CONCEPTUAL ASTROPHYSICS

First Edition

Christopher Sirola

University of Southern Mississippi

SAN DIEGO

Bassim Hamadeh, CEO and Publisher
Angela Schultz, Senior Field Acquisitions Editor
Michelle Piehl, Senior Project Editor
Alia Bales, Production Editor
Emely Villavicencio, Senior Graphic Designer
Greg Isales, Licensing Associate
Natalie Piccotti, Director of Marketing
Kassie Graves, Vice President of Editorial
Jamie Giganti, Director of Academic Publishing

Cover image copyright © 2017 iStockphoto LP/Maximusnd.
Design Image: Source: https://commons.wikimedia.org/wiki/File:Apollo17earth_white.jpg.
Design Image: Copyright © 2008 by Ssolbergj, (CC BY-SA 3.0) at https://commons.wikimedia.org/wiki/File:Terrestrial_globe.svg.

Printed in the United States of America.

cognella® | ACADEMIC PUBLISHING

3970 Sorrento Valley Blvd., Ste. 500, San Diego, CA 92121

To my children, Natalie, Joshua, and Zachary. May they experience the joy of learning and be encouraged in such pursuits as was I when I was a child.

TABLE OF CONTENTS

Acknowledgments

All writers know that their books are in reality collaborative efforts, with contributions from many persons, and this book is no exception. This author wishes to acknowledge the following people:

My wife Susan, whose support, love, and patience (especially patience!) behind the scenes made this project possible;

my parents, Gordon and Gloria, who after many decades still shower their love and help upon their firstborn;

my colleagues at the University of Southern Mississippi, who allowed me the freedom and space needed for this work;

my colleagues at Cognella, who have made this project a joy upon which to work;

agencies and organizations such as NASA that explore space and share their work for the public good;

the website Wikimedia Commons and all the people who post images there for general use, which greatly reduced both the amount of research needed and the costs involved for this project;

Microsoft Word 2016, with which this document was written (and many of its illustrations drawn);

and special thanks to the staff at the Oak Grove Public Library (outside Hattiesburg, Mississippi), who not only provided space and resources (especially Wi-Fi) for this project, but also are wonderfully accommodating of our autistic son, who has found a true second home there. Even in this day and age, not all facilities willingly host special-needs children, especially those with mental and/or emotional handicaps, and we wish to express our deepest appreciation.

Despite our best efforts, unintentional errors and/or omissions crop up in every literary endeavor. All such issues are the sole responsibility of the author, and any constructive assistance in correcting them is appreciated.

INTRODUCTION TO ASTRONOMY

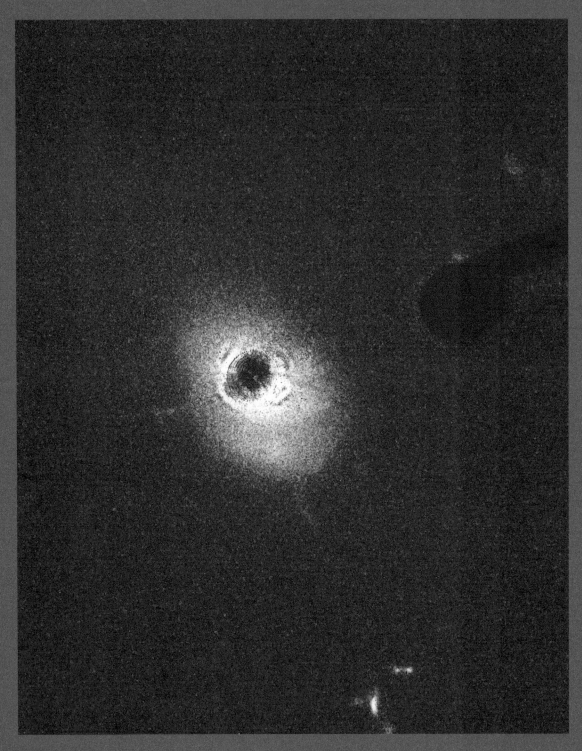

The quasar 3C 273, as imaged by the Hubble Space Telescope's advanced camera for surveys. The center has been blotted out in order to bring out other features. Credit: NASA.

INTRODUCTION TO ASTROPHYSICS

PURPOSE

To introduce the science of astronomy

OBJECTIVES

- To describe the sciences of astronomy and physics
- To introduce the concept of quantity
- To review exponential and scientific notation
- To describe the metric system and associated units of measurement
- To show the utility of ratios
- To review spherical coordinates
- To show how astronomers and physicists set up and solve problems

INTRODUCTION

As we begin our journey to study astronomy, we need to put fundamental concepts and skills into place. Astronomy is a discipline with its own history, its own jargon, and its own ways of addressing problems, so we need to introduce some of these ideas up front. Further, modern astronomy is really a combination of astronomy and physics; that is, astronomers use physics to inform their work. Here, we introduce some necessary skills and knowledge to pursue this topic of astronomy.

KEY TERMS

Astronomical unit (or **au**): The average distance from the Earth to the Sun. Often used by astronomers to express distances within the solar system

Astronomy: From the ancient Greek for the study of stars. More broadly, modern astronomy incorporates the *science* of any object outside of the Earth (or, conversely, in space)

Astrophysics: A combination of *astronomy* and *physics*; specifically, how physics informs the properties and behaviors of astronomical objects

Base-ten logarithm (or **log**): A mathematical operation that reduces a number to its equivalent power of 10

Electromagnetic radiation (or **light** for **short**): Radiation emitted by electrically charged particles under a variety of circumstances. Includes not only visible light, but also radio waves, microwaves, infrared radiation, ultraviolet radiation, x-rays, and gamma rays

Experiments: A way to generate data by performing controlled observations under laboratory conditions. To be distinguished from *observations*

Exponential notation: A method of using powers of 10 in order to make extremely large or extremely small numbers more understandable

Graph: A visual method used to understand relationships between quantities for a set of data. Typically (not always) one quantity is plotted on a horizontal axis and the other on a vertical axis

Light: See *electromagnetic radiation*

Light year (or **ly**): The distance a beam of light travels in a vacuum in a year. Useful for expressing distances to stars

Natural logarithm (or **ln**): A mathematical operation that reduces a number to its equivalent power of *e*, the exponential number (approximately 2.818)

Observations: Virtually all data we receive in astronomy is by remote observation, or "looking" at objects. This is almost always by visible light or another form of electromagnetic radiation, though a few other methods are sometimes employed. To be distinguished from *experiments*

Parsec (or **pc**): Another unit of distance useful for expressing distances to stars. Equal to 3.26 light years. Actually used more often by astronomers than the light year for purposes of convenience

Physics: For simplicity, the study of motion—how we describe investigations into the reasons for the motions of objects, including why objects don't move and why objects change their motions

Polar coordinates: A three-dimensional system for locating an object, using the radius of a disk (circle), the angle around the disk, and a distance above or below the disk

Quantity: A concept that can be expressed as a number

Ratio: Mathematically, a comparison of one quantity to another

Rectangular coordinates: A three-dimensional system of locating objects, using three distances (or "axes") at right angles to each other

Science: Latin for "knowledge." In modern usage, the application of knowledge to the solving of problems regarding nature

Spherical coordinates: A three-dimensional system of locating objects, using two angles and a radial distance

SI ("**systeme internationale**"): In English, "the international standard" system of units. An extrapolation of the metric system used by physicists

Unit: A standardized way to express a measurement. For example, everybody acknowledges the same length when we use the "meter"

Section 0.1: Descriptions of Astronomy and Physics

Before we begin, we should define our terms. Specifically, what are we studying in this textbook?

Astronomy is a term that comes from the ancient Greek and refers to the study of the stars. We need to note that the term "star" itself used to mean any object in the night sky, including what we now term planets and comets.[1] Depending on the culture, the Sun and Moon may also have been considered stars and/or objects in the sky versus objects belonging to the Earth. Much of ancient astronomy was put to practical use, as in the determination of the seasons or the length of the year. Modern astronomy encompasses much more than this now, of course. Astronomy tends to concern itself with objects and phenomena outside of the Earth, whether belonging to the solar system (the first half of this textbook) or among stars and/or galaxies (the second half of the book). Since the invention of the telescope astronomy has expanded to include objects that cannot be seen with the naked eye, or emit visible light in the first place, and even studies the origin of the universe itself.

Physics is a term that covers the study of motion, both descriptions of the motions of objects (how far did it go? When did it get there? How fast is it moving?, etc.) and the reasons for the motions of objects (what made it accelerate? How did it change its direction?, etc.). Modern physics has found that the <u>change</u> of the motion of an object is the most important item to know when describing the status of an object. Physics even includes describing why an object doesn't move; after all, the object might be standing still when we expect it to be moving.

---

[1] Other solar system objects with which we are familiar today, such as asteroids and moons (besides ours) are not visible to the naked eye and are rarely, if ever, mentioned prior to the invention of the telescope.

Astrophysics, an obviously compounded term, gained traction only in the early 20th century. Prior to that, astronomy and physics, though they would occasionally overlap, were considered separate disciplines. Beginning with the discoveries of relativity (special and general) and quantum mechanics, and their subsequent application to astronomy, scientists started to realize the two topics actually share a lot in common. One example we will describe in a future chapter in detail involves the work of Cecilia Payne, who applied quantum mechanics to spectroscopic observations of stars and (among other things) determined that hydrogen is the most common element in the universe. This work came out in the 1920s; today, we would expect this to earn a Nobel Prize in physics, but astronomy was not considered part of physics at the time. Astronomy-related work did not garner attention from the Nobel committee until decades later with the discovery of the cosmic microwave background radiation. Now astronomy-related research is as likely as any other topic in physics to be recognized.

The textbook is designed for a two-semester course. The first half of the textbook teaches the solar system, including basic skills and knowledge of naked-eye astronomy as well as details of the various objects that orbit our star. The second half of the textbook teaches stellar astronomy, which includes their environments and life cycles, and expands to include galaxies and cosmology.

The first major section (part I) deals with old-school astronomy: how astronomers measure space, describe time, and a brief history of our learning about the solar system, covering chapters 1, 2, and 3, respectively. The next major section (part II, naturally) talks about basic physics principles, specifically motion, gravity, and light in chapters 4 and 5 (we will also revisit more science regarding light in chapter 14 as it specifically pertains to the study of stars). Part III gets into the details of the solar system, starting with an overview in chapter 6; then discussing modern models of how the solar system formed (chapter 7); incorporating the role of impacts (chapter 8); describing the geologies, atmospheres, and magnetic fields of solar system objects (chapters 9–11, respectively); and wrapping up with the object for which the solar system was named (chapter 12), the Sun.

Part IV, starting the second half of the textbook, reflects the first three chapters in that it also covers basic knowledge, history, and even properties of light. The difference here for chapters 13–15 is that the focus is now on stars (note that chapter 0 is worth reviewing as well). Part V concerns itself with the life cycles of stars, from their formation (chapter 16) through the middle of their lives (chapter 17) and the wide varieties of ways stars come to their ends (chapters 18–20). Part VI, a shorter section, describes the wider environments in which stars exist, the galaxies. We start with our home galaxy, the Milky Way (chapter 21) and bring in other types of galaxies and arrangements of galaxies next (chapter 22). The final two chapters return to the beginning by discussing origins. Chapter 23 recounts our current thoughts on cosmology, the beginnings of the universe itself, and chapter 24 ends the text with a lighter look at the possibility of life elsewhere besides planet Earth.

The term "science" comes to us via the Latin "scientia," meaning "to know." In modern usage, science has two basic meanings. First, it can refer to individual disciplines, not just astronomy or physics; chemistry, geology, biology, and many others qualify. Second, it can refer to the process of problem solving. Modern science is best viewed not simply as an accumulation of facts and data to memorize, but how to apply problem-solving techniques to answering questions. Or in short, the first usage depicts science as a noun, the second as a verb. In both cases, modern science deals with nature. We will come back to these ideas at the end of this chapter. Going forward, we will discuss the topic of this textbook as astrophysics.

Section 0.2: Quantities, Notation, and Units

Disciplines such as astronomy and physics are dominated by quantities. A *quantity* is simply a concept that can be described by a number, whether the number comes from a measurement or a calculation. This leads naturally to mathematical expressions. While the emphasis in this text is on concepts, we will not shy away from using math to better understand the science. In this section, we cover several methods astronomers and physicists use to express quantities.

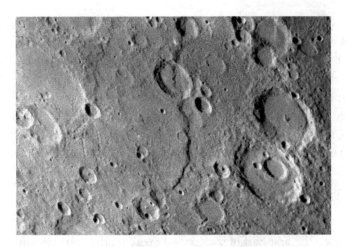

FIGURE 0.1. An image of the surface of Mercury taken by the Mariner 10 spacecraft. Images of Mercury not only showed craters, but also scarps (cliffs) several miles deep, running for hundreds of miles along North-South lines. This particular feature is called Discovery Scarp. Credit: NASA/JPL/Northwestern University.

1. Exponential Notation

Astronomy is different from physics in a number of ways. One is that, with a few exceptions, all of our data in astronomy comes remotely. Objects in astronomy are typically too far away to visit in person and gather materials for analysis in a lab. Rather, astronomers perform *observations*. We wait for information to come to us—most often in the form of light—instead of being able to perform *experiments*, a subset of observations, with the difference being that we have some say in how an experiment is conducted. Observations—at least the type employed by astronomers—are almost always remote, where we have no say at all in how an object behaved (astronomy shares this observational property with other "historical" sciences such as geology and paleontology). Another way in which astronomy is different than other sciences is this near-total reliance on *electromagnetic radiation*, or *light* for short. While there are some instances where information is brought to us from large distances via other methods—neutrinos and gravitational waves are recent examples—astronomers need to understand as much as they can about light in order to get as much out of it they can. Light, or electromagnetic radiation, is of vital importance in astronomy. Astronomers didn't always appreciate this: NASA was reluctant at first to include cameras on their early solar system probes until the images started pouring in and demonstrated the value of being able to look at literally new worlds.

A third way in which astronomy stands out from other sciences is that its quantities are often, well, astronomical. The mass of a typical adult might be about 75 kilograms. The mass of the Earth, which we could call typical for a planet, is 5,980,000,000,000,000,000,000,000 kg! Similar numbers crop up when talking about an astronomical object's age, radius, and distance. On the other hand, astronomy can sometimes deal with very tiny numbers. Electrons, the particles that carry electric charge, have masses of 0.000 000 000 000 000 000 000 000 000 000 091 1 kilograms. It is difficult to understand numbers this far out of ordinary experience. We need some ways in which to make sense of such extremes.

One method to bring these numbers back to Earth (so to speak) is via *exponential notation*. Exponential notation makes use of our decimal number system, citing powers of 10 to allow us to properly compare. For example, let's look at the mass of the Earth again, with the "long" form of the number at left and its representation in exponential notation at right:

$$5{,}980{,}000{,}000{,}000{,}000{,}000{,}000{,}000 = 5.98 \times 10^{24}$$

How do we replace the long form of a number with its equivalent in exponential notation? First, we leave the digits at the front of the number alone. Next, we count the number of columns following those digits. If we place a decimal point after the 5, there are 24 columns of 10 to follow. We express this by multiplying our digits by 10 to that power—in this case, 24.

The mass of an electron can be displayed in a similar manner:

$$0.\,000\,000\,000\,000\,000\,000\,000\,000\,000\,091\,1 = 9.11 \times 10^{-31}$$

The approach is the same, except in this case we use a negative sign to express that the number is smaller than one.

2. Unit Analysis

Another approach to make numbers more accessible is to change the units of expression. For example, let's consider the Earth's average distance from the Sun in units of meters:

$$148{,}000{,}000{,}000 = 1.48 \times 10^{11}$$

We could even express this in words: one-hundred and forty-eight billion meters. But words or exponential notation still aren't all that helpful. To make this more obvious, let's also look at the average distance of Mars from the Sun:

$$228{,}000{,}000{,}000 = 2.28 \times 10^{11}$$

or two-hundred and twenty-eight billion meters. Here is a question: How does Mars's distance from the Sun compare to Earth's? Numbers like these are so large and far from our everyday experience as to make it difficult. Instead, let's change how we express these numbers by changing the *units* we use.

A common unit used by astronomers to express distances within the solar system is the *astronomical unit*, abbreviated *au*. The au is the average distance from the Earth to the Sun (the Earth's orbit is slightly elliptical, so we use the average), or

$$1 \text{ au} = 1.50 \times 10^{11} \text{ meters}$$

We can now recast the average distance from Mars to the Sun via a quick calculation:

$$(2.28 \times 10^{11} \text{ meters})\left(\frac{1 \text{ au}}{1.50 \times 10^{11} \text{ meters}}\right) = 1.52 \text{ au}$$

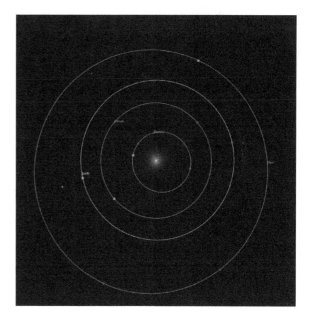

FIGURE 0.2. The orbits of the inner planets, to scale. In order from the center, the orbits are for Mercury, Venus, Earth, and Mars.

It's much easier to say that Mars is about 1.5 times further from the Sun than Earth than to say it is two-hundred and twenty-eight billion meters from the Sun!

Note that both answers—both of the numbers cited for the distance between Mars and the Sun—are correct. The question here is not so much about correctness, but rather appropriateness. Which unit gives us better understanding?

Another method used by astronomers to bring very large (or very small) numbers under control is via logarithms. A logarithm is a way to reduce a number to its equivalent expression as an exponent. Astronomers use two different types of logarithms: *base-ten logarithms* and *natural logarithms*. Let's look at each in turn.

Check Your Neighbor

Mercury's distance from the Sun is roughly 0.4 au of Earth's distance from the Sun. How far from the Sun is Mercury in units of meters?

3. Base-Ten Logarithms and Powers of Ten

The first attempt at any type of logarithm was invented by John Napier of Scotland, who published his results in 1614. While his logarithms are not the same as those we use today, the idea—of reducing a large number via using exponents—is the basis of logs. His invention allowed users to calculate using addition and subtraction instead of multiplication and division, which doesn't sound like much of an advance today, but in the days before calculators it made a huge difference to researchers, including astronomers.

Base-ten logarithms ("logs" for short)[2] take numbers and express them instead as powers of ten. For example, the number 10 can also be written as 10^1, since any number can be expressed as itself to the first power. The base-ten log of 10 is then

$$\log(10) = \log(10^1) = 1$$

The base-ten logarithm is thus the exponent. Similarly, we can say that

$$\log(100) = \log(10^2) = 2$$

$$\log(1000) = \log(10^3) = 3$$

This even works if the number is smaller than 1:

$$\log(0.1) = \log(1/10) = \log(10^{-1}) = -1$$

$$\log(0.01) = \log(1/100) = \log(10^{-2}) = -2$$

$$\log(0.001) = \log(1/1000) = \log(10^{-3}) = -3$$

So far, we've only shown numbers that are exact powers of ten. One of Napier's most important innovations was to extend this idea to numbers between powers of ten. Again, in modern usage, some examples are

$$\log(3.16) = 0.500$$

$$\log(5) = 0.699$$

$$\log(318) = 2.50$$

$$\log(5800) = 3.76$$

$$\log(0.316) = -0.500$$

So, when we read that $\log(5) = 0.699$, we are also learning that $10^{0.699} = 5$, and so on. Note that 5 does <u>not</u> equal $10^{0.5}$.

Before the days of electronic calculators, Napier and other mathematicians would painstakingly calculate as many logarithms as they could and publish the results for others to use. In those days, this was an invaluable service. Now, of course, even cell phones have scientific calculators that can provide us with the results as quickly as we could wish.

Astronomers use base-ten logarithms in several places. The most important is the "magnitude" system, which astronomers use to represent the brightness of stars. Astronomers also use logs to graph data that has an extremely wide range of values—for example, stars can be up to a million or more times as luminous as the Sun, or as low as one one-hundred thousandth the luminosity of the Sun. But $\log(1{,}000{,}000) = 6$ and $\log(1/100{,}000) = -5$, which are much easier numbers to deal with.

---

[2] The base-ten logarithm is also abbreviated as "log" on standard calculators.

4. Natural Logarithms and Exponentials

So-called natural logarithms (abbreviated "ln") are related to the "exponential" number (abbreviated "e"). The number e (approximately 2.818) is just as important in math and science as the more familiar number π (3.1416 ...). As its name suggests, it is useful in situations involving exponential growth and/or decay. If we graph e^x, the slope of the e^x function is the same as the e^x function itself, a property that also comes in handy in astrophysics. Just as the log function gives us the exponent of the number 10, the ln function gives us the exponent of the number e. While this sounds abstract, many natural phenomena act this way. One example in astronomy is the notion of "extinction" of starlight. Imagine a star's light trying to get through a cloud in interstellar space. The further into the cloud we go, the more the light has either been absorbed or reflected away. The best way to express this behavior is that the brightness of the light decreases via an inverse exponential function (i.e., 1/e).

5. The SI System

Our next task is to take another look at this idea of units. How do physicists express the values of their quantities? How do astronomers?

Physicists use the *système international*, or international standard units (abbreviated *SI*), an extrapolation of the metric system. The metric (literally, "to measure") system originated in France in 1790, by the revolutionaries who wanted to standardize the then-patchwork of measures used across their country. The metric system's jumping-off point was the distance from the equator of the Earth to the North Pole, set to equal 10 million meters. This definition was used to set up most of the other units (like the kilogram) familiar to us from the metric system. We are more careful with our units today, but the general principle holds true: Choose a set measurement or number as a basis of comparison and go from there.

Important units that undergird the metric (SI) system of units are found in Table 0.1.

TABLE 0.1. A Sampling of Basic Units of the SI System

Unit Name	Unit Abbreviation	Quantity Being Expressed
meter	m	distance (or length etc.)
second	s	time
kilogram	kg	mass
kelvin	K	temperature
ampere	A	electric current

The United States is one of the few nations that does not officially recognize the metric system (to be fair, we actually don't officially recognize any system of units). Rather, the United States favors units borrowed from England—inches, feet, and miles for distance, for example. The downside of the units common in the United States is that conversions are not related by powers of ten—for example, we are all familiar with 12 inches making 1 foot. If one grows up with our system, it's not too bad for everyday use, but does introduce unnecessary complications when trading with other countries. Internationally, a unit such as the inch is not a standalone notion, but rather the inch's length is described in terms of meters. In this textbook, we will typically cite the SI version of a quantity, but also include a version more familiar to American readers—for example, we could cite an object's speed as 10 meters per second, but also express it as 22.5 miles per hour.

For simplicity in speech, the metric system also uses prefixes. A well-known example is the centimeter. The prefix "centi" here means "one hundred," and therefore 100 centimeters is exactly equal to 1 meter (compare this to our coinage, where 100 "cents" equals 1 dollar). Most (not all) prefixes are bundled in powers of 3; that is, we often go up or down the number scale in factors of 10^3, or 1,000 (Table 0.2):

TABLE 0.2. Some Common Prefixes of the Metric System (SI Units)

Prefix	Prefix Abbreviation	Multiplicative Factor
Giga	G	10^9 (billion)
Mega	M	10^6 (million)
kilo	k	10^3 (thousand)
centi	c	10^{-2} (one hundredth)
milli	m	10^{-3} (one thousandth)
micro	m	10^{-6} (one millionth)
nano	n	10^{-9} (one billionth)

The use of prefixes is, once again, there for our convenience. We might say that the distance from the Sun to a neighboring star is 1.33 parsecs, the distance from the Sun to the center of the Milky Way is 8,000 parsecs, and the distance from the Sun to a far-away galaxy is 300,000,000 parsecs. It is clearer if we say 8 kiloparsecs (8 kpc) for the Milky Way and 300 megaparsecs for the galaxy (300 Mpc) instead.

6. Astronomy-Specific Units

This brings us to our next topic: What units do astronomers use? In our textbook, where appropriate, we will use the SI system; so, for example, the mass of the Sun is 1.99×10^{30} kg. Like we showed with the astronomical unit, it makes our science more understandable to define this mass as one solar mass, or 1 $M_\odot$ (where the symbol "$\odot$" represents the Sun). The Sun is close enough to being an average or normal star that it makes sense for us to use it as the standard of comparison with other stars.

But the au and $M_\odot$ are not SI units. Instead, they have been conceived specifically for the benefit of astronomers. While one could express the distance to a dorm room from the lecture hall in terms of astronomical units, this obscures rather than enlightens. Units in astronomy are almost always best restricted to topics in astronomy. Table 0.3 lists a few of the more common units specific to astronomy.[3]

TABLE 0.3. A Sampling of Units Commonly Used by Astronomers

Quantity	Unit	Equivalent
Angle	Hour Angle (HA)	1 HA = 15°
Angle	arcminute (arcmin or ')	1° = 60 arcmin
Angle	arcsecond (arcsec or ")	1 arcmin = 60 arcsec
Time	year (yr)	1 yr = 3.156×10^7 s
Distance	astronomical unit (au)	$1.498 = 10^{11}$ meters (From Earth to Sun)
Distance	light year (ly)	9.46×10^{15} meters (How far light travels in one year)
Distance	parsec (pc)	3.08×10^{16} meters = 3.26 ly
Mass	solar mass ($M_\odot$)	1.99×10^{30} kg
Radius	solar radius ($R_\odot$)	6.96×10^8 m
Luminosity	solar luminosity ($L_\odot$)	3.96×10^{26} W

---

[3] Professional astronomers sometimes make use of the "cgs" ("centimeter-gram-seconds") system rather than the strictly metric (SI) system. We will stick with SI units in this textbook.

Section 0.3: Ratios and Simple Algebra

Among the best skills for students of astrophysics to have is the ability to manipulate *ratios*. Quite often, we are less interested in the absolute value of a quantity and more in how one quantity compares to another. How far is Mars from the Sun compared to Earth's distance from the Sun? How massive is the Sun compared to Jupiter? How much flux is emitted by the star Rigel compared to that of the star Betelgeuse? These comparisons are often more helpful than knowing the individual numbers.

As an example, let's compare the Sun to Jupiter. A thought that is often expressed in common media (without investigation) is that Jupiter is so large that it almost has enough mass to be a star, and had this happened, we would live in a two-star system.

The smallest stars we know of (in terms of mass) possess 8% the mass of the Sun. Below this, the self-gravity of the object simply isn't strong enough to squeeze the object's interior to the pressures and densities needed to light up nuclear fusion. So, if Jupiter were to have a chance to become a star, its mass should be close to 8% of the mass of the Sun.

Jupiter's mass is 1.90×10^{27} kilograms, and the Sun's mass is 1.99×10^{30} kg. Let's compare them via a ratio:

$$\frac{\text{Jupiter's mass}}{\text{The Sun's mass}} = \frac{1.90 \times 10^{27} \text{ kg}}{1.99 \times 10^{30} \text{ kg}} = 0.000\,955$$

Or, $0.000\,955 = 0.0955\%$, which is a touch less than one-tenth of a percent. Jupiter didn't just miss becoming a star; Jupiter is about 80 times too small, mass-wise, to have become a star. An application of ratios helps us evaluate such statements.

As another example of applying ratios, let's look at the flux emitted by Rigel compared to that of Betelgeuse. "Flux" in astronomy is the amount of light power per unit area emitted by a hot object. Flux ("F") depends on the fourth power of the surface temperature ("T") of the object, or in equation form,

$$F \propto T^4$$

Rounded off, the temperatures of Rigel and Betelgeuse are 12,000 K and 3,000 K, respectively. To help us keep their temperatures and fluxes straight, it is common to use subscripts. If we let "R" stand for Rigel and "B" for Betelgeuse, then their temperatures are

$$T_R = 12,000 \text{ K} \qquad\qquad T_B = 3,000 \text{ K}$$

Now we can take a ratio of the fluxes of Rigel vs. Betelgeuse:

$$\frac{F_R}{F_B} = \frac{T_R^4}{T_B^4} = \left(\frac{T_R}{T_B}\right)^4 = \left(\frac{12,000 \text{ K}}{3000 \text{ K}}\right)^4 = (4)^4 = 256$$

So, Rigel emits 256 times as much power per unit area as Betelgeuse.

It also comes in handy to be able to manipulate simple equations and solve for unknown quantities. A famous equation in cosmology is Hubble's law, which relates the distance to a galaxy, the velocity of the galaxy, and a rate of expansion called the "Hubble constant." The value of the Hubble constant is known to be close to 70 kilometers per second per megaparsec. Suppose we determine the velocity of a galaxy to be 2,100 kilometers per second. Hubble's law states

$$v = H_0 d$$

Where v stands for the velocity, H_0 for the Hubble constant, and d for the distance. To find the distance, divide both sides by the Hubble constant, and we get

$$d = \frac{v}{H_0}$$

To find the numerical value of the distance, plug in the values of the velocity and Hubble constant:

$$d = \frac{2100 \text{ km / s}}{70 \frac{\text{km}}{\text{s}} \text{ / Mpc}} = 30 \text{ Mpc}$$

This galaxy is thus 30 megaparsecs away from us. This is an example of a formula that will help us understand how the universe changes at the largest of distances.

Our purpose in this text is not to use math for its own sake, but for math to enhance our understanding. Whenever we introduce an equation, we will show how to use it.

Section 0.4: Coordinates

Another skill we wish to encourage is the ability to find objects in the sky. Of course, if something is big and/or bright enough, then we can just point at it. But most objects are dim—even too dim to see with the naked eye— and thus we need a system for locating objects. We are also often interested in very small differences in positions. Many catalogs in astronomy label their objects by their coordinates.

A *coordinate* is simply a number assigned to a position, given a reference point. Suppose you are sitting at a table working on an astronomy assignment. Your pen runs dry, and you need to fetch a new one from a desk ten feet away. We can say that the coordinate of the desk, relative to your position, is at the position of + 10 feet (Figure 0.3).

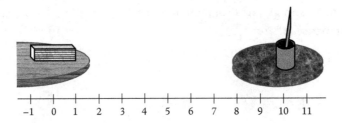

FIGURE 0.3. A coordinate axis showing how to locate a pen from a table.

This example is simple, because it is only depicting the location of an object straight away from the starting position ("origin"). But in physics and astronomy, we usually need to know the location of an object using two or three coordinates.

The French philosopher Rene Descartes told the story of devising a two-dimensional coordinate system while lying on his bed one day. He spotted a fly flitting back and forth across the ceiling, which had rectangular tiles. It dawned on him that he could assign two numbers—one to show the fly's left-right position, the other its back-forth position—using the ceiling tiles. This idea (which can be extrapolated to three dimensions, the third being up-down) is an example of a *rectangular coordinate* system, since the directions are at right angles to each other and can be depicted as rectangles (Figure 0.4):

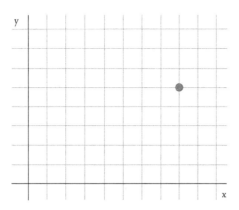

FIGURE 0.4. A rectangular coordinate system. The dark horizontal and vertical lines represent the "x" and "y" axes, our reference lines.

Physicists like rectangular coordinate systems, since they lend themselves to describing the positions and motions of objects in everyday life (for instance, think of how a city is divided into city streets). Astronomers, on the other hand, don't use rectangular coordinates very often. Since objects are so large and far away, and the Earth in comparison is so small, it doesn't make sense to describe an astronomical object as being so many billions of kilometers to the right and another couple of billions of kilometers up. Rather, astronomers find it more convenient to describe locations of objects using angles.

The most common system for astronomers uses *spherical coordinates*. In spherical coordinates, rather than using three separate distances, we use one radial distance and two angles. By "radial" we simply mean its straight-line distance away from us. Examples of spherical coordinate systems are the localized ("alt-azimuth") coordinates useful for astronomers when pointing toward objects in one's sky and the global ("right ascension-declination") coordinates used by everybody to determine the locations of objects. We will describe both systems in further detail in chapter 1; for now, we can see how a spherical coordinate system might be used (Figure 0.5):

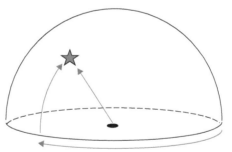

FIGURE 0.5. A spherical coordinate system of the type used by astronomers. The origin of the system is marked by a dark oval. The position of the star is determined by the radial distance (straight arrow), the angle around the disk, and the angle above the disk.

There is an important difference between spherical coordinates used by physicists and astronomers. Since we live on the Earth, and it is convenient to have the Earth at the center (origin) of the coordinate system, we are inside the sphere, so to speak, rather than looking at a sphere from the outside. Astronomy spherical coordinates are somewhat backward compared to physics spherical coordinate systems as a result.

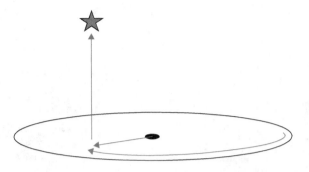

FIGURE 0.6. A polar coordinate system of the type used by astronomers. The origin of the system is marked by a dark oval. The position of the star is determined by the radial distance inside the disk, the angle around the disk, and the distance above or below the disk.

One last type of coordinate system sometimes used by astronomers is a *polar coordinate* system. In this version, we have a circle or disk as our reference. We again use an angle around the disk, but the radial coordinate remains inside the disk, and the third coordinate is straight above or below the disk. The Milky Way (our home galaxy) is dominated by a relatively flat disk, so astronomers find it convenient to use a modified polar coordinate system to describe the motions of stars in the galaxy's disk.

Section 0.5: Graphs

One more method commonly used by astronomers and physicists to interpret data is the *graph*. The reason for a graph is very simple: to be able to see the relationship (or lack thereof) between two quantities. Typically (there are a few exceptions), one of the quantities is plotted along the horizontal axis and the other quantity is plotted along the vertical axis. To explore the utility of graphs, let us view some examples from astronomy.

Table 0.4 shows three different quantities for some stars that are relatively close to our solar system. The stars are all of the same general type ("dwarfs"), so we can fairly compare them. In this table, we have listed each star's mass (in "solar masses"; i.e., their masses compared to that of the Sun), each star's radius (in "solar radii"), and each star's distance (in parsecs). The Sun is included; after all, it is a typical star, too! What can graphs of these properties teach us?

TABLE 0.4. Properties of Some Nearby Stars I

Star	Mass ($M_\odot$)	Radius ($R_\odot$)	Distance (pc)
The Sun	1	1	0
Alpha Centauri A	1	1	1.34
Alpha Centauri B	0.78	0.83	1.34
Barnard's Star	0.28	0.27	1.83
Wolf 359	0.15	0.21	2.39
Sirius A	2.35	1.68	2.63
Epsilon Eridani	0.75	0.81	3.26
BD +4344 A	0.44	0.52	3.45
Tau Ceti	0.83	0.88	3.50
Procyon A	1.30	1.30	3.50
Kapteyn's Star	1	0.60	3.88
HD 88230 A	0.67	0.72	4.69
Altair	1.8	1.6	4.98
70 Ophiuchi A	0.79	0.85	5.03
Fomalhaut	2.4	2.0	6.7

Sirola, C. (2006). "Laboratory Exercises in Stellar Astronomy". Prentice-Hall. (i.e., a lab manual written by the author). http://www.atlasoftheuniverse.com/nearstar.html

Consider the radius vs. mass graph at the left in Figure 0.7. While not a perfectly straight line, there is definitely a trend: The larger across the star, the more massive it is. In fact, we could draw a straight line through the points to display the relationship.

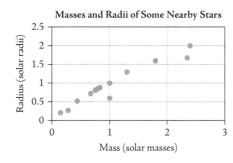
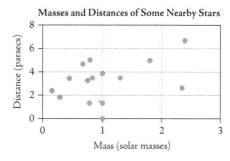

FIGURE 0.7. Left: A graph showing the masses and radii of some nearby stars. Right: A graph showing the masses and distances of the same sample of stars.

Now consider the distance vs. mass graph at the right in Figure 0.7. This is an example of what scientists call a "scatter plot"; that is, the points are scattered all over. There isn't much, if any, trend to see. The distance to a star, it appears, has nothing to do with how massive it is.

Check Your Neighbor

Suppose you gathered data for a group of astronomy students including their weights, heights, and the distances they live from the lecture hall. Imagine plotting the heights of the students vs. their weights and plotting the distances of the students vs. their weights. Which, if either, graph do you expect to show a trend? Which, if either, graph do you expect would not show a trend?

TABLE 0.5. Properties of Some Nearby Stars II

Star	Temperature (K)	Luminosity ($L_\odot$)	log(T)	log(L)
The Sun	5800	1	3.76	0
Alpha Cen A	5800	1.60	3.76	0.20
Alpha Cen B	5200	0.45	3.72	−0.35
Barnard's Star	3400	0.00045	3.53	−3.35
Wolf 359	3100	0.00002	3.49	−4.70
Sirius A	9300	23.5	3.97	1.37
Epsilon Eridani	5000	0.30	3.70	−0.52
BD +4344 A	3700	0.00039	3.57	−3.41
Tau Ceti	5400	0.45	3.73	−0.35
Procyon A	6400	7.65	3.81	0.88
Kapteyn's Star	3900	0.0039	3.59	−2.41
HD 88230 A	4400	0.41	3.64	−0.39
Altair	7800	11.1	3.89	1.05
70 Ophiuchi A	5300	0.43	3.72	−0.37
Fomalhaut	8700	14	3.94	1.15

Sirola, C. (2006). "Laboratory Exercises in Stellar Astronomy". Prentice-Hall. (i.e., a lab manual written by the author). http://www.atlasoftheuniverse.com/nearstar.html

Graphs can also be manipulated in order to clarify trends. As an example, let's graph the surface temperatures and luminosities (i.e., brightness) of the same sample of stars. The data is listed in Table 0.6.

A careful look at the data allows us to see that the hotter the star (i.e., the higher the surface temperature), the brighter the star. This isn't surprising. But when we refer to the graph of luminosity vs. temperature—to the left in Figure 0.8—it is next to impossible to tell anything else.

The graph to the right in Figure 0.8 is much clearer. The trend is still evident—luminosity increases with temperature—but closer to a straight line. To achieve this, we took the base-ten logarithm of both quantities. The reason the first graph looks the way it does is because the numbers for each quantity—especially the luminosity—cover such an extreme range. Taking the base-ten log tamped down the values and made them more accessible. To be sure, the specific behavior takes more work (luminosity depends in part on the fourth power of the temperature), but it does state that a definite relationship exists.

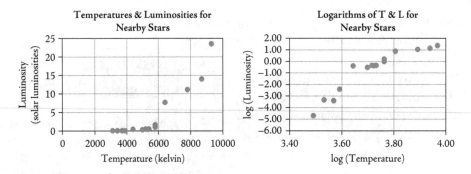

FIGURE 0.8. Left: A graph showing the temperatures and luminosities of some nearby stars. Right: A graph showing the base-ten logarithms of the temperatures and luminosities of the same sample of stars.

Section 0.6: The Solving of Astrophysics Problems

While a fair amount of memorization is necessary for learning astronomy, it is more important to be able to set up and solve problems. As before, it may be best to show some examples.

One of the earliest descriptions of the orbits of planets about the Sun is Kepler's third law, which relates the orbital period of a planet to its average distance from the Sun. Suppose we observe a planet that takes 225 days to complete an orbit. How far is it from the Sun? Let's lay out a strategy for solving this question.

+ Identify the quantities involved. Here, we have two: First, the period of the planet is listed (225 days); second, the question asks us to find the planet's average distance from the Sun.
+ Kepler's third law, in equation form, is

$$P^2 = a^3$$

We need to identify which quantity belongs to which symbol:
  · The symbol for the orbital period of a planet is capital "P"
  · The symbol for the average distance of a planet from the Sun is small letter "a"
+ We also need to make sure we're using appropriate units. Kepler's third law is specifically written for objects in orbit about the Sun. This means we use astronomy-based units rather than SI units:
  · The orbital period P needs to be in terms of years instead of days or seconds. Thus, we need to convert our question's period into years:

$$225 \text{ days} \left(\frac{1 \text{ year}}{365.25 \text{ days}} \right) = 0.616 \text{ years}$$

- The distance from the Sun, when we find it, will be expressed in astronomical units (*au*) rather than meters
- Now that we have the period expressed in years, we can solve for the planet's average distance from the Sun:

$$a = \sqrt[3]{P^2} = \sqrt[3]{(0.616)^2} = \sqrt[3]{0.379} = 0.724 \text{ au}$$

Check Your Neighbor

Consult Table 0.6. Which planet did we find above?

TABLE 0.6. Orbital Properties of the Major Planets

Planet	Period (years)	Average Distance (au)
Mercury	0.24	0.39
Venus	0.62	0.72
Earth	1	1
Mars	1.88	1.52
Jupiter	11.9	5.2
Saturn	29.4	9.5
Uranus	84	19.2
Neptune	164	30.1

Not all problems are mathematical. Astronomy is a very visual subject, and so it is important to tell between types of objects or behaviors just by looking. Consider the North America nebula (Figure 0.9), a cloud of interstellar gas and dust. Three dominant colors are present: pink, blue, and a brownish-black, plus a great number of stars. What are we to make of all this? For that, we need to combine our knowledge of light, conditions in space, and how stars go through their life cycles.

- The pink color represents hydrogen gas. Hydrogen atoms, when both in a rarefied (thin) and high temperature gas, emit specific lines of color. In visible light, these colors show up as thin lines of red, blue-green (sometimes described as cyan), and violet. Blended together, they give the appearance of a pinkish-purple. This tells us the following:
  - Hydrogen gas is very popular. In fact, hydrogen atoms typically make up 90% of all atoms in interstellar space.
  - The gas must be very thin. It is not uncommon for some nebulae to be far more of a vacuum than most physics researchers manufacture in their labs.

FIGURE 0.9. The North America Nebula in visible light. Credit: Keesscherer.

- The gas must be very hot. In order for hydrogen atoms to emit visible light, the temperature usually needs to be near 10,000 Kelvin (18,000 °F).
- This implies that there must be a source of energy nearby to heat the nebula. The most common source for this kind and amount of energy belongs to hot, bright stars. So, the nebula is either near to or contains such stars.

- The blue color comes from the reflection of light off of dust. Much like how the molecules in our atmosphere scatter the Sun's light to make the sky blue, light from stars can be reflected by dust in a nebula. This tells us the following:
  - The nebula must contain a significant amount of dust. It is typical for nebulae to have up to 2% of its mass in terms of carbon-based or rock (silicate)-based dust.
  - Again, there must be a large number of stars near the nebula in order for it to reflect so much light.
  - Blue light is easier to reflect than other colors. We know that both our sky and materials in the lab tend to do this. Seeing that blue is the color reflected hints at what else (besides hydrogen) is contained in the nebula.

- The brownish-black comes from the absorption of light by dust. Again, this is similar to how our atmosphere behaves, but now at sunrise or sunset. The red Sun isn't because the Sun is suddenly emitting more red than other colors, but because blue (and other colors, to lesser extent) are being subtracted via reflection. This tells us the following:
  - The nebula must (again) contain a significant amount of dust.
  - The dust is thicker in some regions of the nebula than others. This may sound obvious, but this also implies
    - if portions of the nebula are thicker than others, then we can expect to find objects hiding inside, such as forming stars ("protostars") and maybe even planets.

Of course, this kind of analysis requires a great deal of learning. We're not expecting beginning students to recognize all these points (or any of them!) at first. But this is part of what we want to teach via this textbook: By looking carefully at the details of an object's appearance, we can tell a great deal about it.

Summary

In this chapter, we did the following:
- Introduced the disciplines of astronomy and physics and how they meld together to form the modern science of astrophysics.
- Spent a great deal of time discussing how to display and interpret the data astronomy generates.
- Briefly showed how astronomers describe how to locate objects via different coordinate systems.
- Demonstrated how astronomers make observations and solve problems.

Questions

1. The average distance from the Earth to the Moon is 384,000,000 meters. Express this number in exponential notation.

2. The mass of a proton is 1.67×10^{-27} kilograms. Express this number in long form.

3. Jupiter is an average distance of 7.79×10^{11} meters from the Sun. How far is this in astronomical units? An astronomical unit is 1.50×10^{11} meters.

4. How many astronomical units are in a parsec? A parsec is 3.09×10^{16} meters.

5. Find the base-ten logarithms of
   + 1,000,000,000,000
   + 0.000 000 000 01

6. How many meters are in a
   + kilometer?
   + micrometer?

7. The Moon has a mass of 7.35×10^{22} kg and the Earth a mass of 5.98×10^{24} kg.
   + What percentage of the Earth's mass is in the Moon?
   + How many times more massive is the Earth compared to the Moon?

8. The amount of light (flux) emitted by a star depends on the square of its radius. Capella Ab is a star with a radius about nine times as large as that of the Sun. How much more flux (in terms of a ratio) does Capella Ab emit compared to the Sun?

9. Suppose we used Table 0.5 to graph the distance (vertical axis) vs. the radii (horizontal axis) of this sample of stars. Do you expect to find a relationship between these two quantities? If so, why? If not, why not?

10. The average distance from Saturn to the Sun is 9.5 au. What is its orbital period in units of years?

11. The Horsehead Nebula (Figure 0.10) is a star-forming region. Referring to the figure, which process—absorption, emission, or reflection—is happening in these regions?
    + The "Horsehead" shape itself
    + The bright blue section to the lower left in the figure

FIGURE 0.10. The Horsehead Nebula in visible light. Credit: Ken Crawford.

Activities

▸ *Astrophysics activity 0.1*: In teams of five or more, each student measures the length and width of a textbook. The data is used to comment on the importance of significant figures.

▸ *Astrophysics activity 0.2*: Use a long string, rods, and a small weight to make a simple pendulum. With a meter stick and stopwatch, use the pendulum to estimate the acceleration of gravity due to the Earth.

Works Referenced

17th Century Maths.com. (n.d). *Some mathematical works from the 17th and 18th centuries*. Retrieved from 17centurymaths.com

Chaisson, E., & McMillan, S. (2002). *Astronomy today*, Vol. 1 (4th ed.). Uppersaddle River, NJ: Prentice Hall.

United States Metric Association (USMA). (n.d.). *Origin of the metric system*. Retrieved from http://www.us-metric.org/origin-of-the-metric-system/

Credits

The closest star system to us: Alpha Centauri (the bright blue star to the left), Beta Centauri (the bright blue star to the right), and Proxima Centauri (the dot at the center of the red circle) are approximately 1.33 parsecs (4.34 light years) from the Earth. Credit: Skatebiker.

MEASURING SPACE

PURPOSE

To find the positions of objects in the sky

OBJECTIVES

- ► To use angular as well as linear measurements for positions
- ► To use the altitude-azimuth (local) coordinate system
- ► To use the right ascension-declination (global) coordinate system
- ► To distinguish between constellations and asterisms
- ► To review the conic sections

INTRODUCTION

Among other questions, students sometimes ask "How far away is that star?" or "What is the furthest one can see?" While astronomers do have answers for these, getting to the point of understanding these answers requires some study. In fact, astronomers tend to start with even simpler questions, such as "Where is it?" "Where is it going?" and "How big is it?"

This chapter is devoted to addressing "where"-type questions in astronomy.

KEY TERMS

Altitude: The angular position of an object in the sky above the horizon

Ante-meridiem ("a.m."): When the Sun is to the East of the local meridian

Arcminute (or "minute of arc"): 1/60th of an angular degree

Arcsecond (or "second of arc"): 1/60th of an arcminute

Asterism: A popular picture made by people out of stars. Not officially recognized by astronomers

Astronomical unit (au): The average distance from the Earth to the Sun, approximately 93 million miles or 150 million kilometers

Azimuth: The angular position of an object along the horizon, often starting from due north and measuring either to the east or to the west

Celestial equator: The equator of the Earth extended to the Celestial Sphere

Celestial Sphere: The notion that the stars are attached to an imaginary sphere completely surrounding the Earth

Conic sections: In ancient mathematics, the resulting possible paths or shapes when slicing across a cone. Among others, the shapes can be circles, ellipses, parabolas, and hyperbolas.

Constellation: An "official" (as determined by astronomers) group of stars. Every object of the sky (not including the solar system) belongs to a constellation. The sky contains 88 constellations

Declination (a.k.a. celestial latitude): The angular position of an object north or south along the celestial sphere

Degree (specifically an angular degree): By definition, there are 360° in a complete circle

Eccentricity: The amount to which an ellipse is stretched out. An ellipse with an eccentricity of zero is a perfect circle; an ellipse with an eccentricity of 1 is actually a parabola

Ecliptic: The apparent path of the Sun across the Celestial Sphere

Foci (singular focus): The two points about which an ellipse is defined

Horizon: Where the ground (or ocean) appears to meet the sky

Hour angle: Angular units typically used by astronomers to depict east-west positions of objects on the Celestial Sphere. There are 24-hour angles in a complete circle

Light year: The distance a beam of light (or photon) travels in one year's worth of time

Local meridian: An arc extending from due south on the horizon, going through the zenith, and continuing to the horizon due north

Local noon: When the Sun crosses the local meridian during daylight hours. By comparison, midnight is when the Sun crosses the local meridian during the night

North Celestial Pole: The North Pole of the Earth extended to the Celestial Sphere

Post-meridiem ("p.m."): When the Sun is to the west of the local meridian

Right ascension (a.k.a. celestial longitude): The angular position of an object east or west along the Celestial Sphere

Semi-major axis: Half of the widest line segment (the "major axis") of an ellipse

Semi-minor axis: Half of the narrowest line segment (the "minor axis") of an ellipse

South Celestial Pole: The South Pole of the Earth extended to the Celestial Sphere

Spherical coordinates: A system used to locate an object in three-dimensional space, using a radial distance and two angles

Zenith: The point on the Celestial Sphere directly above an observer's head

Section 1.1: Angles

The most difficult problem in astronomy is the determination of distances. Even the Moon is some 384,000 kilometers (223,000 miles) from the Earth, and it is easily our nearest celestial neighbor. How then do astronomers describe how to locate objects?

Astronomers use a type of *spherical coordinates*. Spherical coordinates use a radial distance (i.e., a straight-line distance from the observer to the object) and two independent angles in order to locate an object. Although radial distance can be hard to find, it is also irrelevant if all one wishes to do is point toward the object. In other words, all that astronomers require in order to look at an object is its two angular coordinates.

Before we examine specific examples of coordinate systems used by astronomers, we need to review some basic features of angles.

First, what do we mean by the term "angle"? Essentially, an angle (or angular measurement) can tell us how large an object appears to be or how far two objects appear to be apart.

The word "appear" is not merely filler. We will often encounter the notion that astronomers do not automatically know what an object actually "is"; rather, all we know for certain is what an

FIGURE 1.1. A mural engraving of Tycho Brahe sitting inside his gigantic quadrant (i.e., part of a protractor), in order to measure positions of planets and stars.

object is "like." Our primary goal as astronomers in fact is to dig out the reality from the appearance. This can begin with something as simple as comparing how large an object appears to how large it actually is (Figure 1.2):

FIGURE 1.2. The full Moon appears to be one half degree across from Earth. Is this because the Moon is small and close by, or large but far away?

Measuring the angular diameter of an object is a piece of information that can help us determine how large across—the physical diameter—the object really is. But by itself, the angular diameter doesn't fully answer such a question.

So why bother with angles? An angular measurement is the first (and often easiest) piece of information we can learn about an object. Specifically, an angular measurement (or measurements) tells us where to look in the sky to find an object. This might not seem important, until we realize that (a) the vast majority of objects are not visible with the naked eye, and so we need to know where to point our telescopes, and (b) without the determination of precise positions, even for bright objects, we would never have been able to discover even basic knowledge, such as the fact that the Earth orbits the Sun.

Check Your Neighbor

The Sun and the full Moon both subtend an angle of about one half a degree on the sky. Which object is larger? What else would you need to know in order to tell?

1. Angular Units

For interesting historical reasons (see chapter 3), we commonly divide a full circle into 360 angular degrees.[1] As small as this is, the Sun and full Moon both only extend about half of a degree across, and these are the largest appearing astronomical objects in our skies. In other words, for astronomers an individual degree is a very large angle.

Astronomers thus divide degrees into smaller units. Each individual degree can be split into 60 equal *arcminutes* (a.k.a. minutes of arc) and each arcminute further into 60 *arcseconds* (a.k.a. seconds of arc).

Astronomers often signify the arcminute with a single apostrophe (') or by the abbreviation "arcmin" and the arcsecond with a double apostrophe (") or with "arcsec."

To put these units into perspective, the smallest angle distinguishable by a normal person's naked eye is about 1–2 arcminutes. A high-quality telescope is needed for angles smaller than that.

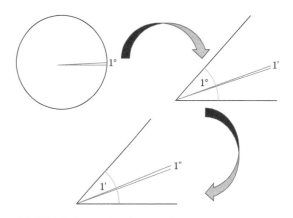

FIGURE 1.3. Successive sketches showing the relative sizes of the angular degree, the arcminute, and the arcsecond.

In some instances, instead of degrees astronomers use a specific unit called the *hour angle*. Just like a complete day has a duration of 24 hours, a complete circle consists of 24-hour angles. Hour angles can also be divided into

---

[1] The word "degree" implies a "step." An angular degree can be seen as a "step" across the sky, a Fahrenheit degree is a "step" up or down in temperature, a bachelor's degree is a "step" up in one's level of education, and so on.

minutes and seconds. Hour angles are almost always restricted to one specific type of measurement called right ascension (see Section 1.3).

Finally, physicists and mathematicians will often describe angles in terms of a unit called the radian, with 2π radians comprising a complete circle. We will rarely encounter the radian in this textbook.

2. Right Triangles

This is not a course on right-triangle trigonometry. Nevertheless, a few basic concepts from trigonometry will come in handy.

Let us designate the sides of a right triangle with letters A, O, and H. We will also use the Greek letter θ ("theta", representing the "th" sound in English) to represent one of the (non-right) angles inside the triangle (Figure 1.4):

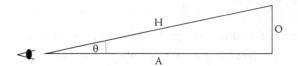

FIGURE 1.4. A right triangle with angle (θ), hypotenuse (H), adjacent side (A), and opposite side (O). The stylized eyeball at the narrow end of the triangle represents the observer.

"H" represents the hypotenuse of the right triangle, which is always the longest leg of the triangle. "A" represents the "adjacent" side of the triangle, or the other side touching (adjacent to) the angle θ. Finally, "O" represents the "opposite" side of the triangle, or the side opposite of the angle θ. Often in astronomy, we place the observer at the corner of the triangle with the angle, and we are looking out into space toward the opposite side.

Four useful relationships between the legs and the angle for a right triangle are as follows:

Equations 1.1

$H^2 = A^2 + O^2$ (a.k.a. the Pythagorean theorem)
$\cos\theta = A/H$ (cosine)
$\sin\theta = O/H$ (sine)
$\tan\theta = O/A$ (tangent)

The most useful of these equations for us will be the tangent ("tan") relation. Let's explore a quick example (Figure 1.5):

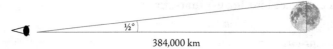

384,000 km

FIGURE 1.5. How large across is the Moon, given it subtends an angle of one half a degree and is 384,000 km from the Earth?

We can measure the angle of the full Moon; suppose it ends up at 0.50 degrees. We can also determine the distance to the Moon to a very high amount of precision;[2] suppose that is found to be 384,000 kilometers (or 223,000 miles). Look at the tangent formula:

$$\tan\theta = O/A$$

---

[2] During the lunar landing missions, astronauts placed mirrors on the surface of the Moon. Astronomers on Earth (from the McDonald Observatory in west Texas) shone laser beams at these mirrors and measured the round-trip travel time of the laser light. From this, they were able to calculate the distance to the Moon.

We know both the angle (θ) and the adjacent side (A). Rearrange the formula to solve for the opposite side, which represents the Moon's diameter:

$$O = A \tan\theta$$

Plug in the numbers (a scientific calculator will be able to handle the tangent piece[3]) and we get

$$O = (384{,}000 \text{ km}) \times \tan(0.50°) = 3350 \text{ km}$$

The Moon's diameter is thus 3,350 km. To find its radius, divide this result by two.

Finally, how might we apply angles expressed in arcminutes or arcseconds? Suppose a crater on the Moon subtends an angle of 10 arcseconds. Scientific calculators don't tend to have settings for arcminutes or arcseconds, so we need to change the units into degrees:

$$\theta = 10'' \times (1' / 60'') \times (1° / 60') = 0.00278°$$

Then we can again calculate the physical length of the opposite side:

$$O = (384{,}000 \text{ km}) \times \tan(0.00278°) = 18.6 \text{ km}$$

The crater therefore has a diameter of 18.6 km, or 11.6 miles.

Section 1.2: Local Coordinates

Our next task is to describe how astronomers locate objects in the sky. Astronomers use two basic systems. Here, we will discuss how astronomers depict angular coordinates of objects from an observer's specific location.

The Earth is nearly a perfect sphere. However, it is so large that, if you are standing in a large open field or on a boat in the ocean, it looks flat to the naked eye. More specifically, it appears that the sky and the ground meet to create a large circle around oneself, which astronomers call the *horizon* (Figure 1.6):

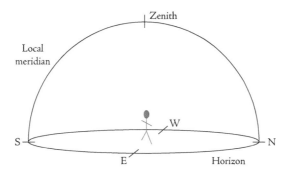

FIGURE 1.6. A depiction of local, or alt-azimuth, coordinates. An observer stands in an open space on the Earth, and the sky appears to be a large dome above the observer.

---

[3] When using a scientific calculator, make sure the calculator is set to the proper units. Some brands of calculators default to units of radians. Every calculator should have a button where you can change the setting from radians to degrees, if necessary.

Another point of interest is the *zenith*, which is directly above the observer's head. The opposite point (below the observer's feet) is called the nadir, but astronomers rarely use it (why?).

Astronomers also find it convenient to divide the sky in east-west halves. Imagine starting due south on the horizon. Then sketch an arc from there, through the zenith, and on to due north, again on the horizon, but now on the opposite side of the observer. This arc is called the *local meridian*.

This terminology, by the way, shows up in everyday life. The Sun rises in the east and sets in the west each day. When the Sun is to the east of the local meridian, we call that "a.m." or "*ante-meridiem*" ("ante" is a prefix that means "before"), and when the Sun is to the west of the local meridian, that becomes "p.m." or "*post-meridiem*" ("post" meaning "after"). The very instant that the Sun crosses the local meridian is called *local noon* by astronomers.[4]

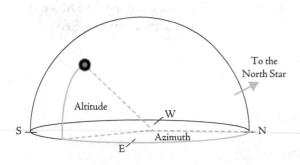

FIGURE 1.7. The altitude and azimuth angles for a star. The direction to the North Star is also depicted. (This is for an observer in the northern hemisphere only.)

Next, we wish to locate objects in the sky. Again, recall that we don't need to know the distance to an object in order to point toward it. This implies that we only need to use angles. Figure 1.7 shows these local coordinates at work.

The *altitude* is the angular height of an object above the horizon. Altitude can range from 0° (at the horizon) to 90° (at the zenith). Note there are no negative altitudes. We again emphasize this is an angular measurement; it makes no sense in astronomy to describe an object's altitude in terms of a length unit such as miles or feet.

The *azimuth* is the angle on an object along the horizon. Azimuth typically starts at 0° (due north) and can go up to 180° either east or west.

Since objects appear to move in the sky (because the Earth actually rotates on its axis), an object's altitude and azimuth change over the course of a night. Further, once an observer travels a large enough distance (a few tens of miles is enough to notice with the naked eye), an object's altitude and azimuth also change. Thus, altitude and azimuth are space and time dependent; we need to specify the location, date, and time for an observer in order to use the alt-azimuth system.

One more item of interest: In our current epoch, the Earth's North Pole points (almost dead-on) toward a star in the sky. This is the North Star, or Polaris. Polaris has the unique property (again, this is an approximation) of remaining still while all other stars move. Further, the altitude of Polaris is the same as one's latitude on Earth. Polaris became an important guidepost for sailors centuries ago, who otherwise wouldn't have any landmarks on the open ocean. Unfortunately, there is no comparable South Star in this period of history—though, if you're willing to wait about 50,000 years, Sirius will be there!

Section 1.3: Global Coordinates

The advantage of local coordinates is that it tells you (the observer) where and when to look for particular objects. The disadvantage is that those local coordinates are different for an observer at a different location and/or time. Astronomers thus also need a system that works for everybody.

What we can call the "global" set of astronomical coordinates is an extension of the latitude/longitude system of coordinates we use for the surface of the Earth, with a few tweaks (see Figure 1.8). The Earth is placed at the center, and objects are imagined to be on the inner surface of the sky, which we call the *Celestial Sphere*:

---

[4] In modern times, we use time zones and daylight-savings time, so noon on one's clock does not necessarily represent an astronomer's local noon anymore.

Since we extend latitude and longitude to the sky, we also extend other aspects of the Earth's geography:

- The *Celestial Equator* (CE) is the extension of the Earth's equator.
- The *North Celestial Pole* (NCP) is the extension of the Earth's North Pole.
- The *South Celestial Pole* (SCP) is the extension of the Earth's South Pole.

In addition, the Earth orbits the Sun, which makes it appear that the Sun moves against the background of the stars (i.e., on the Celestial Sphere). This path is called the *ecliptic*. Since the Earth's axis is tilted by about 23½° compared to the plane of its orbit around the Sun, the ecliptic is tilted by 23½° compared to the celestial equator. The Sun's particular position on the ecliptic depends therefore on the date; when the ecliptic is north of the celestial equator, the northern hemisphere experiences spring and summer while the southern hemisphere has autumn and fall; when the ecliptic is south of the celestial equator, the seasons for each hemisphere are reversed (see chapter 3 for more details).

What about the extensions of latitude and longitude? Sometimes astronomers will (sensibly) call them celestial latitude and celestial longitude, but more commonly they are called declination and right ascension instead (Figure 1.9).

Declination is the easier of the two coordinates to understand. Declination (sometimes abbreviated "Dec" or with the Greek letter "δ") is truly an extension of latitude to the sky. The latitude of Earth's equator is 0°; the declination of the celestial equator is 0°. The latitude of the Earth's North Pole is 90°; the declination of the North Celestial Pole is 90°, and so on. The only variation is that astronomers tend to use the plus sign (+) for northern declinations and the negative sign (−) for southern declinations.

Right ascension (abbreviated "RA" or with the Greek letter "α") contains some alterations compared to earthly longitude. For starters, astronomers don't use degrees to express RA measurements, but rather a unit unique to astronomy called the *hour angle*. Hour angles make use of the notion that the Earth rotates once (relative to the Sun) every 24 hours. This way, an object will move 1-hour angle (from east to west)

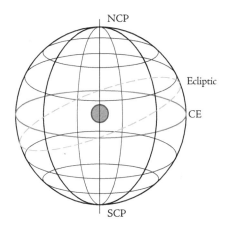

FIGURE 1.8. The Celestial Sphere—the extension of the Earth's latitude/longitude system to the sky.

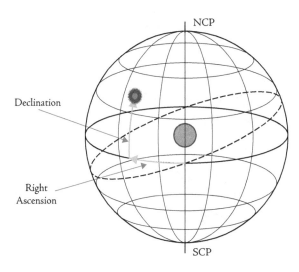

FIGURE 1.9. Right Ascension (celestial longitude) and declination (celestial latitude) applied to the position of an object on the Celestial Sphere.

Check Your Neighbor

What is the approximate declination of the North Star?

for every hour of time. Hour angles are further split into minutes and seconds. Also, on Earth longitude is expressed as degrees east or west from the "prime" meridian (the line of longitude that passes through the town of Greenwich, England); for the Celestial Sphere, RA only goes in one direction and ranges from 0 hours to 24 hours. Finally, hour angles increase going to the left (when one puts north at the top of the page) rather than the typical arrangement where numbers increase going to the right.

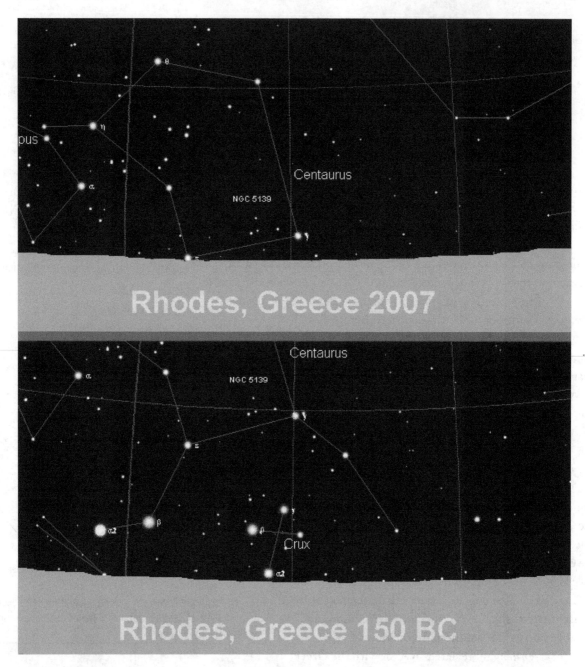

FIGURE 1.10. The effects of physical velocities of stars, the precession of the Earth, and other subtle motions on the global coordinates of stars. The most prominent constellation is Crux, also known as the Southern Cross. Images made using Cartes du Ciel.

Objects in the solar system move quickly enough that astronomers don't assign permanent RA-Dec coordinates to them (although we can and do assign RA-Dec coordinates for solar system objects each day). Objects outside of the solar system—like stars and galaxies—also move through physical space, but because they are so distant, their motions don't noticeably change over days, weeks, or even years. However, some stars move quickly enough so that their positions do become noticed by astronomers over the years (and the solar system itself moves through space, too), and combined with other subtle movements of the Earth itself, primarily precession (see Figure 1.10), means that RA-Dec coordinates of objects are in need of occasional updating. Astronomers therefore (for general use) publish new global coordinates every 50 years. The latest update was in the year ("epoch") 2000, and thus the next will be in 2050. In addition, professionals update coordinates for individual objects of interest as need be. Table 1.1 shows global coordinates for a sample of famous stars.

TABLE 1.1. A Sample of Stellar Global Coordinates (epoch 2000)

Star	Constellation	RA (h m)	Dec (°)
Polaris	Ursa Major	2 32	+89
Algol	Perseus	3 5	+40
Aldebaran	Taurus	4 36	+17
Rigel	Orion	5 14	−8
Betelgeuse	Orion	5 55	+7
Sirius	Canis Major	6 45	−16

Data from van Leeuwen F. (2007) "Validation of the new Hipparcos reduction". Astronomy and Astrophysics 474, 653–364. Also see http://simbad.u-strasbg.fr/simbad/sim-ref?bibcode=2007A%26A...474..653V.

Section 1.4: Constellations

Constellations (in the general sense of the term) are about as old as human history; stories regarding Taurus the Bull and Leo the Lion go back over 5,000 years. The most famous star catalog in antiquity comes from *Almagest*,[5] a compilation of writings from Ptolemy of Alexandria c. 150 C.E. (with many of its star positions derived from the work of Hipparchus several centuries prior). Each culture has created its own pictures out of the stars. But until modern times there was no commonly accepted set of constellations, even amongst astronomers, and most stars were not allotted to any constellation.

> **Check Your Neighbor**
>
> Which stars in Table 1.1 are in the northern portion (hemisphere) of the Celestial Sphere? Which are in the southern portion?

The IAU (International Astronomical Union) changed all that. Starting in 1922, the IAU[6] settled on 88 "official" constellations that (a) include all stars and (b) cover all of the sky. A star does not have to be part of the constellation's picture in order to be part of the constellation; rather, think of stars being like cities belonging to a state. Cities do not have to outline the borders of the state, or form a coherent picture, to be part of the state, and stars are now in a similar relationship to constellations (see Figure 1.11).

Because astronomers have global coordinates already for objects, why do they need constellations? It's less a need than a convenience for many of them. The general locations of constellations are easier to visualize than that of individual stars. Many objects are named or catalogued using their positions in their respective constellations—the North Star, for example, is also known as alpha Ursa Minoris. Like state boundaries, while not perfect or truly permanent, constellations help astronomers organize their knowledge.

In comparison, some of the best-known star pictures are asterisms. The only real difference between an asterism and a constellation is that asterisms are unofficial (according to astronomers) and a constellation is official. Even astronomers sometimes use the terms interchangeably, and it's only a matter of convenience for astronomers to prefer official constellations at times. Some asterisms are identical to their corresponding constellations (for example, the Little Dipper = Ursa Minor), some asterisms are parts of constellations (for example, the Great Square of Pegasus), and some asterisms are borrowed from multiple constellations (for example, the Summer Triangle consists of bright stars from Lyra, Cygnus, and Aquila). Figure 1.12 shows an image with both an asterism and a constellation:

---

[5] Not "*The* Almagest." The prefix "Al" in Arabic already means "the."

[6] The IAU gained public fame in 2006 for their unexpected demotion of Pluto from belonging to the list of "major" planets to one of the newly created categories of "minor" planets. See chapter 7 for more discussion of this event.

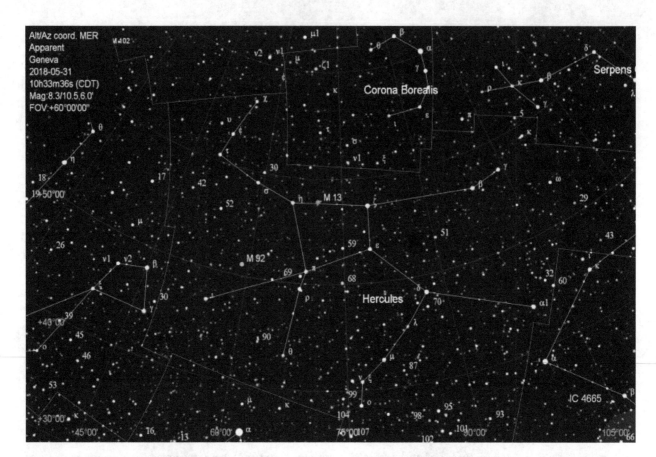

FIGURE 1.11. At top, a star chart showing the constellation of Hercules, with its boundaries with other constellations shaded and its brightest stars connected to show a picture. At right, a map of the state of Mississippi, showing its boundaries with other states and its major cities labeled.

FIGURE 1.12. The asterism of the Big Dipper and its host constellation, Ursa Major. The Big Dipper makes up the back end of the body and the tail of the Great Bear. Credit: Torston Bronger.

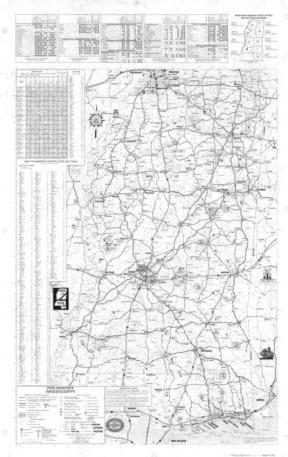

Today's modern constellations, especially those in the northern hemisphere, are primarily named after ancient Greek and Roman myths, for the simple reason that the IAU consisted primarily of European astronomers at the time the constellations were set in the early 20th century. The tenor of naming changes somewhat as one goes well south of the celestial equator; there, constellations tend to have names derived from European sailing voyages of the 15th and 16th centuries. Constellation names also use Latin variations of their popular names ("Ursa Major" instead of the "Great Bear"). Interestingly, star names ("Aldebaran" and others) and coordinate terminology (azimuth, horizon) tend to be borrowed from Arab astronomers c. 1000 c.e.

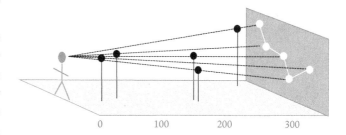

One more thing: Constellations appear to be flat and unmoving, but that is a reflection of their immense distances and that stars appear to us as points on a black background. We have already commented on star movement over time; it is also worth pointing out that stars really exist in three-dimensional space (Figure 1.13), and that observers in different parts of the galaxy will see different constellations.

FIGURE 1.13. A two-dimensional projection of the constellation of Cassiopeia.

Section 1.5: Conic Sections

Ancient Greek mathematicians paid special attention to geometry, and among their discoveries was a class of shapes formed by slicing through a pair of inverted cones: the *conic sections* (Figure 1.14):

Strangely enough, the conic sections have many applications in astronomy. Many large objects such as planets and stars have spherical (the three-dimensional version of a circle) shapes. A parabolic mirror has the advantage of concentrating (via reflection) all of the light from an astronomical object to a single point. All four can represent the path of an object flying through space due to the gravitational influence of another object.

The ellipse deserves some special attention here. As we will see in chapter 3, it shows the simplest path an object such as a planet can take as it orbits the Sun. Let's compare it to the circle, which is a special case of the ellipse (Figure 1.15):

A circle and an ellipse are very similar in origin. But where the circle has one specific center, and all points on the circle are the same distance from the center (the "radius"), an ellipse has two points (*foci*), each equal distance from the center.

An ellipse is a highly symmetrical figure. Drawn correctly, it is widest along one line (the "major axis") and thinnest along another line (the "minor axis"). By definition, the two axes are perpendicular to each other, and each divides the ellipse into two equal halves.

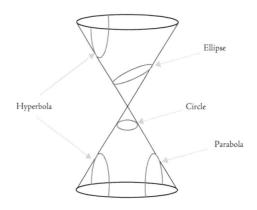

FIGURE 1.14. The conic sections are made by slicing a plane through two identical cones, inverted compared to each other and touching at their tips.

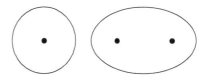

FIGURE 1.15. To draw either a circle or ellipse, make a loop of string. Place one thumb tack at the center, pull the loop taught with a pencil, and go around once; that creates a circle (left). Use two thumb tacks and repeat the process; that creates an ellipse (right).

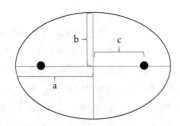

FIGURE 1.16. The semi-major axis (a), the semi-minor axis (b), and the distance from a focus to the center (c) for an ellipse.

In astronomy, it is more convenient to discuss the distance from a furthest point along the ellipse to the center, or half of the major axis; this is called the *semi-major axis* and is denoted in mathematics with the little letter *a*. Half of the minor axis is similarly titled the semi-minor axis, or *b*. Finally, the distance from either of the foci (singular *focus*) to the center of the ellipse does not have an official name but is denoted by the letter *c* (Figure 1.16).

An important consideration for an ellipse is the amount to which it is stretched out, a quantity called the *eccentricity*. The formula for the eccentricity *e* of an ellipse is rather simple:

Equation 1.2

$$e = \frac{c}{a}$$

For example, the eccentricity of a circle is zero, meaning it is not stretched out at all. If the eccentricity of the ellipse gets up to 1, this means one side of the ellipse is "broken," and instead of an ellipse, we have a parabola. Hyperbolas have eccentricities greater than 1. By default, the eccentricity of an ellipse is between 0 and 1.

Let's try a sample calculation. Suppose the distance from one focus to the center of the ellipse in Figure 1.16 is 1.0 inches, and the semi-major axis of the ellipse is 1.5 inches. Then the eccentricity of the ellipse is

$$e = \frac{c}{a} = \frac{1.0 \text{ inches}}{1.5 \text{ inches}} = 0.67$$

Notice that eccentricity is simply a number and has no units.

Summary

In this chapter, we discussed the following:

▸ Basic properties and units of angles

▸ Why astronomers start with angular measurements rather than physical ones

▸ How astronomers find objects from specific locations ("local" or "alt-azimuth" coordinates)

▸ How astronomers find objects in general ("global" or "RA-Dec" coordinates)

▸ Similarities and differences between constellations and asterisms

▸ How star positions change with different positions on Earth, in space, and in time

▸ Review of in-detail properties ellipses

Questions

1. The full Moon subtends about ½ of an angular degree. How large is that in units of arcminutes? Of arcseconds?

2. How many arcminutes are there in a complete circle? How many arcseconds?

3. The ancient Greek scientist Aristarchus found that, despite the Sun and full Moon appearing to be the same size, the Sun was about 20 times further away than the Moon (Note: The modern number is 400). How much larger than the Moon is the Sun, according to Aristarchus?

4. Astronomers at McDonald Observatory sent laser beams to the Moon, which reflected off mirrors set up by astronauts. They measured the round-trip travel time of the light to be 2.56 seconds. How far away is the Moon? Hint: The speed of light is 300,000 km/s.

5. Refer to Section 1.1: What _is_ the radius of the Moon?

6. The Sun subtends an angle of 0.50° and is 150,000,000 km (93,000,000 miles) away. What is the diameter of the Sun?

7. The Sun and the full Moon both subtend an angle of about ½°. The distance to the Sun is about 150,000,000 km whereas the distance to the Moon is about 384,000 km. How much larger (in terms of ratios) is the Sun compared to the Moon? Compare your result to the statement in the third question concerning Aristarchus.

8. A granule is a convection bubble on the surface of the Sun. Suppose a solar telescope finds a granule has an apparent diameter of 1 arcsecond. What is the approximate physical diameter of the granule? Recall the distance to the Sun is about 150,000,000 km (93,000,000 miles).

9. Briefly describe why astronomers tend not to make much use of the nadir.

10. The latitude in Hattiesburg, Mississippi, is approximately 31.5° north. What is the approximate altitude of the North Star in Hattiesburg?

11. Why are there no "east" or "west" stars? What happens to make this impossible?

12. Defend the statement that a circle has an eccentricity of zero. Hint: If there is only one center (or focus), what is the distance from the focus to the center of the circle?

13. The semi-major axis for the Earth is 150 million kilometers, and its eccentricity is 0.0167. How far is the Sun (which is at one focus) from the center of the Earth's orbit?

Activities

▸ *Only possible during a partial or total lunar eclipse:* Draw a circle on a piece of paper 1 inch in diameter. Then sketch the Earth's shadow on the Moon when the shadow covers about half of the Moon. Use this to estimate the relative sizes of the Earth and Moon.

▸ *Astrophysics activity 1.1*: Perform naked-eye observations of the night sky as instructed.

▸ *Astrophysics activity 1.2:* With the instructor's assistance, construct a simple astrolabe, a device used to measure the altitude and azimuth of an object on the sky.

▸ *Astrophysics activity 1.3*: Using an astrolabe or protractor, measure the altitude and azimuth of the Moon each half-hour over a total of 3 hours or more. Plot the results on a graph, using altitude on the vertical axis and azimuth on the horizontal axis. Briefly describe your results.

▸ Using an astrolabe or protractor, measure the altitude and azimuth of the Moon or a bright planet over the course of several weeks, in conjunction with your instructor. Plot the results on a graph, using altitude on the vertical axis and azimuth on the horizontal axis. Briefly describe your results.

▸ With the instructor's assistance, plot the RA-Dec coordinates of a planet over the course of several weeks. Place declination on the vertical axis and right ascension on the horizontal axis. Briefly describe your results.

▸ Write a short report regarding the origins of the modern constellations in the early 20th century.

Credits

Astronomical Clock from Prague

CHAPTER 2

MEASUREMENTS OF TIME

To learn the origins of basic units of time

OBJECTIVES

- ▸ To distinguish between basic types of days
- ▸ To distinguish between basic types of months
- ▸ To review the phases of the Moon
- ▸ To understand the historical origins of the week
- ▸ To review lunar and solar eclipses
- ▸ To compare different versions of the calendar
- ▸ To review the causes of seasons
- ▸ To discuss precession

INTRODUCTION

Many disciplines like to claim they influence our daily lives. In the case of astronomy, that statement may be taken literally.

Our most basic units of time—starting with the day—are due to the motions of celestial objects, including the Earth. The day, week, month, year, and even seasons have their origins in astronomy. Smaller units of time—hours, minutes, and seconds—have different origins, and we will not pursue them here.

Our goal in this chapter is to present the history of units of time.

KEY TERMS

Annular eclipse: A solar eclipse seen from Earth, where the Moon is perfectly centered in front of the Sun but is too far from the Earth for its shadow to completely cover the Sun

Antumbra: The shadow directly behind a blocking object, but where the blocking object is too small to completely cover the eclipsed object

Calendar: A mental device used to keep track of a year. Calendars are usually related to the orbit of the Earth about the Sun, but some versions track the orbit of the Moon about the Earth

Crescent phase (a.k.a. crescent moon): A phase of the Moon where just a curved sliver of sunlight is reflected by the Moon back to the Earth

Equinox: When the Earth crosses the ecliptic, its northern and southern hemispheres theoretically experience equal amounts of daylight and nighttime. There are two equinoxes: the *vernal* (spring) equinox and the *autumnal* (fall) equinox

First quarter: A phase of the Moon where half of the sunlight reflected by the Moon reaches the Earth. The Moon has also traveled one-fourth of its orbit since the new moon phase

Full phase (a.k.a. full moon): A phase of the Moon where all of the sunlight reflected by the Moon reaches the Earth

Gibbous phase (a.k.a. gibbous moon): A phase of the Moon where most, though not all, of the sunlight reflected by the Moon reaches the Earth. "Gibbous" is a word that means "hunchback"

Inclination: The tilt of the Earth's axis compared to the plane of its orbit about the Sun

Lunar phase diagram: A diagram showing both the relative positions of the Earth, Moon, and Sun for each of the eight separate lunar phases, but also the appearance of the Moon for each phase

New phase (a.k.a. new moon): A phase of the Moon where none of the sunlight reflected by the Moon reaches the Earth

Optical infinity: When an object is so far away from us that, for practical purposes, we can assume it is infinitely far away; or, rays of light from the object approach us in parallel lines

Partial eclipse: When a shadow only partially covers the object being eclipsed. All eclipses are at least at some point in time partial

Penumbra: A partial shadow, or where light mixes with shadow, creating a lighter shadow as a consequence

Precession: The wobbling of the direction of the Earth's axis; approximately 26,000 years

Sidereal day: The amount of time for the Earth to rotate once relative to the background of stars

Sidereal month: The amount of time for the Moon to orbit the Earth once relative to the background of stars

Sidereal year: The amount of time for the Sun to return to the same position relative to the stars

Solar day: The amount of time for the Earth to rotate once relative to the Sun

Solar year: The amount of time for the Earth to orbit the Sun

Solstice: When the Earth is tilted as much toward or away from the Sun (or, is at its maximum or minimum positions on the ecliptic). There are two solstices, summer and winter

Synodic month: The amount of time for the Moon to orbit the Earth once relative to the Sun

Third quarter (a.k.a. last quarter): A phase of the Moon where half of the sunlight reflected by the Moon reaches the Earth. The Moon has also traveled three-fourths of its orbit about the Earth since new moon phase

Total eclipse: When a shadow completely covers the object being eclipsed

Tropical year: The amount of time for the Sun to go from the vernal equinox to the next vernal equinox

Umbra: The darkest part of a shadow, directly behind the light-blocking object

Waning moon: The portion of the Moon's orbit (and corresponding phases) where the amount of sunlight reflected back to the Earth decreases day after day

Waxing moon: The portion of the Moon's orbit (and corresponding phases) where the amount of sunlight reflected back to the Earth increased day after day

Week: A unit of time composed of several days. The standard week is seven days in duration

Section 2.1: The Day

The most important astronomical object (besides the Earth itself) is the Sun, and the cycle of time used to track its apparent motion is the day. But the day we know from normal life is actually a combination of real motions of the Earth. Let's explore the basics of this unit of time.

The Earth is (almost) a sphere and rotates about its axis. This rotation occurs regardless of whether the Earth or other objects are moving (or, we might say it is an <u>intrinsic</u> property of the Earth). How fast does the Earth spin, and how do we measure its spin?

Stars are so distant that, for this purpose, we can assume they are infinitely far away,[1] a notion called *optical infinity*. This is an important statement to make up front, since we (hopefully obviously!) can't draw pictures of infinitely distant objects. Any pictures we show are necessarily not to scale.

With that in mind, let's imagine the Earth floating by itself in space, with its intrinsic rotation its only motion (Figure 2.1), starting at local noon.

If we watch carefully, the Earth requires 23 hours, 56 minutes, and 3.92 seconds to complete a rotation relative to the background stars. Since astronomers (like many other professionals!) enjoy using ancient languages for simple concepts, we call this the Earth's *sidereal day* (from the Latin *sider*, meaning star).

You probably noticed something odd. We all grow up learning the day consists of 24 hours, exactly. What happened?

FIGURE 2.1. A location on Earth points through the Sun toward a distant background of stars, so that the Sun appears to be in front of a set group of stars. The Earth rotates counterclockwise from this orientation. The figure is <u>not</u> to scale.

Check Your Neighbor

How might you go about measuring the Earth's sidereal day? What instrument(s) would you need?

If the Earth were indeed floating still, with rotation being its only motion, this would be the complete story. However, the Earth does not sit still, but orbits the Sun. Let's explore the consequences of including this additional motion (Figure 2.2).

If the Earth were not revolving about the Sun,[2] the Sun would appear to be in front of the same group of stars after one complete rotation. But since the Earth does move (at least a little) about the Sun while this happens, the Sun and stars will not be aligned as before. To bring the Sun back around to local noon, the Earth needs to move (both rotating and revolving) just a little more. But that guarantees the Sun will <u>not</u> appear in front of the same set of stars.

The duration from one local noon to the next is called the *solar day*, and this is our familiar 24 hours.

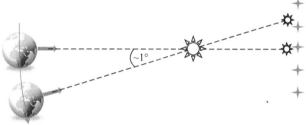

FIGURE 2.2. The same picture as Figure 2.1, but now the Earth also orbits the Sun. The Earth both rotates counterclockwise <u>and</u> orbits counterclockwise from this orientation. The Sun now appears to be in front of a different group of stars. The figure is <u>not</u> to scale.

In order for this to happen compared to the sidereal day, the Earth has to continue to move for nearly 4 extra minutes. In terms of angles, the Earth moves through its orbit almost a full angular degree.

One more thing: In our figures, we have oriented the Earth so that its rotation and revolution both are counterclockwise. By definition, we are therefore looking down on the North Pole of both the Earth and the solar system (we are ignoring the tilt of the Earth's axis for the moment). This also means that, from the Earth's perspective, the Sun appears to have moved—compared to the background stars—to the <u>east</u>. This is not the same as the Sun's apparent motion in the sky

Check Your Neighbor

What is the origin of the degree symbol? Hint: How many degrees are there in a complete circle, and how many days are there in a year?

---

[1] The nearest star system to ours, Alpha Centauri, is over 200,000 times further from us than the Sun.

[2] In astronomy, the term "rotation" refers to an object spinning about its axis, whereas the term "revolve" refers to an object orbiting about another object.

during the day, which is east to west; we are talking here about the Sun's apparent motion relative to the constellations.

Section 2.2: The Month

The story behind the month, and its corresponding lunar phases, is similar to that of the day. To fully understand it, we need to incorporate multiple motions.

Again, start by assuming the Earth does not orbit the Sun. But here we now include the Moon and its orbit about the Earth. For simplicity, we also assume the Moon's orbit is constant and circular, and all motions are counterclockwise (see Figure 2.3):

FIGURE 2.3. A location on Earth points through the Moon toward the Sun and then a distant background of stars. The Moon orbits the Earth counterclockwise from this orientation. The figure is <u>not</u> to scale.

Since the Moon is in the daytime sky, and the bright side of the Moon is facing away from the Earth, we do not typically see the Moon in this orientation. This is called the *new* phase of the Moon (see Section 2.3 for more details).

Similar to a sidereal day, the amount of time for the Moon to orbit the Earth such that it appears in front of the same group of stars is called the *sidereal month*. A sidereal month is about 27 1/3 days long. Note that when we use the term "day" without a qualifier, we mean the solar (24-hour) day.

Again, however, in reality the Earth also orbits the Sun. In order to return to the next new moon, the Earth and Moon both need to continue moving (see Figure 2.4).

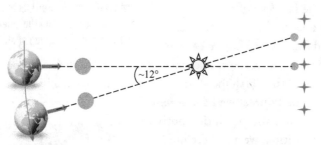

FIGURE 2.4. The same picture as Figure 2.3, but now the Earth also orbits the Sun. Both the Earth orbits the Sun and the Moon orbits the Earth counterclockwise from this orientation. The Moon now appears to be in front of a different group of stars. The figure is <u>not</u> to scale.

For historical reasons, instead of calling this the "solar" month, the time between successive new moons is called the *synodic month*. Like the solar day, the synodic month is longer than its sidereal counterpart—in this case, the synodic month is about 29 ½ days.

We pictured the synodic month as going from new moon to new moon, but it is the same for any phase—from first quarter to first quarter, from full moon to full moon, and so on.

Do any of these issues arise for other planets and moons? The answer is yes; we will discuss some of these consequences in their turns in later chapters for the planets Mercury and Venus, and some select moons (like Io and Triton) in the outer solar system.

Check Your Neighbor

Toward which direction does the Moon appear to move compared to the background stars each successive night: east or west?

Section 2.3: Lunar Phases

Whenever it is in the sky, the Sun shows up as a smooth yellow-white disk. The Moon, on the other hand, looks different at different times, going through a cycle of appearances astronomers call *phases*.

Some people think that the Earth's shadow is responsible for the phases of the Moon. This is a misconception. Rather, the phases of the Moon come about due to our changing vantage point—or, the changing relative positions of the Earth, Moon, and Sun.

We have already mentioned the new moon phase. When does this happen? Refer to Figure 2.5 during this discussion (we have darkened the night sides of both the Earth and Moon):

FIGURE 2.5. At left is the arrangement of the Earth, Moon, and Sun during a new moon. At right are the positions of the Sun and Moon as seen from Earth during a new moon. The figure is <u>not</u> to scale.

During a new moon phase, the Moon is in between the Sun and the Earth. Because the Moon and Sun are approximately the same angular size, one might expect the Moon to block the light from the Sun. While this looks guaranteed, the Moon's orbit about the Earth (in three-dimensional space) is slightly tilted compared to the Earth's orbit about the Sun. For most new moons, the Moon is either above or below the Sun.

Why don't we see the Moon during a new moon phase? Most importantly, the Sun is incredibly bright, and its glare tends to wash out the Moon. Also, the side of the Moon reflecting sunlight is pointed away from us. These two effects make it virtually impossible to see the new Moon with the naked eye.

If the Moon didn't move, then this would be its only phase. Of course, the Moon does actually orbit the Earth. Suppose we go forward about seven to eight days, which is one-fourth of the duration of the Moon's orbit. Then the relative configuration of Earth-Moon-Sun looks like this (Figure 2.6):

FIGURE 2.6. At left is the arrangement of the Earth, Moon, and Sun during a first quarter phase. At right are the positions of the Sun and Moon as seen from Earth during a first quarter phase. The figure is <u>not</u> to scale.

If you look carefully at the configuration of a first quarter phase, you will notice that only half of the lit side of the Moon is pointing toward the Earth. On top of that, only half (of course) of the Moon is ever lit by the Sun. Half of a half is one quarter—which is another way to remember the name and meaning of the phase.

Let's look at one more common phase. A full moon phase occurs when the Moon and Sun are on opposite sides of the Earth (Figure 2.7). Again, more often than not, the Moon is either above or below the Sun, and a lunar eclipse is relatively rare.

FIGURE 2.7. At left is the arrangement of the Earth, Moon, and Sun during a full moon phase. At right is the appearance of the full moon. The Sun is not next to the full Moon at right (why not?). The figure is <u>not</u> to scale.

Astronomers also distinguish phases between these major phases: A crescent moon occurs when just a rounded sliver of the Moon appears, and a gibbous phase occurs when most (though not all) of the Moon is lit. The phases also behave according to a set pattern; when the lit amount of the Moon is increasing, we term this a *waxing* moon; when the lit amount is decreasing, we term this a *waning* moon.

All the phases of the Moon can be depicted in a *lunar phase diagram* (Figure 2.8):

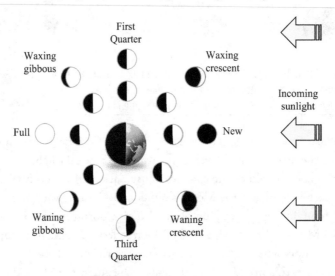

FIGURE 2.8. A lunar phase diagram. Sunlight comes from the right. The inner ring shows the position of the Moon for each phase, with its lit side facing the Sun; the outer ring shows the appearance of the Moon as seen from Earth. The figure is <u>not</u> to scale.

Careful consideration of this diagram allows one to derive facts for each phase. For example, the new moon is in the middle of the sky (i.e., crosses the local meridian) at local noon. Since the Moon takes (on average) 12 hours to go across the sky, this implies the new moon rises around 6 a.m. and sets at 6 p.m. Conversely, a full moon rises at 6 p.m., crosses the local meridian at midnight, and sets at 6 a.m. The quarter phases are in between the new and full phases, and the crescent and gibbous phases are in between all of these. For example, the waxing gibbous will rise at 3 p.m., cross the local meridian at 9 p.m., and set at 3 a.m.

Check Your Neighbor

Assume the night sky lasts from 6 p.m. to 6 a.m. Which phase do you see during the entire night? Which phase is never visible at night?

Section 2.4: The Week

The week is a bit of a misfit of a time unit—it is not obviously related to a simple occurrence such as the day or month. Yet it is useful to create a unit of time somewhere (somewhen?) between the day and month, and many cultures have done so. "Weeks" have been as short as 4 days (western Africa) to as long as 10 days (ancient Rome, revolutionary France). The commonplace feeling that a 7-day week is "natural" has more to do with familiarity than with any external source.

Check Your Neighbor

In which section of the sky—east or west—would you expect to see a first quarter moon?

Many astronomy textbooks, for whatever reason, leave out a discussion of the week as a unit of time. Yet our common 7-day-long week has significant astronomical origins, mixed in with some interesting history and mythology, and the names of the days themselves are related to objects in the solar system. Let's review a short presentation of the origin of the week, which is due to the ancient Babylonians.

First, consider that the Moon has four major phases—in order, new, first quarter, full, and third quarter. The synodic period, the time for the lunar phases to repeat, is about 29.5 days. Dividing by 4 gives us 7 3/8 days—neither exactly 7 nor 8 days. This suggests either a 7- or 8-day week, but which one?

The Babylonians[3] had a new moon festival called "sappatu," which would occur either after 29 or after 30 days, depending. They further split the month into four sections for each major lunar phase—but, rather than dividing up the days equally, or changing the days to match each phase, apparently they set the time between each phase to be exactly 7 days, then adjusted to match the new moon at the end (Figure 2.9):

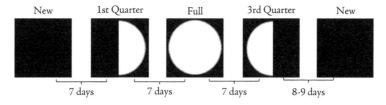

FIGURE 2.9. Durations between lunar phases, according to ancient Babylon.

Keeping to a variable schedule is difficult, however. At some point, the Babylonians fixed on 7 days for the duration of their week, but why?

The second determining factor for a 7-day week lies in what the ancients called "wanderers." As stated earlier, astronomical objects tend to rise in the east and set in the west, due to the Earth rotating on its axis. But seven bright objects exhibit an extra, longer-term motion, "wandering" compared to the star background. We have already discussed the Sun and Moon; the other five are Mars, Mercury, Jupiter, Venus, and Saturn. The ancient Greeks gave us their name—the term "planet" comes from *planētes asteres*, or "wandering stars." The Babylonians were perhaps the first culture to have a coherent description (via cuneiform tablets from the 7th century B.C.E.) of the motions of these objects. The Babylonians also gave each object an individual name and associated them with various deities.

In modern English, our names for the planets come to us from ancient Rome, whereas our names for the days of the week come from Norse tradition. But a side-by-side listing of the days and planets in other languages (such as French, a romance language) and the corresponding mythological figure—all are Nordic except for Saturn—reveal the connections (Table 2.1):

---

[3] The Babylonians had a base-60 number system, apparently in part because 60 is an easy number to divide into whole number parts. They thus are also responsible for 60 minutes per hour, 60 seconds per day, and 360 degrees for a complete circle.

TABLE 2.1. Connections Between the Days and the Planets

Day (in English)	Mythological Figure	Ancient Planet	Day (in French)
Monday	Mani	Moon	lundi ("luhn-dee")
Tuesday	Tui or Tyr	Mars	mardi ("mahr-dee")
Wednesday	Woden or Odin	Mercury	mercredi ("mehr-kruh-dee")
Thursday	Thor	Jupiter	jeudi ("zhuh-dee")
Friday	Frigga or Freya	Venus	vendredi ("vahn-druh-dee")
Saturday	Saturn	Saturn	samedi ("sahm-dee")
Sunday	Sol	Sun	dimanche ("dee-mahnsh")

Modern English is a Germanic language, sharing much of its structure with languages such as German and Dutch. But English also has a large vocabulary derived from Latin and therefore has this in common with languages such as French and Spanish.

The connections are further illustrated if we consider the word "week" itself. "Week" is derived from an old English word meaning "change" (as in, the changing appearance of the Moon). While "week" and "change" aren't alike, their equivalents in modern German, "woche" (week) and "wechsel" (change), make it easier to spot.

The combination of major phases of the Moon plus the ancient wanderers in the sky have thus given us our modern 7-day week.

Finally, recall "sappatu", the name of the Babylonian festival. It was in the 6th century B.C.E. that leading citizens of Judea were taken into captivity to Babylon. In an attempt to retain their traditions and religion while surrounding by a conquering alien culture, they put into writing what we now know as the first books of the Bible. The very first book, Genesis, describes how the world (i.e., the universe) was created in six days, with a seventh day set aside for rest[4]—which in English comes to us as "Sabbath."

Section 2.5: Eclipses

While not a basis for time measurement—being at first glance irregular—lunar and solar eclipses are also consequences of the relative motions of the Earth, Moon, and Sun.

Most figures in textbooks of the Earth and Moon system are not to scale. The reason is simple: If the distance between them is to scale, then the Earth and Moon are very small. Nevertheless, here is a scaled picture (Figure 2.10):

Check Your Neighbor

Suppose Uranus was also extremely bright (it really isn't) and ancient peoples therefore recognized it as a planet. Would a week still be 7 days long, or could you argue for a different result? And if so, how long would a week be?

FIGURE 2.10. The Earth and Moon to scale.

This is worth remembering as we discuss how eclipses work.

Eclipse is the term we use when the shadow of an object covers, or comes close to covering, another object.[5] The objects don't need to be close in physical size (diameter) but should be close in angular size. The Moon and Sun

---

[4] The origins of a 2-day, as opposed to a 1-day, weekend has nothing to do with astronomy; its origins lie in labor movements of the early 20th century.

[5] When a very large object cuts in front of a very small object (again, in terms of angular size), astronomers call that an *occultation*. When a very small object cuts in front of a very large object, astronomers call that a *transit*. We will see both terms again later in this book.

are almost exactly the same angular size—though we will see details matter, here—and thus eclipses are possible, if not common.

If the Moon orbits the Earth, why don't we have both a lunar eclipse and a solar eclipse each month (See Figures 2.5 and 2.7)? If the Moon's orbit about the Earth and the Earth's orbit about the Sun were in the same plane, we would. But the Moon's orbit is actually tilted by about 5° compared to the Earth's orbit, which means the Moon is more often either above or below the Earth (Figure 2.11):

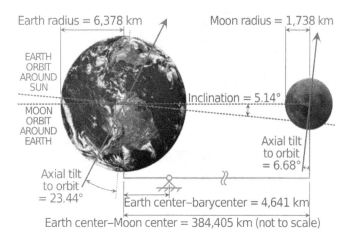

FIGURE 2.11. The inclination (tilt) of the Moon's orbit about the Earth compared to the Earth's orbit about the Sun. The figure is **not** to scale.

A second factor is that the Moon's orbit is not a perfect circle, but elliptical instead. The Moon's apparent (angular) size noticeably changes, meaning that sometimes the Moon's shadow will be large enough to cover the Sun, and sometimes not. The Earth, in comparison, is always large enough that its shadow can cover the Moon if it is lined up.

Let's take a look at some details.

1. Lunar Eclipses

In this case, the Earth's shadow covers part or all of the Moon (Figure 2.12):

FIGURE 2.12. The Earth's shadows during a lunar eclipse.

If the Earth's shadow only covers part of the Moon, then we call that a *partial lunar eclipse*. If the Earth's shadow covers all of the Moon, we call that a *total lunar eclipse*. Since the Moon appears to move through the sky, it enters the Earth's shadow gradually (and also leaves it gradually), so every total eclipse really also includes a partial eclipse.

While the Sun is 93 million miles away, because the Sun is physically much larger than the Earth and Moon (the Sun is roughly a million miles across!), light from the Sun is not perfectly passing the Earth and Moon in parallel lines. This creates two sections of shadow. Directly behind the Earth, where the Sun is completely blocked, we have the *umbra* (or umbral shadow); on the outskirts of the Earth, where part of the Sun is blocked but part is not, we have the *penumbra* (or penumbral shadow). The Moon often passes through the penumbra, but because the penumbra is so light, we often don't even notice it.

Perhaps surprisingly, the Moon does not go completely dark. Rather, sunlight refracts (bends) through the Earth's atmosphere, reflects off the Moon, and comes back to Earth. Since red light refracts better than other colors, the Moon takes on a copper-red tone during a total lunar eclipse (Figure 2.13):

FIGURE 2.13. The Moon during the total lunar eclipse of April 15, 2014.

Lunar eclipses are visible somewhere on Earth on average about two times per year. From start to finish (i.e., when the Earth's umbral shadow first touches the Moon, until the umbra leaves the Moon) they usually take several hours. Totality can last over an hour and a half, depending.

2. Solar Eclipses

In this case, the Moon's shadow covers part or all of the Earth (Figure 2.14).

Similar to lunar eclipses, solar eclipses can also come in partial and total versions. The difference is that the

Check Your Neighbor

What is the phase of the Moon during a lunar eclipse?

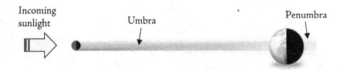

FIGURE 2.14. The Moon's shadows during a solar eclipse.

Moon is much smaller than the Earth, and so is its shadow. Therefore, it is not possible for the entire Earth to experience the same solar eclipse at the same time, while solar eclipses happen as often as lunar eclipses in general (about two per year), a solar eclipse for any individual location on Earth is less common. Further, while a solar eclipse from start to finish still takes several hours, totality at maximum only lasts up to 7 minutes.

While lunar eclipses are entertaining, total solar eclipses are especially valuable to astronomers, even now. Sunlight can pass through valleys on the Moon's surface, showing up as a phenomenon called Baily's beads, and right before or after totality, the same process can yield a diamond ring effect (Figure 2.15). Further, the disk of the Sun (the "photosphere") is about a million times brighter than the other outer layers of the Sun, so we can't normally see them without either a total solar eclipse or a special device called a "coronagraph" placed on board

Check Your Neighbor

What is the phase of the Moon during a solar eclipse?

a solar telescope in space. Either allows us to view the chromosphere, a region where atoms emit spectral lines, and the corona, an ever-changing region of thin gas escaping the surface of the Sun[6] (Figure 2.16):

FIGURE 2.15. The Moon and Sun during the total solar eclipse of August 21, 2017.

FIGURE 2.16. The chromosphere and corona during the total solar eclipse of August 21, 2017.

Because the Moon's orbit is noticeably elliptical, sometimes it is far enough away that the Moon's disk is not large enough to completely cover the Sun, even if it is perfectly aligned with the Earth. This situation is called an annular eclipse (Figure 2.17):

FIGURE 2.17. The Moon's shadows during an annular solar eclipse.

The Earth is too far from the Moon to be within its umbra. However, it does reside within the Moon's *antumbra*, where the shadow becomes dark again. Any spot on the Earth inside the antumbra sees a ring (Latin *annulus*) of sunlight around the Moon.

What does the near future hold for solar eclipses? The next solar eclipse in North America will be an annular eclipse, on October 14, 2023, and the next total solar eclipse in North America will be on April 8, 2024. Figure 2.18 shows a global map showing the paths of total solar eclipses for North America during the 21st century.

---

[6] We will study these layers—the chromosphere and the corona—in more detail in the chapter on the Sun.

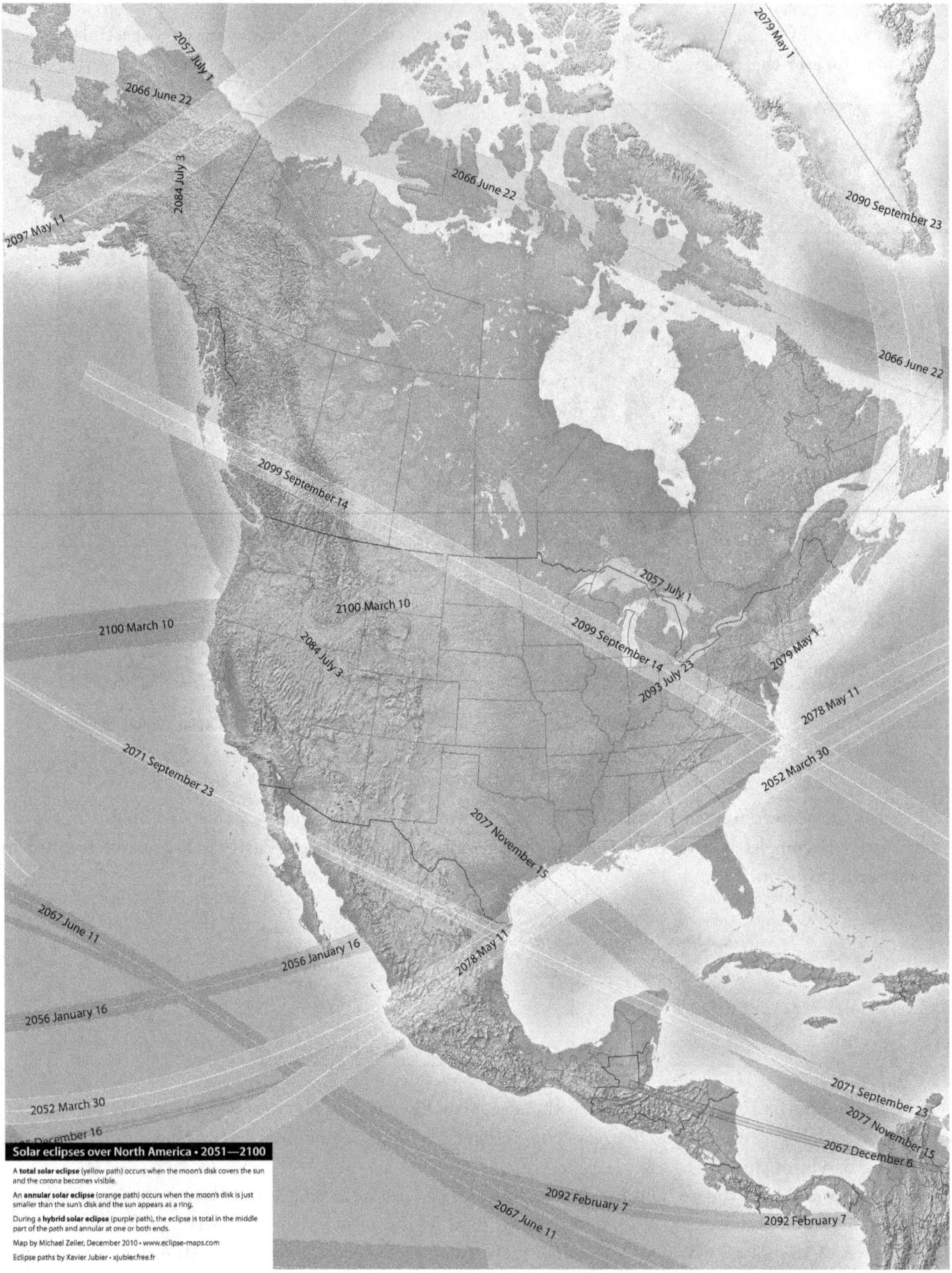
2057 July 1
2066 June 22
2079 May 1
2084 July 3
2097 May 11
2066 June 22
2090 September 23
2066 June 22
2099 September 14
2057 July 1
2100 March 10
2100 March 10
2099 September 14
2084 July 3
2079 May 1
2093 July 23
2078 May 11
2052 March 30
2071 September 23
2077 November 15
2067 June 11
2056 January 16
2078 May 11
2056 January 16
2071 September 23
2052 March 30
2077 November 15
December 16
2067 December 6
2092 February 7
2067 June 11
2092 February 7
Solar eclipses over North America • 2051—2100
A **total solar eclipse** (yellow path) occurs when the moon's disk covers the sun and the corona becomes visible.
An **annular solar eclipse** (orange path) occurs when the moon's disk is just smaller than the sun's disk and the sun appears as a ring.
During a **hybrid solar eclipse** (purple path), the eclipse is total in the middle part of the path and annular at one or both ends.
Map by Michael Zeiler, December 2010 • www.eclipse-maps.com
Eclipse paths by Xavier Jubier • xjubier.free.fr

FIGURE 2.18. Total solar eclipses in North America for the years 2051–2100. The thin line in each stripe represents the maximum path of totality.

Section 2.6: The Year and the Calendar

1. The Egyptian Solar Calendar

Like the story of the week, our modern calendar has a complicated history. In this case, we start with ancient Egypt.

The original Egyptian calendar was based on the Moon, with 12 months—such lunar calendars are still used across the world, often for religious observances. But 12 months of 29.5 days results in a year of 354 days—over 11 days short. The length of the "tropical" year, that is, one that tracks the Earth's orbit about the Sun, is over 365 days. If we wish to accurately track the seasons, we need a Sun-based calendar.

The Egyptians seem to have invented a Sun-based calendar c. 3000 B.C.E. and to have adopted it permanently for civic purposes c. 2500 B.C.E. Why they did is not known for sure, although the flooding of the Nile River (important for irrigation of crops) is roughly in tune with the seasons. They also appear to have tracked the rising of the bright star Sirius instead of the Sun to devise their solar calendar.

The Egyptian solar calendar used 12 months of 30 days each. They were well aware that the year is longer than that; to compensate, 5 extra ("intercalary") days were attached to the end of the year.

This presented a problem, of which the Egyptians themselves were aware. The actual length of the tropical year is closer to 365 ¼ days, which means that,

FIGURE 2.19. Egyptian hieroglyphs (from the Kom Ombo Temple calendar) showing the transition from month XII to month I. The extra 5 days normally placed at the end of the Egyptian calendar are not shown.

without proper adjustments, the calendar will be out of phase with the seasons by 1 day every 4 years. Even though a solution was proposed by Ptolemy III in 238 B.C.E.—to have 6 intercalary days once every 4 years—resistance was strong and the fix was abandoned after Ptolemy's death (Ptolemy was of Greek origin, and his rule was resented by the native priests).

2. The Julian Calendar

The Roman calendar, up through the middle of the 1st century B.C.E., had 12 months (with mostly the same names as we have today), but only totaled 355 days, which made time keeping difficult for officials. During his time in Egypt, Julius Caesar noted the superior Egyptian solar calendar. Hoping to remove the calendar from the vagaries of Roman officialdom, Caesar incorporated the leap day, realigned the calendar with the seasons, and the new calendar began on January 1, 45 B.C.E.

In addition to adding the leap day every 4 years (it was placed at the end of February from the beginning), the lengths of several months were extended to bring the total number of days up to 365 (for example, April went from 29 days to 30 days). In 8 B.C.E., the month of Quintilis was renamed Julius (modern July) in recognition of Caesar's work (it was also the month of his birth), and the month of Sextilis was renamed Augustus (modern August) after Julius's adopted nephew and the first Roman Emperor.[7]

---

[7] Other Roman emperors attempted to change the names of other months. This did not take; otherwise, the beginning of autumn would occur in the month of Germanicus, and so on.

FIGURE 2.20. A bust of Julius Caesar (left); a portrait of Pope Gregory XIII (right).

Unfortunately, Caesar's fix was not accurate enough. The length of the tropical year is closer to 365.24219 days, not 365.25, and so the Julian calendar is a little too long. Although this doesn't matter much from one year to the next—the error is only 0.002%—it does introduce an over counting of 1 day every 128 years. By the 16th century c.e. this had caused an 11-day shift compared to the seasons.

3. The Gregorian Calendar

As with the Julian calendar reform, the Gregorian calendar (a) was promulgated by a powerful official and (b) the actual work was done by astronomers behind the scenes. And, in this case, the transition was quite messy.

JULIAN 1582	\multicolumn{5}{c}{October}	Gregorian 1582	
Sun	Mon	Tues	Wed	Thurs	Fri	Sat
	1	*2*	*3*	*4*	15	16
17	18	19	20	21	22	23
24	25	26	27	28	29	30
31						

FIGURE 2.21. A pictorial description of the shift made during the switch from the Julian to the Gregorian calendar in most of Europe in 1582.

Evidence exists that suggests ancient Greek astronomers were aware of the problem, but for some unknown reason Caesar went with the less-accurate fix. The council of Trent originally authorized Pope Paul III to reform the calendar, and it was brought to completion during the reign of Pope Gregory XIII. Astronomers, led by Aloysius Lilius and Christopher Clavius, came up with the following:

+ Keep the leap day once every 4 years, but now subtract 3 leap days every 4 centuries. This adjustment means the calendar will only be 1 day out of alignment every 3030 years

+ Move up the dates by 11 days to bring the calendar back into alignment with the seasons

While the move worked, it encountered some resistance. For example, the month of October would only contain 20 days instead of its usual 31. Renters were inclined to only pay 2/3 of the monthly rent, whereas landlords demanded a full month's worth. Catholic countries tended to follow the Pope's lead, Protestant and Orthodox nations did not (England, for example, did not make the switch until 1752, and Russia not until 1918).

Today the Gregorian calendar is the officially recognized calendar for international business. The Gregorian calendar assumes the year to be 365.2425 days long; this is close enough that, although some further modifications have been proposed, no other calendars have been adopted.

Section 2.7: The Seasons

While the specific seasons (and how many of them) recognized by people depend largely on where they live, astronomers talk about four distinct seasons thanks to the specific behavior of the Earth in its orbit—and the tilt of its axis.

The Earth is not straight up and down compared to the plane of its orbit (Figure 2.22). Rather, its rotational axis is tilted by 23½°.[8]

FIGURE 2.22. The tilt of the Earth's axis ("inclination") compared to the plane of its orbit about the Sun.

How is the Earth's tilt related to its seasons? When the northern hemisphere of the Earth is tilted toward the Sun (remember that the Sun is so distant that its rays come in parallel), the rays are relatively concentrated (see Figure 2.23). At the same time, the southern hemisphere will be tilted away from the Sun, and the Sun's rays will be relatively diluted. This spurs the northern hemisphere to experience summer and the southern hemisphere to experience winter. Six months later, the situation is reversed.

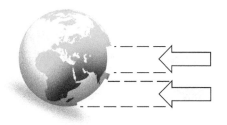

FIGURE 2.23. During Northern summer, the Sun's rays are relatively concentrated in the northern hemisphere and relatively diluted in the southern hemisphere.

Recall from chapter 1 that the apparent path of the Sun is called the *ecliptic*. The ecliptic also represents the actual path of the Earth in its orbit about the Sun, with its tilt taken into account.

When the Earth's northern hemisphere is tilted as much toward the Sun as it can, the Sun will reach its highest altitude possible at local noon. Because the Sun takes longer to cross the sky during summer (there are more hours of daylight in summer), we call this the *summer solstice* (Latin for "stand still"). Of course, this is true only for the north; at the same time, the southern hemisphere will see the Sun reach its lowest possible altitude at local noon and is at its *winter solstice*. Summer and winter solstices trade places half a year later.

When the Earth is tilted sideways—that is, neither the north nor the south hemisphere points toward or away from the Sun—the Earth (everywhere!) theoretically experiences equal amounts of daylight and nighttime.[9] Therefore this is called the *equinox* (Latin for "equal night"). The equinox after winter and leading into summer is the vernal (spring) equinox, and after summer and leading into winter is the autumnal (fall) equinox. Figure 2.24 shows each of these four points in time, with the approximate dates.

---

[8] While the axial tilts—"inclinations"—of planets range from 0 to 90°, Earth, Mars, Saturn, and Neptune all have axial tilts in the 20-degree range. This is likely a coincidence.

[9] We say "theoretical" because the bending of light by the Earth's atmosphere extends daylight by a few minutes.

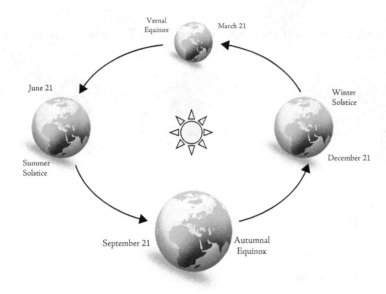

FIGURE 2.24. The results of the Earth's relative tilt compared to the plane of the Earth's orbit. All terms and approximate dates are given for the northern hemisphere.

A common misconception regarding the Earth's seasons is that the Earth is farther away from the Sun during winter and closer to the Sun during summer. Unfortunately for simplicity, that wouldn't work for the opposite hemisphere; more importantly, the Earth's orbit, while not a perfect circle, is only a few percentage points from being one, and the Earth gets about the same amount of sunlight regardless of its position. In fact, the Earth is actually closest to the Sun on January 3, and farthest from the Sun (this is an easy date for U.S. students to remember) on July 4.

Section 2.8: Precession

Hipparchus was probably the greatest astronomer of antiquity. Among various other discoveries—the relative distances to the Moon and Sun, a detailed catalog of the stars (i.e., Celestial Sphere), the first astronomical magnitude (brightness) system for stars—he is credited with the discovery of the effect of *precession*.

Check Your Neighbor

If it is the autumnal (fall) equinox in Hattiesburg, Mississippi, which of the four major points in time is it in Sydney, Australia?

Left to itself, the Earth would rotate with its axis of rotation always oriented in the same direction.[10] But because the Earth also experiences sideways forces (gravity) from the Sun and Moon, it wobbles, much like a toy top (Figure 2.25). This has some interesting consequences.

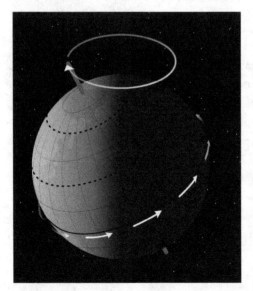

FIGURE 2.25. The Earth's processes as it rotates, much like a toy top.

---

[10] The *amount* of the Earth's axial tilt also changes slightly with time.

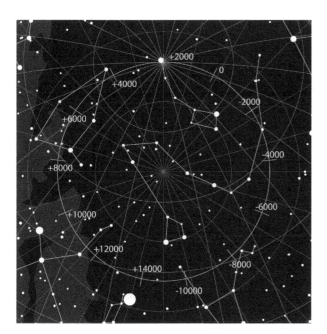

FIGURE 2.26. The circle represents the movement of the Earth's North Celestial Pole due to precession. The circle also shows the years (+ for C.E., − for B.C.E.) for the position of the NCP. Polaris is the bright dot near the top of the figure, whereas the very bright dot near the bottom of the figure is the star Vega. Vega was the North Star 14,000 years ago.

First, the period (the amount of time for Earth to make one full wobble, or precession) is about 26,000 years. This means the effect is rather subtle and requires observations taken over many decades, if not centuries, to uncover. Second, it means the Earth's North Pole has not always pointed at the same position in the sky. The object we know as the North Star—Polaris—wasn't the North Star over 1000 years ago. Nor will it be the North Star forever. Other stars—Vega is the most prominent—have served as the North Star in the past, and most of the time there wasn't a North Star at all.

Check Your Neighbor

Refer to Figure 2.26—about when will Polaris no longer be a North Star?

One last question: Is there a "South Star"? Currently, the answer is no. But, interestingly enough, a combination of precession and the actual motion of the star Sirius—the brightest star in the night sky—will bring it close enough to the South Celestial Pole to serve as the South Star around the year 67,000 C.E. Our distant descendants will enjoy one of the brightest possible pole stars in human history.

Summary

In this chapter, we have discussed the following:

▶ The difference between the physical rotational period of the Earth and what we think of as the day

▶ The difference between the physical orbital period of the Moon and what we think of as the month

▶ How lunar phases are made

▶ The historical roots of the week as a unit of time

▶ How the calendar was refined over history

▶ The physical origins of the seasons

▶ How the rotational axis of the Earth changes over long periods of time

▶ The physical origins of partial, total, and annular lunar and solar eclipses

Questions

1. The solar day for the Earth is a little bit longer than its sidereal day. What would happen if the Earth spun clockwise instead, while continuing its counterclockwise orbit about the Sun? Would the solar day be longer, shorter, or the same duration as the sidereal day?

2. Recall the degree symbol "°" refers to the concept of a "step." Who, or what, is stepping when we discuss the solar day?

3. The Earth's solar day is about 4 minutes longer than a sidereal day. How many times does the Earth do this during a full year? For this calculation, divide the number of seconds contained in a 24-hour day by the number of seconds contained in 4 minutes. Does the result look familiar?

4. Round off the duration of the month to 30 days and the year to 360 days. About how many degrees does the Moon appear to move—compared to the background stars—from one night to the next? Would this be easy or difficult to confirm with the naked eye?

5. In Figure 2.27, the Moon is crossing the local meridian (i.e., it is local noon) and the Sun is just setting over the western horizon. Each constellation is about 30° apart. Answer the following:
   - What is the phase of the Moon in this figure?
   - In which direction (east or west) will the Moon and Sun move during the course of a day? Which motion of the Earth is responsible for this?
   - In which direction (east or west) will the Moon and Sun move compared to the background of constellations? Which motion of the Earth is responsible for this?
   - Where will the Moon be in about 6 hours?
   - Where will the Sun be in about 6 hours?
   - In front of which constellation will we see the Moon in about 6 hours?
   - In front of which constellation will we see the Sun in about 6 hours?
   - In front of which constellation will we see the Sun in about 1 day?
   - In front of which constellation will we see the Moon in about 2–3 days?
   - In front of which constellation will we see the Sun in about 30 days?

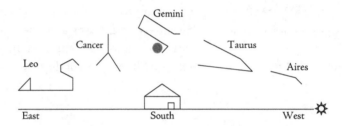

FIGURE 2.27. Possible positions of the Moon and Sun compared to background stars.

6. Which side of the Moon (east or west) is lit during a first quarter phase? During a third quarter phase?

7. Which phase of the Moon are you most likely to see—a first quarter or a third quarter? Hint: At which times are these phases visible in the night sky?

8. Approximately from which time of day to which time of day would one experience a full moon? A new moon?

9. Which part of the sky would one see a first quarter moon at night? Which part of the sky would one see a third quarter moon at night?

10. When will a waxing crescent be visible? When will a waning crescent be visible? Assume night lasts from 6 p.m. to 6 a.m. and that the crescent moon will be difficult to see during daylight.

11. What is the *angle* between the Sun and the first quarter moon, as seen from Earth?

12. Suppose the year was about 365 1/5 days long, rather than 365 1/4 days. How often would we have a leap year?

13. Suppose it is September 21. Which season begins in the northern hemisphere? The southern hemisphere?

14. Is "North Star" a description of a particular object or a title? Briefly defend your answer.

Activities

▶ Measure the sidereal day yourself. Plan ahead—which device(s) or instrument(s) would you need for this task? Try to achieve precision to a few seconds of time. Briefly report on your findings.

▶ Similarly, measure the solar day for yourself and briefly report on your findings. Consider how you can keep your eyes safe (it is dangerous to look at the Sun with the naked eye).

▶ With classmates, walk through the sidereal and solar days. One student stands still to represent the Sun, one student rotates and moves sideways to represent the Earth, and a third keeps track of the results. Students should also take turns so each gets a chance to experience how the Earth moves.

▶ With classmates, walk through the synodic and solar months. One student stands still to represent the Sun, one student moves sideways (slowly!) to represent the orbit of the Earth, and a third represents the Moon and its orbit about the Earth. Students should also take turns.

▶ For the appearance of the Moon during a full moon phase (refer to Figure 2.7), the Sun is not depicted. Where is it?

▶ *Only possible during a lunar eclipse:* Take pictures during the process of a lunar eclipse, from first to last contact.

▶ *Only possible during a lunar eclipse:* Take a picture of the Moon while about half-way covered by the Earth's shadow. Use this to estimate the relative sizes of the Earth and Moon.

▶ *Only possible during a solar eclipse:* Take pictures during the process of a solar eclipse. Use proper safety precautions!

Works Referenced

Clagett, M. (1995), *Ancient Egyptian science: A source book, Vol. II: Calendars, clocks and astronomy.* Philadelphia, PA: American Philosophical Society.

Depauw, M., Arlt, C., Elebaut, M., Georgila, A., Gülden, S. A., Knuf, H., ... & Kromer, M. (2008). *A chronological survey of precisely dated demotic and abnormal hieratic sources.* Köln/Leuven.

Mary Greeling News, "We Owe Seven-Day Week to Babylonians". (1991) Retrieved 2019-04-19. https://www.nytimes.com/1991/08/25/opinion/l-we-owe-seven-day-week-to-babylonians-627291.html

Nothaft, C. Phillip E. (2018). *Scandalous Error: Calendar Reform and Calendrical Astronomy in Medieval Europe.* Oxford University Press. https://books.google.com/books?id=dz5MDwAAQBAJ&dq=moyer+1983+Coyne+Hoskin+Petersen&source=gbs_navlinks_s Retrieved 2019-04-19.

NASA Eclipse Web Site. https://eclipse.gsfc.nasa.gov/solar.html

Parker, R. A. (1950). *The calendars of Ancient Egypt, studies in ancient oriental civilization.* Chicago, IL: University of Chicago Press.

Credits

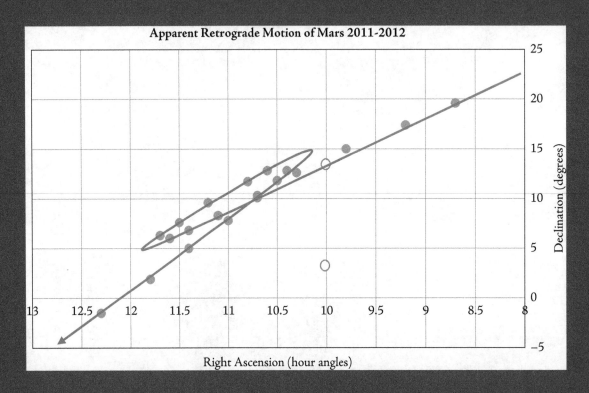

The position of Mars from October 2011 until July 2012, starting from the upper right and going to the lower left (with a loop in between).

CHAPTER 3

THE BIRTH OF MODERN ASTRONOMY I

The Solar System

PURPOSE

To describe the history leading up to our modern understanding of the solar system

OBJECTIVES

- To estimate the size of the Earth
- To estimate the distances to and relative sizes of the Moon and Sun
- To compare geocentrism with heliocentrism
- To cite the three laws of planetary motion
- To review early discoveries with the telescope
- To compare the changing definitions of the term *planet*

INTRODUCTION

Astronomy is perhaps the most ancient of the branches of human knowledge. Even so, it was once as much mysticism as science, as much wild speculation as careful record keeping, until just a few centuries ago. What did people know in ancient times about the skies, and how were ancient misconceptions adjusted? Who were the people who brought astronomy into modern times?

This chapter tells of the birth of modern astronomy, with the emphasis on our understanding of the solar system.

KEY TERMS

Arclength: The physical distance along the arc of a circle or sphere

Astrology: A pseudoscience, proposing the notion that the positions of planets and stars affect a person's personality and/or fate

Astronomy: The study of the stars and planets (and all other phenomena and objects outside of the Earth)

Deferent: Ptolemy's name for the original circle (or crystal sphere) of a planet's orbit in his geocentric system

Ellipse: One of the conic sections; also the shape of a closed orbit of a relatively small object due to the gravity of a relatively large object

Epicycle: An off-set wheel or gear, moving in uniform circular motion, connected to the original crystal sphere (deferent) in Ptolemy's geocentric system. Its purpose was to account for retrograde motion

Geocentrism (a.k.a. geocentric theory): The notion that the Earth is at the center of the universe and all astronomical objects move about it

Heliocentrism (a.k.a. heliocentric theory): The notion that the Sun is at the center of the universe and all astronomical objects (including the Earth) move about it

Laws of motion: Three rules, consolidated by Isaac Newton, describing how all objects move

Laws of planetary motion: Three rules, derived by Johannes Kepler, governing how planets (and other objects) orbit the Sun

Orbital period: The amount of time an object requires to complete an orbit

Nova: A term coined by Tycho Brahe for what he took to be the birth of a new star; later astronomers found it was actually an example of the death of a star

Retrograde motion: Officially "apparent" retrograde motion; the apparent backward (east to west) motion of planets compared to the constellations

Semi-major axis: Half of the largest axis (or largest distance across) of an ellipse. Equivalent to the average distance from the Sun for a planetary orbit

Uniform circular motion: When an object moves in a circle at constant speed in the same rotational direction

Telescope: A device that allows one to see distant objects

Zodiac: Traditionally 12 constellations that cross the ecliptic, most of which are named after animals

KEY INDIVIDUALS

Aristarchus: An ancient Greek astronomer who devised the first heliocentric model

Aristotle: An ancient Greek astronomer who devised the first detailed geocentric model

Brahe, Tycho: A Danish astronomer of the late 16th century; he was the best astronomical observer in the world before the invention of the telescope

Copernicus, Nicholas: A Polish astronomer of the mid-15th century; he revived the heliocentric model for modern times

Eratosthenes: An ancient Greek astronomer living in Egypt who was the first to measure the circumference of the Earth

Hershel, William: A German-English astronomer of the late 18th/early 19th century who discovered the planet Uranus

Galilei, Galileo: An Italian physicist and astronomer of the early 17th century who was the first to apply the telescope to astronomy

Kepler, Johannes: A German astronomer of the early 17th century who devised the laws of planetary motion

Newton, Isaac: An English physicist and astronomer of the late 17th/early 18th century who devised the laws of motion and the law of gravity, invented calculus, and invented the reflecting telescope

Ptolemy, Claudius: An ancient Greek astronomer living in Egypt who introduced modifications to the geocentric model

Section 3.1: Astrology versus Astronomy

Astronomy is one of the oldest, and most useful, of the sciences. It provided our first basic units of time: the day, the month, and the year. Many phenomena on Earth are related to its seasons—the growth of wild edible plants, the migrations of animals, the times to sow and reap crops are just a few. Even before Polaris was available to us as a North Star, familiarity with the constellations allowed sailors to navigate on the open seas.

But alongside astronomy grew the notions that the positions of planets and stars, especially during one's birth, determines one's future. Whether one might grow up with a gentle nature, violent tendencies or a life of misfortune could be ascribed to the appearance of Jupiter, Mars and/or Saturn in the right (or wrong) constellation. The reading of the fates in the skies was often restricted to official personnel in many countries, under pain of death. Superstition shared the stage with rationality.

The people who measured the positions of the planets to great precision were the same as those who cast horoscopes; in other words, the modern distinction between astronomers and astrologers was rarely recognized. Even historically famous astronomers such as Kepler actually made most of their livelihoods via astrology.

Unfortunately for astrologers, no evidence exists that it is a viable science. There are a variety of problems; what follows is a small sampling of them:

+ In careful tests, astrologers know nothing beyond chance about persons if they are only given the time and date of a person's birth.
+ No physical mechanism exists that would affect a person's personality from a planet, star, or constellation.
+ In tests, astrologers do not come to the same conclusions regarding a person's personality and/or fate, given only the time and date of birth.
+ Twins (whether identical or fraternal) should always share extremely similar personalities and/or fates; this does not always happen.
+ Astrological horoscopes are not really predictions; rather, they are vaguely constructed bits of advice.

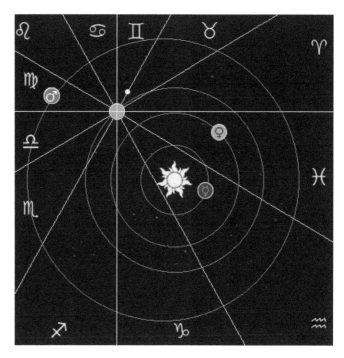

FIGURE 3.1. Zodiac constellations and planets on January 30, 1980.

Suppose we think that athletic ability may be related to one's astrological sign. To examine this, we searched out the signs for 120 professional award-winning athletes in one of the four major team sports (baseball, basketball, football, and hockey) in North America.[1] If the claim had merit, we would expect at least one sign to have a significantly larger number of athletes above the average. The results are shown in the histogram in Figure 3.2.

A quick glance at the histogram shows quite clearly that no sign really (with statistical significance) dominates the other signs. One's astrological sign, in other words, is not a predictor of athletic ability.

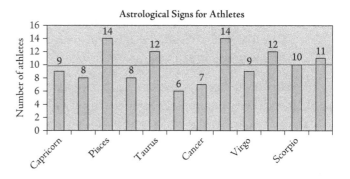

FIGURE 3.2. A histogram showing the astrological signs of award-winning professional athletes in North America. The red line represents the average number per sign.

Astrologers claim we are connected to the planets and stars, but these ultimately turn out to be trivial and meaningless. Astronomers too claim we are connected to the skies, but in much deeper and meaningful ways. Here is a short list:

+ We _are_ under the influence of a star: the Sun! Its light supplies the energy to warm the planet to a livable temperature, to drive weather and climate, to allow plants to grow and thereby give us food, and so on. Its gravity keeps the Earth in orbit about it, so that the flow of energy from the Sun remains virtually constant.
+ We also feel the influence of the Moon. Besides providing a bright light (especially during its full phase) at night, its gravity drives ocean tides, stabilizes the tilt of the Earth's axis, and may have helped mix molecules together in the early Earth to spark the origin of life.

---

[1] The study was performed in 1995. By "awards," we mean major achievements and/or official awards given to athletes in each sport—for example, the Cy Young award for the best pitcher in major league baseball.

- Faraway supergiant stars (both in terms of distance and time) exploding as supernovae helped spread heavy elements—including common ones such as carbon and oxygen—throughout the galaxy, which were picked up by the forming Earth, and eventually (again) life on Earth.
- Asteroids and comets may have contributed an important fraction of the Earth's water supply.
- Radioactivity (from heavy elements in the Earth, supplied by supernovae) and cosmic rays can spark mutations in DNA, therefore contributing to the evolution of life on Earth.
- The very matter we are made from (protons, neutrons, and electrons) were formed within the first few minutes of the life of the universe itself.

This is by no means complete. But we present these items to show what astronomy (the science) has discovered. We will be discussing much of these events later in this textbook. Astrology, by comparison, has nothing remotely as consequential to offer.

Astronomy is not the only science with pseudoscientific partners—alchemy vs. chemistry is probably another pair you recognize. The popularized notion of UFOs as alien spacecraft (as opposed to real scientific efforts to locate life elsewhere in the galaxy) is another example we will encounter in this textbook. How then can we tell the difference between a real science and a pseudo (i.e., fake) science?

We will study science as a way of gaining knowledge throughout this book. But we can distinguish real science from fake using a few basic guidelines:

- A real science offers a model or theory, that is, a comprehensive explanation.
- A real science offers a unified and consistent method for solving problems and making predictions.
- A real science can be tested via observations and/or experiments (it is "falsifiable"), so that if it is wrong, or has sections of it that are wrong or incomplete, these issues can be identified.
- A real science is "fecund"; that is, it not only addresses current questions, but also opens up new questions for investigation and study.

If a field uses ad-hoc explanations (i.e., one explanation for this problem, a separate explanation for another); if a field is vague or useless for solving problems; if a field ignores observational evidence when convenient; if a field leads to no new knowledge or discoveries, it is not a science.

Section 3.2: The Size and Shape of the Earth

Although the popular notion is that all ancients thought the Earth to be flat, in fact educated people have known of the Earth's sphericity for thousands of years. This goes back at least to the 6th century B.C.E., and while contemporaries tended to credit Pythagoras[2] with the discovery, we actually don't know for sure who originated the idea.

Why might people think of the Earth as spherical? One possibility is that the Earth's shadow on the Moon during a lunar eclipse is rounded. Another is that sailors noticed the disappearance of a ship's mast last as it recedes into the distance. A modern approach is to simply take photographs of the Earth from space. (Figure 3.3).

FIGURE 3.3. The Iberian Peninsula (Portugal and Spain) seen from the International Space Station, looking from over the Atlantic Ocean toward the east.

---

[2] Pythagoras is, of course, most famous for the theorem that bears his name. Neither the notion of a spherical Earth nor the Pythagorean theorem can be definitively ascribed to Pythagoras.

But the three-dimensional nature of the Earth was not confirmed until the work of Eratosthenes (c. 276–c. 195/194 b.c.e.), a Greek in charge of the library of Alexandria, Egypt. One version of the story has him reading about how, at local noon on the longest day of the year, the light of the Sun goes directly to the bottom of a well in the city of Syene (modern Aswan) and how a vertical obelisk casts no shadow. These events do not happen in Alexandria.

If the Earth were flat and the Sun were directly overhead in Syene, then it should also be overhead in Alexandria. If the Earth were flat and the Sun was at an angle in Alexandria, it should also be at the same angle in Syene. The only way to have both at the same time—overhead in Syene, at an angle in Alexandria—is for the Earth to be curved (Figure 3.4):

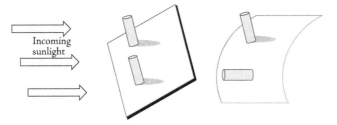

FIGURE 3.4. Parallel light shines on a pair of cylinders. If the cylinders are on a flat sheet, they both project the same shadow. If the cylinders are on a curved sheet, their shadows can be different.

Eratosthenes needed two sets of measurements: one, the distance between Alexandria and Syene; two, the angles of the shadows cast at each location. Stories again differ on how he got his data, whether it was knowledge already available at the library, or whether he hired an assistant to walk from Alexandria to Syene and back. He also assumed Alexandria is perfectly north of Syene, which it isn't, and there is some debate about the modern value of the length units (the "stade") he used. Nevertheless, most scholars think his result was within at worst 15% of the correct answer, and perhaps much better.

Figure 3.5 shows the measurements and geometry of Eratosthenes.

Eratosthenes worked out the circumference of the Earth in these steps:

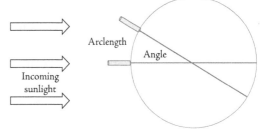

FIGURE 3.5. Parallel rays from the Sun reach upright obelisks on the Earth. We can use geometry to triangulate the center of the Earth and from that, the diameter of the Earth.

+ The relative angle of the shadows between Alexandria and Syene was 7°.
+ The arclength (the physical distance between Alexandria and Syene) was 5,000 stadia, or 800 kilometers/500 miles.
+ 7° is about 1/50 of 360°, a full circle.
+ The circumference of the Earth must be 50 times the arclength between Alexandria and Syene:

50 × 800 km = **40,000 km** (or 25,000 miles).

For simplicity, we are presenting the best-case calculation for Eratosthenes. Nevertheless, his estimation was an incredible achievement.

A historical postscript: Instead of 25,000 miles, Columbus went with a much smaller 18,000-mile circumference. Only then could he sell his notion—to sail west and reach the Far East from Europe. If the Americas had not been there, his voyage would have failed.

Check Your Neighbor

Suppose we did the same trick on the Moon. Let the angle again be 7°, but now the distance from one location to the next is 200 km. What is the circumference of the Moon?

Section 3.3: Heliocentrism versus Geocentrism, Part I

What lies at the center of all things? We don't tend to ask this question anymore, at least in astronomy, because it's an irrelevant question (see the chapter on cosmology for more details). But it was asked often in the past, and for most of history, people thought they had the answer.

Check Your Neighbor

Were Columbus's sailors truly worried about sailing off the edge of the world? If not, what might they have been worried about instead?

1. Aristarchus

Aristarchus was a Greek scientist[3] from the island of Samos in the 3rd century B.C.E. (c. 310 B.C.E. to 230 B.C.E.). Only one document survives from his own hand, "On the Sizes and Distances of the Sun and Moon," though his work is also mention in Archimedes's "The Sand Reckoner." In short, he estimated the relative distances to the Sun and Moon, and correspondingly their relative sizes, by careful observations of first- and third-quarter lunar phases (Figure 3.6):

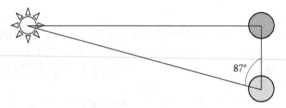

FIGURE 3.6. Angles estimated by Aristarchus during a first-quarter moon.

Aristarchus estimated the angle between the Sun and Earth during a first-quarter moon to be 87°. Note this is not the same as the 90° angle at the Earth, which is what determines the first-quarter moon in the first place.

From these measurements, Aristarchus realized that the Sun must be further from the Earth than the Moon. Also remember that the Sun and Moon subtend about the same angular diameter (each about 0.5°) on the sky. If two objects <u>look</u> to be the same size, but one is farther away than the other, then the farther object must be physically larger (Figure 3.7):

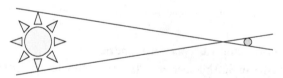

FIGURE 3.7. If the Sun and Moon subtend the same angle on the sky, but the Sun is further away, then the Sun must be larger than the Moon.

Another important step for Aristarchus was to estimate the relative sizes of the Earth and Moon. Since the Earth is a sphere, its shadow on the Moon during a partial lunar eclipse must be curved (Figure 3.8). We can extend the curve of the Earth's shadow to reconstruct the size of the entire shadow, and thereby estimate the relative size of the Earth itself compared to the Moon.

Aristarchus determined that the Earth is about four times larger across than the Moon (essentially correct). Then from his angle measurements during quarter moons, he subsequently estimated that the Sun was 20 times

---

[3] Our usage here is anachronistic, as the term "scientist" wasn't invented until the beginning of the 1800s by William Whewell. If titles were used at all, such a person as Aristarchus would have been termed a "natural philosopher."

farther from the Earth than the Moon (and therefore the Sun was five times larger across than the Earth). From this, he proposed that the Sun, rather than the Earth, should be at the center of everything—a *heliocentric* (Sun-centered) system.

This is the correct conclusion. Aristarchus's work did have some problems—most importantly, it is not possible to measure the angle as precisely as he did (it may be that he knew this and suggested 87° as a lower value). The modern value is 89.5°, which can only be found with modern instruments. With the updated information, we find the Sun is about 400 times, not 20 times, farther from us than the Moon, and therefore 400 times larger than the Moon (and about 100 times larger than the Earth). Regardless of the specifics, the big picture result is true: The Sun is much larger than either the Earth or the Moon and is at the center of the solar system.

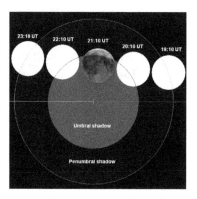

FIGURE 3.8. The Earth's umbral shadow across the Moon during the partial lunar eclipse of August 16, 2008.

FIGURE 3.9. Eratosthenes (left), Aristarchus (center), and Aristotle (right).

2. Aristotle

Despite Aristarchus's work, few people accepted the idea of the Sun at the center. Why not? Most importantly, it wasn't well known. It's not merely that only scraps of his original writings have survived until modern times; in an age before widespread literacy, printed books or the Internet, information was difficult to disseminate. Most educated people, and probably all uneducated people, never heard of it in the first place. Second, it goes against common sense. In order for Aristarchus's proposal to work, the Earth would need to both move through space and rotate on its axis. But then we should feel the motion, shouldn't we? Even now, do you feel like we are moving? In contrast, it's the Sun, Moon, planets, and stars that all go around us, right?

Aristotle (384 B.C.E. to 324 B.C.E.) spent much of his life at the northern reaches of Greece, specifically in the country of Macedonia.[4] He was a great synthesizer of human knowledge, writing on virtually all scientific topics of the day, including astronomy, biology, geography, and physics. His work tended to rely on everyday observations and common sense, though he also advocated for exploration and experiment.

Unfortunately for posterity, there were two major problems with his work. First, important concepts were often wrong. Second, later scholars (especially in medieval Europe) elevated his work to the pinnacle of human intellectual achievement, which stifled future development.

What did Aristotle have to say about astronomy and physics? Some of his conclusions went like this:

+ Astronomical objects revolve around the Earth at constant speed in the same rotational direction (physicists call this "uniform circular motion").

---

[4] One of his claims to fame is that he tutored a young man who became known to history as Alexander the Great.

- Objects on Earth rise or fall according to the "elements" they are made from. Aristotle's elements include earth, water, air, and fire.[5]
- Objects in the sky are made of a fifth "element," or "quintessence," and are perfect.
- The laws of nature are different for objects in the sky than they are for objects on Earth.
- Only the observable (what can be seen, heard, tasted, etc.) is real.

These (and other) thoughts had the effect of seriously restricting inquiry into how nature works. Ironically, it is likely Aristotle would not have approved of this attitude and instead preferred we continue to study nature without these intellectual blinders.

It is difficult sometimes for us to understand such attitudes—the blind acceptance of ancient authority as the final word. But our society has changed markedly since ancient times. The prevailing paradigm in science is that of continued questioning and improvement. In days when most people lived at a subsistence level, where most children died before reaching adulthood and the life expectancy was decades less than today, when disease and violence were part of everyday life, it seemed to many people that they needed something permanent to rely on—such as the skies.

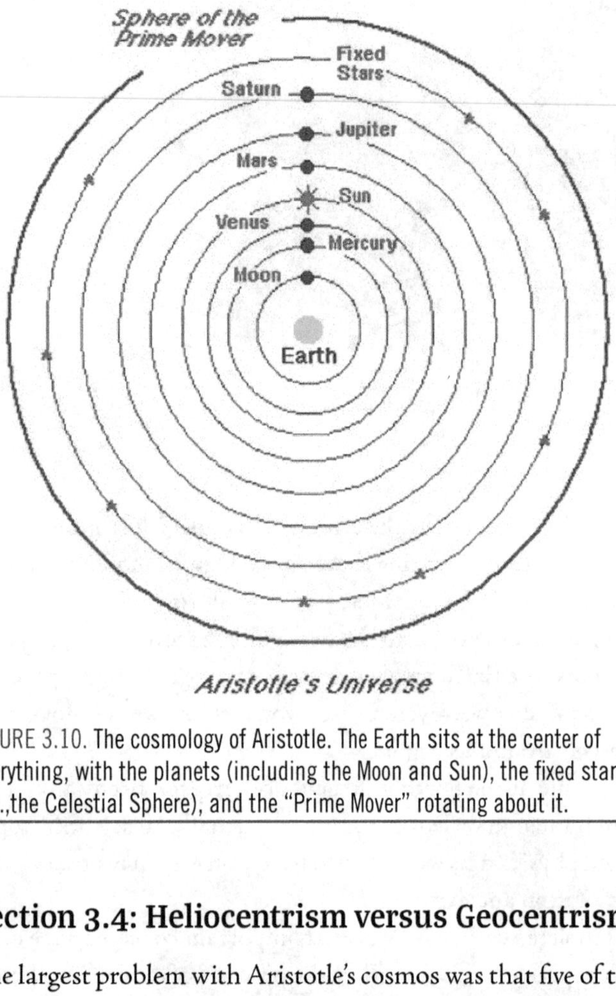

How did Aristotle arrange his universe? Figure 3.10 shows his cosmology.

The Earth sits at the center of everything—what we now call a *geocentric* system. All astronomical objects are attached to transparent, crystal spheres. As the spheres rotate via uniform circular motion about the Earth, they carry their respective objects along with them.

Aristotle (and other ancients) knew the relative positions of the planets correctly out to Saturn. Beyond Saturn was the sphere of fixed stars, the "Celestial Sphere." Beyond that was the sphere of the "Prime Mover." Identified usually as some divine agency, such as gods or angels, the Prime Mover would be attached to the other crystal spheres. As the Prime Mover rotated, it would in turn (via a complex of gears, perhaps?) make the other spheres rotate.

This system of Aristotle gave a general, common-sense explanation for how the skies worked. It also had some important flaws, known even to the ancients.

FIGURE 3.10. The cosmology of Aristotle. The Earth sits at the center of everything, with the planets (including the Moon and Sun), the fixed stars (i.e.,the Celestial Sphere), and the "Prime Mover" rotating about it.

Section 3.4: Heliocentrism versus Geocentrism, Part II

The largest problem with Aristotle's cosmos was that five of the seven ancient planets did not behave properly. The Sun and Moon—or their corresponding crystal spheres—can be modeled relatively well (though not perfectly) with uniform circular motion. But the other ancient planets, Mercury, Venus, Mars, Jupiter, and Saturn, cannot. These objects occasionally exhibit something called *retrograde motion*.

---

[5] As astronomers have radically changed the usage of the term "planet" since ancient times, so have chemists done with "element."

Objects in the sky tend to rise in the east and set in the west each day. Objects like the Sun and Moon also have a more gradual motion from west to east compared to the Celestial Sphere (see chapters 1 and 2). Retrograde motion (or, more officially, *apparent* retrograde motion) is when a planet moves from east to west compared to the background of stars (Figure 3.11):

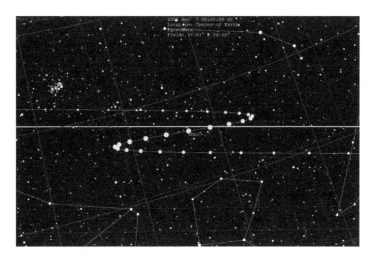

FIGURE 3.11. Apparent retrograde motion of Mars during 2005.

This presents an enormous problem for Aristotle's geocentrism. These objects are definitely <u>not</u> exhibiting uniform circular motion. While this doesn't automatically eliminate the Earth from being the center of the system, it certainly makes it harder to accept.

1. Ptolemy

A solution was proposed by another Greek (historians tend to think[6]) who also lived in Alexandria, Egypt, but several centuries after Eratosthenes and Aristotle. Claudius Ptolemy (c. 100 C.E. to c. 170 C.E.) was a synthesizer of knowledge, like Aristotle, and spanned the topics of mathematics, astronomy, music, geography, and optics. His largest work, *Almagest*,[7] was his compilation of astronomical knowledge from Babylon, Egypt, and Greece. Its value came in its clear writing style, an updated star catalog (containing 48 constellations, many of which we still use today), and tables of data useful for making predictions of future positions of planets. Ptolemy's *Almagest* was translated into Arabic and subsequently into Latin for medieval astronomers, and like Aristotle's work, was accepted as the gold standard for centuries.

Ptolemy's largest contribution was a solution to retrograde motion. The major feature of Ptolemy's geocentric model was to add a system of gears, or offset wheels, called *epicycles*. A planet would be attached to the edge of the epicycle, and the original circle (or crystal sphere, now called the *deferent*) and epicycle would still move in uniform circular motion. Ptolemy could adjust the size and speed of the epicycle to fit the observations of the planets well enough for naked eye observations for years into the future. Ptolemy also made other small-scale modifications (for example, moving the Earth slightly off center) to better fit the observational data. Figure 3.12 shows the basics of Ptolemy's modifications.

---

[6] Ptolemy's origin is unknown. "Ptolemy" is a Greek name, suggesting he was either a Greek living in Egypt or a Hellenized Egyptian, but "Claudius" is Roman, suggesting citizenship in the Roman Empire. Despite "Ptolemy" being the name of Greek kings and "Claudius" of a Roman emperor, it is unlikely he himself was of royal lineage.

[7] "Almagest" is "The Greatest" in Arabic, reflecting its translation and wide usage by medieval Arab astronomers. The prefix "al" means "the," so it is not technically correct to speak of "The Almagest."

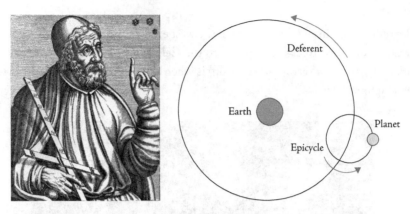

FIGURE 3.12. An early baroque artist's interpretation of Ptolemy (left). Ptolemy's geocentric system for an individual planet, retaining uniform circular motion (right).

With this gears-on-gears approach, Ptolemy was able to both keep uniform circular motion and to account for the loop-the-loop behavior of the planets.

Ptolemy's system introduced its own problems. The crystal spheres of Aristotle would need to be abandoned, or somehow be able to pass through each other while still remaining attached. Odd objects such as comets did not fit in the scheme, though most astronomers tended to claim such phenomena belonged to the Earth, not the skies. It became incredibly complex and therefore difficult to manage. And, of course, it was wrong.

2. Copernicus

Ptolemy's model worked well enough, in a hand-to-mouth fashion at least, to retain primacy amongst astronomers for many centuries. It wasn't until modern times that it sustained a real challenge.

Nicholas Copernicus (the Latinized version of his name) was born on February 14, 1473, in Poland. As with many of the people discussed in this chapter, he was adept in a number of disciplines—for example, he made key contributions to the emerging field of economics. But his most famous work came in astronomy. His father died when Nicholas was 10 years old, and an influential uncle apparently made sure he got a strong education, including the University of Krakow; although he did not earn a degree, he was exposed to the theories of Aristotle and Ptolemy. He was

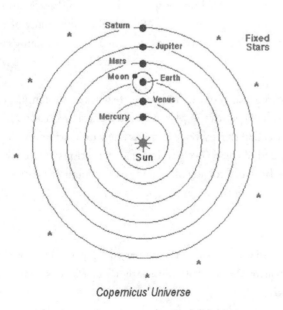

FIGURE 3.13. The heliocentric universe (left) and a statue of Copernicus (right).

never ordained as a priest, but he did serve in various capacities as a lay (non-religious) official at a variety of Catholic churches during his life.

Copernicus had an interest in astronomy—we might call it a hobby—that he pursued, on and off, throughout his adult life. Observations of Mars, Saturn, and the Sun led him to conclude that the Earth's orbital eccentricity is variable—a correct conclusion. That, and requests from Catholic officials to investigate calendar reform (see chapter 2), seems to have led him to reevaluate how the solar system was arranged. He also had access to the work of Aristarchus, though he eventually decided not to cite Aristarchus in his own publications.

Copernicus was seriously thinking about heliocentrism since at least 1514 (he put forth preliminary results in a 40-page manuscript titled the "Little Commentary") and by 1532 had essentially finished his book *De Revolutionibis Orbium Coelestium* ("On the Revolutions of the Heavenly Spheres"). He delayed its release, but the encouragement of a former pupil encouraged him to publish it in 1543, and legend has it he received a copy on his deathbed. He seems to have feared criticism of his work, but even today historians are not sure whether this was of a scientific and/or religious nature.

Its most important change, of course, was that Copernicus placed the Sun, rather than the Earth, at the center. We now can truly call this a "solar" system, although Copernicus still retained a sphere of fixed stars, uniform circular motion, and other features of the Aristotelian/Ptolemaic geocentric system. The definition of a planet now changes; rather than being an object moving compared to the constellations, it is now an object that orbits the Sun. Since the Moon remains in orbit about the Earth, it is no longer a planet either.

The largest benefit of Copernicus' heliocentric system was its more natural explanation for retrograde motion. Planets such as Mars do not actually move backward at times; rather, they appear to move backward when being passed by (or passing by) the Earth. In other words, retrograde motion isn't real; it's an optical illusion (Figure 3.14).

You can experience retrograde motion for yourself in everyday life. Suppose you are riding (not driving!) in a car on a highway or county road, where there is a background with distant objects. As your car passes by another car, watch the position of the other car carefully, compared to the background. For that instant, it will appear to move backward, even though it is definitely moving forward.

One of the hallmarks of a good scientific theory is that it predicts future

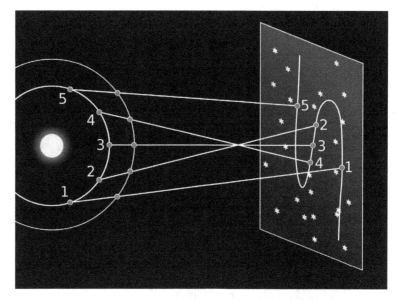

FIGURE 3.14. Suppose we have two planets, Earth (in blue) and Mars (in red). Because Earth is closer to the Sun, it moves more quickly than Mars. While Mars always moves forward, it appears to move backward compared to the fixed stars while Earth passes it by.

events. Copernicus's model was just as successful at predicting the future positions of the planets as was Ptolemy's. Another important feature for a scientific theory is that it presents a unified problem-solving strategy; here, Copernicus's model fell short, as it still included many ad hoc concepts such as an offset Sun and uniform circular motion.

Astronomers in the last half of the 16th century were left with the following debate: Which theory—geocentrism or heliocentrism—is correct? For several decades, astronomers were unable to resolve the argument—until a combination of precise measurement and improved theory was able to decide the issue.

Section 3.5: Heliocentrism versus Geocentrism, Part III

1. Tycho Brahe

The evidence that eventually tipped the scales to the heliocentric model was gathered by an astronomer who was at best ambivalent about it. Like Copernicus, Tycho Brahe (1546–1601) was part of an affluent family and had a driving interest in astronomy from youth. However, whereas Copernicus worked other jobs and held astronomy more as a hobby, Brahe convinced his family to allow him to pursue his passion full time. Eventually, Brahe would create the first modern research institute ("Uraniborg")[8] for this purpose.

Tycho died before the invention of the telescope. But he had access to every contemporary astronomical instrument, including a quadrant—essentially part of a protractor—large enough for him to sit in! (See the opening to chapter 1) Over his career he made several important discoveries, including the following:

+ He made detailed observations of the supernova of 1572. The true nature of such events wouldn't be discovered for centuries, but Tycho kept detailed observations of it, including brightness and position, and wrote a short book about it called *De stella nova* (Latin for "The New Star"), because it had appeared in the sky without any warning. The term *nova* (and later supernova) was given to this type of phenomenon. He also showed that the nova was part of the Celestial Sphere, or at least as far away as the stars. Ironically, though *nova* means "new," the actual physical event denotes the explosive death of a star (see chapter 19 for details).

+ He also made detailed observations of a comet that flew past the Earth in 1577. He noted its tail always pointed away from the Sun and that it moved between the orbits of the planets (thereby destroying the notion of crystalline spheres).

FIGURE 3.15. Tycho Brahe (left); a map of Uraniborg (right).

Tycho had an abrasive personality. Upon the death of his patron, King Frederick in 1588, he lost his support in Denmark and eventually ended up working for the Holy Roman Emperor Rudolf in Prague (now in the Czech Republic). In his youth, he had gotten into a sword fight with a companion and had the tip of his nose cut off; he wore a prosthetic ever after. His death was likely caused by a burst bladder; one story states he refused to leave a dinner party in honor of a superior, despite having drunk far too much for his own good.

---

[8] Uraniborg (named by Tycho after the Greek muse of astronomy) was cited as Tycho's private island of Hven, a gift from the Danish king.

More to the point, he came up with his own "Tychonic" theory, where objects in the solar system revolved about the Sun, but the Sun in its turn revolved about the Earth; therefore, he was neither an Aristotelian (geocentrist) nor a Copernican (heliocentrist).

Don't worry if you haven't heard of the Tychonic theory; it disappeared quickly after Tycho's death. Tycho's legacy isn't in his theoretical work, but in the quality of his observations.

2. Kepler

Johannes Kepler's (1571–1630) early life was much different than that of the affluent Tycho. His father was a mercenary who abandoned his family, and Kepler grew up relatively poor. His inherent brilliance, however, enabled him to gain an education at various schools, and he himself briefly taught at a school in Graz, Austria. A devout Lutheran during the age of the Reformation living in Catholic countries, he endured exile several times, and lost much of his family to epidemics spread by soldiers. His original gravesite is unknown. Poor eyesight prevented him from making quality observations, even with the telescope. Yet he is perhaps the first true astrophysicist in history.

Combining mystical tendencies with mathematics, he originally attempted to describe the orbits of the (then six) known planets by way of geometric shapes known as the five perfect solids[9] and by musical scales (sometimes referred to as the "Harmony of the Worlds"). Although he never completely abandoned these thoughts, he soon realized published observations available to him did not support this notion very well. Having gained a reputation as an astronomical scholar, he was invited by Tycho to join Tycho's research group in Prague; when Kepler's ruler (archduke Ferdinand) exiled Protestants from his lands upon pain of death or conversion, Kepler decided to accept Tycho's offer in 1600.

Although Tycho and Kepler (a very straight-laced person, much different from Tycho in terms of personality) clashed often, Tycho's sudden death in 1601 left Kepler in the position of imperial mathematician. Kepler was able to retrieve Tycho's observations (though not without the opposition of Tycho's family) and use them to determine the true shape of a planet's orbit about the Sun.

Here, the notion of precision of measurement was of utmost importance to history. Whatever Tycho's other failings, he excelled at precision angular measurements; his tables represented the best data before the invention of the telescope, and are probably as good as any measurements can be with the naked eye. Figure 3.16 shows a comparison between the full Moon and Tycho's estimated uncertainty.

A short digression: In science, it is not sufficient merely to report a result of a calculation or measurement; it is necessary to also supply a number representing the confidence we have in the result. It is common in a discipline such as astronomy to do this via an uncertainty, an estimation of the reliability of the measurement. For example, we could say that the width of the full Moon is 0.50°. If we say the uncertainty is plus or minus (+/−) 0.01 degrees, then we are saying we believe the width of the full Moon is anywhere between 0.49° and 0.51°.

FIGURE 3.16. The red circle at upper right denotes the approximate precision from Tycho Brahe's observations of angular positions of the planets. The full Moon is shown for comparison.

---

[9] Each of the five perfect solids has faces of only one particular regular polygon (a triangle, square, or pentagon); in no specific order, we know them as the cube, icosahedron, dodecahedron, tetrahedron, and octahedron. Don't worry about memorizing these; it is the first and last time we will deal with them in this book.

Tycho's angular uncertainties for the positions of planets were as low as 2 arcminutes (recall there are 60 arc-minutes in an angular degree). The human eye is unable to do much better than this, and Tycho achieved such precision only due to the excellence and size of his instruments.

A Copernican, Kepler originally also kept uniform circular motion. But Tycho's data made it a difficult fit. Kepler came to realize orbital shapes could not be circular, but it only was after much experimentation that he settled on the ellipse. Kepler also realized that the speeds of the planets in their orbits behaved a specific way, and these first two results were published in 1609. A third rule, relating the sizes of the orbits of the planets to their periods, was discovered later and published in 1619.

Kepler's First Law of Planetary Motion

> *A planet orbits the Sun in an ellipse, with the Sun at one focus of the ellipse.*

The Sun is not at the center of the ellipse (Figure 3.17) but offset to the side along the major axis at one of the focus positions. The other focus is empty space. The reason for these details would wait until Isaac Newton came up with the laws of motion and the universal law of gravity.

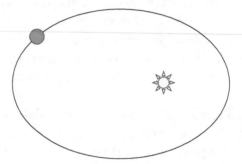

FIGURE 3.17. Kepler's first law of planetary motion: Each planet orbits the Sun in an ellipse, with the Sun at one focus of the ellipse. Note that each planet's ellipse is different.

Kepler's Second Law of Planetary Motion

> *A planet sweeps out equal areas in equal times.*

Draw an imaginary line between the planet and the Sun (Figure 3.18). As the planet moves, this line sweeps out an imaginary wedge. The wedge will have different shapes for different sections of the planet's orbit, but the wedge will cover the same area over the same amount of time.

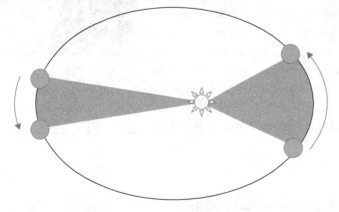

FIGURE 3.18. Kepler's second law of planetary motion: A planet sweeps out equal areas in equal times.

Kepler's Third Law of Planetary Motion

The square of the period of the orbit of a planet is directly related to the cube of its semi-major axis.

This law is better expressed as an equation:

Equation 3.1

$$P^2 = a^3$$

In the equation, *P* represents the period of the planet's orbit, expressed in Earth years, and *a* the semi-major axis of the orbit, expressed in astronomical units. Astronomers express Kepler's third law this way for simplicity; we will look at it again in chapter 4.

The third law compares planets to each other. The third law also applies to any object orbiting the Sun independently, like comets and asteroids, and the general version of the third law applies to any object in orbit about another object due to gravity. Kepler speculated about an invisible force emanating from the Sun that would pull planets toward it; a generation later, Newton would describe the force in detail in his universal law of gravitation.

Check Your Neighbor

Where does a planet move fastest in its orbit—when closest to the Sun, when furthest from the Sun, or at a constant speed?

Check Your Neighbor

Suppose astronomers discover a new planet that has a semi-major axis of 4 au. What is the semi-major axis of its orbit?

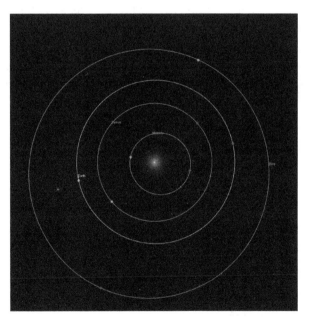

FIGURE 3.19. Kepler's third law of planetary motion: The amount of time to orbit the Sun (period) is directly related to the size of the orbit (semi-major axis). At left are shown the orbits of the four inner planets, Mercury, Venus, Earth, and Mars.

3. Galileo Galilei

Contemporary with Kepler was (1564–1642) was Galileo Galilei. But where Kepler was socially awkward, Galileo was outgoing, personable, and rather egotistical. Kepler was a Protestant in Germany and frequently in conflict with authority; Galileo was a Catholic in Italy and on personal terms with the pope, at least during the first part of his career. Kepler's ability to conduct quality astronomical observations was restricted by poor eyesight; Galileo's fame as an astronomer comes from his telescopic observations—though, again, his eyesight failed him in his later years. Although they corresponded via letter, the two men never met in person.

FIGURE 3.20. Johannes Kepler (left), Galileo Galilei (right).

A polymath like Kepler (and many of the other figures in this chapter), Galileo also made important discoveries in physics, some of which we will detail in the next chapter. Here, we focus on his work with the telescope.

The invention of the telescope was one of the great accidents of history. Lenses and reading glasses had been around for centuries prior to 1608. A popular story holds that some young boys wandered into the eyeglass shop of Hans Lippershey (1570–1619) and began playing with some lenses. After shooing away the boys, Lippershey checked for himself what the boys had done, and within a few days had constructed the world's first telescope (Figure 3.21).

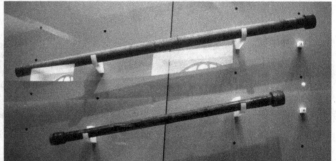

FIGURE 3.21. Hans Lippershey (left); two of Galileo's telescopes (right).

Lippershey[10] ("Lipperhey" is an alternate spelling) was born in Wesel, in western Germany, but immigrated to the Netherlands in 1594 and became a citizen of the province of Zeeland in 1602. He applied for a patent on October 2, 1608, to the Dutch government for a device "for seeing things far away as if they were nearby." While he did not get the patent (there were many claimants for similar devices), the Dutch government paid him well for the use of his design. Lippershey's original version supposedly was capable of magnification of up to three times.

---

[10] Although in English the two letters "sh" are often combined, the letters are separated here; thus, Lippershey is pronounced "Lippers-hey."

Word of the "Dutch perspective glass" (the term *telescope*, meaning "to see far away," was not coined until 1611) spread throughout Europe. Galileo constructed his own versions—eventually creating a version capable of 30-times magnification—and almost immediately (a) began to sell them to merchants and (b) turn them to the skies. Others (understandably) were interested in the business and military applications of the telescope, but Galileo was the first to use it for astronomy. By coincidence, as Kepler was publishing his first two laws of planetary motion, Galileo was doing the same regarding his observations with the telescopes.

Galileo made five distinct discoveries that, once and for all, defeated the geocentric theory and placed the Sun at the center of the solar system. He also destroyed Aristotelean physics in the process.

Features on the Moon

It wasn't that Galileo discovered that the Moon has features; we can all see that with the naked eye. What he did was map individual features, give names to regions of the Moon, and—most importantly—measure the sizes of the features. We take it for granted today that the same laws of nature apply to space as to the Earth, but this was not the case in Galileo's time. The terms "mare" (Latin for seas) and "terrae" (Latin for lands) are due to Galileo, who assumed the dark and light patches on the Moon represented its versions of oceans and continents. To be fair to Galileo, nobody before him had ever seen this before.

Sunspots

Others—notably Chinese astronomers—knew about sunspots before Galileo. But again, he performed what we can call modern scientific exploration on the Sun. Specifically, Galileo observed that sunspots move across the face of the Sun. From this, he deduced that the Sun rotates on its axis about once per month. This, and his work on the Moon, also denied the claim by Aristotle that the heavens are populated with unblemished, "perfect" objects.

The Milky Way

The term "Milky Way" originated with the notion that the band of smooth, white material that goes across the sky at night. It's not as famous in modern times, since so many of us live in cities where light pollution wipes it out, but for those in ancient times, or those of us who have been fortunate to see it, the Milky Way is impressively bright and extensive. Alternatively described as spilled milk, a staircase, or the spine of a gigantic creature, Galileo showed that it actually consists of numerous stars, each too dim to see individually. Another of Aristotle's notions, that nothing exists outside our senses, disappeared as a consequence.

FIGURE 3.22. A panoramic view of the Milky Way.

Venus

In theory, in the geocentric system it should be possible to see a full phase of the planet Venus. That this is never seen is a problem for Aristotle's model. The Ptolemaic solution of epicycles could address this, but either Venus

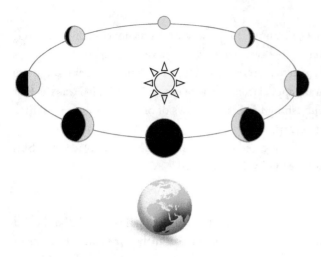

FIGURE 3.23. The group of phases of Venus observed by Galileo are only possible in a heliocentric system with Venus having a smaller orbit than the Earth.

could have only crescent and new phases or gibbous and full phases. Galileo's observations showed that Venus has all possible phases besides full (Figure 3.23), which is only possible in a heliocentric system with Venus having a smaller orbit than the Earth.

Moons of Jupiter

Perhaps the most iconic of Galileo's discoveries were the moons of Jupiter. Galileo found four objects moving back and forth across the face of Jupiter (Figure 3.24). We now know of over 60 individual moons orbiting Jupiter, but these four were found first due to their brightness and size (each is about as big as our Moon, or larger). Nobody had thought any objects could orbit something besides either the Earth or Sun; in a few weeks, Galileo found that many objects can orbit many other objects.

Galileo is also famous for the heresy trial he endured in 1633 and his subsequent house arrest. The Catholic Church had originally shown some positive interest in the heliocentric theory, but as the Reformation gained prominence, Catholic officials felt it necessary to take a hard line in defending the Bible's version of creation, which was definitely geocentric. Also, Pope Urban VIII—formerly Cardinal Maffeo Barberini, and a former personal friend of Galileo's—was under pressure to be harsher in defense of church doctrine.

RECENS HABITAE. 23

dentalis proxima min. 2. ab hac vero elongabatur occidentalior altera min: 10. erant præcisè in eadem recta, & magnitudinis æqualis.

Die quarta hora ſecunda circa Iouem quatuor ſtabant Stellæ, orientales duæ, ac duæ occidentales in eadem ad vnguem recta linea diſpoſitæ, vt in proxima figura. Orientalior diſtabat à ſequenti min. 3. hęc verò à Ioue aberat min. 0. ſec. 40. Iuppiter à proxima occidentali min 4. hæc ab occidentaliori min. 6. magnitudine erant ferè ęquales, proximior Ioui reliquis paulo minor apparebat. Hora autem ſeptima orientales Stellæ diſtabant tantum min. 0. ſec. 30. Iuppiter ab orientali viciniori aberat min. 2. ab occidentali verò ſequente min. 4. hæc verò ab occidentaliori diſtabat min. 3. erantque æquales omnes, & in eadem recta ſecundum Eclypticam extenſa.

Die quinta Cœlum fuit nubiloſum.

Die ſexta duæ ſolummodo apparuerunt Stellæ me-

dium

FIGURE 3.24. Sketches from Galileo's 1610 book *The Starry Messenger*, showing the four giant moons of Jupiter.

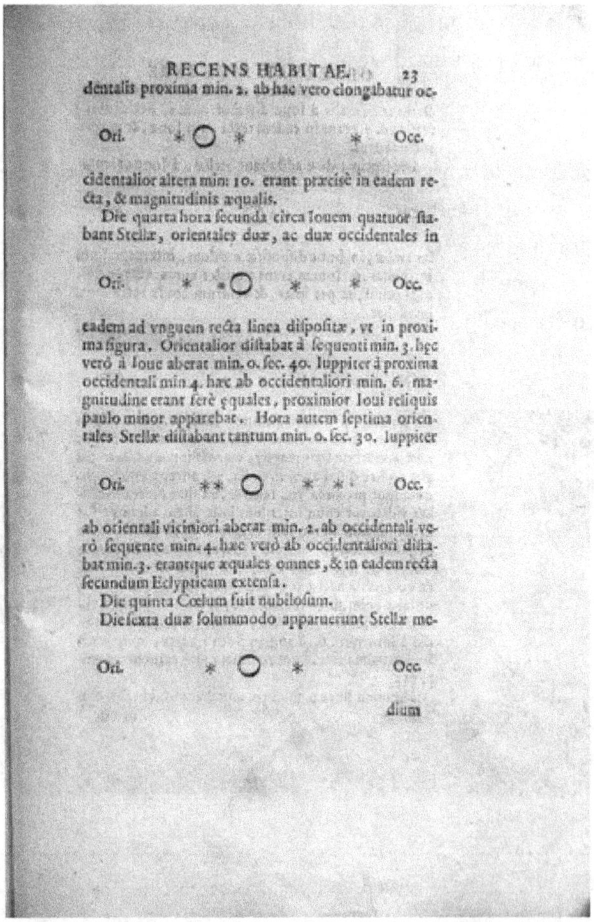

Section 3.6: A New Planet

Modern astronomy was born with the work of Copernicus, Tycho, Kepler, Galileo, and others we have not mentioned. But there is an interesting postscript to the story.

Recall that the ancients had recognized seven "planets": objects that wandered across the sky compared to the background of the stars. The replacement of the geocentric system by the heliocentric one changed that number: The Sun and Moon were removed and the Earth was included, leaving us with six planets. Moreover, the usage of the term "planet" changed dramatically; now, a planet was a celestial object directly orbiting the Sun.

William Hershel (1738–1822) was born in the German electorate of Hanover, which was under the rule of the English king, George II. When war with France threatened (the "Seven Years War" from 1756–1763), his father Isaac sent William and his brother Jakob to England for safety. William was accused of desertion, but was later pardoned by the next English king, George III, with whom he was to have a friendship. Hershel anglicized his name from "Wilhelm" to "William" and remained in England the rest of his life.

Hershel came from a musical family, and his primary means of support during his early career was via music—six of his symphonies were recorded as recently as 2002. William's interest in astronomy was sparked by a fellow musician in England, and soon after his sister Caroline came to live with him permanently. The sister-brother team built over 400 telescopes and became the best telescope-lens grinders in the world at the time. We will cover more of Hershel's work in later chapters, but his fame mainly rests on the discovery of a new planet.

 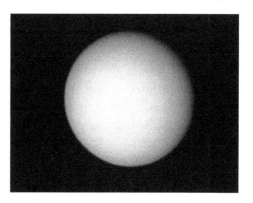

FIGURE 3.25. William and Caroline Herschel grinding a lens (left), the planet Uranus (right).

In March 1781, while searching for double stars, Hershel came upon a blue disk. At first he thought it might be a star or planet, but after repeated observations concluded it must be a new planet beyond the orbit of Saturn. He originally suggested *Georgium Sidus* ("George's Star") after his patron king George III, but nobody else recognized the name as official, and eventually "Uranus" was suggested.

There are some tantalizing hints that other people had seen Uranus previously; Galileo may have spotted it as many as three separate times. But Uranus is very dim compared to the other planets (although it is officially visible to the naked eye) and moves extremely slow against the stars, so nobody until Hershel realized its true nature.

While the heliocentric theory had been well established by Herschel's day, the discovery of Uranus was yet another blow to ancient ways of thinking. And, ironically, he restored the number of planets to seven.

Check Your Neighbor

If Hershel had his way, we would be discussing planets with names like Mars, Jupiter, Saturn, and George. Instead of planet George, we have Uranus. Can you think of a reason why the name Uranus is especially fitting?

Summary

In this chapter, we have discussed the following:

- The properties of a healthy science
- How ancient astronomers determined the size and shape of the Earth
- How ancient astronomers debated the size and distances to the Sun and Moon
- The debate between Earth-centered and Sun-centered systems
- Apparent retrograde motion
- The three laws of planetary motion
- Observations with the telescope
- The discovery of a new planet

Questions

1. Compare astrological predictions for the same sign on the same day from two or more different astrology columns.

2. What do you think we mean by a term such as "statistically significant"?

3. Consult a star chart with modern boundaries of constellations drawn.

   + How many constellations actually cross the ecliptic?
   + Does each zodiac constellation cover the same area (i.e., number of days)?
   + Do modern star chart dates for zodiac constellations agree with the dates of astrological signs?

4. Two cities, along a direct north-south line, are 1,300 miles apart. Each city has a tall, vertical tower. On midsummer's day at local noon, the shadow at the southern city is at an 8° angle, and the shadow at the northern city is at a 20° angle. Using this information, show how to estimate the circumference of the Earth.

5. How fast are you currently moving due to the Earth's rotation? The Earth's speed at its equator is its circumference divided by its rotational period (24 hours). To get more specific, look up your latitude. Multiply the equatorial speed by the cosine of the latitude.

6. List the planets acknowledged by astronomers before and after Copernicus. How many objects were considered planets in each case?

7. Suppose you measure the full Moon to be 30 arcminutes across, with an uncertainty (precision) of 2 arcminutes. What is the fractional (or percentage) uncertainty?

8. Which of Galileo's five major discoveries would you say was the most important? Briefly defend your opinion.

9. If William Hershel's original name had been adopted, we would have had planets, going outward from the Sun, named Mercury, Venus, Earth, Mars, Jupiter, Saturn, and George. Briefly comment on why "Uranus" was adopted instead of "George."

10. Officially, Uranus is visible to the naked eye, but just barely, and its apparent retrograde motion is also extremely slow. Uranus was not discovered until well after the invention of the telescope. Briefly relate these two statements.

Activities

▸ Comb through an astrology column (they can be found in newspapers, magazines, or online) and review its "predictions" for at least one day. Rate each prediction or statement as extremely vague, somewhat vague, somewhat specific, or extremely specific. Briefly discuss your results.

▸ Follow an astrology column for at least 1 week for a classmate's astrological sign (it needs to be a different sign than your own), and have the classmate do the same for you. At the same time, keep a journal of daily events for the same period of time. At the end of the week, share the predictions with your classmate. Comment on the accuracy and/or usefulness of the predictions. It is imperative to <u>not</u> share until the end of the week.

▸ Your instructor may give the class a personality "quiz" based on horoscopes. Follow the instructions carefully and honestly. Briefly describe the results.

▸ Reproduce the athletic achievement study for astrological signs. Or, instead of athletes, choose any other successful human endeavor—members of the U.S. Senate, famous actors/actresses, winners of cooking competitions, etc.—anything where you can get birthdates, and therefore astrological signs, for a large sample of people (100 is probably a lower limit). Briefly report on your results.

- *Astrophysics activity 3.1:* With data either provided by the instructor or found online, plot the position of a planet showing apparent retrograde motion.

- Write a short paper on the importance to history of the solution to the retrograde motion problem.

- Create a spreadsheet calculating the amount of time spent in retrograde motion for each of the eight major planets, using the following formula:

$$t = \frac{2\pi cos\left[cos^{-1}\left\{\dfrac{a + \sqrt{a}}{1 + a^{3/2}}\right\}\right]}{2\pi\left(1 - \dfrac{1}{P}\right)}$$

where *a* is the semi-major axis (in astronomical units) and *P* the period (in years) of the planet in question. Compare the results from the formula to the observations listed (Mercury and Mars have a range of times, due to their highly eccentric orbits):

Planet	Time in Retrograde (Days)
Mercury	18 to 25
Venus	41
Mars	59 to 81
Jupiter	121
Saturn	138
Uranus	151
Neptune	158

- *Astrophysics activity 3.2:* Review one of the five major discoveries (Jupiter, Milky Way, Moon, Sun, Venus) made by Galileo with his original telescopes. Consulting with others, rank the discoveries in order of importance (1 = most important) and be prepared to defend your answer.

- *Astrophysics activity 3.3:* Watch Episode 7 from the original *Cosmos* series, "The Backbone of Night," about ancient astronomers. Answer questions as instructed. The video is available online.

- *Astrophysics activity 3.4:* Watch Episode 3 from the original *Cosmos* series, "Harmony of the Worlds," about the life and works of Johannes Kepler. Answer questions as instructed. The video is available online.

Works Referenced

Conner, C. (2005). *A people's history of science: Miners, midwifes and low mechanics.* Nation Books, New York, NY.

King, H. C. (1951–1952). *The history of the telescope.* Ph.D. Thesis, University of London (External).

Kitcher, P. (1982). *Abusing science: The case against creationism.* Boston, MA: MIT Press.

West, M. (2017, July 22). Soundly proving the curvature of the Earth at Lake Pontchartrain. Retrieved from https://www.metabunk.org/soundly-proving-the-curvature-of-the-earth-at-lake-pontchartrain.t8939/

Credits

Fig. I.4: Source: https://www.astro.com/swisseph/ae/2000/ae_2011.pdf and https://www.astro.com/swisseph/ae/2000/ae_2012.pdf.

Fig. 3.1: Source: https://commons.wikimedia.org/wiki/File:Location_of_the_inner_planets_and_their_Zodiac_signs_on_January_30,_1980.png.

Fig. 3.2: Source: Sporting News.

Fig. 3.3: Source: https://commons.wikimedia.org/wiki/File:Barcelona,_Spain_-_Flickr_-_NASA_Goddard_Photo_and_Video.jpg.

Fig. 3.8: Source: https://commons.wikimedia.org/wiki/File:Lunar_eclipse_chart_close-08aug16.png.

Fig. 3.9a: Source: https://commons.wikimedia.org/wiki/File:Eratosthenes.jpg.

Fig. 3.9b: Copyright © by Eliseevmn (CC BY-SA 4.0) at https://commons.wikimedia.org/wiki/File:Aristarchus_of_Samos.jpg.

Fig. 3.9c: Source: https://commons.wikimedia.org/wiki/File:Aristotle_Altemps_Inv8575.jpg.

Fig. 3.10: Source: https://www.physicsoftheuniverse.com/images/cosmologies_aristotelian.jpg.

Fig. 3.11: Copyright © by Tomruen (CC BY-SA 4.0) at https://commons.wikimedia.org/wiki/File:Mars_motion_2005.png.

Fig. 3.12a: Source: https://commons.wikimedia.org/wiki/File:PSM_V78_D326_Ptolemy.png.

Fig. 3.13a: Source: https://www.physicsoftheuniverse.com/images/cosmologies_copernican.jpg.

Fig. 3.13b: Copyright © by René Klein (CC BY-SA 3.0) at https://commons.wikimedia.org/wiki/File:Torun03-MonumentToCopernicus.JPG.

Fig. 3.14: Copyright © by Brian Brondel (CC BY-SA 3.0) at https://commons.wikimedia.org/wiki/File:Retrograde_Motion.bjb.svg.

Fig. 3.15a: Source: https://commons.wikimedia.org/wiki/File:Tycho_Brahe.JPG.

Fig. 3.15b: Source: https://commons.wikimedia.org/wiki/File:Uraniborgskiss_45.jpg.

Fig. 3.16: Copyright © by Kiefer (CC BY-SA 2.0) at https://commons.wikimedia.org/wiki/File:07.Sep.2014_(14992545629).jpg.

Fig. 3.19: Source: https://commons.wikimedia.org/wiki/File:Inner_Planet_Orbits.jpg.

Fig. 3.20a: Source: https://commons.wikimedia.org/wiki/File:Johannes_Kepler_1610.jpg.

Fig. 3.20b: Source: https://commons.wikimedia.org/wiki/File:Justus_Sustermans_-_Portrait_of_Galileo_Galilei,_1636.jpg.

Fig. 3.21a: Source: https://commons.wikimedia.org/wiki/File:Hans_Lipperhey.jpg.

Fig. 3.21b: Copyright © by Sailko (CC BY-SA 3.0) at https://commons.wikimedia.org/wiki/File:Galileo_galilei,_telescopi_del_1609-10_ca..JPG.

Fig. 3.22: Copyright © by ESO/H.H. Heyer (CC BY 4.0) at https://commons.wikimedia.org/wiki/File:360-degree_Panorama_of_the_Southern_Sky.jpg.

Fig. 3.24: Source: https://commons.wikimedia.org/wiki/File:Sidereus_Nuncius_Medicean_Stars.jpg.

Fig. 3.25a: Copyright © by Wellcome Collection Gallery (CC BY 2.0) at https://commons.wikimedia.org/wiki/File:Sir_William_Herschel_and_Caroline_Herschel._Wellcome_V0002731.jpg.

Fig. 3.25b: Source: https://apod.nasa.gov/apod/ap010826.html.

THE INTERSECTION OF PHYSICS
AND ASTRONOMY

The top of Mount Everest is about 5 miles above sea level. Why not a hundred miles?

CHAPTER 4

GRAVITY AND MOTION

PURPOSE

To relate the laws of motion and gravity to the solar system

OBJECTIVES

- To review the laws of motion
- To investigate how mass and distance relate to gravitational forces
- To relate the laws of motion and gravity to the laws of planetary motion
- To tell why many astronomical objects are spherically shaped
- To introduce the concept of angular momentum
- To discuss gravity tides

INTRODUCTION

In our previous chapter, we discussed the laws of planetary motion. These laws are good for describing how planets orbit the Sun, or how the Moon orbits the Earth, or how stars orbit each other. But they don't apply to how objects move on Earth, or why ocean tides roll in and out, or why the planets tend to orbit the Sun in the same plane.

In the last half of the 17th century, Isaac Newton introduced (among other concepts) a set of laws—laws of motion and gravity—that handle nearly all types of motions of astronomical objects. Other facts, such as the rotations and even the shapes of objects, are described by Newton's findings. In this chapter, we apply Newton to solar system astronomy.

KEY TERMS

Acceleration: The rate at which the velocity of an object changes with respect to time

Angular momentum: For a small object in orbit about a large object, its mass multiplied by its speed multiplied by its distance from the Sun. The angular momentum of such a small object is conserved; that is, it does not change unless another significant outside force acts on the small object

Center of mass: For any object, or series of objects, we can show that the object(s) act as if all the mass is located at a particular point

Centripetal acceleration: "Center-seeking" acceleration, often seen in astronomy when a small object orbits a large object due to gravity

Escape speed: The speed at which a small object needs to be moving in order to "escape" the gravitational pull of a large object

Force: A "push" or "pull" given by one object to another

Gravitational potential energy: The energy stored by the gravitational attraction between two masses

Gravity assist: The use of a planet's gravity to "slingshot" space probes, so that they can move much faster than without the assist

Kinetic energy: The energy expressed by a moving object

Mass: The resistance to the change of velocity of an object (acceleration)

Migration (also planetary migration): In some cases—shepherd moons or giant planets in the distant past—objects can "swap" orbits due to their gravitational interactions

Newton's first law of motion: Often nicknamed "the law of inertia," it states that an object will keep its velocity constant unless acted upon by an outside (external) force

Newton's second law of motion: Usually expressed as an equation (F = ma), it states that an object's acceleration, or change of velocity, depends on the net (total) external force acting upon it and inversely upon the mass of the object

Newton's third law of motion: Often nicknamed the "action-reaction law," it states that if an object exerts a force on a second object, the second object exerts an equal (in amount) and opposite (in direction) force on the first object

Orbital resonance: When the gravity of a massive object has locked the motion of a smaller object (its rotation and/or orbit) into a simple ratio. The example we see

each month is the Moon: Its sidereal rotation (rotation with respect to the stars) equals its sidereal orbit, a ratio of 1 to 1, so that it always shows us the same face. Ratios do not need to be 1:1; other whole-number options are known

Rings (also ring particles): Billions of relatively tiny particles orbiting a planet, looking like a solid ring from a distance

Shepherd moons: Mountain-sized ring particles whose gravity keeps or "herds" other smaller ring particles so that they stay confined to the ring rather than dissipating. Shepherd moons always come in pairs

Spin-orbit coupling: See *orbital resonance*

Tides: The difference between forces of gravity acting on an object, due to differences in distance

Uniform circular motion: When an object moves in a circle at constant speed and in the same rotational direction

Universal gravitational constant: Represented by the capital letter "G," it determines the scale of the force of gravity between objects

Universal law of gravity: This states the amount of gravity force between two objects depends on the amount of mass of each object and inversely on the square of the distance between the objects. A constant of nature ("G") sets the scale of the force

Weight: The force of gravity on a small object on the surface of an astronomical object like a moon or planet, equal to the acceleration due to gravity ("g") multiplied by the mass of the small object

KEY INDIVIDUALS

Cavendish, Henry: An English scientist who late in the 18th century first determined the value of the universal gravitational constant ("G") to good precision

Galilei, Galileo: An Italian scientist in the early 17th century who, among other things, performed experiments on the motions of objects

Newton, Isaac: An English scientist in the late 17th/early 18th century who, among other things, devised the laws of motion and the law of gravity, invented calculus, and invented the reflecting telescope

Section 4.1: Isaac Newton

Whilst he was pensively meandering in a garden it came into his thought that the power of gravity (which brought an apple from a tree to the ground) was not limited to a certain distance from earth, but that this power must extend much further than was usually thought. Why not as high as the Moon said he to himself & if so, that must influence her motion & perhaps retain her in her orbit, whereupon he felt a calculating what would be the effect of that supposition.

So wrote John Conduitt, an assistant of Isaac Newton's at the Royal Mint and husband of Newton's niece, describing a famous event from Newton's life. The legend often states that an apple hit Newton on his head while he sat under a tree, but that appears not to be true. That Newton saw an apple fall from a tree and related its motion to that of the Moon was stated by several of Newton's acquaintances.

Whether or not the event happened as described, the importance of the story is not that gravity exists (people have noticed objects falling as long as there have been people), but that the same force of nature that pulls an apple to the ground is also responsible for keeping the Moon in orbit about the Earth. This is a further demonstration of Galileo's argument several decades prior, that the laws of nature are universal and apply everywhere.

FIGURE 4.1. Gravity works on both apples and the Moon.

Isaac Newton is possibly the smartest person who ever lived—the only real competitor in many minds is Einstein. But from where did such genius originate?

Newton was born on Christmas Day in 1642,[1] so tiny his mother famously said he could fit into a quart mug. Newton's father had died 3 months before he was born, and he never reconciled himself to his mother remarrying, even fantasizing about killing her and his stepfather. In 1659, his stepfather died, and Newton's mother wanted to bring him home from school to take over the family farm; the school's headmaster convinced her to allow Newton to continue his schooling, where he excelled, spurred on in part as revenge against a bully.

In 1661, Newton was admitted to Trinity College in Cambridge, where he acted as the equivalent of a work-study student until earning a scholarship in 1664. Despite hints at his talents—he worked out a generalized binomial theorem and the beginnings of calculus—his career as a student was apparently unremarkable until he was sent home to avoid an outbreak of plague in 1665.

Instead of farming, which Newton despised, he spent his time in thought and experiment—in hindsight, the most productive extended spring break in history. Before returning to Cambridge a year and a half later, Newton formulated the laws of motion, the universal law of gravity, showed how white light consists of a continuous spectrum of colors, invented the reflecting telescope, and further developed the first version of calculus.

Newton's abilities were recognized soon after his return to school in April 1667; by October of 1667 he was elected as a fellow of Trinity; he received his MA in 1668; in 1669 he

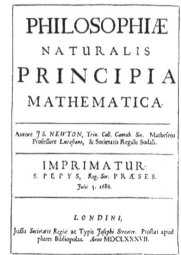

FIGURE 4.2. Statue of Isaac Newton at Trinity College chapel (left); the title page of the *Principia* (right).

---

[1] That is, under England's old calendar (see chapter 2). England, not being Catholic, didn't switch to the new and improved Gregorian calendar until after Newton's death. In the updated calendar, Newton was born January 4, 1643.

replaced his mentor Isaac Barrow as Lucasian professor, a highly regarded position; by 1672 he was elected as a fellow of the Royal Society.

As hinted at, Newton was a prickly personality. He was very guarded in allowing others to see details of his work and engaged in several disputes over priority, most notably with Gottfried von Leibniz over calculus and Robert Hooke[2] over various issues in mechanics. Newton was the president of the Royal Society, presided over the Royal Mint, and even served two brief unconnected terms as a member of Parliament. He was only the second scientist to be knighted in England (Roger Bacon was the first), in 1703 by Queen Anne. Much of his later career was also spent on alchemy and religious studies. He died in his sleep in 1727 and was buried in Westminster Abbey, an honor reserved only for the most famous and important of British citizens.

What is it that Newton discovered? We will investigate his studies regarding light in a future chapter, and most of his mathematics (especially calculus) lies outside the scope of this book. This chapter is devoted largely to his work on the laws of motion and gravity, to which we now turn.

Section 4.2: The Laws of Motion

Kepler's laws, as useful as they are, are really an application of more general principles. Kepler discovered how planets orbit the Sun; Newton discovered how all objects move, laying out a set of laws in his most famous work, the *Principia*.[3] In modern terms, his laws can be stated thusly:

1. **"The law of inertia."** An object at rest tends to stay at rest; an object in motion tends to stay in motion. This introduces the concept of velocity (or momentum), the combination of an object having both a relative speed and direction. The law states that an object will keep a constant velocity ("inertia") unless an external force acts on it. This brings us to the next law.

2. **F = ma.** The most obvious mathematical of the laws of motion, it states that an object will have a change of its velocity—also called acceleration—if a net external force acts on it. For our purposes, a "force" can be thought of as a "push" or a "pull." The amount of acceleration also depends on the mass of the object—the more mass, the less acceleration. This leads to a physics-way of defining mass: Mass is not merely the amount of "stuff" an object contains, but, more specifically, the resistance to a change of an object's velocity.

3. **"Action-reaction."** If an object exerts a force on a second object, it will feel an equal and opposite force in return—equal in amount, opposite in direction. This law relates objects to each other.

The laws of motion were not exclusively constructed by Newton (science is always a process of discovery built on prior work); for example, Galileo performed experiments elucidating the first law decades before Newton's birth. But Newton introduced modern terminology, adduced new concepts (such as "centripetal" motion) and, most importantly, realized these three statements make a complete set of rules for the motion of all objects, astronomical or not.

The first law states that a moving object will continue with that motion (velocity) unless an external force acts on it. This appears to contradict what we see in everyday life; for example, if you're driving along a highway and you take your foot off the gas pedal, the car immediately and noticeably begins to slow down. Why?

> ## Check Your Neighbor
>
> You're driving your car down the highway when a bug hits your windshield. Which object exerted more force during the collision: the bug on the car, the car on the bug, or (perhaps) both objects exerted the same amount of force on each other?

---

[2] Upon Hooke's death, Newton supposedly burned all portraits of Hooke at the Royal Society. We don't have any reliable images of Hooke even today.

[3] The full title is *Philosophaie Naturalis Principia Mathematica*, or in English, the *Mathematical Principles of Natural Philosophy*.

A car has several external forces acting upon it; for example, the car's tires push against the road, meaning the road pushes back, propelling the car forward. The car also feels friction between the tires and the road and air resistance (drag) trying to keep it moving forward. This is why you need to keep your foot on the gas pedal—when you remove your foot, you remove the force propelling the car forward, leaving only forces (friction, drag) acting to slow the car.

In astronomy, we generally have a simpler situation. Space is virtually a vacuum, meaning there is essentially no friction or air drag. Given this, a planet like the Earth should continue moving in a straight line, essentially forever. Yet it doesn't. Why not? Because there is one more important external force to consider: gravity.

Section 4.3: Gravity and Motion

Everyone, of course, has known about gravity all along—if you drop an object, or throw it in the air, it always falls back to the ground. What Newton did was (a) discover that gravity not only acts for objects on Earth, but for objects in space, and (b) all objects feel and exert gravity; in other words, Newton's law of gravity is *universal*. The equation expressing the amount of gravitational force between two objects can be expressed as

Equation 4.1

$$F_G = -G \frac{m_1 m_2}{r^2}$$

Check Your Neighbor

For the previous question, which object experienced a larger acceleration during its collision: the bug, the car, or (perhaps) they both experienced the same acceleration?

FIGURE 4.3. A bug versus a car—who wins?

Check Your Neighbor

Suppose your car is moving at a constant speed of 55 mph due north along a highway. How does the amount of force from the car's tires propelling it forward compare to the total amount of force from friction and drag trying to slow it down?

In this equation, the negative sign indicates the objects always attract each other; G is the "universal gravitational constant," which determines the scale (amount) of the force; m_1 and m_2 are the two individual masses; and r is the distance between the centers of each object.[4]

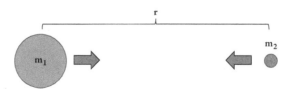

FIGURE 4.4. The amount of gravitational force acting between two objects depends on (a) the individual masses of the objects and (b) inversely on the square of the distance between the objects. Distances are measured from the centers of each object. Gravity always acts to attract objects toward each other.

---

[4] More precisely, between the centers of mass of each object. The *center of mass* of an object is the point in space where we can pretend all the mass of the object is located. This makes it easier to calculate gravity, for instance.

An aside: Physicists tend to express calculations in "standard" units, an extension of the metric system. Distance comes in meters, time in seconds, mass in kilograms, and force in newtons—named, obviously, after Isaac Newton.[5] A newton is a combination of a kilogram multiplied by a meter and divided by a second squared. For those of us more familiar with English units, a pound is about the same as 4½ newtons.

Gravity always pulls, or attracts, objects toward each other. This is as true for the Moon and the Earth as well as an apple falling from a tree toward the ground. So why doesn't the Moon simply crash into the Earth?

The first law of motion indicates that, left to itself, the Moon should go off into space in a straight line. The third law of motion (applying gravity) indicates that the Moon should be pulled into the Earth. It is the combination of these two laws—and the second as well—that explains the Moon's actual motion in space. One of Newton's major achievements was to use the laws of motion and the law of gravity to show that not only will the Moon orbit the Earth (or planets orbit the Sun, etc.), but the shape of the orbit must be an ellipse—precisely what Kepler discovered several decades earlier. Newton's mathematical solution even includes the notion that the larger object will be at one focus of the ellipse. In other words, Newton's laws of motion and gravity explain Kepler's first law of planetary motion.

How else does gravity affect astronomical objects? Let's explore some of these other issues.

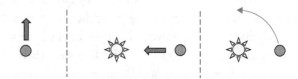

Check Your Neighbor

Two students are standing 1 meter apart, facing each other. They then each take a step backward so that they are now standing 2 meters apart. How much gravitational force acts upon them when separated by 2 meters, compared to when they were separated by 1 meter?

FIGURE 4.5. If left to itself, Earth would move in a straight line (left). If the Earth only felt gravity, it would be pulled toward the Sun (center). The Earth's actual motion represents the combination of these two behaviors.

1. Acceleration Due to Gravity

Gravity does one thing: It tries to pull objects together. This includes what we might call the self-gravity of an object. Each particle (such as atoms) contained in an object exerts a gravitational force on every other particle in that object. For objects in everyday life, the amount of self-gravity doesn't mean much and is usually undetectable, since gravity is a very weak force. But gravity matters if the object in question is (literally) astronomical. A rough rule of thumb is that gravity dominates when an object is about 200 miles across or larger.

Consider this: Every atom in your body is trying to pull every other atom in your body, the net attempt being to pull you into a point at the center of "you." But other forces—the material forces of bone, for example—are so much stronger that there is no possibility of you ever being squeezed into a point. On the other hand, the Earth has so much mass that it does try to pull itself toward a point. Material forces for the Earth (it being made of substances such as metal and rock inside) keep it from shrinking away to nothing, but the net result is that the Earth takes on a round shape, since the gravitational pull is, for the most part, directed toward the center of the Earth equally in all directions (this isn't quite true, an idea we will address next).

FIGURE 4.6. The reason astronomical objects are spherically shaped. Gravity (green arrows) tries to pull an object toward a common central point; other forces (red arrows) push back.

---

[5] Many units of measurement used by physicists are named after famous scientists. To distinguish between the person and the unit, we use capital vs. small letters; thus, "Newton" refers to the person, whereas "newton" refers to the unit.

Objects in astronomy are made from a variety of substances, but we can make some generalizations. Relatively small objects like comets and asteroids tend to be made of water-ice and/or rock; medium-sized objects like large moons or terrestrial (Earth-like) planets tend to be made from metal and rock; very large objects, like giant planets or stars, tend to be made of hydrogen and helium gas. In almost every case, the material exerts an outward pressure to "fight" against gravity, which always exerts an inward pressure. If an object doesn't have much mass, gravity isn't as important and its shape is lumpy or oblong; if an object has a lot of mass, its shape tends to be spherical (see Figure 4.7).

How can we express the "strength" of a planet's (or moon's, etc.) self-gravity? One way is to use the acceleration due to gravity at its surface. Designated little "g," this number helps us understand how much an object will weigh and how fast an object will fall if dropped near the surface of the planet. The formula for determining g is

Check Your Neighbor

Mauna Kea, one of the tallest volcanic mountains on Earth, reaches over 5 miles from its base to its peak. Why not 100 miles tall?

FIGURE 4.7. The effects of self-gravity on shape: Ida, an asteroid (left); Ganymede, a moon of Jupiter (right).

Equation 4.2

$$g = G\frac{M}{R^2}$$

Here, the capital M stands for the mass of the planet (again, or moon, etc.) and R for the radius of the planet. Note that we don't have a second object—specifically, the mass of a second object—in this formula. This equation describes the self-gravity of the planet, regardless of any other object involved.

Check Your Neighbor

Mars has an acceleration of gravity of 3.71 m/s². Which planet is more likely to possess taller volcanoes, Earth or Mars? Briefly defend your answer.

Sample Calculation

Let's do this for the Earth. The mass of the Earth is 5.98 × 10²⁴ kg and its radius is 6.37 × 10⁶ m, and the universal gravitational constant G = 6.67 × 10⁻¹¹ N·m²/kg²:

$$g_{Earth} = G\frac{M}{R^2} = (6.67 \times 10^{-11} N \cdot m^2 / kg^2)\frac{(5.98 \times 10^{24} kg)}{(6.37 \times 10^6 m)^2} = 9.81 \text{ m/s}^2$$

Now compare this to the acceleration of gravity on the surface of the Moon. The Moon is smaller both in terms of mass (7.35 × 10²² kg) and radius (1.74 × 10⁶ m). A lower mass implies a smaller acceleration, but a smaller radius implies a larger acceleration (because the mass is more concentrated).

$$g_{Moon} = G\frac{M}{R^2} = (6.67 \times 10^{-11} N \cdot m^2 / kg^2)\frac{(7.35 \times 10^{22} kg)}{(1.74 \times 10^6 m)^2} = 1.62 \text{ m/s}^2$$

In this case, the mass of the Moon is so much less than the Earth's (about 1/81) that its smaller radius (about one-fourth) that the Moon's surface gravity comes out weaker than the Earth's.

A useful shorthand for expressing the force of gravity acting on a small object (like a person) on the surface of an astronomical object (like the Earth) is its *weight*:

Equation 4.3

$$w = mg$$

where m is the mass of the small object and g is the acceleration due to gravity, previously described in Equation 4.2.

Sample Calculation

Suppose you are an astronaut, and you (with your spacesuit and associated gear) have a mass of 100 kilograms. What is your weight on (a) the Earth and (b) the Moon?

For Earth: $w_{\text{Earth}} = mg_{\text{Earth}} = (100 \text{ kg})\left(9.81 \frac{\text{m}}{\text{s}^2}\right) = 981 \text{ N}$

For the Moon: $w_{\text{Moon}} = mg_{\text{Moon}} = (100 \text{ kg})\left(1.68 \frac{\text{m}}{\text{s}^2}\right) = 168 \text{ N}$

2. Centripetal Motion

Recall that we earlier defined velocity as speed <u>and</u> direction. Further, acceleration is the change of velocity over time—meaning that if <u>either</u> the speed <u>or</u> the direction of an object changes, we have acceleration. The simplest way to have an acceleration when the object's speed is constant but its direction changes is *uniform circular motion.*[6]

An object undergoing uniform circular motion moves in a perfect circle at constant speed in the same rotational direction (i.e., either clockwise or counterclockwise). Although objects in astronomy rarely exhibit uniform circular motion, it often serves as a good starting point for discussing more complicated motions, such as the elliptical paths taken by planets orbiting the Sun.

To have an object moving in uniform circular motion (or other closed paths like ellipses), we need two things: (a) the object already has a velocity not pointed either directly toward or directly away from the center of its circle, and (b) a force to keep trying to pull the object toward the center of the circle. This results in a continual change of the object's velocity, which itself has a special term: *centripetal acceleration.* Any force that tries to pull the object toward the center of its circle will do. In everyday life, examples can include turning a car (friction between the car's tires and the road supplies the force) or whirling a rock around one's head using a string (tension in the string supplies the force). For planets orbiting the Sun, the force behind the centripetal acceleration is gravity.

The amount of centripetal acceleration of an object is related to both its speed v and the radius r of its circle:

Equation 4.4

$$a_c = \frac{v^2}{r}$$

Where do we see this in everyday life? Probably the most familiar experience is riding in a car. When you take a sharp turn, it feels as if you're thrown sideways away from the direction of your turn. In fact, this is another example

---

[6] If this sounds familiar, it should. Uniform circular motion was assumed to be how planets moved, from Aristotle to Copernicus, and was only shown to be incorrect by Kepler.

of the combination of all the laws of motion. For example, law 1 (inertia) means that you (the passenger[7]) will have a tendency to go forward in a straight line; law 2 (force) means you feel a force from the door (or dashboard, etc.); and law 3 (action-reaction) means the reason you feel a force from the door is because you exerted a force on it. It feels like you are being thrown outward, but in reality there are forces trying to push you inward.

Where does this show up in astronomy? Isaac Newton himself noticed that the Earth cannot be a perfect sphere due to this effect. Because the Earth rotates, objects at the Equator move quickly (over 1,000 mph!) whereas objects at the poles barely rotate at all. Therefore, Newton argued that the diameter of the Earth measured across the Equator must be larger than the diameter of the Earth measured from North to South Pole—and so it is.

The Sun rotates at a relatively slow rate—once per month, on average—and so the "distortion" of the Sun is minimal. Astronomers used to think virtually all stars have slow rotations, and for the most part that still appears to be true. But there are some interesting cases involving significant centripetal motion. Over a century ago, the bright star Vega was used as the standard of comparison for star brightnesses ("magnitudes"). But an unspoken assumption assumed Vega was a perfect sphere, because its brightness would look different from different angles (vantage points) if it had an oblong shape. Interferometric observations indicate Vega rotates at 236 km/s at its equator, making it 19% larger

FIGURE 4.8. The Sun (left) and Vega (right) to scale.

at its equator than between its poles. Because Vega is smaller at its poles, its self-gravity is larger there, making its surface temperatures higher there. Vega is about twice as bright at its poles compared to its equator—therefore actually making it a poor choice to serve as a standard star.

Another effect of centripetal motion involves orbits. Even if the motion is not perfectly circular, the acceleration at any given point of (for example) a planet about the Sun is still determined by the same formula. Further, because the force in astronomy responsible for centripetal motion is gravity, we can set Newton's law of gravity to equal the mass of the planet multiplied by its centripetal acceleration; or, in other words, we can make use of Newton's second law of motion to state

Equation 4.5

$$G\frac{Mm}{r^2} = \frac{mv^2}{r}$$

where M is the mass of the Sun (or larger object) and m is the mass of the planet (or smaller object). We can use this to show that the speed v of the planet as it moves through space depends on its distance from the Sun r:

Equation 4.6

$$v = \sqrt{\frac{GM}{r}}$$

Sample Calculation

How fast does the Earth travel through space in its orbit about the Sun? Use the mass of the Sun (in kilograms) and the average distance of the Earth from the Sun (in meters).

$$v = \sqrt{\frac{\left(6.67 \times 10^{-11} \ \text{N} \cdot \text{m}^2 \middle/ \text{kg}^2\right)\left(1.99 \times 10^{30} \ \text{kg}\right)}{1.50 \times 10^{11} \ \text{m}}} = 30{,}000 \ \text{m/s} = 30 \ \text{km/s or } 18 \ \text{miles/s}$$

---

[7] If you want to try this, please do so as a passenger and not as a driver. Thanks!

While astronomers are often interested in a planet's speed, what they can measure directly is the period of the planet's orbit. Let's assume the shape of the planet's orbit is a perfect circle (it turns out that the result will be the same if we use an ellipse; the derivation is simpler with a circle). Speed in general is distance traveled divided by the time needed to make the trip. If the planet moves in a circle, the distance is the circumference of the circle, and the time to complete the orbit (circle) by definition is the planet's orbital period:

Equation 4.7

$$v = \frac{2\pi r}{T}$$

If we combine this formula for speed with Equation 4.5, and do some rearranging, we can create an equation relating the orbital period to its distance from the Sun:

Equation 4.8

$$T^2 = \left(\frac{4\pi^2}{GM}\right)r^3$$

If this looks familiar, it should. Compare this to Kepler's third law:

$$P^2 = a^3$$

Kepler's third law applies specifically to objects independently orbiting the Sun. Newton's version of the third law (Equation 4.8) is more general; it applies to any small object orbiting any large object due to gravity. Another difference between the two formulae is that Kepler's third law uses units from astronomy (the year and the au) whereas Newton's version uses standard physics units (seconds and meters).

Sample Calculation

What is the orbital period of the Earth, given its average distance from the Sun is 1.50×10^{11} m?

$$T = \sqrt{\left(\frac{GM}{4\pi^2}\right)r^3} = \sqrt{\left(\frac{\left(6.67 \times 10^{-11} \; N \cdot m^2/kg^2\right)\left(1.99 \times 10^{30} \, kg\right)}{4\pi^2}\right)\left(1.50 \times 10^{11} \, m\right)^3} = 3.2 \times 10^7 \, s$$

... which is 1 year.

The disadvantage (if we want to describe it as such) is that Newton's version of Kepler's third law is more complicated than Kepler's original version. The advantage is that Newton's version is more general: It can be applied to any situation where one object orbits another, whereas Kepler's is limited to describing objects in units of solar masses.

Suppose we want to determine the mass of an astronomical object, such as a planet. We can't put the planet on a scale, so what can we do? We can measure the effect of its gravity on other objects—in other words, watch a much smaller object orbit the planet.

The Moon has a semi-major axis of 384,000 km and a sidereal orbital period of 27.3 days. What is the mass of the Earth?

First, convert each given number into standard units (i.e., meters and seconds):

$$384,000 \text{ km} \times \left(\frac{1000 \text{ m}}{1 \text{ km}} \right) = 3.84 \times 10^8 \text{ m}$$

$$27.3 \text{ days} \times \left(\frac{86,400 \text{ s}}{1 \text{ day}} \right) = 2.36 \times 10^6 \text{ s}$$

Then manipulate Newton's version of Kepler's third law (Equation 4.7) to find the mass:

$$M = \left(\frac{4\pi^2}{G} \right) \left(\frac{T^2}{r^3} \right) = \left(\frac{4\pi^2}{6.67 \times 10^{-11} \text{ N} \cdot \text{m}^2 / \text{kg}^2} \right) \left(\frac{[3.84 \times 10^8 \text{ m}]^3}{[2.36 \times 10^6 \text{ s}]^2} \right) = 6.0 \times 10^{24} \text{ kg}$$

3. Energy and Momentum

In physics, we can think about force being a push or pull. Energy is perhaps a more abstract term, but we can think about energy representing a specific type of quality contained in an object; for example, the gasoline in your car's tank stands for a type of chemical energy, which you (and your car) can use to move the car. For our purposes, we will only look in detail at two types of energies: kinetic and gravitational.

We can see without much trouble that a moving object has something that a non-moving object does not. Physicists call this *kinetic energy*, and it has the following formula:

Equation 4.9

$$K = \frac{1}{2}mv^2$$

Where, as you might expect, m is the mass of the moving object and v is its velocity. The standard physics units for energy (kinetic or otherwise) are called *joules*; for comparison, it takes over 4 thousand joules to make up one food calorie.

It also takes energy to raise an object above the ground, or more generally, to move two objects apart against their mutual gravitational pull. This is called *gravitational potential energy*:

Equation 4.10

$$U = -G\frac{m_1 m_2}{r}$$

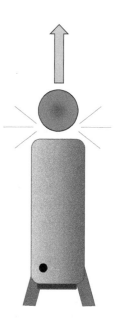

FIGURE 4.9. Can you shoot a cannonball fast enough that it escapes the gravity of the Earth?

As you've no doubt noticed, if you throw an object up in the air, it falls back down. Suppose you had an extremely strong cannon—how fast would you have to shoot an object straight up in order so that it never fell back down? Or, how fast would you have to shoot an object so that it could escape the Earth's gravity?

By comparing Equations 4.9 and 4.10, we can show that the *escape speed* of an object off the Earth will be

Equation 4.11

$$v_{esc} = \sqrt{\frac{2GM}{R}}$$

Where, assuming we start on the surface of the Earth, M is the mass of the Earth and R is the radius of the Earth. This doesn't have to just be the Earth; this equation works for escaping any object's gravity.

Sample Calculation

Compare the escape speed of the Earth to the escape speed of the Moon. Briefly describe how this helps us understand why the Earth has an atmosphere and the Moon does not.

$$\text{For Earth: } v_{Earth} = \sqrt{\frac{2GM_{Earth}}{R_{Earth}}} = \sqrt{\frac{(2)\left(6.67 \times 10^{-11} \text{ N} \cdot \text{m}^2\middle/\text{kg}^2\right)(5.97 \times 10^{24} \text{ kg})}{6.37 \times 10^6 \text{ m}}} = 11{,}200 \text{ m/s}$$

Or 11.2 km/s or about 7 miles per second

$$\text{For Moon: } v_{Moon} = \sqrt{\frac{2GM_{Moon}}{R_{Moon}}} = \sqrt{\frac{(2)\left(6.67 \times 10^{-11} \text{ N} \cdot \text{m}^2\middle/\text{kg}^2\right)(7.35 \times 10^{22} \text{ kg})}{1.74 \times 10^6 \text{ m}}} = 2{,}400 \text{ m/s}$$

Or 2.4 km/s or about 1.5 miles per second

Earth's escape speed is significantly higher than that of the Moon, so gas particles will have a much more difficult task escaping the Earth than the Moon.

As the example hints, we can use escape speed to help us understand how a planet can hold onto an atmosphere. It also matters when we think about sending space probes off of Earth to other locations in the solar system. And it matters when we examine the damage an asteroid or comet makes when it hits the surface of a planet. We will discuss these ideas more fully in future chapters.

Check Your Neighbor

Do <u>you</u> have an escape speed? If so, how large do you expect it to be? Briefly defend your answer.

Finally, another related concept to energy is called *linear momentum*. The linear momentum of an object is the mass of the object multiplied by its velocity (velocity including both the speed of the object and its direction). This idea also comes into play when, for instance, an asteroid hits the surface of a planet.

4. Center of Mass and Mutual Orbits

Earlier, we presented the motion of a planet about the Sun as an orbit, wherein the planet does all the moving and the Sun stands still. While close, this is not an exact description of the situation. Instead, both the Sun and planet will move about a point called the *center of mass*.

The center of mass of such a system is a weighted average of the positions of the two objects—rather than being at the geometric center (i.e., exactly between the two objects) the center of mass will be skewed toward the more-massive object:

Equation 4.12

$$r_{CM} = \frac{m_1 r_1 + m_2 r_2}{m_1 + m_2}$$

Where m_1 and m_2 are the masses of the objects and r_1 and r_2 are their respective positions.

Sample Calculation

Where is the center of mass of the Earth-Moon system? Express your answer as a distance from the center of the Earth.

Let the position of the Earth be at "zero" and the position of the Moon be at 384,000 km (3.84×10^8 m), the semi-major axis of its orbit. Then,

$$r_{CM} = \frac{(5.98 \times 10^{24}\,\text{kg})(0) + (7.35 \times 10^{22}\,\text{kg})(3.84 \times 10^8\,\text{m})}{5.98 \times 10^{24} + 7.35 \times 10^{22}\,\text{kg}} = 4.66 \times 10^6 \text{ m}$$

The Earth's radius is 6.37×10^6 m, so the center of mass of the Earth-Moon system is inside the Earth, some 1,700 kilometers (just over 1000 miles) below the Earth's surface. The exact position of the center of mass relative to we on the surface of the Earth changes as the Earth rotates, the Moon moves in its orbit, and (now) the Earth pivots about this point. Astronomers often describe this as a "wobble" by the Earth, or by the much larger object in any such similar situation.

FIGURE 4.10. The orbit of a planet about a star, ignoring the center of mass (left); the orbit of a planet and the "wobble" of a star, including the center of mass (center); the mutual orbits of two stars about the center of mass (right).

This means we need to modify our equations to incorporate these ideas. Let's look specifically at Kepler's third law, which now becomes

Equation 4.13

$$\frac{a^3}{P^2} = M_1 + M_2$$

Since even a planet like Jupiter is far less massive than the Sun, these differences don't amount to much, and it's still proper to describe Jupiter orbiting the Sun, rather than stating the more correct but longer-winded version of Jupiter and the Sun moving about a common center of mass. But this does come into play when we search for planets in other star systems, or view binary stars, where the individual objects do have similar masses. We will return to these ideas in detail in other sections of the book.

Section 4.4: Angular Momentum

Newton's laws of motion as presented are specifically applied to objects moving in straight lines. But they also apply to objects moving in curves, including (for example) planets orbiting the Sun or planets rotating on their axes.

One of the most important laws in physics is the conservation of angular momentum. Angular momentum is the rotational equivalent of linear momentum. An object that rotates about its own axis, or orbits another, larger object, has a constant angular momentum. What does that mean?

For example, the formula for the angular momentum of a small object (such as a planet) orbiting a large object (such as the Sun) looks like this:

Equation 4.14

$$L = mrv$$

where m is the mass of the moving object, r is its distance from the larger object, and v is the speed of the object.[8] Kepler's first law discusses how objects that orbit the Sun do so in ellipses, so they are sometimes close to the Sun and sometimes far from the Sun, so the distance of the object from the Sun is continuously changing.

The law of conservation of angular momentum means that the <u>combination</u> of mass, distance, and velocity (or speed) stays the same, or "constant" as physicists like to say. Since the mass of the planet basically stays the same in its orbit, this implies the distance and speed are inversely related to each other—the closer a planet is to the Sun, the faster it moves; the further a planet is from the Sun, the slower it moves. Or, another way to express it is that a planet sweeps out equal areas in equal times—which is Kepler's second law of planetary motion.

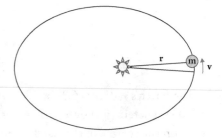

FIGURE 4.11. Applying angular momentum to Kepler's second law of motion.

To sum up, we have shown how Newton's laws of motion, combined with Newton's law of gravity, can be used to derive Kepler's laws of planetary motion.

Section 4.5: Tides

Another effect of gravity upon the behavior and appearance of an astronomical object is *tides*. Tides are the differences between gravity forces on an object due to differences in distances (see Figure 4.12):

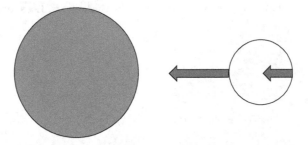

FIGURE 4.12. The acceleration due to gravity from a planet (blue disk at left) acting on opposite sides of a moon. The longer arrow on the side of the moon nearer the planet indicates the acceleration is relatively large, and the shorter arrow on the side of the moon further from the planet indicates the acceleration is relatively small. For clarity, the figure is not to scale, and the differences in acceleration arrow lengths have been exaggerated.

Suppose we have a large object (such as a planet) exerting gravity on a smaller object (such as a moon). To determine how the moon orbits the planet, we use the distance from the center of mass of the planet to the center

---

[8] By the way, physicists are aware there is no "L" in the term "angular momentum." Sometimes we simply run out of letters for our quantities and need to use others.

of mass of the moon. But in reality, all parts of each object attract each other. We can imagine the planet's gravity acting on the side of the moon closest to the planet separately from the planet's gravity acting on the side of the moon. Because the force of gravity drops with the square of the distance, the amounts of gravity won't be the same on opposite sides of the moon.

Usually tides are not very important, but sometimes they matter. Io, a moon of Jupiter, is a good example. The tides from Jupiter are strong enough to "flex" the surface of Io by several miles as Io orbits. The flexing is strong enough that the interior of Io is almost entirely molten. A moon that otherwise should have cooled completely solid billions of years ago is the most volcanically active object in the solar system.

 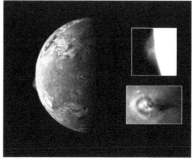

FIGURE 4.13. Flexing a paper clip generates heat at the point of flexing; flexing a moon like Io via tides generates enough heat to create active volcanoes.

In extreme cases, the tides from a large object (large in terms of mass, specifically) can potentially be larger than the forces that hold a smaller object together. This is one hypothesis concerning the origin of the rings of Saturn, and the tides of Jupiter shredded a comet (Shoemaker-Levy 9) into over two dozen pieces when the comet made a close approach to Jupiter in 1992.

FIGURE 4.14. The tides of Jupiter shredded Comet Shoemaker-Levy 9 into pieces during a close approach of the comet in 1992.

It's not only the case that large objects exert tides on small objects. Earth is famous for experiencing tides from the Moon, of course. The tides from the Moon tilt the Earth back and forth as it both orbits us and as the Earth rotates. The amount of tilting is rather small, only 1/10,000 of a degree, but several behaviors intensify the effects. By coincidence, the Earth's oceans have a resonant frequency near 12 hours, which is similar to half an Earth day (remember, the tides act to distinguish between opposite sides of the Earth); the oceans are thousands of miles across, which adds up; and local changes in the shape of the shoreline all make the ocean tides larger than the small amount of rocking might otherwise indicate.[9] Also, the Moon is not the only object involved; the Sun also

---

[9] Textbooks often show the Earth's tides as "pulling" water off the surface of the Earth. This notion is unfortunately very misleading as to how ocean tides actually work.

exerts noticeable tides on the Earth, though the Moon's effects are over twice as important. The gravitational pull of other planets can (very) slightly affect the Earth's orbit, but their tides are virtually undetectable.

How else do tides—again, tides are merely gravity forces at different distances—affect objects in the solar system? Here are a few consequences and/or related phenomena.

1. Planetary Rings

The rings of Saturn were first spotted by Galileo in 1609, though his telescope's quality was not enough for him to understand what he was looking at. Within a few decades, Christiaan Huygens discovered the fact that we are looking at rings surrounding Saturn that nowhere touch the planet. In the mid-nineteenth century, the famous physicist James Clerk Maxwell showed the rings cannot be solid, but rather must consist of numerous tiny individual particles. Or, each tiny particle is really a moon of sorts, each in its own orbit about Saturn. While Saturn's rings are spectacular, all the giant planets have rings.

Even so, rings are still not stable. Ring particles are crowded enough that they frequently collide with each other. Collisions should knock some particles toward the planet and some away, meaning within a relatively short time (within a person's lifetime) even rings as large as Saturn's should dissipate. Yet Saturn's rings appear much the same as they did 400 years ago, and the rings of Jupiter and Uranus (Neptune's are more of a mystery) also seem stable. Why?

Jupiter is a special case. The tides of Jupiter acting on Io keep Io molten inside, making Io the most volcanically active object in the solar system. Material blasted during violent eruptions can escape Io's gravity and instead be drawn into orbit about Jupiter. So, Jupiter's rings are constantly being replenished.

The same isn't true for Saturn or Uranus. Rather, they possess an interesting phenomenon called *shepherd moons*. Like a sheep dog, shepherd moons act to "corral" wayward ring particles, confining them to their ring. Shepherd moons (unlike sheep dogs) always come in pairs, on opposite sides of the ring (i.e., one closer to the planet than the ring, one further away). If a ring particle moves away from the ring, the gravity of a shepherd moon acts to pull it back into the ring. While an average ring particle is the size of a softball or adult's fist, a shepherd moon is more like a floating mountain, several tens of kilometers across.

Interestingly, when the shepherd moons get close to each other, they swap places: the shepherd moon farther from the planet now becomes the closer moon, and the closer moon becomes the farther moon. Shepherd moons have been observed for both Saturn and Uranus. Shepherd moons have not been seen for Neptune's rings; further, Neptune's rings are more like arcs than complete circles, indicating they are either still forming or perhaps disintegrating. Unfortunately, with the exception of Saturn's rings, the rings of the other giant planets are extremely dark (like coal dust), and observations are difficult from Earth. Various space probes have made many trips to Jupiter and Saturn, but Uranus and Neptune have each only been visited once (by Voyager II), in 1986 and 1989, respectively.

FIGURE 4.15. Two shepherd moons bracketing the "epsilon" ring of Uranus.

Check Your Neighbor

A sheep dog has to run constantly around the herd to supervise all the animals. How can a shepherd moon "run" around its ring? Hint: What are the shepherd moons' orbital periods, or orbital speeds, compared to that of the ring?

2. Resonance

If you look carefully at the Moon night after night, you'll notice that it shows the same side to us. Why? The Earth rotates—why doesn't the Moon?

FIGURE 4.16. The near side of the Moon, which we always see from Earth (left); the far side of the Moon, which we never see from Earth (right).

We've already mentioned how the Moon's tides rock the Earth back and forth. This has several consequences. One is that the oceans "rub" back and forth on the ocean floor, generating friction, acting to slow the Earth's rotation. This isn't something to worry about during your lifetime, or even from your grandparents to your (future?) grandchildren, but it does add up over many millennia. Dinosaurs had a day a few hours shorter than ours. Further, because the Earth's spin contributes to the overall angular momentum of the Earth-Moon system, and angular momentum is conserved, the Moon is literally inching away from us. The Moon's semi-major axis gets larger by a few inches each year. Again, nothing you'll notice during your lifetime, but the dinosaurs (they're easy to pick on) had a Moon closer to Earth, and therefore larger in the sky, than we do.

The same frictional slowing happened to the Moon as is currently happening to us. But because the Earth has more mass, and the Moon was originally much closer, gravity tides from the Earth were (and still are) much larger than what we receive from the Moon. The Moon probably stopped spinning independently of the Earth billions of years ago.

This is called *orbital resonance*, or alternatively *spin-orbit coupling*. "Resonance" is simply a word that means periods of time match up. For example, suppose you are pushing a child on a swing, and the child wants to go higher. In order to get the best results, you push the child at the end of the child's backswing. By pushing at just the right moment, you add energy to the child-swing system.

A similar notion can occur in the solar system, but instead of adding energy to an object, energy is taken away. Our Moon is hardly the only Moon tidally "locked" to its planet; nearly all moons in the solar system behave this way. In fact, our Moon is a bit of an anomaly for planet-moon relationships. The Moon has about 1.2% of the Earth's mass, which sounds small, until we compare it to like situations for other moons and planets. For example, Io is similar in size and mass to our Moon, but instead of the 80 to 1 ratio of Earth's mass to the Moon's mass, the ratio of Jupiter's mass to Io's is over 21,000 to 1. Surprisingly, ring particles still rotate and tumble as they

FIGURE 4.17. In order to have a child swing to a large height, it helps to push the child at just the correct moment.

orbit; this is because tides are differences in gravity due to different distances, so when an object is that small, the tides are virtually nonexistent.

Resonance isn't just for spins and orbits of moons. While the other planets are too far for tides to matter this much, Mercury is close enough to the Sun that it is also tidally locked. But, due in part to its elliptical orbit, Mercury's ratio is not 1 to 1. Rather, Mercury's spin (its sidereal rotation) is about 60 Earth days long, and its orbit (sidereal again) is about 90 days, so it has a 2:3 ratio instead.

Resonance is also not confined to spins versus orbits. One of the arguments against Pluto remaining in the list of "major" planets is that it orbits the Sun twice for every three orbits of its neighboring planet, Neptune. Neptune is easily the more massive object, and so we recognize that the gravity of Neptune has forced Pluto into this arrangement. Similar situations exist for other objects beyond the orbit of Neptune and for various groups of asteroids under the influence of Jupiter.

3. Migration and Gravity Assists

One more effect to describe is *migration*. We've already noted that shepherd moons can occasionally swap orbits. This may have happened for planets in the early days of the solar system.

Current hypotheses of the origins of the solar system suggest that Jupiter and Saturn, the two largest planets, formed furthest from the Sun, with Uranus and Neptune forming closer in. In the early days of the solar system, the plane of the solar system would have contained a good amount of gas and dust. Drag (akin to friction) between the materials of the plane would have dragged Jupiter and Saturn closer in from their original positions. In the process, the gravities of these larger planets would have swung Uranus and Neptune outward, to their current positions. (It is suspected that Jupiter's inward trek only stopped when it ran out of drag material.) We will explore these ideas further in the chapter on the formation of the solar system.

One final effect to explore. Objects in the solar system are very far apart—tens of millions of miles or more being the rule. We do not currently have the ability to send manned spacecraft to other planets, so we send robot probes. But even there, we need help; the chemical rockets in our possession are simply not powerful enough to get the probes to where they need to be, at least without incurring unsupportable costs.

Instead, we borrow energy from planets via *gravity assists*. Imagine sending a space probe near a planet. The intent is not to land (or crash!) on the planet, but rather to pass close by. The gravity of the planet acts like a slingshot, in that it "grabs" the probe and slings it past at a faster speed than it originally had. Astronomers treat this as a near-collision problem, and we can use details of conservation of energy and angular momentum to show the probe will acquire energy while the planet loses it. The planet is so large compared to the probe that it doesn't notice the transfer, but the energy gained is sufficiently large from the probe's viewpoint that the probe's speed changes dramatically. Without this gravity assist, missions to the outer solar system are next to impossible and, even if performed, would require much more fuel than they can carry. In the occasional cases where we send probes closer to the Sun—to examine Mercury or Venus, for example—the probes move in the opposite direction so that their gravity assists make them slow down and allow them to get closer to the Sun that much easier.

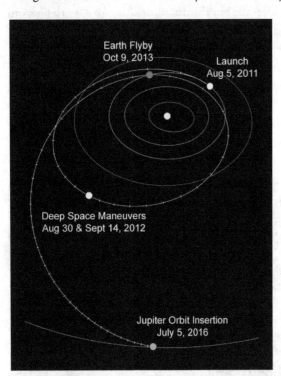

FIGURE 4.18. The space probe Juno, currently in orbit around Jupiter, required a gravity assist from Earth to reach its destination.

Summary

In this chapter, we have discussed the following:

- ▸ The laws of motion
- ▸ The law of gravity
- ▸ Shapes of astronomical objects
- ▸ Orbits of astronomical objects
- ▸ Angular momentum
- ▸ Gravity tides
- ▸ Planetary rings
- ▸ Planetary resonance and migration

Questions

1. You hold an apple in your hand at rest, then let it go. The apple has a mass of about 0.25 kg and the Earth a mass of 6×10^{24} kg.

   - ◆ Which object exerts more gravitational force on the other: the apple on the Earth, the Earth on the apple, or (perhaps) the amount of force is the same?
   - ◆ Which object experiences a larger acceleration: the apple, the Earth, or (perhaps) they both accelerate at the same rate?

2. A refrigerator magnet sticks to your fridge at home. But the Earth's gravity is trying to pull it down. What does this imply about the relative strengths of magnetism and gravity as forces of nature?

3. Jupiter has a mass of 1.90×10^{27} kg and an equatorial radius of 7.15×10^7 m. Find the acceleration of gravity at its cloud tops (Jupiter has no solid surface as such). Is this greater or less than that of the Earth?

4. Using the result from the previous question, what would be the weight of an astronaut with a mass of 100 kg at the cloud tops of Jupiter? Compare this to the astronaut's weight of 981 N on Earth.

5. Miranda, a moon of Uranus, has some of the tallest and most dramatic features of any solid object in the solar system. Its mass is 6.59×10^{19} kg and its radius is 2.36×10^5 m. Use the mass and radius to help explain the sizes of Miranda's features.

6. The distance from the Earth to the Moon is 384,000,000 meters.

   - ◆ Use this fact and the mass of the Earth to find the acceleration due to gravity from the Earth at the Moon.
   - ◆ Use the acceleration of gravity from the Earth at the Moon and the distance from the Earth to the Moon to find the speed of the Moon as it moves about the Earth.
   - ◆ We assumed the Moon's orbit is a perfect circle. In fact, it is noticeably eccentric. Does the Moon have a larger or smaller acceleration when it is closest to Earth ("perigee") in its orbit?
   - ◆ Does the Moon have a larger or smaller acceleration when it is furthest from the Earth ("apogee") in its orbit?

7. The Earth moves with an average speed of 30 km/s (30,000 m/s) in its orbit about the Sun. What is the value of its centripetal acceleration?

8. The Sun has a mass of 1.99×10^{30} kg, and the Earth is an average distance from the Sun of 1.50×10^{11} m. What is the value of g from the Sun at the Earth's distance? How does this answer compare to the Earth's centripetal acceleration?

9. How fast does the Earth move in its orbit at perihelion? At aphelion? Hint: Use information from chapter 3 to help answer this question.

10. Io is a moon of Jupiter's. It has a period of 1.769 days and a semi-major axis of 421,700 km in its orbit about Jupiter. What is the mass of Jupiter?

11. Suppose a spaceship visited the Jupiter system and landed on Ganymede, one of its moons. Would it be relatively easy or difficult for the spaceship to leave Ganymede (compared to leaving the Earth)? Hint: Find the escape speed of Ganymede. The mass of Ganymede is 1.48×10^{23} kg and the radius of Ganymede is 2,634 km.

12. Referring to the previous question, would it be easy for the spaceship to leave the Jupiter system after landing on Ganymede? Hint: Find the escape speed of Jupiter at Ganymede's distance from Jupiter and compare it to that of Earth. The distance from Jupiter to Ganymede is 1,070,000 km and the mass of Jupiter is 1.90×10^{27} kg.

13. Saturn is noticeably not spherical in shape. Why not? Use the following facts to address specific questions about Saturn:

> Saturn's equatorial radius is 60,268 km
> Saturn's polar radius is 54,364 km
> Saturn has a rotational period of 10.55 hours
> Saturn has an acceleration of gravity at its equator of 10.44 m/s²
> Saturn has a density of 0.687 g/cm³

   + Convert the radii into units of meters (Hint: 1 km = 1000 m).
   + Convert the rotational period into units of seconds (Hint: 1 hour = 3600 s).
   + How fast is a point moving at the equator of Saturn? Hint: Either use the centripetal acceleration formula or v = 2pr/T, where T is the rotational period.
   + Briefly describe why you think Saturn is much larger at its equator than its poles, using data and calculations from previous questions.

14. Jupiter is the largest planet in our system, and the one most easily detected from another star. How much of a wobble would an astronomer see? To do that,

   + find the center of mass of the Sun-Jupiter system. Set the Sun at the "zero" position and use Jupiter's semi-major axis (7.78×10^8) km as Jupiter's position; and
   + find the speed at which the Sun would "wobble." Assume the Sun's wobble is a circle, and that the period of Jupiter's orbit is 11.9 years. Express your answer in units of kilometers per second.

Activities

▶ Suppose an astronomer in a distant solar system looked back at ours and observed Jupiter orbiting the Sun. Discuss which kinds of data our distant astronomer would need in order to determine the mass of the Sun.

▶ *Astrophysics activity 4.1:* Using simulations as instructed, analyze how the force of gravity changes with changing combinations of masses and distances. Also apply this knowledge to various planets and tidal forces.

▶ *Astrophysics activity 4.2:* Using simulations as instructed, analyze the mutual orbital motions between various combinations of stars and planets.

Works Referenced

The effect of rotation on the shape of the star Vega is discussed in Aufdenberg, J. P., et al. (2006). First results from the CHARA Array: VII. Long-Baseline Interferometric Measurements of Vega Consistent with a Pole-On, Rapidly Rotating Star? *Astrophysical Journal, 645*(1), 664–675. doi:10.1086/504149

Newton's apple tree/Moon story is recalled in several places. The quote here is from Conduitt, J. (2004). Draft account of Newton's life at Cambridge. *Newton Project*. Retrieved from http://www.newtonproject.ox.ac.uk/view/texts/normalized/THEM00167

Keynes, M. (2008, September 20). Balancing Newton's mind: His singular behavior and his madness of 1692–23. *Notes and Records of the Royal Society of London*, 62(3): 293. doi:10.1098/rsnr.2007.0025

Levenson, T. (2009). *Newton and the counterfeiter: The unknown detective career of the world's greatest scientist*. Boston, MA: Houghton Mifflin Harcourt.

London Gazette. (1727, April 1). No. 6569. Retrieved from https://www.thegazette.co.uk/London/issue/6569/page/7

Newton. (1729). *Principia*. (Trans.)

NPR. (2009). Isaac Newton: Physicist and ... crime fighter? Retrieved from https://www.npr.org/templates/transcript/transcript.php?storyId=105012144 2019-04-20

Levenson, Thomas (2009). *Newton and the Counterfeiter: The Unknown Detective Career of the World's Greatest Scientist*. Houghton Mifflin Harcourt. Boston/New York.

For a good treatment of the effects of the tides of our Moon upon the Earth, see Quincey, P. (1994). Why we are unmoved as oceans ebb and flow. *Skeptical Inquirer*, 8(15), 509–515. Retrieved from https://www.csicop.org/si/show/why_we_are_unmoved_as_oceans_ebb_and_flow

Biographical information on Newton comes from Storr, A. (1985, December). Isaac Newton. *British Medical Journal (Clinical Research Edition)*, 291(6511), 1779. doi:10.1136/bmj.291.6511.1779

University of Cambridge. (n.d.). Newton, Isaac (RY644J). *A Cambridge Alumni Database*. Retrieved from http://venn.lib.cam.ac.uk/cgi-bin/search-2016.pl?sur=&suro=w&fir=&firo=c&cit=&cito=c&c=all&z=all&tex=RY644J&sye=&eye=&col=all&maxcount=50

A student-friendly force-of-gravity calculator (complete with astronomy-related examples) can be found at http://astro.unl.edu/classaction/animations/renaissance/gravcalc.html

A complete description of the shepherd moons of Uranus can be found with its picture at https://commons.wikimedia.org/wiki/File:Uranus_rings_and_two_moons.jpg

Credits

The 40-inch refracting telescope at Yerkes Observatory, Wisconsin.

LIGHT I

To discuss several properties of light which are important for basic astronomy

OBJECTIVES

- To introduce properties of waves
- To review the visible light spectrum
- To apply geometric optics
- To investigate optical telescopes
- To review other types of telescopes
- To investigate non-light telescopes

INTRODUCTION

A leading candidate for the most important scientific instrument of all time must be the telescope. Few other devices have completely reinvented an entire science (its companion, the microscope, did the same for biology) like the telescope. There is a huge divide in the history of science—astronomy done before the telescope and astronomy done after the telescope. Without the telescope, it was a toss-up between an Earth-centered and a Sun-centered cosmos; with the telescope, astronomers were not only able to settle that debate, but to go far beyond it. Notions of universal laws only became plausible with the discoveries of the telescope.

We have previously reviewed Galileo's findings with the first astronomical telescopes (chapter 3), so we will not recapitulate them, here. Instead, this chapter is devoted to the telescope as a scientific instrument—how telescopes are constructed, used, and even located.

Before we look at telescopes, we need to spend some time looking at some basic properties of light. What is a light wave? What kinds of light waves are out there? Which ones reach us here on Earth from space? And how can we manipulate light in order to better understand the information it brings?

KEY TERMS

Adaptive optics (also **active optics**): The combination of using lasers to create artificial stars and computer-controlled activators to flex mirror shapes in order to adapt to atmospheric turbulence so as to allow for clearer images from telescopes

Alt-azimuth mount: A telescope mount allowing the user to move the telescope vertically (altitude) and horizontally (azimuth)

Amplitude: The "strength" of a wave. For light waves, the amplitude is related to the brightness of the wave

Astrometry: The science of determining positions of astronomical objects

Chromatic aberration: When different colors are not focused the same by lenses in telescopes

Clock drive: A motor (mechanical or electrical) that can move a telescope to track an astronomical object as it moves across the sky

Concave: The shape of a lens or mirror which is thinner in the middle and thicker at the edges

Convex: The shape of a lens or mirror which is thicker in the middle and thinner at the edges

Electromagnetic radiation: These are waves made when <u>any</u> charged particles accelerate. EM radiation includes visible light, but ranges all the way from radio waves (smallest frequencies, longest wavelengths) to gamma rays (largest frequencies, shortest wavelengths)

Equatorial mount: A telescope mount allowing the user to move the telescope along right ascension (celestial longitude) and declination (celestial latitude). Such a telescope can track astronomical objects parallel to the celestial equator

Frequency: The number of cycles (wave crests) passing by an observer per unit time; alternatively, the number of oscillations per unit time for a vibrating object. Frequency is also the inverse of the period of an object or wave

Gravitational waves: Waves that stretch and compress space/time, due to vibrating masses

Intensity: The amount of power per unit area of a wave

Interferometry: The science of comparing the light of objects from slightly different vantage points, using the property of light called "interference"

Light: See *visible light*

Longitudinal waves: Waves that oscillate in the same direction as they propagate. Sound waves are common examples

Magnification: The ratio of the size of an image to the size of the original object

Neutrinos: Subatomic particles, electrically neutral, that almost never interact with matter

Period: The amount of time it takes for an object or wave to return to its original conditions. For a wave, the period is the inverse of the frequency

Photometry: The science of measuring the amount of light from an astronomical object

Polarization: The effect (and science) of light waves being forced to vibrate along the same axis

Primary: The largest lens or mirror of a telescope. The primary determines the amount of light brought in by and the resolution of the telescope

Propagation: How physicists describe the motion of waves. Waves "propagate" in all directions from a small vibrating object (a "point source"), for example

Reflection: When a wave or ray "bounces" off of a surface

Reflector (a.k.a. reflecting telescope): A telescope using a series of mirrors to better observe objects at a distance

Refraction: When the direction of a wave or ray changes, crossing the border between one substance (medium) to another. Also see *transmission*

Refractor (a.k.a. refracting telescope): A telescope using a series of lenses to better observe objects at a distance

Resolution: The ability to see fine detail

ROYGBIV: An acronym identifying the visible colors of the rainbow: red, orange, yellow, green, blue, indigo, and violet

Secondary: The second mirror of a reflecting telescope, used to redirect light from the primary mirror to the eyepiece

Seeing: A term used by astronomers to represent the clarity of astronomical images when observed through the atmosphere

Spectroscopy: The science of measuring the spectra of light from astronomical objects. Among other items, the spectrum of an astronomical object can yield information about the object's composition, temperature, velocity, rotation and density

Telescope: See *reflector* and/or *refractor*

Transmission: When waves or rays pass through a medium. Often discussed regarding the amount of the wave (intensity) that passes through. Also see *refraction*

Transverse waves: Waves that oscillate perpendicular to the direction in which they propagate. Light waves are common examples

Visible light: The electromagnetic waves that humans can perceive ("ROYGBIV"), ranging from red (shortest frequencies, longest wavelengths) to violet (largest frequencies, shortest wavelengths). Visible light is but one small section of all possible *electromagnetic radiation*

Wavelength: The distance between successive wave crests

Wave speed: The speed of an individual wave crest as it travels ("propagates")

Section 5.1: Properties of Waves

Often when discussing motion, we automatically think about objects. But objects are not the only way in which "things" travel from one location to another.

Vibrating an object can create a disturbance in a substance ("medium") that travels outward from the vibrating object, or source. This is true for all types of waves—waves in string, water waves, earthquake waves, sound waves, and (pertinent to astronomy) light waves. Because waves are disturbances, rather than objects, physicists often describe their motion with the term *propagation*. Sound waves will "propagate," or spread outward in all directions, from an alarm, for instance. This is different from an object, which can only travel in one direction at a time.

Waves tend to take one of two forms: *longitudinal* waves, which shake back and forth in the same direction as they propagate, and *transverse* waves, which shake back and forth at right angles to the direction in which they propagate. Examples of longitudinal waves include sound and some earthquakes waves; examples of transverse waves include water and light waves.

FIGURE 5.1. A longitudinal wave (left) and a transverse wave (right). In both cases the waves travel ("propagate") to the right. The longitudinal wave stretches and compresses in the direction of propagation; the transverse wave oscillates up and down perpendicular to the direction of propagation.

When we sketch waves, we will use transverse waves, even if the wave in question is a longitudinal wave, for a few reasons: One, it is a much easier picture to understand; second, all the other properties of waves behave the same, regardless of which type of wave it is. Finally, since we in astronomy work with light more than any other wave, and light is a transverse wave, we will use transverse waves in our discussions regarding light.

One more thought: Waves can take many forms, but we will restrict ourselves to analyzing sinusoidal waves. Such waves are easily made in nature by vibrating objects—like electrons—and light waves are best modeled by this shape.

Because waves are disturbances and not objects, we have different ways to characterize them. If we imagine freezing a wave (Figure 5.2), we would notice the distance between successive peaks (or successive troughs) is the same for all neighboring waves. This property is the *wavelength* of the wave. The standard units for wavelength in physics is the meter, but visible light waves are very small, so astronomers often use nanometers (billionths of a meter) or angstroms (10-billionths of a meter) instead.

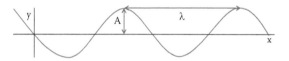

FIGURE 5.2. The behavior of a sinusoidal wave in space, showing the properties of wavelength λ and amplitude A.

We can also talk about how "high" or "strong" the wave is, which is called the *amplitude* of the wave. Different types of waves have different ways of expressing their heights or strengths. A water wave's amplitude is best expressed as an actual height, but a sound wave's amplitude helps tell us how loud the wave is, and a light wave's amplitude helps tell us its brightness. The units used to express the strength of a wave depends on the type of wave.

On the other hand, if we imagine watching the vibrating object move up and down over time (Figure 5.3), we can measure the amount of time it takes to move from peak to trough

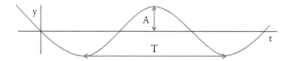

FIGURE 5.3. The behavior of a sinusoidal wave in time, showing the properties of period *T* and amplitude *A*.

and back to peak. This property is the *period* of the wave, and the second is the standard unit used to express it. Note that the amplitude is the same, whether we analyze the wave as a function of space or as a function of time.

For a variety of reasons, astronomers often discuss the *frequency* of a wave. Frequency is the number of wave crests that pass by per unit time, and is the inverse of the wave's period:

Equation 5.1

$$f = 1/T$$

Frequency (and wavelength) can be perceived by people—for sound, different frequencies refer to different pitches; for light, different frequencies refer to different colors. The units of frequency are in inverse seconds or cycles per second, which are given their own name: hertz (abbreviated Hz). For light waves, the frequency is usually very large—on the order of 10^{14} power Hz for visible light. Finally, how fast does a wave propagate? It is equal to the wavelength of the wave multiplied by its frequency:

Equation 5.2

$$v = \lambda f$$

All these quantities and relationships apply to all waves, not just light waves. Let's take a moment to compare some of them.

Sample Calculation

Suppose a water wave, a sound wave (in air), and a light wave each have the same wavelength of 0.75 meters. The speed of propagation of the water wave is 3.0 meters per second, that of the sound wave is 340 m/s, and that of the light wave is 300,000,000 m/s. What is the frequency of each of these waves?

For each wave, the algebraic solution is the same: $f = v/\lambda$. Then,

<u>for water</u>: f = (3.0 m/s) / (0.75 m) = **4.0 Hz**

<u>for sound</u>: f = (340 m/s) / (0.75 m) = **453 Hz**

<u>for light</u>: f = (300,000,000 m/s) / (0.75 m) = **400,000,000 Hz (or 4.0×10^8 Hz)**.

Section 5.2: Properties of Electromagnetic Waves

Rainbows are familiar phenomena. But how do they form? And what do they have to do with waves?

Light waves all share the same speed in vacuum, approximately 3.00×10^8 m/s (you may be more familiar with its speed as 186,000 miles per second). Suppose we have a source of white light (like the Sun), which combines many different frequencies. But different frequencies of visible light travel at slightly different speeds when going through transparent materials such as water. This means the different frequencies—which we perceive as different colors—take slightly different paths. Or, the white light is spread out into its constituent rainbow, or spectrum, of colors.

Before people understood the origin of rainbows, however, they needed to understand that white light is a blending of the rainbow in the first place. The person who did the first conclusive experiments was Isaac Newton. He darkened his bedroom, allowing only a sliver of sunlight to pass into the room. The light was sent into a prism, which separated the white light of the Sun into its constituent colors. Newton then performed the second part of the experiment, which was to take those colors and send them into another prism, which recreated the white light of the Sun.

FIGURE 5.4. A double rainbow over Ohrid Lake in Macedonia.

Newton did not conceive of light as consisting of waves (see chapter 15), and good values for the wavelengths (and frequencies) of light did not become available until the 19th century. But we can routinely measure wavelengths now.

The visible light spectrum ranges from 400 nanometers to 700 nanometers (or 4,000 angstroms to 7,000 angstroms). The shortest wavelengths are violet and the longest red. The corresponding ranges for frequencies are 4×10^{14} Hz for red light and 7×10^{14} Hz for violet. The entire visible light spectrum, or rainbow, is often abbreviated as "ROYGBIV":

FIGURE 5.5. White light enters a prism and is separated into its rainbow of colors. Sending the rainbow into another, upside-down prism recombines the colors into white light.

Red-Orange-Yellow-Green-Blue-Indigo-Violet

Human vision does not match up perfectly with these individual colors. Humans have two different types of light sensors in their eyes, rods and cones. Rods more or less are simply brightness detectors, whereas cones detect red, green, and blue. Other colors we "see" are interpolations performed by our brains. It turns out astronomers do something similar; we often use color filters to look at different aspects of astronomical objects (we will discuss this in more detail later in the book).

It turns out that visible light is actually just a very small portion of the entire range of light. Theoretically, there are no limits to how large or small a wavelength (or frequency) can be. Because light is ultimately made when electrons vibrate, and the waves created thereby are a mix of electric and magnetic waves, in general we call light *electromagnetic radiation*. People did not know (more specifically, recognize) other types of EM radiation until William Herschel discovered infrared light in 1800.

Electromagnetic radiation runs from radio waves (low frequencies, long wavelengths) through microwaves, infrared, visible, ultraviolet, x-rays to gamma rays (high frequencies, short wavelengths). Only visible light and most of the radio waves from space penetrate the atmosphere and reach the ground; to see other regions of the EM spectrum, astronomers must use balloons, aircraft, or satellites to get above the Earth's air. Nevertheless, whether x-rays or microwaves, all forms of EM radiation are just different types of light, and all travel at the speed of light in vacuum. We will be discussing uses of both visible and other regions of the EM spectrum throughout this textbook.

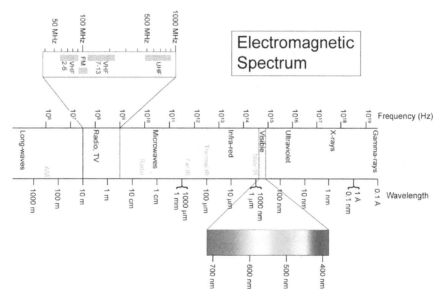

FIGURE 5.6. The electromagnetic spectrum, showing details of radio waves and the visible light spectrum.

Section 5.3: Geometric Optics and Telescopes

Optics is the science of visible light. Geometric optics is a subset that treats light as if it (mostly) travels in straight lines. This becomes very useful when constructing telescopes.

We will review how light is generated in other chapters. For now, we are concerned with how light interacts with objects via reflection and refraction. *Reflection* (also called scattering) is how we describe a light ray hitting a surface and bouncing off; *refraction* (also called transmission) is how we describe a light ray passing through a transparent substance (see Figure 5.7):

FIGURE 5.7. Reflection and refraction off a slab of glass.

Reflection is relatively easy to describe: The angle at which a light ray comes into a surface of an object (is "incident upon," to use physics lingo) equals the angle at which a light ray leaves a surface. This is true whether the object in question is a mirror or not, whether the surface of the object is flat or curved, or whether the surface is smooth or rough. Astronomers are interested in reflection off of mirrors for telescopes, of course, but they also need to understand how light reflects (scatters) off of rough surfaces, when we study objects like planets or asteroids, for example.

Refraction is a little more difficult. When a light ray passes through a transparent substance, it slows down. Different materials slow light by different amounts, and even for the same substance, different wavelengths can be slowed by different amounts (refer to Figure 5.4 for an example of the consequences).

The most important components manipulating light in telescopes are lenses and mirrors. Lenses make use of refraction and mirrors make use of reflection. Lenses and mirrors are usually curved in order to focus light, as seen in Figure 5.8.

If a lens or mirror is thick in the middle and thin at the edges (it doesn't matter whether it is a lens or a mirror), the shape is called *convex*. If a lens or mirror is thin in the middle and thick at the edges, the shape is called *concave*.[1] A convex lens will bend light inward and a concave lens will bend light outward; it is the opposite situation for mirrors. This brings us to the two basic types of telescopes. We have already covered some of the history of the invention of the telescope (see chapter 3); it is time to show how telescopes operate.

---

[1] An easy way to remember the distinction between convex and concave is that a concave shape is "caved" in, or resembles the entrance to a cave. Convex is then the opposite shape.

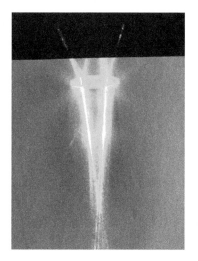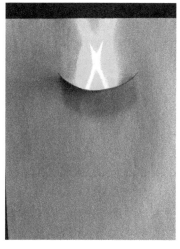

FIGURE 5.8. Light rays focused by a convex lens (left) and a concave mirror (right).

1. Refracting Telescopes (a.k.a. Refractors)

The first telescope used in astronomy was built by Galileo, who placed a concave and a convex lens together in order to form an image. This type of telescope is called a refracting telescope, or *refractor* for short, since it uses the refraction from two or more lenses to form its images. Galileo's telescope ensured that images appear right-side up but was limited in how wide the telescope would show clear images. A more common way to construct a refractor is to hold two convex lenses together. The image from this arrangement will be inverted (upside-down), but will give a more reliable image than Galileo's original version.

Astronomical objects are all so distant that rays of light from them come in parallel lines. The front lens (the "primary" or "objective") of a refracting telescope takes those rays (Figure 5.9) and bends the rays inward, where another lens (the "eyepiece") focuses them.

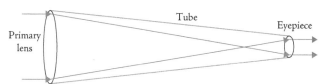

FIGURE 5.9. The basic structure of a refracting telescope.

What benefits do we get from a telescope?

+ First, incoming light is concentrated, so that images are <u>brighter</u> than the objects appear to the naked eye. Not only do dim objects appear brighter, but objects we otherwise can't see with the naked eye become visible. This was shown by Galileo when he discovered that the blur or fuzz of the Milky Way actually consisted of many stars packed tightly together but individually invisible.

+ Second, images show <u>more detail</u> than objects do to the naked eye, an idea astronomers call *resolution*. Without a telescope, we can see that the Moon has features; with his primitive telescope, Galileo was able to measure the heights and diameters of individual craters.

+ Third, and perhaps surprisingly, telescopes magnify images.[2] Making images larger is actually low on the list of wants for astronomers. After all, if we can't see the object in the first place, magnification doesn't help; and, if we have a very blurry image, magnifying a small blur into a large blur also doesn't help.

---

[2] To be honest, "magnification" in optics simply means the ratio of image size to object size. An image can be smaller than the object—think of an image of a nearby car in your rear-view mirror—though all astronomical telescopes make images larger than objects as a matter of course.

The larger the primary, the more light the telescope can gather. So, ideally, we want to have as large a telescope as possible. Unfortunately, light has to go through the primary lens. This means the lens can only be supported (held) at its edges, which limits the weight of the lens.

Astronomers compensate for these problems by making the primary as thin as possible and by using other optics (lenses and/or mirrors) to adjust the image. Nevertheless, refractors are limited in size. The largest refracting telescope in the world is a 40-inch (1.02 meter)[3] telescope at Yerkes Observatory in Williams Bay, Wisconsin. The telescope was constructed in 1893, which indicates that astronomers long ago knew, in order to build larger telescopes, they needed to go in a different direction. Run for decades by the University of Chicago, Yerkes Observatory was closed to the public on October 1, 2018.

Check Your Neighbor

Lack of support limits the size of a primary lens for a refractor. Suggest other potential problems for large refractors.

2. Reflecting Telescopes (a.k.a. Reflectors)

The other option is the reflecting telescope, or *reflector*. Reflectors have several advantages over refractors, all stemming from the fact that, because primary mirrors can be supported from underneath, the apertures can potentially be unlimited in size.

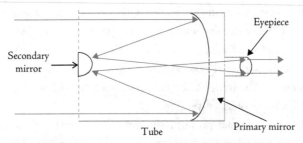

FIGURE 5.10. The basic structure of a reflecting telescope.

All the reasons to use a telescope—increased brightness, resolution, magnification—are all improved with a larger primary. In the case of a reflector, of course, the telescope is using a mirror instead of a lens as its primary. Since a primary mirror can be made larger than a primary lens, astronomers favor reflectors over refractors for modern research telescopes. The largest refractor in the world (now retired) is just over 1 meter in diameter; several reflectors are over 10 meters in diameter.

Nevertheless, reflectors do have issues. Because reflected light goes away from the mirror, we won't see the light unless we bring it back to us somehow. The most common solution is to use a *secondary* mirror, which redirects the primary's reflected light rays back to the eyepiece and the observer.

Check Your Neighbor

List some advantages and disadvantages of reflectors compared to refractors.

Reflectors are still by far preferred by researchers. It is the area, not the diameter, of the mirrors that matters most; by making the secondary as small as possible, the loss of light is not critical. Neither are reflectors so much more complicated that they cost more, or are more difficult to construct, compared to comparably sized refractors.

Spherical aberration is a more serious problem. Parabolas do reflect parallel rays to the same point, so ideally we would use parabolic surfaces for mirrors; unfortunately, parabolic shapes are extremely difficult to manufacture. Astronomers therefore tend to use optics (lenses and/or mirrors) at the eyepiece end of the telescope to adjust the image.

---

[3] Telescope sizes are defined by the diameters or "apertures" of their primary lenses or mirrors.

Another approach, which has gained traction in recent decades, is to use a segmented mirror. Therefore the telescope must remain centered on the object in question, or the object's image will become streaked.

Section 5.4: Putting Telescopes to Work

In order to get the best possible results from any telescope, we need to do the following:

+ Hold the telescope steady and follow the sky as it rotates
+ Record a clear image
+ Perform specific types of science

Let's see what astronomers do in order to learn the most we can.

1. Telescope Mounts (How to Hold a Telescope Steady)

In order to get a clear image, we need to hold the telescope as steady as possible. While we're at it, we also need to move the telescope to track objects as they move across the sky. This sounds like we have an inherent contradiction, but they are in practice reconcilable.

FIGURE 5.11. The Otto Struve reflecting telescope at the McDonald Observatory in west Texas.

Smaller portable telescopes—like those used by an amateur hobbyist—typically rest on portable tripods (literally, "three feet"). Larger telescopes are housed in permanent shelters, which are usually dome shaped, and the telescope itself bound to a large column or the floor. In either case, we say the telescope is placed on a *mount*.

But we also need to aim the telescope. The simplest way to point a telescope toward its target is to move it vertically and horizontally—or, as we called them in chapter 2, in altitude and azimuth. An *alt-azimuth mount* is the simplest type of mount to use, especially for a beginner. The downside for an alt-azimuth mount is that (with three specific exceptions), astronomical objects don't move along the vertical or horizontal; instead, they move at various angles across the sky. So an alt-azimuth mount makes it easier to point toward an object but doesn't allow us to easily track that object.

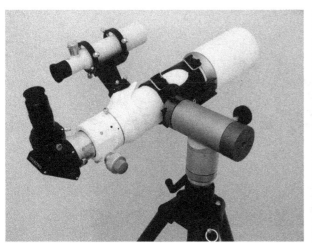

FIGURE 5.12. A telescope on an alt-azimuth mount (left); an equatorial mount (right).

The other major option is an *equatorial mount*, which tracks celestial longitude and latitude (or, as you may recall from chapter 2, "Right Ascension" and "declination"). It's more difficult to use for a beginner (though it doesn't take too much practice to become proficient), but it does a better job of tracking astronomical objects. Once an object is centered in the telescope, the telescope can remain at its declination setting and only needs to move along celestial longitude in order to follow the object.

The motor that moves the telescope tube to track objects is called a *clock drive*. In years past, a clock drive could be powered mechanically by falling weights (which could be manually reset each night) or nowadays electrically. The name hints at its other function; a clock drive also keeps time.

Finally, a large telescope—and/or a telescope which will have heavy instrumentation attached to it—will use a counterweight to help with its balance.

Check Your Neighbor

We stated that a telescope needs to move in order to track objects as they move across the sky. Is the sky actually moving? If not, what makes it look like it's moving?

2. Achieving and Recording Clear Images

Tracking an object with a clock drive is not simply to keep an object centered in a telescope. It's also to record clear images. Even in a relatively small telescope (such as an 8-inch aperture portable telescope), an image will noticeably move, and go "off screen" within a few minutes. Although one might think a picture only requires an instant to be taken, in fact most astronomy pictures require several seconds, minutes, or (for very dim objects) even hours of exposure time. Therefore the telescope must remain centered on the object in question for the duration of the exposure, or become a streak rather than be clear.

How else can astronomers try to ensure images are clear? Another difficulty is the air itself. While air is nice to have around (breathing is a good thing!), air distorts images. Even though air appears clear, it can absorb light, especially when humid (think of how fog blurs our vision). Air can refract different colors of light slightly, so colors don't always focus as well as they should. If the air is turbulent, pockets of air can be at different temperatures, which also refracts light differently … and so on. The quality of our (and our instruments') vision through the air is referred by astronomers as *seeing*.

FIGURE 5.13. Telescope domes at Las Campanas Observatory in the Andes Mountains of South America.

The most common solution for modern research telescopes is to find a good location. Most high-quality locations share at least one of several criteria: high elevations (to be above as much of the atmosphere as possible), arid environments (to cut down on humidity), air that flows at constant rates (astronomers don't mind a small breeze, as it helps equalize air temperatures), and a location far away from city or other artificial lights. In the continental United States, the southwest is generally regarded as good for visible light astronomy; some important telescopes are also sited in Hawaii. Several observatories are located in the Andes Mountains of South America for similar reasons. Of course, if we want to avoid air completely, the best possible seeing is in space—a topic we will address later in this chapter.

An approach becoming common in recent decades for modern ground-based telescopes is called active or *adaptive optics*. First, a powerful laser is beamed upward from an observatory in order to create an artificial star. Since it is the observatory that shines the laser light, the observatory astronomers know how it should look. Second, the observatory's equipment watches the artificial star as its image slightly shifts back and forth due to atmospheric turbulence. Finally, this data is fed into actuators—little motors—attached to the back of the primary mirror (or mirrors) to flex the mirror in order to compensate for the distortions caused by the atmosphere. The net result is that ground-based telescopes can often rival the seeing conditions of their compatriot telescopes in space.

The next step is to <u>record</u> images. Up until relatively modern times, astronomers at best could only describe and/ or sketch images. With the advent of chemical photography

FIGURE 5.14. A laser used to make an artificial star at Paranal Observatory, Chile.

in the mid-19th century, astronomers could finally procure permanent images, so a large element of subjectivity (i.e., each person's opinion) was removed. Nevertheless, chemical photography had some strong disadvantages, mostly centered on the fact that chemical photography is very inefficient—only about 1% of the light incident upon a photographic plate is actually recorded. The other major difficulty with a chemical photograph is that it can only be used once.

Beginning in the late 1970s, astronomers began using charge-coupled devices (CCDs)—the now-familiar square wafer consisting of a grid of numerous tiny pixels, or picture elements. By the 1990s, astronomers had almost entirely switched over to CCDs or other electronic detectors, and in our era where a person's cell phone has still picture and video capabilities, chemical photography has virtually disappeared.

By the late 1980s, it was becoming common for research astronomers to use CCD chips with 1,000 by 1,000 grids— that is, a million pixels on a chip about a square centimeter in area. Size, reliability, number, computer speed, and storage capacities have all improved dramatically over the past few decades, making it possible (for example) for astronomers to image hundreds of objects simultaneously.

CCDs have several advantages for astronomers. First, they are electronic, meaning that they can be used over and over. Second, they are efficient—many tens of times better than chemical photography—so that images may be taken in short amounts of time, or ever-fainter objects can be seen.

FIGURE 5.15. A CCD, or charge-coupled device, chip. The square-shaped chip is 2/3 of an inch, or 1.7 centimeters, on a side.

Third, the images can be electronically modified to reduce background light, to ensure the image is flat (i.e., the same) across the chip, and to account for individual pixels that are too sensitive or not sensitive enough. Fourth, astronomers can directly make measurements from an electronic image; for example, if we want to determine the brightness of a star, we can (or have the computer software) literally count individual particles of light from that star on our image. Last, astronomers can apply computer programs to manipulate images—for example, to search for hidden features or behaviors.

Finally, for various reasons, astronomers often use color filters to limit the colors (wavelengths) of light to be recorded. Filters, like most other instruments, are typically attached at or near the eyepiece. Typical filter colors are red, yellow (or "visible"), and blue; ultraviolet and infrared filters are also available. The Moon and Sun are special cases; since they are so bright (especially the Sun), their light can actually swamp or damage digital cameras. "Neutral density" or polarizers are common for lunar digital photography, since they simply cut down the total light across all visible wavelengths. More specialized filters are used for the Sun; in order for a telescope (or person) to be safe, the Sun's light must be darkened by a factor of a million (!) times. Astronomers have a variety of solar filters, perhaps the most used is a "hydrogen alpha" filter which only lets a specific spectral line through.

FIGURE 5.16. Sample green, yellow, and red filters used for digital cameras.

3. Science with Telescopes

All of this is fine, but what do astronomers actually study? Or, what kinds of science are they actually performing with images from telescopes?

Astrometry

The very first type of scientific inquiry done with astronomical images—aside from noting the existence of an object in the first place—is *astrometry*. While "astronomy" is the overall scientific discipline dealing with space, astrometry, or "star-measuring," is specifically concerned with noting the <u>positions</u> of astronomical objects.

People have of course noted positions of stars and planets throughout human history: Hipparchus noted effects such as proper motion and precession using records from naked-eye observations thousands of years ago, and the culmination of Tycho Brahe's work was Kepler's laws. But of course modern telescopes have made wonderful improvements. The motion of Barnard's Star, one of our closest stellar neighbors, is now possible to follow over even just a few years, and careful measurements of the positions of stars near the center of the galaxy have allowed astronomers to estimate the mass of the supermassive black hole residing there.

FIGURE 5.17. The 30-inch refracting Thaw Telescope at Allegheny Observatory in Pittsburgh, Pennsylvania, has searched for exoplanets using astrometric methods.

Photometry

Another basic datum we might want from an astronomical object is simply its brightness. We will investigate in detail how astronomers describe brightness in chapter 15; for now, we will just note that an object's brightness is one of the most basic intrinsic properties (i.e., a property that belongs to the object itself, and not just because of how we see it) we can know.

Brightnesses of objects can be used to estimate their sizes and distances, especially for stars. Other objects can vary their light outputs—many stars pulsate, for instance, and other exotic objects, such as QSOs,[4] hint at large disks of material being swept into supermassive black holes. In recent decades, astronomers have used "transits," where small objects cut in front of large objects, to search for planets orbiting other stars—a method so successful that several thousand "exoplanets" are now known. Photometry also includes image processing, that is, computer-based manipulation of the image in order to make it more clear or bring out hidden features.

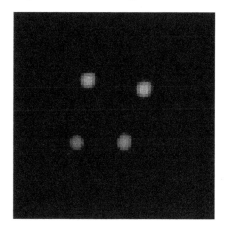 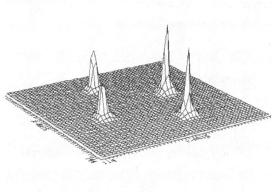

FIGURE 5.18. A false-color Hubble Space Telescope image of the "Cloverleaf" QSO (left). Image processing of the four components of the "Cloverleaf" (right).

An interesting historical case of photometry involves the (now "dwarf") planet Pluto, discovered in 1930. Early photographs indicated a relatively large object, perhaps larger across than the Earth. As telescopes and imaging improved, astronomers continually revised its size (diameter) downward until a combination of astrometry and photometry revealed it to be much smaller across than our Moon. We now know the confusion arose because Pluto's surface is made of various ices that reflect light much better than rock, and so Pluto looked larger than it really is because image quality was not as good in the past as it is today.

FIGURE 5.19. The northern hemisphere of Pluto, courtesy of the New Horizons spacecraft.

---

[4] The acronym "QSO" is short for "quasi-stellar object," something we will examine in chapter 20.

Spectroscopy

Spectroscopy is the science of spreading apart visible light into its constituent colors. We will investigate spectroscopy further as a physical process in chapter 14; for now we note that, among other items, astronomers can identify the composition (i.e., the atoms and molecules), the temperature, speed toward or away from us, and rotational velocity of an object. Spectroscopy is harder to perform than photometry, because while photometry can typically just pay attention to the light from the object, spectroscopy requires smearing out the light, and therefore requires more light to begin with; it is not uncommon for an observation to last ten times longer in order to take a spectra compared to just its image. However, because of its versatility, if astronomers are asked about which type of data they most prefer, they will typically want spectra.

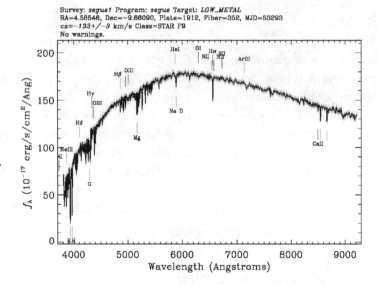

FIGURE 5.20. A spectrum of a star observed by the Sloan Digital Sky Survey (SDSS). The graph plots relative brightness versus wavelength. Some individual elements are identified.

Spectra are often plotted in graphs using relative brightness on the vertical scale and wavelength or frequency on the horizontal scale. Spectra from solid objects are often fairly complex, but spectra from stars tend to be relatively smooth, due to the fact that stars emit visible light according to their surface temperatures. Often superimposed upon such a smooth curve are various thin peaks and dips, which help astronomers identify the presence and abundance of various atoms and/or molecules. Examining details of these "spectral lines" can yield even more, and different, information about the star in question.

Interferometry

Because light is a wave phenomenon, it possesses the interesting property of "superposition." That is, instead of crashing when two objects collide, waves can add to or subtract from each other when they meet. Equivalently, when we observe the same object from slightly different locations, the light waves coming toward (incident upon) those two locations can superimpose upon each other. This specific type of superposition is often called interference, and the science of studying interference is *interferometry*.

The benefits of using interferometry are cited previously. The downside is that we need to know the distance between the two observing locations to great precision, compared to the wavelength of light used. This isn't so critical when using radio telescopes (see the next section), but is incredibly difficult to achieve for visible light telescopes, due to their fantastically small wavelengths. It also requires long exposure times, even more than spectroscopy, to gather enough light to make it work.

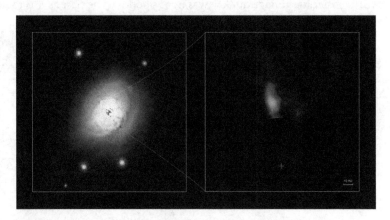

FIGURE 5.21. The young protostar H100546 and its protoplanetary disk in visible light by the Hubble Space Telescope (left) and in infrared light by the Very Large Telescope (right). The VLT image in particular reveals a possible protoplanet. Courtesy of ESO/NASA/ESA/Ardilia et al.

Nevertheless, optical interferometry is now a reality. The pair of Keck telescopes atop Mauna Kea in Hawaii combine many of the desired properties we have discussed: It is an excellent site for seeing (the telescopes are at an altitude of nearly 14,000 feet and have virtually no light pollution and extremely stable air, being in the middle of the Pacific Ocean), large primary mirrors (each telescope is actually composed of 36 hexagonal mirror segments yielding an aperture over 10 meters) and has the most modern instrumentation. Most importantly, the distance between the telescopes is known to nanometer precision.

Polarization

Suppose you are playing with a long jump rope. Shake the rope, and if the rope is somewhat taut, you can send waves along the rope. Recall these waves are called "transverse" by physicists, meaning that the vibration is perpendicular to the direction of propagation.

Next, string the rope through a picket fence, where the pickets are arranged vertically. If you shake the rope up and down, the wave will pretty much travel through the fence unaffected. If you shake the rope left and right (horizontally), the wave will be stopped by the fence. If you shake the rope at an in-between angle, some of the wave will make it through, but will be diminished in amplitude, and now vibrate only vertically.

Light is also a "transverse" wave. Usually, light that reaches us consists of an extremely large number of waves, all mixed together (called "incoherent" light), meaning some light waves are (relative to us) vertical, some horizontal, some at in-between angles. But we can make the waves vibrate together in unison with devices called polarizers (Figure 5.22). A polarizer will cut down the intensity (brightness) of light by 50%, but ensures the remaining light is "coherent." If we place two polarizers on top of each other and rotate one of the polarizers 90° relative to the other, virtually no light passes through them, since the waves can't travel through the equivalent of both "vertical" and "horizontal" pickets. The overall effect is called *polarization*.

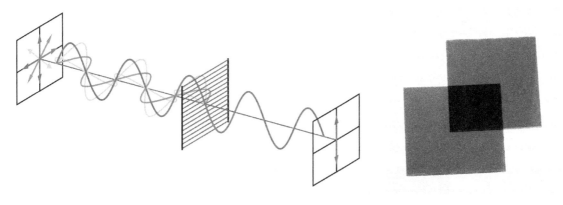

FIGURE 5.22. How a polarizer works (top); two polarizers rotated at 90° relative to each other (above).

This is polarization caused by a device. Can nature do this? In order for this to happen, there must be the equivalent of "pickets." The daytime sky is a good example. Nitrogen and oxygen molecules have elongated shapes, and so light from the Sun, reflecting off these molecules, can show some polarization—enough that polarized sunglasses are commonplace.

In astronomy, we have several possible ways that nature might polarize light. One is that a gas, like our atmosphere, consists of molecules with elongated shapes. Another is that magnetic fields can align atoms and/or molecules in a gas. By using polarizers, astronomers can use this effect to get information about how the particles are arranged and why.

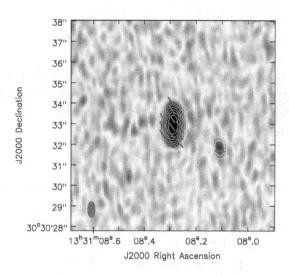

FIGURE 5.23. The quasar 3C 286 seen in polarized light. Credit: ALMA (ESO/NAOJ/NRAO), Nagai et al.

Section 5.5: Telescopes Using Other Regions of the EM Spectrum

Visible light, as versatile as it is, only covers a minute fraction of all of the electromagnetic spectrum. In order to fully understand astronomical objects, we need to study as much of the EM light coming from them as possible.

Besides visible light, radio waves are able to pass through the Earth's atmosphere. Astronomers have been using radio telescopes since the 1930s when Karl Jansky discovered radio waves coming from the center of the Milky Way. We will discuss Jansky's work in more detail in the chapter on the Milky Way; here, we wish to present a little about radio astronomy in general.

FIGURE 5.24. Karl Jansky's original radio telescope from the 1930s. Image courtesy of NRAO/AUI.

Radio waves were discovered by Heinrich Hertz in 1888 by showing how radio waves induce a spark in a modified antenna. While they don't produce sparks (!), many older passenger cars used to have long antennae for receiving radio waves. In the first few decades of radio astronomy, observers also tended to use various arrangements of antennae to capture radio waves. Nowadays, radio telescopes tend to look more like optical reflecting telescopes, with a curved disk acting as the reflecting surface and an electronic detector or "feed" at the focal point.

Because radio wavelengths can be very long (from centimeters to tens of kilometers), radio telescopes must be very large. Radio research telescopes can be as large as tall houses; until recently, the largest radio telescope in the world is at Arecibo, Puerto Rico, with a dish 1,000 feet (305 meters) in diameter, larger than a football stadium.

The Arecibo dish is built into the hollow of a valley (you can walk underneath it). At that size, not surprisingly, it cannot move; rather, astronomers simply wait for the Earth to rotate underneath their objects in order to take observations. The dish is spherically shaped so that its focus is not a point but rather a line, and feeds are hung in the focal plane in order to receive the radio waves.[5]

FIGURE 5.25. A radio telescope at the Kennedy Space Center (left); the Arecibo radio telescope in Puerto Rico (right).

What have astronomers discovered using radio waves? The following is but a sampling, and not remotely a comprehensive list:

- The rotational period of Mercury, which is about 60 days, and 2/3 of its orbital period
- The temperature of the planet Venus, which turns out to be extremely hot due to a runaway greenhouse effect
- The magnetic field of the planet Jupiter, the largest such in the solar system
- Pulsars, rotating neutron stars beaming radiation toward us
- Sagittarius A*, the center of the Milky Way, thought to host a supermassive black hole
- Quasars (more generally quasi-stellar objects), themselves powered by supermassive black holes in ancient galaxies
- The "cosmic microwave background radiation," leftover heat from the early days of the Big Bang

After visible light, radio has been the most fruitful region of the EM spectrum for astronomers—in part because we can also site radio telescopes on the ground, and in part because a very wide variety of objects emit radio waves for many different reasons.

One more comment about the usefulness of radio telescopes: For observations at very long wavelengths, radio telescopes can be electronically linked to perform interferometry and act as gigantic binoculars. Some projects have combined observations from radio telescopes from across the globe, essentially turning the entire planet into a gigantic radio telescope.

Other telescopes, using wavelengths outside either visible or radio, need to get above the Earth's atmosphere. Some observations can be done at high altitudes—such as infrared instruments lifted by aircraft or balloons—but some can only be done from space, such as gamma rays. Each new regime of the EM spectrum examined yields new information, sometimes even discoveries of objects and/or phenomena of which we weren't previously aware.

---

[5] Fortunately, Hurricane Maria did relatively little damage to the Arecibo telescope and facility in 2017.

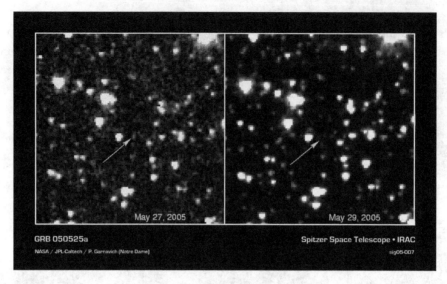

FIGURE 5.26. Observations from the Spitzer telescope linking an infrared (heat) signature to a gamma-ray burst.

Perhaps the most dramatic such cases are gamma-ray bursts. Given their wavelength, duration, and distance, gamma-ray bursts are the most powerful individual events in the universe. But until the launching of gamma-ray telescopes, nobody knew about or even postulated their existence. Combining observations over many different wavelengths—and including data from non-EM spectrum detectors—it seems that gamma-ray bursts are caused when black holes collide. It's a revealing thing to say; until the past few decades, the brightest events in the universe went completely unnoticed, in large part because they emitted a type of light we can't see from the ground.

Section 5.6: Non-Light Telescopes

The reception of visible light, and other wavelength bands of the EM spectrum, are the most common methods we possess to study astronomical objects. There are a few important reasons for this: Space is very large, objects are very far away, and nothing travels faster than light. Moreover, much of nature interacts (emits, absorbs, etc.) EM radiation, so by studying various forms of light, we learn about many different kinds of objects and behaviors. Nevertheless, nature does deal in more than EM radiation, and astronomers are making efforts to utilize these other sources of information. At the top of this list are neutrinos and gravitational waves.

1. Neutrinos

Neutrinos are subatomic particles emitted during certain subatomic reactions—as the name indicates, they are electrically neutral, just like photons (particles of light). However, neutrinos have very different properties than light. Once speculated to be massless, physicists now know that neutrinos do possess mass, though much less than even electrons. Because they have mass, neutrinos can move close to, but not at, the speed of light. More importantly, neutrinos barely react with matter. To get across how transparent the universe appears to neutrinos, consider the following: Imagine owning a flashlight that emits a beam of neutrinos rather than a beam of visible light. Then shine the beam into a solid cylinder (tube) of lead, a light year long. About half of the neutrinos will eventually emerge on the other side!

FIGURE 5.27. If a beam of neutrinos traveled a light year through a solid tube of lead, about half of the neutrinos would emerge out the other side.

Because neutrinos are so "shy," they can't be focused or recorded in the same manner as visible light photons. An example of a reaction a neutrino can have is with a water molecule. Upon such an impact, the neutrino generates a cone of other subatomic particles, which can be detected. However, because the reaction is so rare, we need an enormous amount of water to make this work. Also, because many other subatomic particles are running about, we need to shelter the detectors so only the neutrinos are counted. Neutrino "telescopes" are rather built like gigantic swimming pools than empty tubes.

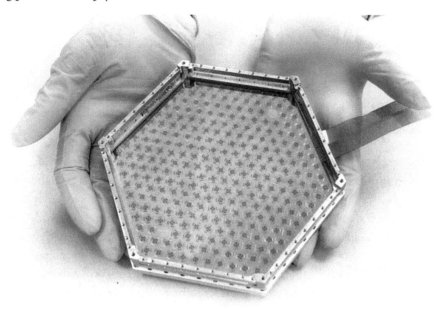

FIGURE 5.28. A neutrino detector for the South Pole Telescope. Credit: U.S. Department of Energy.

One example of a neutrino telescope is the South Pole Telescope (SPT), funded by the U.S. Department of Energy. Its purpose is to better determine the masses of individual types ("flavors") of neutrinos, which helps inform us about the conditions of the very early universe. The largest neutrino observatory in the world is called "Ice Cube" and is located at the South Pole. It covers a square kilometer on the surface, and special optical detectors are sunk to depths from 1,450 to 2,450 meters. Special hot-water drills were used to bore holes for the detectors, and the water was allowed to refreeze after they were installed. The sensors, "digital optical modules," or DOMs, consist of photomultiplier tubes and associated electronics, which amplify signals and determine their angle of approach, so researchers can estimate their points of origin on the sky. Because of the size and cost, there are but a handful of neutrino observatories around the globe.

What have neutrino telescopes found? One of the early discoveries occurred in 1987, when a handful of neutrinos (25, considered a "burst" by astronomers) were discovered by three separate facilities. These neutrinos were backtracked to a supernova in a satellite galaxy of the Milky Way, the Large Magellanic Cloud, and remains the closest supernova to us (at 50,000 parsecs) since the early 17th century. Other neutrino research covers the Sun (it emits neutrinos during its generation of energy via nuclear fusion) and investigations into the nature of dark matter.

2. Gravitational Waves

The newest major contributor to astronomy is gravitational waves. Predicted by Einstein in 1915, gravity waves are a consequence of the motions of massive objects stretching and compressing space/time itself. Theoretically, any moving object (including you and me!) makes gravity waves; in practice, only the most massive and most concentrated objects create waves we can potentially detect. Gravity's ability to bend space (and time; clocks move relatively slower near a strong gravity field) has been observed directly and indirectly since Arthur Eddington's total solar eclipse mission of 1919. Even so, it is only in the past few years—a century after Einstein—that the existence of gravitational waves themselves has been confirmed, a discovery so important that its lead investigators won the 2017 Nobel Prize in physics.[6]

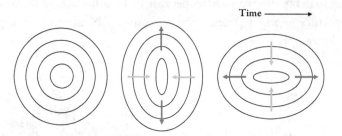

FIGURE 5.29. The flexing of space/time by a passing gravitational wave (greatly exaggerated).

As gravity waves pass by a region of space, they stretch it back and forth—first along one axis (vertical, for example), then another (horizontal). In other words, space itself acts like a spring, though only as the gravity wave passes by. Gravity waves, like light waves, travel at the speed of light, so they pass by quickly.

The world's premier gravity wave detector actually combines observations from three widely separated sites—one in Livingston, Louisiana, one in Hanford, Washington, and one near Pisa, Italy[7]—so that spurious detections at one or the other site can be ruled out. Each observatory is in the shape of an "L" to compare and contrast changes in space, again to rule out false signals and confirm true ones. The sensitivity is phenomenal: Vibrations of several orders of magnitude smaller than a proton can be sensed; or, the gravity waves caused by a person coughing in the control room can be detected.

The first recognized discovery occurred on September 14, 2015. Signals were independently recorded at both American locations. Investigators tracked the signal to the shockwave (lasting about 1 second) from the collision of two massive black holes, one about 29 times the mass of the Sun and the other 36 times the mass of the Sun. The resulting much-more-massive black hole is about 1.3 billion light years away, meaning the event itself occurred 1.3 billion years ago. The shockwaves of several other like events—collisions between black holes and/or neutron stars—have since been captured. Gravitational waves are fast becoming an important tool for observing and understanding distant events in the cosmos.

Summary

In this chapter, we have examined properties of light and telescopes, including the following:

▸ General properties of waves

▸ Refraction, reflection, lenses, mirrors

▸ Refracting and reflecting telescopes

▸ Telescopic instruments

▸ Telescopes at other wavelengths

▸ Non-light telescopes

---

[6] A previous study of the decay of the mutual orbits of two neutron stars, due to their emission of gravity waves, won the Nobel Prize in physics in 1993 for Joseph Taylor Jr. and Russell Hulse. This, however, was an indirect discovery. Einstein did not win the Nobel Prize for his work on gravity.

[7] The two American gravity wave facilities are operated jointly by CalTech and MIT (and funded by the National Science Foundation) and go jointly under the acronym "LIGO," or "Laser Interferometer Gravitational-Wave Observatory." The Italian facility is titled "Virgo."

Questions

1. A nanometer is one-billionth of a meter, and an angstrom is one ten-billionth of a meter. How many angstroms in a nanometer?

2. If the wavelengths of visible light range from 400 nm to 700 nm, what is their range expressed in angstroms?

3. The frequency of a wave on a string is 9.0 Hz and the speed of the wave is 3.0 m/s. Determine the wavelength.

4. The Sun emits most of its light near 500 nm. What is the frequency of this light?

5. The Sun emits most of its light near 500 nm. What is the color of this light? Does this agree with what you expected?

6. For the following examples, identify whether they represent the process of reflection or the process of refraction:
   + A person wears prescription eyeglasses.
   + A family watches TV channels delivered via a satellite dish.
   + The driver of a car looks at her rearview mirror for traffic.
   + A straw placed in a glass of water appears bent at the boundary between air and water.

7. In general, the size (diameter or "aperture") of a telescope should be many times larger than the wavelength of light being analyzed. The Aricebo telescope in Puerto Rico observes wavelengths from 3 centimeters to 1 meter. Which of the following is the aperture of the Aricebo dish?
   (a) 1 millimeter   (b) 3 centimeters   (c) 1 meter   (d) 1,000 meters

8. The main telescope at the Yerkes Observatory (near Lake Geneva in Wisconsin) has a diameter (aperture) of 1.02 meters (40 inches) and the tube is 18 meters (60 feet) long. What type of telescope is this—a reflector or a refractor?

9. During an observation run, a graduate student views a binary system with one red star and one blue star. The graduate student finds that when he focuses on the red star, the blue star appears very blurry, and when the graduate student focuses on the blue star, the red star appears very blurry. What is the name of this problem, and what type of telescope was used by the graduate student?

10. What is the most important reason to use a telescope? What is the second most important reason?

11. Which type of telescope, reflector or refractor, is favored by research astronomers? Why?

12. Which type of mount best helps an astronomer track the motion of an object across the sky over time?

13. To what does the term *seeing* refer?

14. *Adaptive optics* are used to make images from ground-based telescopes as clear as possible. To what are the optics "adapting"?

15. List at least three advantages electronic detectors (CCDs) have over other methods of recording astronomical observations.

16. Astronomical filters decrease the amount of light reaching the observer. Cite a reason why an astronomer might use a filter.

17. Match the type of science performed with astronomical observations with a short description:

    Astrometry: _____   (a) Used to achieve high-resolution images
    Interferometry: _____   (b) Used to determine the composition of an object
    Photometry: _____   (c) Used to detect magnetic fields and dust grains
    Polarimetry: _____   (d) Used to determine the brightness of an object
    Spectroscopy: _____   (e) Used to determine the position of an object

18. Besides visible light, which region of the electromagnetic spectrum most easily passes through the Earth's atmosphere?

19. Which type of telescope can potentially "see" into the core of the Sun?

    (a) Infrared   (b) Neutrino   (c) Radio   (d) Visible

20. An optical lens "bends" or changes the direction of light via the process of refraction. Astronomers have discovered many examples of "gravitational lenses" in space. Briefly describe how a gravitational lens might work.

Activities

▸ *Astrophysics activity 5.1*: Construct a refracting telescope using two convex lenses. Determine the magnification of the telescope from the focal lengths of each lens.

▸ *Astrophysics activity 5.2*: Investigate a spacecraft sent to study a(n) object(s) in the solar system, excluding the Earth. Write a short report detailing your findings. Include samples of new knowledge brought to us by the spacecraft.

▸ *Astrophysics Activity 5.3*: Use simulations to study how to operate an astronomical telescope.

Works Referenced

Neutrino emission and detection from Supernova 1987A is described in Arnett et al. (1989). Supernova 1987A. *Annual Review of Astronomy and Astrophysics, 27*, 629–700. doi:10.1146/annurev.aa.27.090189.003213

A press release concerning the 2017 Nobel Prize in physics is found in The Guardian. (2017, Ocoober 3). Nobel prize in physics awarded for discovery of gravitational waves: P825,000 prize awarded to Rainer Weiss, Barry Barish and Kip Thorne for their work on Ligo experiment which was able to detect ripples in the fabric of spacetime. Retrieved from https://www.theguardian.com/science/2017/oct/03/nobel-prize-physics-discovery-gravitational-waves-ligo

Information about photometry etc. performed on the Cloverleaf QSO is described in Turnshek et al. (1997). Hubble Space Telescope observations of the gravitationally-lensed Cloverleaf Broad Absorption Line QSO H1413+1143: Imaging. *Astrophysical Journal. 485*, 100–111. Retrieved from http://iopscience.iop.org/article/10.1086/304395/pdf

Specific details concerning the 40-inch refractor at Yerkes Observatory can be found at https://physical-sciences.uchicago.edu/content/yerkes-updates. Retrieved 2019-04-20.

Information about the Keck telescopes can be found at http://www.keckobservatory.org/

Information about the Ice Cube neutrino experiment can be found at https://icecube.wisc.edu/science/icecube/detector

More information about LIGO and its collaborator Virgo can be found at https://www.ligo.caltech.edu/

Credits

Fig. 5.15: Copyright © by Sphl (CC BY-SA 3.0) at https://commons.wikimedia.org/wiki/File:CCD_Image_sensor.jpg.

Fig. 5.16: Source: https://commons.wikimedia.org/wiki/File:55mm_optical_filters.jpg.

Fig. 5.17: Copyright © by Niagara (CC BY-SA 3.0) at https://commons.wikimedia.org/wiki/File:Thaw_Refractor,_Allegheny_Observatory_2.jpg.

Fig. 5.18a: David Turnshek et. al., "Hubble Space Telescope Observations of the Gravitationally-Lensed Cloverleaf Broad Absorption Line QSO H1413+1143: Imaging," The Astrophysical Journal, vol. 485, no. 1, pp. 102. Copyright © 1997 by The American Astronomical Society. Reprinted with permission.

Fig. 5.18b: David Turnshek et. al., "Hubble Space Telescope Observations of the Gravitationally-Lensed Cloverleaf Broad Absorption Line QSO H1413+1143: Imaging," The Astrophysical Journal, vol. 485, no. 1, pp. 112. Copyright © 1997 by The American Astronomical Society. Reprinted with permission.

Fig. 5.19: Source: https://apod.nasa.gov/apod/ap160227.html.

Fig. 5.20: Source: https://commons.wikimedia.org/wiki/File:Star_SDSS_J001820.5%E2%80%93093939.2_Spectrum.png.

Fig. 5.21: Copyright © by ESO/NASA/ESA/Ardila et al. (CC BY 4.0) at https://commons.wikimedia.org/wiki/File:VLT_and_Hubble_images_of_the_protoplanet_system_HD_100546.jpg.

Fig. 5.22a: Copyright © by Bob Mellish (CC BY-SA 3.0) at https://commons.wikimedia.org/wiki/File:Wire-grid-polarizer.svg.

Fig. 5.22b: Copyright © by NielsB (CC BY-SA 2.5) at https://commons.wikimedia.org/wiki/File:Polarizer_sheet_perpendicular.jpg.

Fig. 5.23: Copyright © by ALMA (ESO/NAOJ/NRAO), Nagai et al. (CC BY 4.0) at https://commons.wikimedia.org/wiki/File:Quasar_3C_286_as_observed_with_ALMA.jpg.

Fig. 5.24: Copyright © by NRAO/AUI (CC BY 3.0) at https://commons.wikimedia.org/wiki/File:JanskyatAntenna_hi.tif.

Fig. 5.25a: Source: https://commons.wikimedia.org/wiki/File:KSC_radio_telescope.jpg.

Fig. 5.25b: Copyright © by David Broad (CC BY 3.0) at https://commons.wikimedia.org/wiki/File:Arecibo_radio_telescope_observatory_Puerto_Rico_-_panoramio_(3).jpg.

Fig. 5.26: Source: https://commons.wikimedia.org/wiki/File:Gamma-Ray_Burst_050525a.jpg.

Fig. 5.28: Source: https://commons.wikimedia.org/wiki/File:U.S._Department_of_Energy_-_Science_-_270_122_001_%2822599935022%29.jpg.

THE SOLAR SYSTEM

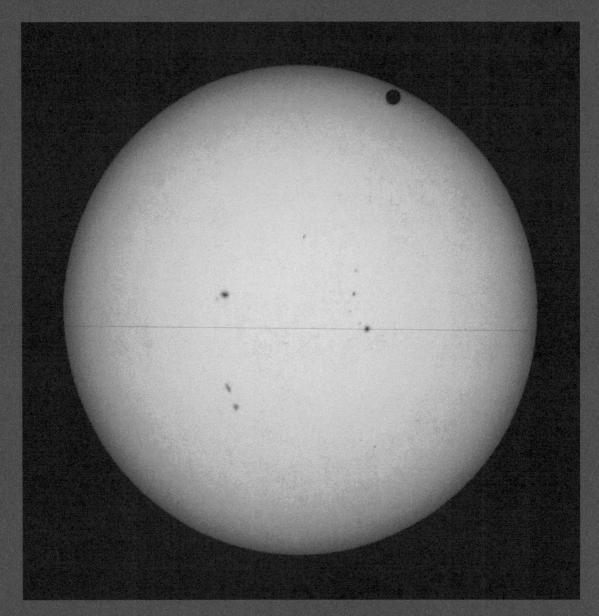

The transit of Venus across the Sun in the summer of 2012.

CHAPTER 6

PREVIEW OF THE SOLAR SYSTEM

PURPOSE

To preview the major constituents of the solar system

OBJECTIVES

- ▶ To compare different classes of solar system objects
- ▶ To show how different classes of objects are arranged in the solar system
- ▶ To discuss the case of Pluto

INTRODUCTION

When we think of the solar system, we tend to think about the planets—eight or nine of them, depending—orbiting the Sun. While more or less true, it is quite incomplete, both in numbers and classes of objects. Planets are now split into "major" and "dwarf" categories. Hundreds of asteroids are known, and while most of them are concentrated in a "belt" surrounding the Sun, many more are scattered in the inner solar system. We also know of hundreds of comets; the vast majority originate in regions beyond the outer major planets. Hundreds of moons orbit the planets (with two interesting exceptions), but moons have also been spotted orbiting asteroids. The solar system is embedded in a vacuum-thin haze of dust, which affects the appearances of many airless objects. Finally, the object at its center, the object after which the system is named, contains over 99% of all its mass.

   In this chapter, we preview the layout of the solar system, focusing on the various classes of objects, their basic properties, and locations. The next chapter will review current models for the formation of the solar system and incorporate recent knowledge from other solar systems.

KEY TERMS

Asteroid: A relatively rocky, relatively small object orbiting close to the Sun

Asteroid belt: A doughnut-shaped region between the orbits of Mars and Jupiter where the majority of asteroids reside

Comets: A relatively icy, relatively small object orbiting far from the Sun. A comet can grow a "tail" and become very bright if it approaches the Sun

Density (also mass density): The amount of mass per unit volume for an object. Can be used as a diagnostic for determining the types of materials in an object

Dwarf planet: One of several medium-sized objects orbiting the Sun. A "dwarf" planet should be close to spherical in shape and not be in orbit about another planet, but does not dominate its orbit gravitationally, and is noticeably smaller than several moons

Eccentricity: The deviation of an ellipse from being a perfect circle. An eccentricity of zero is a perfect circle; an eccentricity of 1 indicates the ellipse is so stretched that it is a parabola instead

Icy dwarf: An object, usually a dwarf planet or candidate for such, made mostly of ice and rock

Inclination: The tilt of the plane of an object's orbit about the Sun compared to the ecliptic (the plane of the Earth's orbit)

Inner solar system: Generally, the part of the solar system closer to the Sun than the orbit of Jupiter

Jovian planet: A sub-category of a major planet, which is many times more massive than the Earth, consists primarily of hydrogen and helium gas, and orbits between 5 and 30 au from the Sun

Kuiper belt: A torus-shaped region extending tens of astronomical units beyond the orbit of Neptune that is thought to potentially contain thousands or more comet nuclei and is the source of short-period comets

Major planet: One of eight relatively large objects orbiting the Sun. A "major" planet must be nearly spherical in shape and be the dominant object (in terms of gravity) in its orbit. Mercury is the least massive major planet and Jupiter the most-massive

Moon: An object orbiting another object besides the Sun

Obliquity: The tilt of an object's axis compared to the ecliptic. The obliquity of an object whose equator aligns with the ecliptic has an obliquity of zero degrees; the obliquity of an object whose north and south rotational poles aligns with the ecliptic has an obliquity of 90 degrees

Occultation: When a relatively large object passes in front of a relatively smaller object

Oort cloud: A spherical region perhaps up to 1 light year from the Sun, where millions of comet nuclei reside and is thought to be the source of long-period comets

Outer solar system: Generally, the part of the solar system starting from the orbit of Jupiter and outward from the Sun

Planet: See *major planet* and *dwarf planet*

Planetary rings: Small debris (rocks and/or chunks of ice) that orbit a planet in a doughnut-shaped region. Only found around Jovian planets

Star: An object that generates energy via nuclear fusion

Terrestrial planet: A sub-category of a major planet, which is similar in mass to the Earth, consists primarily of metal and rock, and orbits between 0.3 and 1.5 au from the Sun

Trojan asteroids: Two sets of asteroids that either lead or follow Jupiter in its orbit, held in place by the mutual gravitational pull of Jupiter and the Sun

KEY INDIVIDUALS/ORGANIZATIONS

International Astronomical Union (IAU): The international body which, among other responsibilities, names and defines astronomical objects

Kuiper, Gerald: A Dutch astronomer of the 20th century who speculated on the structure and origin of comets

Lagrange, Joseph-Louis: An Italian mathematician and physicist of the late 18th century who made important advances in among others celestial mechanics

Oort, Jan: A Dutch astronomer of the 20th century who also speculated about comets

Tombaugh, Clyde: An American astronomer of the 20th century who discovered the (now "dwarf") planet Pluto

Section 6.1: A Short History of the Term "Planet"

An astronomical bombshell exploded (figuratively speaking) on all of us when the International Astronomical Union—the body responsible for naming and categorizing astronomical objects—decided in 2006 that Pluto, considered a planet since its discovery in 1930, no longer qualified. Not everyone was happy with the decision, including some astronomers. But the number of planets has always been a fuzzy concept.

The ancients knew of seven "wanderers," which has come down to us from the Greeks as "planets." Originally simply objects that move relative to the star background, the notion that planets are objects orbiting the Sun was reintroduced by Copernicus in 1543, which changed not only the definition of a planet, but also their number from seven to six. The number went back up to seven with William Herschel's discovery of Uranus in 1781—which is where we left the story earlier in chapter 3.

By then astronomers knew to high precision the relative sizes of the orbits of the planets. A math formula called Bode's law appeared to predict the semi-major axes of the planets, out to Uranus, with one exception: There is a gap between Mars and Jupiter. According to Bode's law, there should be a planet 2.8 au from the Sun (see Table 6.1).

TABLE 6.1. Bode's Law

Planet	Bode's Law prediction (au)	Actual Semi-Major Axis (au)
Mercury	0.4	0.39
Venus	0.7	0.72
Earth	1	1
Mars	1.6	1.52
?	2.8	?
Jupiter	5.2	5.2
Saturn	10.0	9.5
Uranus	19.2	19

In 1801, Italian astronomer Guiseppe Piazzi discovered an object at a distance of 2.77 au, which was subsequently named Ceres.[1] The gap seemed to have been filled. Ceres was observed to be noticeably smaller than Mars, though its true size wouldn't be known for many years.

With Ceres, it appeared to many that the solar system was complete, as least as far as planets are concerned. But within just a few years, three other objects were found at almost exactly the same distance from the Sun (Pallas, Juno, and Vesta), each of them smaller than Ceres. This presented astronomers with a conundrum: Should each of these be counted as planets? Assuming we do so, the number of planets jumped from 7 to 11 in a space of 6 years.

The situation hung until the next discovery, that of Neptune in 1846. Neptune was such a large object, compared to the small sizes of Ceres and its companions, that astronomers dropped these objects—now called "asteroids"—but added Neptune, changing the total from 11 to 8.

Pluto was found in 1930 by Clyde Tombaugh and was immediately added to the list of planets, raising the total to nine. However, even early on, Pluto didn't fit well with the others, being obviously much smaller than Neptune and the other gas giants. In 2003, with the discovery of Eris, another very small object, the debate regarding Pluto gained steam, and Pluto was reclassified in 2006, returning the number of planets back to eight.

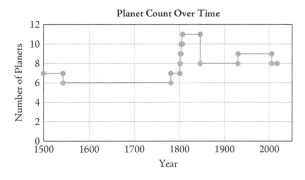

FIGURE 6.1. The change in the number of recognized planets over the past few centuries.

---

[1] In keeping with the Greco-Roman theme for naming planets, Ceres is the Roman name (Greek Demeter) of the goddess of agriculture. The other three large asteroids described here also share the same naming convention.

We will return to the story of Pluto at the end of this chapter. But the lesson should be clear: Despite all the hand-wringing regarding Pluto, how we define a planet has always been a fungible concept. Finally, while this was a discussion regarding the number of planets (now "major" planets) in our solar system, several thousand planets are now known outside of our solar system—meaning our ideas about planets are still in flux.

Section 6.2: Solar System Objects

Our preview of the solar system begins with a census of its different classes of objects.

Categories in an observational science such as astronomy are not hard and fast. Pluto's "demotion," and the split between "major" and "dwarf" planets, happened as recently as 2006. Comets and asteroids, once thought to be distinct, are not always so different. Objects have been found that orbit asteroids, giving a new meaning to the term "moon." Planetary rings may originate from shredded moons. New categories include "KBOs" (Kuiper Belt Objects), "TNOs" (Trans-Neptunian Objects), and so on.

Since it is called the "solar" system, let's start with the Sun.

1. Stars

The Sun is the dominant object in the solar system. Its mass is 330,000 times that of the Earth, and it is over 100 times larger across. Even Jupiter, otherwise rightfully termed a "giant" planet, is less than 1/1,000 the mass of the Sun and less than 1/10 the Sun's diameter. Or, as the joke goes, the Sun is over 99.9% of the solar system.

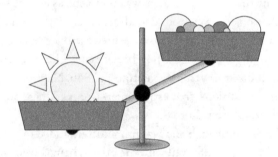

FIGURE 6.2. The Sun easily outweighs everything else in the solar system.

We will devote a future chapter to the details of the Sun. For now, our purpose is to recognize the Sun as belonging to a completely different class of object than any other in the solar system—a *star*.

With a few exceptions (the occasional planet or galaxy), every dot we see with the naked eye in the night sky is a star. Stars are quite numerous—astronomers usually estimate we have over 400 billion of them alone in our galaxy, the Milky Way. Stars exist in a variety of "living arrangements"—many single, many in pairs ("binaries"), others in groups ("clusters") of hundreds to hundreds of thousands of inhabitants. Astronomers speculated for many decades that the Sun might have a dim, invisible (to the naked eye) companion star, but it does not. The Sun is a single star.

What is a star? Briefly, a star is a natural object, made of various gases, whose mass is so large that it uses nuclear fusion as an energy source to support itself against its own weight. The Sun consists of 90% hydrogen and 9% helium (by element), though its core is roughly a 50–50 split between those two elements. The Sun does possess other elements, but they are rare in comparison. This is another immediately obvious difference between the Sun and the Earth: the Sun is made of a much different mix of materials.

FIGURE 6.3. The Sun and planets to scale.

The other obvious difference between the Sun and all the other solar system objects is its brightness. The Sun is so hot—about 6,000 kelvin, or 11,000 °F—on its surface that it glows in visible light, which is true of no other solar system object. It also emits a prodigious amount of heat (infrared), a small but significant amount of ultraviolet, and even smaller but measurable amounts of other regions of the electromagnetic radiation. Roughly 1,400 watts of energy, spread out per meter squared, reaches the Earth each second, even at a distance of 150 million kilometers (93 million miles). The Sun also boasts, as you now might expect, the largest magnetic field in the solar system.

The Sun supports itself (literally) by nuclear fusion, turning hundreds of millions of tons of hydrogen nuclei into helium nuclei every second. Despite this, the Sun is so large that it has a lifespan estimated at 10 billion years. We are about halfway there, so the solar system has many years ahead of it before the Sun dies.

Having 99.9% of the total mass of the solar system, it is fair to say all objects orbit the Sun. As we saw in chapter 4, the gravity that planets exert on the Sun can make it "wobble," and if we observed our system from a nearby star, we could detect this effect. Nevertheless, there is no comparison; we truly live in the Sun's domain.

2. Major Planets Part I: Terrestrials

For over a decade now, the number of "major" planets recognized by astronomers is eight. But even within that category, there are two—maybe three—subcategories of planets. We will look at the *terrestrial planets*, those most like the Earth, first.

"Terrestrial" of course means "Earth-like," so the term itself is a hint. But what specific properties and behaviors qualify as "Earth-like"? Mercury, for example, has no atmosphere to speak of. Venus has a worldwide temperature of 900 °F. Mars, even though the most common planet in science fiction for humans to inhabit, is a barren, frozen desert world, deadly to life. So why are these objects lumped in with the Earth?

FIGURE 6.4. The terrestrial planets in order from the Sun, left to right. Their sizes are to scale, though not their distances.

The terrestrials share many bulk properties in common, even though they are very different in the specifics. These properties fall into two related sets:

1. Location, location, location: All four major terrestrial planets are within a few astronomical units from the Sun. This is not true of other classes of planets, or most other objects, for that matter
2. Composition: All four are made primarily of the same materials—metal and rock

Taken together, these general ideas lead us to other shared properties:

1. Quick orbital periods, to go with their short semi-major axes. Mercury only needs 3 months to orbit the Sun. Mars, the furthest of the planets, still needs less than 2 years to complete an orbit
2. Relatively high surface temperatures—even Mars, which is frigid compared to the Earth, is much warmer than objects in the outer solar system
3. High densities. Being made of metal and rock, each of them is several times thicker than liquid water
4. Similar interior structures. Each terrestrial has a core made of a mix of iron and nickel, surrounded by a thick layer of heavy rock (mixing iron and magnesium in with the silicon and oxygen that makes up the basic chemistry of rock) and topped by a thin layer lighter rocks, basalt and granite
5. Relatively thin atmospheres. Mercury's surface is essentially in vacuum. Mars only has an air pressure at its surface about 1% that of Earth. Even Venus, with its intense 90 atmospheres of pressure, pales in comparison to the millions of atmospheres of pressure deep inside Jupiter
6. Solid surfaces. Only Earth has a liquid (water) covering most of its surface, but even then the liquid is a thin layer compared to the rest of the planet, and it is solid underneath its oceans
7. Evidence of past geologic activity, Earth being the only one currently active
8. Impact craters. Mercury and Mars in particular are saturated with them. Venus and Earth have a few hundred each
9. Few moons and no rings. Mercury and Venus each have no moons at all. Earth has many artificial satellites, but only one natural satellite (the Moon). Mars has two small, mountain-sized moons which are either captured asteroids or debris from ancient impacts

FIGURE 6.5. To scale: Vesta, Eros, and Ceres (all asteroids); Charon and Pluto.

We can lump in two other objects into the terrestrial mix, if we wish to put aside the requirement of "major planet" status. The Moon shares virtually all these properties, except that it orbits the Earth; were it orbiting the Sun independently, we would be tempted to call it a planet (when we examine the Moon more carefully later in the book, we will discuss its probable origin as part of an independent protoplanet in the early days of the solar system). The largest of the asteroids, Ceres, is far too small to be considered a planet (it is slightly less than 1,000 kilometers in diameter and only the 33rd-most massive object in the solar system) and lives in the asteroid belt, accompanied by thousands, if not millions, of other asteroids. Yet it too shares most of the other properties of terrestrial planets, although its metal core is minimal at best. Ceres does contain an estimated 1/3 of the mass of all asteroids and is massive enough to be spherical, the only asteroid able to make that claim; a current space probe (Dawn) has been orbiting Ceres since 2015, the first spacecraft to visit Ceres. We should learn a great more about Ceres in the next few years.

3. Major Planets Part II: Jovians

The other subcategory of major planets is the Jupiter-like, or *Jovian*[2] planets, and they in many ways are the opposites of the terrestrials. Where terrestrials live close to the Sun, the Jovians live far way. Where terrestrials are solid, the Jovians are gaseous. But probably the most significant difference is simply the size: The Jovians are gigantic planets. Jupiter has well over 300 times the mass of the Earth, and its volume is such that over 1,000 Earths could fit inside it. Even the smallest of the Jovians, Uranus, is still 14 times more massive than the Earth.

FIGURE 6.6. The Jovian planets in order from the Sun, left to right. Their sizes are to scale, though not their distances.

Specific properties of the Jovians, especially when compared to the terrestrials, include the following:

1. Longer orbital periods, to go with their large semi-major axes. Jupiter has the shortest orbit, requiring just under 12 years to complete an orbit. Neptune is so far from the Sun—30 au—that even though it was discovered in 1846, it only finished its first complete orbit since its discovery in 2010
2. Relatively low surface temperatures—each planet's upper atmosphere is incredibly cold; several hundred degrees below zero (Fahrenheit) is standard
3. Low densities. Being made primarily of hydrogen and helium, they are just barely thicker than water, except for Saturn, which would float in a big enough tub
4. Thick atmospheres. Each has a relatively small solid core, but the majority of each planet is gaseous. In fact, there are no places where any astronaut or spacecraft could land
5. They do not possess any "geologic" activity as such; on the other hand, each has incredibly active weather systems
6. Being gaseous, there is no evidence for impacts, even though they must occur, being the largest targets (aside from the Sun) in the solar system. We know this can happen, because pieces of a comet (Shoemaker-Levy 9) hit Jupiter in 1994, which was observed worldwide
7. Large numbers of moons, not surprising since each is so massive. Jupiter and Saturn each have over 60 identified moons
8. Each possesses a set of rings

---

[2] "Jove" is simply another name for Jupiter. And "Jupiterian" sounds awkward.

Having said this, the individual differences amongst the Jovians are even greater than those amongst terrestrials. We can argue that they should be split into further subcategories: Jupiter and Saturn in one set, Uranus and Neptune in another.

The observation that immediately strikes the eye is that Uranus and Neptune are shades of blue, whereas Jupiter and Saturn's colors are dominated by white and yellow. By itself, a color difference doesn't necessarily matter; all the Jovians possess methane as a constituent of their atmospheres, but Uranus and Neptune simply have more of it, percentage-wise (methane absorbs red and infrared light well, yielding blue in return). However, the differences are more than skin deep. Deep in the interior of Jupiter and Saturn, pressures become so intense (millions of times that at the Earth's surface) that hydrogen is squeezed into a liquid, metallic state. Uranus and Neptune do not reach such pressures (though they are still immense compared to pressures inside the Earth); rather, their interiors appear to have superheated ionized water instead. Jupiter and Saturn are an order of magnitude (i.e., power of ten) more massive than Uranus and Neptune.

4. Dwarf Planets

We will tell the story of Pluto toward the end of this chapter. For now, it is sufficient to describe a relatively new class of object in the solar system—the *dwarf planets*.

The most important reason for placing objects like Pluto and Ceres into a new "dwarf" planet category is simple: mass. Excluding the Sun, Pluto is only the 16th most-massive object in the solar system. Several moons—including our own—are larger than Pluto. But why then give objects the "planet" designation?

A dwarf planet, in essence, is an object with enough mass to pull itself into a spherical shape (with at least one exception) and orbits the Sun rather than another object but is not otherwise very massive. Mercury serves as the boundary, at least in our solar system, for such objects to retain the "major" title. Another reason is that the orbits of some of the dwarf planets are affected by the gravitational pull of nearby major planets—for example, Pluto and Neptune's orbital periods are linked in a 2:3 ratio, due to Neptune's influence.

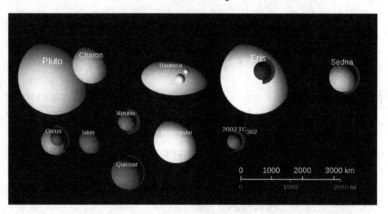

FIGURE 6.7. An artist's renditions of dwarf planets (and candidates) with their moons.

Pluto and perhaps Ceres are familiar to the average person; the other dwarf planets are probably not, being relatively new (new, in that they were recently discovered, not new in terms of their ages, which average about 4 1/2 billion years). The other objects currently on the dwarf planet list are Eris, Haumea, and Makemake (pronounced "mah-kay-mah-kay"); other candidates include Sedna and Quaoar ("kwar"). You probably noticed that only Eris comes from Greco-Roman tradition; astronomers have run out of names from the ancient Greeks and Romans, so they are tapping others—Makemake is Hawaiian, for example. We only have close-up images for Pluto and Ceres—what may look like close-ups of the others are artistic renditions.

What are other arguments for objects being termed "planets"? One is that they have moons. Each dwarf planet has at least one moon (Makemake has a recently discovered moon) and Pluto has five. Others are that they are active geologically and/or have atmospheres. But these are characteristics shared by other classes of objects—several asteroids have moons (Ida, for example, has a moon named Dactyl), several moons show geological activity (Io is not alone; Enceladus of Saturn shows continuous geyser eruptions), and a few moons (Titan of Saturn, Triton of Neptune) have atmospheres.

The body recognized by astronomers with the responsibility for naming and categorizing astronomical objects is the International Astronomical Union, or IAU.[3] In 2006, the IAU revisited the definition of a planet and decided on the following criteria:

1. The object must orbit the Sun
2. The object's mass must be enough to pull it into a nearly spherical shape
3. The object must clear the neighborhood around its orbit

The first criterion excludes objects like moons, which can be spherical but orbit planets instead, and the second criterion excludes objects like comets, which orbit the Sun but are not massive enough to be spherical. The third criterion is the most interesting (and most controversial). But what does it mean for a planet to "clear" its neighborhood?

First, it's not that space around a planet has to be empty—the Moon (and thousands of artificial satellites) orbit the Earth, after all. Rather, what it means is that any object not directly orbiting the planet, but that comes near the planet, will be shunted away by the immense gravity of the planet. If an object can do that—keep sweeping its vicinity of debris—then we can call it a planet. Several groups have worked on numerical methods to discriminate between planets and non-planets, and the results easily distinguish between our current eight "major" planets and other objects.

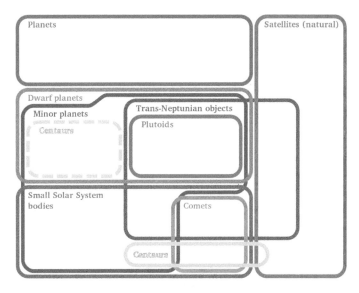

FIGURE 6.8. A diagram suggesting a way to organize objects in the solar system (besides the Sun).

Dwarf planets are not the only (relatively) new category of solar system object. "Centaurs" are objects orbiting the Sun between Jupiter and the Kuiper Belt. The Kuiper Belt is a torus- (doughnut) shaped region far from the Sun where comets originate; objects larger or different in composition from comets are "Kuiper Belt Objects" or KBOs—Pluto is an example. There are also "trans-Neptunian objects" or TNOs, and so on. Consequently, there is also a lot of overlap between categories.

---

[3] It is important to realize that the IAU is a scientific body, not a legal one. Its rulings reflect the consensus of its members and are subject to revision with further debate and knowledge.

5. Moons

Briefly, *moons* are natural satellites of other objects that orbit the Sun. Originally, astronomers thought that only (major) planets could have moons, but moons are now known to orbit dwarf planets and even asteroids. In most cases, moons form along with their hosts; some moons are debris from collisions between objects, with the smaller object falling into a closed orbit about a larger object; on rare occasions, a small object might be "captured" by the gravity of a larger object.

FIGURE 6.9. Some moons in the solar system: Prometheus (tiny dot) transits Saturn's rings while Dione transits Titan in the background. From the Cassini mission (NASA).

Moons have perhaps an even wider array of properties than planets. We are familiar with our moon (the Moon), but it is rather an exception to the rule, being very large compared to its host. Some moons are significantly larger than ours, but most are not. A few moons have atmospheres and several are geologically active. Many moons are massive enough to be spherical in shape, but most are not. Some are icy, though most are made of rock. By and large, the smaller a moon, the more common it is.

FIGURE 6.10. The asteroid Ida and its moon Dactyl, 10,500 km (6,500 miles) away by the space probe Galileo Credit: NASA/JPL.

6. Asteroids

The term *asteroid* is usually reserved for relatively small, rocky objects orbiting the Sun from roughly the orbit of Jupiter and closer. Ida (Figure 6.10) is a fair example; asteroids are generally too small (in mass) to be spherical, and therefore tend to have oblong shapes (like a potato!). Ida is nearly 60 kilometers long, which makes for a large rock, but is far too small for gravity to greatly distort its shape. An astronaut who landed on Ida could theoretically jump into orbit about it. Nevertheless, Ida is an example of an asteroid with a moon (named "Dactyl").

Some asteroids orbit the Sun on their own, but most asteroids are in two general locations. First, the space between Mars and Jupiter has thousands of known, and perhaps millions more, asteroids and has the nickname of the *asteroid belt*. Asteroids in the belt are not all evenly spread throughout the belt; rather, the gravitational influence of Jupiter gently confines them to set distances from the Sun. Ceres is the largest member of the belt (see Section 6.1), but even if all the asteroids of the belt were combined into a single object, it still would be far smaller than our Moon.

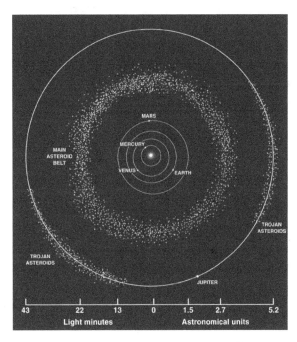

FIGURE 6.11. The solar system out to Jupiter, showing the asteroid belt and Trojan asteroids (asteroids not to scale). Courtesy: NASA.

The other place asteroids congregate is in orbit with Jupiter, two sets collectively called the *Trojan asteroids*. Jupiter's gravity combines with the Sun's to create regions of stability either 60° in front of Jupiter or 60° behind Jupiter as it orbits the Sun; that is, one group of asteroids leads Jupiter and one follows. The effect is not too strong, and asteroids in both locations are rather spread out, though centered at both 60° angles front and back. This is an interesting effect of gravity noted originally by the Italian mathematician Joseph-Louis Lagrange (1736–1813), who realized that regions of stability will exist in several locations around two astronomical objects, depending on their separation and relative masses. Astronomers sometimes make use of this notion to locate space probes.

Both regions—the asteroid belt and Trojans—are depicted in Figure 6.11. At first glance, it appears that these spaces are filled with asteroids. However, we need to keep in mind the scale of such pictures. Each dot represents the possible location of an asteroid but is much larger than the asteroid is; if we drew the asteroids correctly to scale, each would be about as large as an average bacterium and invisible to the naked eye. It would also then be evident that there is plenty of space between each asteroid. In fact, when NASA or other space agencies send probes

FIGURE 6.12. Joseph-Louis Lagrange (artist unknown).

through the asteroid belt to explore the outer solar system, they worry very little about collisions with asteroids. In fact, it's hard to make a probe hit an asteroid, even if you're trying on purpose!

Asteroids consist almost entirely of rock, though some trace amounts of metal can be found. Astronomers also suspect many asteroids incorporate water ice in their interiors. We are only in recent years getting results from flyby and/or orbiting missions about asteroids to get close-up images and detailed measurements of their compositions.

Some asteroids are more or less on their own, some orbiting within the inner solar system and rarely (fortunately!) coming near the Earth. Tiny asteroids are sometimes called "meteoroids" (there is not a set distinction) and can hit the Earth or other planets and moons. A meteoroid that enters the Earth's asteroid will heat up due to enormous air resistance and can be seen for a second or two as a bright dot streaking across the sky as a "meteor." Most meteors are small pebbles that disintegrate tens of miles above the surface, but occasionally some reach the surface, these remnants being termed "meteorites."

Meteorites can actually fetch a large price from museums and dealers, since they are rare and are scientifically valuable. Meteorites come in several varieties, though all are made of rocks of various kinds, and some are iron rich. In fact, stony-iron meteorites are more popular, percentage-wise, than stony-iron meteoroids and asteroids, since while rock can burn up on entry, iron is tougher and has a better chance to survive to reach the ground. We will further discuss in detail impacts of asteroids and comets in chapter 8.

7. Comets

Our final stop in the solar system brings us to comets. Astronomers in centuries past made observations of comets; for example, Johannes Kepler was one of several who noted that comet tails always point away from the Sun. The physical nature of comets was not understood until several decades ago, however. The astronomer Fred Whipple suggested a process to create the extremely long tails of comets, and a nickname: comets are "dirty snowballs." As a comet nears the Sun, the comet's snow (or ice) melts and evaporates (or sublimates), sending geysers of water and other ices streaming off the comet. The radiation and solar wind of the Sun push the chunks of ice and dust away from the Sun, thus the tail. The ices can spread out over a million miles, making the "head" of the comet, before streaming backward to form a tail—or tails, as the case may be (see Figure 6.13).

The Sun's light supplies pressure—yes, light can "push"—on neutral (not electrically charged) ice and dust particles. The pressure is very gentle, so this material arcs gracefully away from the comet rather than going in a straight line. But the Sun also gives off the "solar wind"—a stream of charged particles, mostly protons—that interact with charged particles thrown off by the comet. This pressure is stronger, so the ionized material goes away from the comet in more or less a straight line.

A comet's head is about a million miles across, and its tail can extend for hundreds of millions of miles. What object is responsible for all this? It turns out a typical comet nucleus, like an asteroid, is so small that it looks more like a potato than anything else (Figure 6.14). Starting in 1986 with Comet Halley, several spacecraft have gotten up-close looks at comet nuclei

FIGURE 6.13. Comet Hale-Bopp with two tails, in 1997. Courtesy of the European Space Observatory.

and (with a few exceptions) when they are far enough from the Sun that the Sun's heat does not produce a comet head and tail.

These observations also imply something about the locations of comets: They must usually live far from the Sun. Astronomers consider two general sources, both named for Dutch astronomers.

The *Kuiper Belt* is named after Gerard Kuiper (pronounced like "viper"), who in 1951 theorized that a torus-shaped region beyond the orbit of Pluto containing various bodies had existed at the beginning of the solar system but has since dissipated. Despite the fact that Kuiper thought the region no longer exists, the name has stuck. The Kuiper Belt officially begins outside the orbit of Neptune at 30 au and extends to 50 au or 100 au from the Sun (Figure 6.15). As with our depictions of the asteroid belt, any picture we sketch of the Kuiper Belt is misleading, since we can't draw the comets to scale and still see them. Since it is much further from the Sun and much thicker, the Kuiper Belt probably contains hundreds or thousands of times more mass than the asteroid belt.

Today, we think the Kuiper Belt is the source of "short-period" comets, comets whose orbits are often several decades long. Suppose we consider a comet nucleus originally orbiting the Sun at an average distance of 50 au. The comet nucleus is disturbed somehow—perhaps by the gravity of Neptune—and falls toward the Sun. As it travels toward the Sun, it is unlikely to collide with a planet (though that is possible), especially at first, but its chances of getting close to a planet and having its orbit further perturbed are larger, and close encounters between comets and planets are virtually inevitable given astronomical time scales (millions or billions of years). The chances of close encounters are enhanced if the comet's orbit is inclined (tilted) similarly to the planets, that is, if the comet is roughly in the same plane as the planets. If the orbit of the comet nucleus is further shrunk, it can end up getting close enough to the Sun so that it grows a head and tail. Short-period comets tend to return during a person's lifetime, and some (like Comet Halley) become famous.

The *Oort Cloud* was proposed separately by Jan Oort (pronounced with a long "o") in 1950. Astronomers, culminating with Oort, had speculated about the source of "long-period" comets, those which have such large semi-major axes that their orbital periods are in the thousands of years or longer. Their story is similar to that of comet nuclei in the Kuiper Belt, except that the

FIGURE 6.14. The nucleus of Comet Wild 2, from the Stardust probe (NASA).

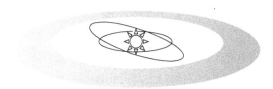

FIGURE 6.15. The Kuiper Belt (gray torus), about 100 au from the Sun. The orbits of Neptune and Pluto are shown roughly to scale.

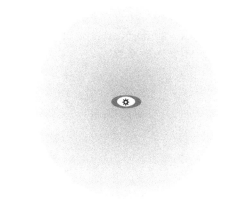

FIGURE 6.16. The Oort Cloud (grey sphere), about a light year from the Sun, surrounding the Sun and Kuiper Belt. The figure is not to scale.

likely source of any disturbances is a passing star. The Oort Cloud is thought to be anywhere from a few thousand to several tens of thousands of au from the Sun—so far that this is one way in which astronomers define the boundary of the Sun's influence. Indeed, Oort Cloud comet nuclei are so distant that they are not held onto very well by the Sun's gravity, and such objects might be floating free between stars, or traded between them. The various comet nuclei and other debris or dust in the Oort Cloud were possibly thrown outward from their original locations during the early days of the solar system as Jupiter and Saturn migrated inward (we will see more about this in the next chapter).

The sharing of objects between stars appears rare, but not impossible. An object was observed by the Pan-STARRS1 survey telescope on Hawaii in October of 2017 approaching the Sun which, with follow-up observations, was confirmed to having a trajectory originating from outside the solar system. The object is designated 1I/2017 U1, or "'Oumuamua" (derived from Hawaiian for "scout") and is thought to be an asteroid rather than a comet, since even though it reached as close as 0.25 au from the Sun, it showed no cometary activity. 'Oumuamua also has an elongated shape, and the Sun's gravity produced a slingshot effect on 'Oumuamua, and it is already heading back to interstellar space (Figure 6.17).

FIGURE 6.17. Left: An artist's portrait of 'Oumuamua, the first known visitor from another solar system. Right: 'Oumuamua's path through the solar system. Both images courtesy the European Southern Observatory.

What are comets like inside? While asteroids are thought to essentially be large rocks, comets are more like large snowballs, and very thin snowballs at that. From flybys of comets, astronomers have been able to estimate the densities of comet nuclei, and rather than being solid ice or packed-in dirty snowballs, they are so light a better description would be more like fluffy snow. Water ice appears most prevalent, but other ices—ammonia, carbon dioxide, methane—are also present. A comet nucleus is also thought to have a relatively thin "skin" of sorts, made from dark, sticky dust gathered by the comet nucleus as it moves through the otherwise-seeming vacuum of the solar system (Figure 6.18):

FIGURE 6.18. An excellent representation of the nucleus of a comet.

As a comet nucleus nears the Sun, the Sun's light heats up the dark carbon-loaded surface, which transfers energy to the ices trapped below. Hot spots can develop, melting the ices below and creating pressure, which can burst through as geysers or jets. The light mass of the comet nucleus means that these jets escape its gravity, potentially spreading out hundreds of thousands or millions of miles before solar radiation and the solar wind shape the comet's head and tail. The irony is that a comet, when developed, is extremely large and bright, whereas the nucleus is small and coal-dark.

Check Your Neighbor

What eventually will happen to a comet nucleus if it continues to make close approaches to the Sun (so it grows a head and tail)? Hint: Where do the materials making up the head and tail go?

Section 6.3: The Organization of the Solar System

Despite the wide variety of objects flying about in the solar system, they aren't randomly spread out. Rather, it is organized, if somewhat loosely. Terrestrial planets and asteroids congregate relatively close to the Sun, Jovian planets and moons far from the Sun, and icy bodies like Pluto and comets very far from the Sun. What determines these arrangements?

To ferret out the reasons, let's consider how different properties behave given their location in the solar system. By location, we really mean distance from the Sun.

One question to ask is about the kinds of materials in the solar system. Without detailed analysis of an object—which implies landing probes and perhaps astronauts on it, which is difficult if not impossible—we can't answer such a question to great precision. But we can get an overall idea via proxies. One of the simplest identifiers a material can have is its *density*, the amount of mass it has per unit volume. A pure substance, in a specific phase or state (such as gas, liquid, or solid) will have a constant density. For example, suppose you wanted to tell if an ancient coin consists of pure gold. If you determine its density is 19.3 grams per cubic centimeter, then you can be reasonably assured it is.

We expect that astronomical objects will be mixes of various materials, and density can change with depth inside an object (due to increasing pressure), so this isn't a tell-all measurement. Nevertheless, density is a good starting point. Figure 6.19 depicts the densities of a sample of objects (planets, moons, asteroids, and comets) with increasing distance from the Sun.

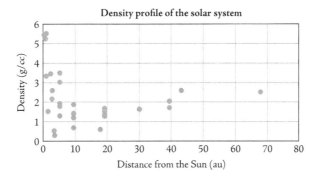

FIGURE 6.19. The density of selected objects as a function of distance from the Sun.

What can we learn from this graph? First, the highest densities tend to be close to the Sun—densities greater than 3 grams per cubic centimeter are not found beyond Jupiter. Second, the density appears to level off afterward. Third, we need to note that the further we go from the Sun, the less density data we have; very few comets have their densities determined, and those are exclusively short-period comets. Astronomers suspect comets and other "icy" bodies in the Kuiper Belt and Oort Cloud will have very low densities, but we don't have the measurements to confirm this yet.

Another way to pose this question is to look carefully at the types of materials or substances that we do know are popular in the solar system. For example, water—as a solid—is a very common substance, especially in the outer solar system. How close can solid water (water ice) get to the Sun before the Sun's heat melts it? Or, conversely, how far from the Sun does water need to be before it can solidify? We can call this the *condensation distance*, and the material in question will become solid below the *condensation temperature*. Table 6.2 depicts a list of common solar system substances and their corresponding condensation temperatures and distances.

TABLE 6.2. Properties of Common Substances in the Solar System

Substance	Density (g/cc)	Condensation Temperature (K)	Condensation Distance (au)
Iron-Nickel alloy	7.9	1470	0.36
Oxide minerals	3.2	1450	0.37
Feldspars[1]	2.8	1000	0.61
Troilite[2]	4.6	700	0.98
Carbonates	2.9	400	2.07
Water ice	0.92	293	3.44
Carbon Dioxide ice	1.56	216	4.70
Ammonia ice	0.82	195	5.39
Methane ice	0.53	91	14.9
Nitrogen ice	0.88	63	24.3

[1] "Feldspar" represents a class of rocks common in the crust of the Earth and other terrestrial objects.
[2] The chemical formula for troilite is FeS, or iron sulfide. Troilite is found on the Moon, Mars, and in meteorites.

We can arrange these substances into four broader categories: carbon, ices, rocks, and metals. A quick glance at the table suggests that we can expect them to predominate in very specific regions of the solar system. Again recall that real astronomical objects tend to be mixes of different substances. Finally, the two most popular substances in the solar system—hydrogen and helium—are not included because they tend to remain gaseous and require very large amounts of gravity to be retained in important amounts, which restricts them primarily to the Sun and the Jovian planets.

We can think of the condensation temperature as the "toughness" of a substance and compare the condensation temperature to the density of the substance. Figure 6.20 shows a definite relationship between the two quantities.

We can combine these various ideas by graphing the densities of these substances with their corresponding condensation distances (Figure 6.21):

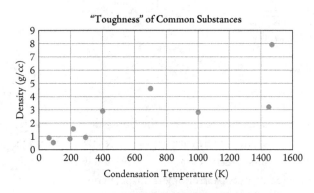

FIGURE 6.20. The temperature at which common substances in the solar system melt or evaporate, compared to their densities.

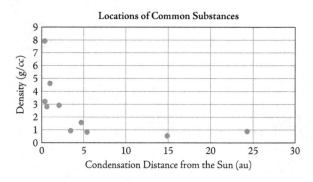

FIGURE 6.21. The densities of common solar system substances versus the distance from the Sun at which they melt or evaporate.

Compare the graphs from Figures 6.19 and 6.21; they show the same overall profile. They aren't identical by any means, but the trend is there. The basic lesson is this: There are reasons why different types of objects are located where they are.

Check Your Neighbor

Which general type of material—ice, metal, or rock—is most likely to be the most popular closest to the Sun? Why?

Section 6.4: Case Study: So, What Happened to Pluto?

Check Your Neighbor

What do these results suggest about the temperatures in the early solar system, as a function of distance from the forming Sun?

August 24, 2006, is a day that will live forever in infamy—according to some people. For others, it was merely the confirmation of what many astronomers already suspected. This is the day the IAU removed Pluto from the list of planets.

How did this come to be? How can Pluto be a planet one day and not the next? If Pluto was never a planet, why was it ever called a planet? To examine the case of Pluto is to examine how we define the world—the universe—around us.

Pluto was discovered by the American astronomer Clyde Tombaugh (1906–1997) in 1930. Tombaugh grew up outside of Streator, Kansas. He always had an interest in astronomy, but a bad hailstorm in 1922 damaged the family's crops and kept him from attending college. By 1926 he was grinding lenses and mirrors to construct homemade telescopes. He had the clever idea of digging a deep pit in which to place his mirrors for testing, in order to keep a consistent temperature and humidity; the family also used the pit for storage and as an emergency shelter. He sent sketches of Jupiter and Mars to Lowell Observatory in Arizona, which impressed the astronomers there enough that they offered him a position in 1929.

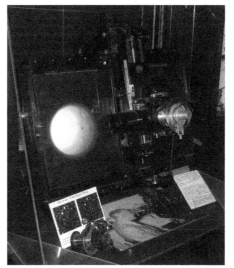

FIGURE 6.22. Clyde Tombaugh and his homemade 9-inch telescope (left); the blink comparator he used to discover Pluto (right).

He was quickly given the task of searching for "Planet X." Neptune had been discovered in 1846 by considering gravitational anomalies in the orbit of Uranus, and the same appeared to be happening again. Astronomers Percival Lowell and William Pickering therefore predicted another undiscovered planet's gravity would be the culprit.

Tombaugh used a 13-inch reflector to take pictures of the sky, several nights apart, around the regions where Planet X was expected to be. He then would align the separate images in a "blink comparator." The comparator

FIGURE 6.23. Pluto, as seen by the New Horizons spacecraft
Credit: NASA.

would light up one image at a time. By flicking a switch on the comparator, Tombaugh could flip back and forth between images. Stars would stay in the same place, but a moving object such as a planet would appear to move. Perhaps surprisingly, he found Pluto in February 1930, soon after beginning the search. Pluto's name was suggested by an 11-year-old English girl (Venetia Burney), in part because it kept the same theme of using Greco-Roman deities, and in part because the first two letters (P and L) make up the initials of Percival Lowell.

At first, Pluto was thought to be fairly large—Lowell thought it might be as much as 6.6 times as massive as the Earth—in order to account for gravitational disturbances in the orbit of Uranus. At that size, Pluto was expected to be a gas giant, much like Uranus or Neptune.

But if this was the case, then Pluto didn't look right. If Pluto were truly a gas giant, it should have been relatively bright, invisible without a telescope (like Neptune) but still something fairly easy to see. Instead, Pluto was on the order of 40 times dimmer (or more) than expected.

Pluto's distance from the Sun was soon calculated, revealing a semi-major axis of about 40 au, compared to 30 au for Neptune and 19 au for Uranus. At this distance, given Pluto's apparent brightness, it could not be a gas giant after all. For a few decades, Pluto was informally classified as a terrestrial planet—begging the question as to how a terrestrial planet would be in a completely different section of the solar system as the other terrestrials.[4]

As astronomers studied Pluto, other observations came to light arguing that Pluto didn't fit the traditional schemes:

+ The other planets orbit the Sun in almost the same plane, which we call the ecliptic. The smallest of the other planets, Mercury, has an orbital tilt ("inclination") of 7°. To put this into perspective, if we shrunk the orbits to scale, they would all fit inside a standard pizza box. Pluto doesn't follow; its orbital inclination is 17°.

+ The other planets have close to circular orbits, which is why astronomers thought they were circular for so long. Again, Mercury is the most extreme, with an eccentricity of 0.206. Pluto's orbit is highly eccentric at 0.2488. This means its perihelion (i.e., closest approach to the Sun) is 29.5 au and its aphelion (furthest distance from the Sun) is 49.2 au. Oddly, this sometimes brings Pluto closer to the Sun than Neptune, an event which last occurred from 1979 to 1999. This does not mean Pluto will ever crash into Neptune, as the orbital inclination ensures that can't happen.

+ Pluto's rotational period is 6.4 days. Most of the other planets have 24 hour-long days or shorter, the two exceptions being Mercury and Venus. Mercury's 59-day rotational period is due largely to the tides from the Sun; Venus seems to have been struck by a large object early in its history which flipped it upside-down and slowed its rotation to 117 days. Pluto doesn't fit any of these narratives.

---

[4] Author's note: I remember as a child in the early 1970s reading my father's astronomy books, which explicitly labeled Pluto as a terrestrial planet. I also remember being a little confused by this—which, as it turns out, was the same reaction as that of the professional astronomers of the day.

+ On top of that, Pluto's axis is tilted by 122.53° to the ecliptic. Most planets are tilted by 30° or less, although Venus is upside down and Uranus's tilt is 98°. Axial tilt (obliquity) isn't a guarantee of anything, but Pluto's tilt is still different than most.

However, the most telling facts about Pluto are its mass and radius. Astronomers for decades tried various tricks to estimate both quantities, with limited success.

A measurement that confirmed Pluto's small size was an attempted occultation. An *occultation* occurs when a relatively large object moves in front of a relatively smaller object, cutting off the light from the smaller object. Pluto was expected to occult a dim star in the constellation of Leo on April 25, 1965, but it missed the star completely. This set a maximum diameter for Pluto at 5,790 kilometers, with the possibility that Pluto could be even smaller. For comparison, the Earth's diameter is 12,700 km and the Moon's is 3,500 km.

Mass is much trickier to determine just by looking at an object. An object might be very small, but very dense, so its mass is high; or, conversely, an object might be very large but have a low density, so its mass is low. This is the situation for Saturn; Saturn is almost as large across as Jupiter, but its density is about half of Jupiter's, so Saturn is less than 1/3 the mass of Jupiter. A similar situation shows Uranus is less massive than Neptune. This simply means we can't tell an object's mass without more information.

The best way to calculate an astronomical object's mass is to observe the orbit of another, smaller object about it. We can't put the Earth on a scale, for instance, but we can watch the orbit of the Moon, or any of the thousands of artificial satellites in orbit about us. For Pluto, astronomers either needed to find a natural moon of Pluto's or send a spacecraft to fly by Pluto.

In 1978, the American astronomer James Christie discovered a "bump" on images of Pluto that moved about Pluto once every 6.4 days. This turned out to be a moon about half the diameter of Pluto and some 20 times closer to Pluto than our Moon is to us. This newly discovered moon, named Charon (pronounced either "Kay-ron" or "Shā-ron"), is tidally locked to Pluto, showing Pluto the same face as it orbits. This is expected; what was <u>not</u> expected is that Pluto, in its turn, is tidally locked to Charon. If Pluto were to be considered a planet, it should be massive enough that its moon not so dramatically affect its behavior.

TABLE 6.3. "The Incredible Shrinking Planet"

Year	Mass (Earth masses)	Astronomer(s)
1915	6.6	Lowell (prior to discovery)
1931	1	Nickolson & Mayall
1948	0.1	Kuiper
1976	0.01	Chruikshank, Pitchers, & Morrison
1978	0.0015	Chrisy & Harrington
2006	0.00218	Buie et al.

The New Horizons flyby mission of 2015 confirmed the mass of Pluto, though it did update its diameter to 2,370 km. This also means its density is 1.879 grams per cubic centimeter, indicating Pluto is a mix of ice and rock—which tells us Pluto cannot be a terrestrial planet in any real sense of the term. Instead, Pluto and like objects in its vicinity are sometimes called *icy dwarfs*.

The next step in our story brings us to 2003. A team of astronomers led by Mike Brown was searching for trans-Neptunian objects (TNOs, i.e., objects further from the Sun than Neptune), and had made prior discoveries including Sedna and Quaoar. Images taken in 2003 by the Schmidt telescope at Palomar Observatory were reexamined in 2005 and showed the presence of another TNO, and follow-up work revealed it has a moon. The IAU eventually gave them the names Eris and Dysnomia.[5] Since Eris has a moon, Brown's team was able to get a

---

[5] Eris is the goddess of discord in Greek mythology—a fitting name, as you'll see.

precise estimate of its mass, which at 1.66×10^{22} kilograms is about 27% more than Pluto's mass. Astronomers were also able to track images of Eris in records as far back as 1954, and therefore have a fairly good orbit worked out for Eris: Its semi-major axis is 68 au and its orbital period is 558 years.

And therein lay the problem. If Eris is more massive than Pluto, then why can't we consider Eris a new planet? For a short while, Eris was in serious consideration to be planet number 10. On the other hand, both Pluto and Eris are very small—much smaller than our Moon and several other moons—so is Pluto large enough to be considered a planet?

Despite all this, Pluto officially remained on the list of planets, which brings us to <u>who</u> makes these decisions. The *International Astronomical Union*, or IAU, is the governing body recognized by astronomers in charge of giving names to astronomical objects and their features. Founded in 1919, the IAU has nearly 10,000 active members from 101 countries. The IAU is not a legal organization—their rulings do not carry the force of law—but astronomers in general adhere to their decisions in these areas.

FIGURE 6.24. The vote on the status of Pluto and dwarf planets in Prague, August 23, 2006.

With the Eris/Pluto question in the air, the IAU held an impromptu vote on the status of Pluto and Eris and ended up revamping the definition of a planet (see section 6.1). The key difference between Pluto and other major planets is that Pluto has not "cleared" its neighborhood. For example, recall Pluto's orbital period is 248 years and Neptune's is 168 years, which works out to be a 3:2 ratio; that is, for every three orbits Neptune makes about the Sun, Pluto makes two orbits. This is how Pluto was redefined and became the most famous member of the new class of "dwarf planets."

How did people react? A good number of astronomers agreed with the reassigning of Pluto's status, though there were some concerns with how the decision was made. Some astronomers disagree with the decision, in part due to the historical significance of Pluto's discovery. The public was confused[6]—virtually everybody

---

[6] In a local newspaper, one young sixth-grade girl recited the mnemonic and then plaintively asked: "What do we do now?"

alive had grown up memorizing the names and order of the planets with Pluto at the end, using mnemonics such as

"My Very Eager Mother Just Served Us Nine Pizzas."

Astronomy magazine even ran a contest, asking readers to come up with a new mnemonic. The winning entry was

"My Very Eager Monster Just Scared Us Nuts."

It's been long enough since 2006 that current children won't personally remember a time when Pluto was one of the nine planets. As we have seen, the meaning of the term "planet" has changed—and will likely change again, as we continue to learn more about our solar system.

FIGURE 6.25. An update of a cartoon published in a student newspaper (the *Student Printz* at the University of Southern Mississippi) after the news about Pluto broke in 2006.

Summary

In this chapter, we have discussed the following:

- The history of how we look at planets
- The different types of objects in the solar system
- The locations of different types of objects in the solar system
- The history of how we look at Pluto

Questions

1. Eris has a density of 2.2 grams per cubic centimeter. What is Eris mostly made from: ice, gas, metal, or rock?

2. Triton is about the same size (diameter) and mass as Pluto, but Triton orbits Neptune. To which category does Triton belong?

3. Mercury has a density of 5.44 g/cc and Mars a density of 3.93 g/cc. Both objects are thought to contain metal and rock. Which object has a larger proportion of rock?

4. Vesta is an asteroid. Which is more likely its semi-major axis: 2.8 au or 40 au?

5. How many "major" planets are currently recognized as such in the solar system?

6. The number of recognized "major" planets has changed over time. Briefly discuss an example of when the number changed, including why the change was made.

7. A solar system object independently orbits the Sun, is massive enough to be round, and "dominates" its orbit. Which type of object is it?

8. A solar system object independently orbits the Sun, is <u>not</u> massive enough to be round, and consists primarily of various ices. Which type of object is it?

9. Object A has a density of 5 g/cc and object B a density of 3 g/cc. Which object is more likely (on average) to be closer to the Sun?

10. Mercury and Ganymede have approximately the same diameter, but Mercury's density is about twice that of Ganymede. Which object has a higher density?

11. Cite at least three reasons for reinstating Pluto to the list of "major" planets.

12. Cite at least three reasons for removing Pluto from the list of "major" planets.

Activities

▶ *Astrophysics activity 6.1*: Use a common food or drink—cake, candy bars, popcorn, sweet tea, etc.—to illustrate the relative masses of objects in the solar system. For example, if a planet holds 10% of the total mass of objects (excluding the Sun) in the solar system, then that planet represents a slice containing 10% of the total amount of cake.

▶ *Astrophysics activities 6.2a and 6.2b*: What would it be like to visit another terrestrial object? Specifically, imagine being an astronaut and stepping out of your spaceship. What would be similar to being on Earth? What would be different?

▶ *Astrophysics activity 6.3*: Host a debate regarding the status of Pluto. Create a list of reasons in favor of Pluto being restored to "major" planet status and another list in favor of keeping Pluto as a "minor" planet.

Works Referenced

A short history of the status of Pluto, prior to 1989, is given in Asimov, I. (1987, March). The incredible shrinking planet. *Magazine of Fantasy and Science Fiction, 72,* 3.

Hills, J. G. (1981). Comet showers and the steady-state infall of comets from the Oort Cloud. *Astronomical Journal, 86,* 1730–1740. doi:10.1086/113058

Statements about the International Astronomical Union, its duties and specifics regarding the status of Pluto can be found in International Astronomical Union. (n.d.a.). About the IAU. Retrieved from https://www.iau.org/administration/about/

International Astronomical Union. (n.d.b.). Resolution B5: Definition of a Planet in the Solar System. Retrieved from https://www.iau.org/static/resolutions/Resolution_GA26-5-6.pdf

The Kuiper Belt is discussed in Jewitt, D. (n.d.). Why Kuiper Belt? *University of Hawaii.* Retrieved from http://www2.ess.ucla.edu/~jewitt/kb/gerard.html

Kuiper, G. P. (1951). *Astrophysics: A topical symposium.* (J. A. Hynek, Ed.). New York, NY: McGraw-Hill.

One way to describe how planets "clear" their "neighborhoods" is in Margot, J. L. (2015). A quantitative criterion for defining planets. *Astronomical Journal, 150*(6), 185. doi:10.1088/0004-6256/150/6/185

Minor Planet Center. (n.d.a). *MPEC 2017-U181: COMET C/2017 U1 (PANSTARRS)*. Retrieved from https://www.minorplanetcenter.net/mpec/K17/K17UI1.html

Minor Planet Center. (n.d.b). *MPEC 2017-V17: NEW DESIGNATION SCHEME FOR INTERSTELLAR OBJECTS*. Retrieved from https://minorplanetcenter.net/mpec/K17/K17V17.html

The discovery and other information about the interstellar asteroid 'Oumuamua (catalog # 1I/2017 U1) can be found at NASA. (2017, October 26). *Small asteroid or comet "visits" from beyond the solar system*. Retrieved from https://www.nasa.gov/feature/jpl/small-asteroid-or-comet-visits-from-beyond-the-solar-system

The Oort Cloud is discussed in Oort, J. (1950). The structure of the cloud of comets surrounding the solar system and a hypothesis concerning its origin. *Bulletin of the Astronomical Institutes of the Netherlands, 11*, 9–110.

Data concerning the solar system can be found in Sirola, C. (2005). *Laboratory exercises in solar system astronomy*. Upper Saddle River, NJ: Prentice Hall.

Estimates of the mass and radius of Pluto come from the following sources:

Buie, M. W., et al. (2006). Orbits and photometry of Pluto's satellites: Charon, S/2005 P1, and S/2005 P2. *Astronomical Journal, 132*(1), 290–298. doi:10.1086/504422

Christy, J. W., & Harrington, R. S. (1978). The satellite of Pluto. *Astronomical Journal, 83*(8), 1005–1008. doi:10.1086/112284

Croswell, K. (1997). *Planet quest: The epic discovery of alien solar systems*. New York, NY: Free Press.

Kuiper, G. P. (1950). The diameter of Pluto. *Publications of the Astronomical Society of the Pacific, 62*(366), 133–137. doi:10.1086/126255

Nicholson, S. B., & Mayall, N. U. (1931, January). Positions, orbit, and mass of Pluto. *Astrophysical Journal, 73*(1). doi:10.1086/143288

Tavernier, L. (2015, July 16). NASA's New Horizon Mission flies by Pluto. *Jet Propulsion Laboratory*. Retrieved from https://www.jpl.nasa.gov/edu/news/2015/7/16/how-to-make-nasas-pluto-flyby-a-teachable-moment-for-students/

Tombaugh, C. W. (1946). The search for the ninth planet, Pluto. *Astronomical Society of the Pacific Leaflets, 5*(209), 73–80.

The history of discovery of Eris and its properties are discussed in the following sources:

Brown, M. (2006). The discovery of 2003 UB313 Eris, the largest known dwarf planet. *Cal Tech*. Retrieved from http://web.gps.caltech.edu/~mbrown/planetlila/

Brown, M. E., & Schaller, E. L. (2007, June 15). The mass of dwarf planet Eris. *Science, 316*(5831), 1585.

NASA. (n.d.c). JPL small-body database browser: 136199 Eris (2003 UB313). Retrieved from https://ssd.jpl.nasa.gov/sbdb.cgi?sstr=Eris

Credits

An artist's depiction of the planets of Kepler-90 compared to the Sun. The planet sizes are to scale; their distances from their stars are not. Credit: NASA/Ames Research Center/Wendy Stenzel

THE FORMATION OF THE SOLAR SYSTEM

PURPOSE

To review the conditions and laws of nature that form solar systems

OBJECTIVES

- To discuss the nebular hypothesis
- To relate the laws of physics to the formation of solar system objects
- To compare other solar systems to our own

INTRODUCTION

Are there planets orbiting other stars? Until a few decades ago, we didn't know the answer to this question. Since 1995, astronomers—amateurs and professionals alike—have discovered thousands of them. Why does it matter? Here are a few reasons:

- We learn more about how our solar system formed
- We learn how diverse solar systems can be
- We advance the search for life beyond the Earth

The purpose of this chapter is thus not only to discuss how our solar system came to be, but also to review some of the recent and exciting findings regarding other solar systems. Astronomy has entered a "golden age" of sorts regarding the discovery of planets around other stars, "exoplanets" for short, and as of this writing well over 2,000 planets are now known to orbit other stars in the Milky Way. All this has come about since the mid-1990s. And with major efforts and expertise being put to work, we can expect our abilities to compare solar system with others to expand enormously within the next few years.

KEY TERMS

Adaptive optics: A method whereby instrumentation adjusts for the turbulence of the air, so that a telescope behaves as if it were in vacuum instead

Differentiation: The sifting of different materials into different layers inside a protoplanet due to its being molten (liquid)

Exoplanet (also **extrasolar planet**): A planet orbiting a star besides the Sun

Habitable zone (also **Goldilocks zone**): A region surrounding a star where liquid water might be possible for a planet to possess

Hot Jupiter: An exoplanet similar to Jupiter in mass so close to its parent star that its temperature is often 1,000 kelvin or higher

Migration (also planetary migration): A process wherein a planet dramatically changes its distance from its star

Nebula: A cloud of gas and dust in space

Nebular hypothesis: The proposal, originally made in the 18th century that the solar system formed out of a swirling disk of gas and dust

Planetesimal: A relatively small solid object, likely made of rock, existing as part of a protoplanetary disk, which could eventually join other planetesimals to form a planet

Proplyd: A forming solar system seen from a distance as a dark disk surrounding a protostar

Protoplanet: An object in the process of becoming a planet

Protoplanetary disk: A swirling disk of material around a protostar wherein planets etc., are forming

Protostar: An object in the process of becoming a star

Super Earth: An exoplanet estimated to be up to several times the mass of the Earth, but still be made primarily of rock rather than gas

Velocity curve: A graph showing the velocity of a star over time. If a star has a velocity curve that shows it moving or "wobbling" back and forth, it is evidence for a massive companion

KEY INDIVIDUALS

Kant, Immanuel: A German philosopher of the 18th century who worked out a preliminary version of the *nebular hypothesis* for the formation of the solar system

Laplace, Pierre-Simon: A French scientist who proposed at the end of the 18th century a detailed version of the *nebular hypothesis* for the formation of the solar system

Section 7.1: The Updated "Nebular Hypothesis"

> In the beginning there was nothing, a void only, but this lay between two regions, one freezing and misty called Niflheim, one hot and sparking called Muspel. A river flowed into the great void, and froze over, layer upon layer. Where the hot and cold areas touched, the ice melted and formed a frost giant, Ymir, from whom are descended all of the frost giants of the world. Then it formed a cow, Audhumla, that licked the salty frozen ice. As it licked, a figure of human shape was formed out of the block, and this was Buri, from whom most of the great gods are descended. The gods Odin, Vili and Ve killed Ymir, and from his body made the structure of this world, of the sea, the sky and clouds. (Graham-Campbell, 1994, p. 110)

This is a summary of creation according to the ancient Norse. Many (not all) creation myths share the theme of distilling an ordered world out of an original chaos. While by no means a prediction or accurate scientific account of how the Earth and solar system came to be, the general idea of filtering order from chaos is one astronomers recognize.

For most of human history, people have thought the Earth to be at the center of all things. Even when Copernicus reopened the debate regarding the organization of the solar system, virtually everyone assumed all its objects to have been here forever, or at least since the beginning of time. And only in recent centuries have we begun to think that the solar system has an origin, and a separate one at that from the rest of the universe.

The first person apparently to suggest a natural process formed the solar system was the Swedish theologian and scientist Emanuel Swedenborg, in 1734. This was elaborated by the German philosopher Immanuel Kant (1724–1804), whose idea was that a cloud of gas and dust (a *nebula*) would slowly shrink and flatten under the influence of gravity, out of which the Sun and planets would form. Independently, the French scientist and mathematician Pierre-Simon Laplace (1749–1827) published a more detailed work in 1796, imagining a nebula

FIGURE 7.1. Immanuel Kant (left); Pierre-Simon Laplace (right).

heating and spinning as it shrunk, flattening into a disk and eventually breaking off rings of material which would become planets, leaving the center to become the Sun. The nebular hypothesis gained traction as astronomers such as William Hershel began imaging "spiral nebulae," which looked like other solar systems in formation (though we now know these were actually spiral galaxies).

As you might expect from these early models, they suffered from some serious physics problems. The most glaring difficulty is that of angular momentum. You may recall that we briefly encountered the principle of conservation of angular momentum in chapter 4, which states that the total angular momentum—the combination of mass, distance, and speed for an object or system of objects moving in circles or loops—is constant. As the nebula shrinks, its rate of spin ("angular" or "rotational velocity") should increase. This implies that the Sun, being at the very center of the solar system, should possess most of the solar system's angular momentum. Instead, the Sun rotates rather slowly (about once per month) and the planets instead together possess 99% of the angular momentum of the solar system. The Kantian and Laplacian models do not account for this observation.

Another critique came from the Scottish scientist James Clerk Maxwell, who pointed out that since different sections of the collapsing disk of material must be moving at different speeds (differential rotation), it would be next to impossible for such materials to condense due to gravity. As Maxwell was the preeminent theoretician of the 19th century, his word carried weight. Astronomers tended afterward to ditch the nebular hypothesis and look elsewhere for potential methods to build the solar system. Although a variety of other ideas were put forth, none others proved satisfactory either.

Nevertheless, astronomers kept coming back to the nebular hypothesis. The Soviet astronomer Viktor Safronov (1917–1999) revitalized it in 1969 by showing how smaller bodies about 1 kilometer across—now called *planetesimals*—could gather together to form larger bodies and eventually full-sized planets. This notion was carried further starting in the 1970s by the American geologist George Wetherill (1925–2006), who was interested in the composition and orbital properties of meteorites and asteroids. Wetherill devised a numerical technique to calculate the development of swarms of planetesimals and how their accretion could become a runaway process. He also made the first reasonable predictions of the positions of the terrestrial planets and showed how the gravity of Jupiter actually acts to shield the inner solar system from incoming asteroids and comets.

Safronov and Wetherill did not address how planetesimals form out of tiny dust particles. Gravity can't be the answer, since the masses are just too small. Instead, astronomers believe that dust particles attract each other via static electric charges, much like how dust particles are sticky in one's home. Electrical forces pull carbon- and rock-based dust particles together until they reach the planetesimals stage, where gravity becomes important.

Where do the dust particles come from? Star (and planet) formation starts with nebulae—specifically, very cold nebulae. Such nebulae might have temperatures as low as 10 K (about −440 °F!) and densities around a million particles (atoms and molecules) per cubic meter, which sounds high, until we realize that the density of the air we're breathing is around 10^{25} particles per cubic meter. The low density means that individual particles don't get near each other very easily; the low temperatures translate to slow speeds, meaning the particles are less likely to bounce off each other when they do meet.

FIGURE 7.2. The protoplanetary disk of HL Tauri (from the Altacama Large Millimeter Array).

Dust tends to extinguish visible light—that is, reflect and/or absorb visible light—so much of star and planet formation was hidden for most of our history. But telescopes using other wavelengths, such as infrared and radio, are able to see deep inside nebulae to image individual planetary disks. A good example of such a disk is HL Tauri (see Figure 7.2), a nebula in the constellation of Taurus the Bull. HL Tauri is a forming star system about 450 light years (130 parsecs) distant. Astronomers used the Atacama Large Millimeter Array (ALMA) in Chile to take a close-up picture of the system: The disk spans about 1,500 light minutes (180 au) across and shows details as small as 40 light minutes (5 au). The most striking part of the image is that the disk shows gaps, which are likely to be due to protoplanets sweeping up material as they form. HL Tauri is estimated to be "only" 1 million years old, so it is a bit of a mystery as to how protoplanets formed so quickly.

This does a good job of describing how rocky objects form—terrestrial planets, asteroids and the like. But how do gas giants form? As the nebula shrinks, it also heats up, and the closer to the center, the hotter. Rocks and metals can condense under the high temperatures (thousands of degrees), but ices and gases will evaporate. So the gas giants, icy moons, and comets need to form far from the center. Furthermore, the forming star at the center has enough gravity to gather in virtually all the gas nearby, leaving none for any potential gas giant. But the larger gas giants, Jupiter and Saturn, are actually closer than the smaller gas giants Uranus and Neptune. This is an issue that has puzzled astronomers until recently.

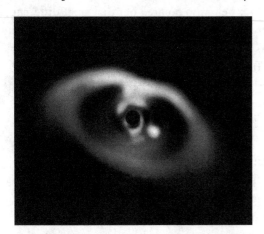

FIGURE 7.3. An image from the Very Large Telescope of the European Southern Observatory, showing PDS 70b (bright dot right from center), a new exoplanet. The parent star, PDS 70, is artificially blocked out at center.

Figure 7.3 hints at some of the answers. This is an image of the PDS 70-star system, made from multiple wavelengths in infrared light by the Very Large Telescope (yes, that's its name!) at the European Southern Observatory in the Atacama Desert of Chile. The telescope uses a device called a *coronagraph* that blocks out the light of the star (or protostar) in order to let the light from a planet shine through. The telescope also used very impressive image processing tricks and techniques to make the planet, termed PDS 70b, visible.

PDS 70b is estimated to be two to three times the mass of Jupiter and orbits its parent star at a distance of 3 billion kilometers, or close to the distance of Uranus from our Sun. As the planet is continuing to pull debris to itself, the gravitational energy from this process is transformed into heat, and thus the surface temperature of PDS 70b is about 1,000 K. Nevertheless, its mass is high enough that it is thought to have a thick atmosphere. The image also shows that PDS 70b is clearing its orbit of debris.

Jupiter's core is possibly as large as 17 times the mass of Earth. This allows it to hold onto very light gases, even hydrogen and helium as well as water vapor, ammonia, methane, and others. As the temperatures eventually drop (many thousands or even millions of years into the future), many of these substances themselves should condense into liquids.

The further away a proto-gas giant, the better its chances of forming—to a point of course, because the nebula will eventually thin out too much to form planets at a far-enough distance from the center. Generally, then, the further away the planet from its star, the better its chances of becoming a gas giant. That brings us back to a question we posed earlier: How then is it that Jupiter and Saturn, our systems true gas giants, are closer to the Sun than Uranus and Neptune, which are each an order of magnitude lighter?

Check Your Neighbor

In discussing the formation of our solar system, we keep referring to other, currently forming solar systems. Why?

Astronomers have been searching for planets orbiting other stars, called 'extra solar planets' or *exoplanets* for short, for decades, if not centuries. But only since the early 1990s have astronomers had the technology and techniques needed to find them—indirectly at first, later by direct observation.

The first exoplanet orbiting another star was discovered by Michael Mayor and Didier Queloz in 1995.[1] The star, 51 Pegasi, is actually visible to the naked eye and is in the constellation of Pegasus, which can be seen during the autumn in the Northern hemisphere. The planet itself wasn't imaged; rather, Mayor and Queloz used Doppler shift measurements of the star's spectral lines in order to show it was "wobbling" back and forth in a regular pattern. Such wobbling motion requires the star to be in a common orbit about a center of mass with another massive object, which in this case turned out to be a planet, designated 51 Pegasi b. Figure 7.4 shows the *velocity curve* for 51 Pegasi; its sinusoidal pattern indicates the presence of an unseen companion and even allows astronomers to estimate the planet's semi-major axis, period, and mass.

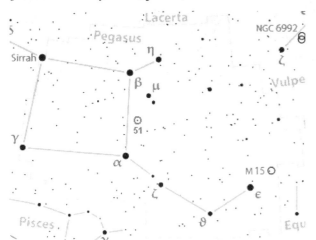 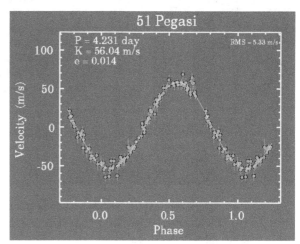

FIGURE 7.4. The location of 51 Pegasi in the sky (left); a velocity curve for 51 Pegasi, from the Planetary Society (right).

However, the properties of the planet were puzzling. First, the planet's orbital period is barely over 4 days long. Given the mass of the star, this tells us the planet must be extremely close to its star, in this case only 0.05 au away. Even Mercury, the closest planet to the Sun in our system, has an orbital period of nearly 90 days and a semi-major axis of 0.4 au. Second, the mass of the planet is at least 47% of the mass of Jupiter, and possibly much larger.[2] Also, because the planet is so close to its star (which is much like the Sun), its surface temperature is a blistering 1,284 K (1,850 °F). The planet was quickly nicknamed a *hot Jupiter* as a consequence. Further, if Peg 51b was unique, this would be a special case, but it isn't; in fact, most of the exoplanets found in the following decade were also hot Jupiters.

How did Peg 51b get so close to its star, if gas giants can't form so close in? The answer is that Peg 51b didn't. Instead, it migrated.

Planetary migration is a process whereby a planet dramatically changes its semi-major axis, either getting much closer or much further away from its parent star. A protoplanetary disk is thought to have a lifespan on the order of a few million years, after which nearly all its material has been swept up by planets, moons, and asteroids. While a planet is embedded inside the disk, its sweeping-up of material creates a kind of friction that shrinks the orbit of the planet. The planet also slingshots smaller objects (asteroids or smaller planetesimals) outward, which also pushes the planet inward. Each slingshot or frictional interaction is slight, but the planet has potentially millions of years to feel these effects.

---

[1] 51 Peg b is not the first planet discovered outside the solar system; planets were found orbiting a neutron star a few years prior. Mayor and Queloz were awarded Nobel Prizes in physics in 2019 for their discovery.

[2] The reason this is a minimum mass for the planet is that we don't know enough about its orbit. Specifically, the planet's orbit is tilted at an angle from our vantage point, and without that information, we can't set a specific value for the planet's mass.

Terrestrial planets near their star can experience migration, but the migration is limited because the central protostar is sweeping up most of the stray debris. Larger planets forming very far from the Sun have the opportunity to experience larger amounts of migration. In some circumstances, the planet might migrate inward so much that it expels other, smaller planets on its journey and becomes the closest planet to its star.

What happened in our solar system? Jupiter and Saturn probably formed out several tens of astronomical units from the Sun, with Uranus and Neptune forming much closer in. Planetary migration and slingshot effects swapped the positions of these planets, so today we see Jupiter just barely over 5 au from the Sun. Jupiter obviously halted its inward plunge, likely because by the time it got to 5 au from the Sun, the disk of material had dissipated or otherwise been swept up by the terrestrials or the Sun.

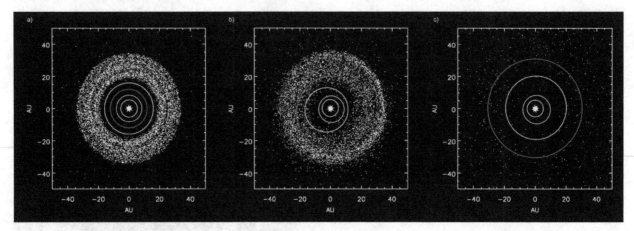

FIGURE 7.5. A simulation of planetary migration in the early solar system. Left: The original orbits of the gas giants and Kuiper Belt objects. Center: The scattering of Kuiper Belt objects outward as Neptune shifts its orbit outward. Right: After the final ejection of Kuiper Belt objects and the settling of the orbits of the gas giants.

The strong gravitational forces exerted by the gas giants slingshot most of the remaining planetesimals outward into what we now see as the Kuiper Belt. Finally, gravity also locked some objects into orbital resonance, Pluto and Neptune (3:2 ratio of periods) being an example, though many others (the Trojan asteroids about Jupiter, certain asteroids in the asteroid belt to Jupiter, Mercury about the Sun) are also now recognized. The Moon-Earth situation is a special case of sorts, which we will discuss in a different chapter.

Finally, what about the angular momentum issue? Recall we stated earlier that stars like the Sun often spin far slower than expected, though there are some exceptions (the stars Vega and Altair are bright examples). During the final stages of star formation, the interactions between hot, ionized material in the protoplanetary disk and the protostar's nascent magnetic field can shoot jets of material in opposite directions away from the protostar, perpendicular to the disk. This and other processes involving the magnetic field of the protostar are suspected of bleeding away excess angular momentum, though the specifics of these hypotheses are still being worked out.

Section 7.2: Recap: The Formation of the Solar System

It will be useful to recap the story so far, but in order of time. Before we do that, let's review some of the important physics concepts that govern how this works:

+ **Gravity:** Gravity is the force of nature that has all objects pulling each other together. Here, the gravity of a nebula can collapse the nebula.
+ **Density:** Density is the measure of the concentration of mass, usually expressed per unit volume. The higher the density of an object, other things being equal, the stronger its surface gravity.

- **Angular momentum:** For an isolated system, the conservation of angular momentum tells us that as a nebula collapses, (a) it will spin faster and (b) it will tend to flatten into a disk.
- **Gas pressure:** We didn't discuss this earlier as such, but we did mention temperature. The higher the temperature, the faster particles move inside a gas. The faster particles move, the more often and more violently they collide with each other. The net effect is that the gas exerts an outward pressure.
- **Friction:** When objects rub up against each other, a process we call friction, they tend to (a) slow each other down and (b) generate heat.
- **Electricity:** Small objects such as dust particles can carry static electric charges. Electric charges can exert strong attractive or repulsive forces on each other.
- **Magnetism:** Similar to electricity, moving electric charges can exert magnetic forces on each other.

The formation of the solar system can be broken down into various steps or stages. To some extent, these stages are arbitrary, and there are usually no obvious boundaries or distinctions between one step and the next. Nevertheless, we will see large changes from start to finish. Also, we are mostly concerned here with the formation of planets and smaller objects in the solar system; the details of the formation of the Sun are left for another chapter.

1. Start with a nebula. A nebula is a "cloud" of gas and dust in space. A nebula best suited for the formation of stars and planets etc., often termed a molecular cloud, will be relatively cold and thick. Also, it is common for a nebula to be tens or even hundreds of light years across.
2. The nebula begins to collapse under its own weight (gravity). This can often be spurred by external shocks, such as a nearby exploding star (a.k.a. supernova).

FIGURE 7.6. Barnard 68, a molecular cloud (left); the Horsehead Nebula, a star-forming region (right). Credit: ESO.

3. The nebula is not perfectly smooth but has regions inside it of with relatively high and relatively low density. Since higher-density regions have larger amounts of gravity, the nebula fractures or separates into many different concentrated pieces. It is not uncommon for a nebula to produce several hundred or even several thousand of these pieces.
4. Now consider an individual piece, perhaps a light year across. The "sifting" of individual clumps of relatively high densities continues. In many cases, the center pulls the majority of gas and dust to itself on its way to becoming a single star; in other cases, two or more stars may form. Since our current story concerns the solar system, we will discuss the case of just one star at the center. The process so far has taken at least 100,000 years.

5. Up until now, the collapse has been slow enough that the infalling gas and dust has been more or less evenly distributed (i.e., in a spherical shape). As the collapse speeds up, the material begins to flatten into a swirling disk. Seen from a distance, the combination of protostar and infalling material is called a *proplyd*.

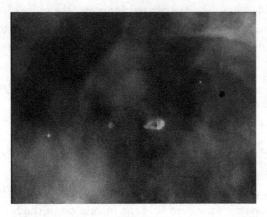 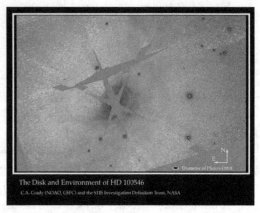

FIGURE 7.7. Proplyds in the Orion Nebula (left); a protoplanetary disk in HD 100546 (right). The spikes in the figure at right represent glare from the protostar that has been removed.

6. Individual parts of the disk also begin to filter or sift themselves out, as static electric charges bring dust particles to form planetesimals. Planetesimals can grow to 1 kilometer across or larger via this process; after this, positive and electric charges tend to cancel each other's effects, and gravity becomes more important. When the disk contains planetesimals, we call it a protoplanetary disk.

7. Energy as heat is released as the growing center becomes larger (the center, our Sun, trapped literally over 99.9% of the total mass of the solar system), which starts blowing gas away from itself, eventually halting its accumulation of gas.

8. In the protoplanetary disk, energy as heat is also released as individual planetesimals collide with each other or with still free-floating gas and dust. Also, the closer the planetesimals to the center of the disk, the higher the temperature due to the heat being released by the forming Sun. Thus, most of the planetesimals become hot—the larger the planetesimals, the hotter—so much that the largest ones are at least partially molten rock and metal.

9. Gravity, not static electricity, is more important when the planetesimals reach sizes of about 1 kilometer across or larger. Many planetesimals congregate together to form objects large enough to become rounded by their gravity, so we can start calling them protoplanets.

10. The molten nature of protoplanets means that different substances start sifting themselves in their interiors; in other words, very dense substances such as iron and nickel sink toward their centers and relatively less dense substances such as rock rise in comparison. This process is termed *differentiation*, meaning large objects like planets will have distinct layers.

Check Your Neighbor

Why does it matter that the protoplanet be molten (liquid) in order to sift itself into different layers?

11. The planetesimals relatively close to the Sun have a smaller amount of disk material available—both because the gravity of the forming Sun takes it away and because there is simply a smaller volume of space—and so the planetesimals tend to be limited in size. Planetesimals further from the Sun have less competition from the Sun's gravity and a larger volume of space to draw from, and so they become larger. For example, the core of Jupiter is thought to be about 17 times the mass of the Earth, but also made of rock and metal.

12. Between their own high temperatures, the heat of the Sun and their weak gravities, protoplanets near the Sun tend to retain little in the way of atmospheres. Protoplanets far from the Sun are able to gather various gases, the most popular being hydrogen and helium, but also including water vapor, carbon dioxide,

methane, ammonia, nitrogen, and a few others. The gathering of gas is not trivial; 95% of Jupiter's mass is thought to be hydrogen and helium, its core of metal and rock only making up 5% of its total.

13. Friction between the protoplanets and the protoplanetary disk induces the protoplanets to migrate inward toward the forming Sun. The more massive the protoplanet and the thicker the disk, the larger the migration effect (Figure 7.8):

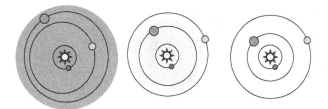

FIGURE 7.8. Planetary migration. Left: The masses of the protoplanets increases with increasing distance from the protosun. The dark grey represents the protoplanetary disk of gas and dust. Center: The most massive planet has migrated closer to the Sun due to friction with the disk, in the process swapping places with another planet. The disk is lighter in color to represent how it is being swept up or expelled by the protoplanets. Right: The most massive planet has halted its inward migration as the disk has nearly vanished. Note that the sizes of the planets and their orbits are indicative and not to scale. The number of planets is also kept to three for clarity.

14. Gravitational "slingshot" effects between planets can swap their orbits. As Jupiter and Saturn migrate inward, their larger masses sling Uranus and Neptune further from the Sun. This process was not as important in the inner solar system, as the Earth and other terrestrial planets were never as massive. Instead, repeated impacts among protoplanets and planetesimals are more important there.

15. The migration of Jupiter and Saturn continues until the protoplanetary disk becomes so thin that friction becomes negligible. The orbits of the major planets (especially the Jovians) stabilizes.

16. Left-over planetesimals have several possible fates, if they are not swept up by protoplanets or the Sun. One is to fall into "orbital resonance" (see chapter 4) with more massive objects; examples are the Trojan asteroids that both lead and follow Jupiter in its orbit, or Pluto's relationship to Neptune. Another is to become a moon of a planet (a few moons become round due to gravity in their own right)—several dozen orbit the Jovians. A third option is another "slingshot" effect, where planetesimals are thrown outward past the orbit of Neptune to become part of the Kuiper Belt.

17. As planets cool, water condenses on their surfaces, becoming liquid or solid, depending on the temperature and presence (or absence thereof) of an atmosphere. The water comes from two general sources: outgassing from deep within the protoplanet (water is often contained within rock, even molten rock) and later bombardment by comets. Earth of course has water, and there is much evidence that Mars once had oceans of water. Even Venus may have initially had water, though this is not confirmed. Mercury was probably always too close to the Sun and too small for water to be a significant component on its surface. Further from the Sun, water was gathered up in large amounts by Uranus and Neptune, and icy moons are prevalent in the Jovian systems. Finally, outgassing releases many other compounds besides water, which can become part of the planet's atmosphere.

This is the story, as we currently know it, of the origin of our solar system. We will discuss the further effects of impacts between protoplanets and/or planetesimals (now asteroids and comets) with protoplanets in the next chapter. The origin of our Moon is also a topic for the future, though its story follows from what we have discussed here.

Section 7.3: The Discoveries of Other Solar Systems

Given the spiral forms observed starting in the late 18th century, combined with the nebular hypotheses of Kant and Laplace, astronomers briefly thought they had in fact discovered forming solar systems. That turned out to be

FIGURE 7.9. Left: A view from a helicopter of lava flows from the Pāhoehoe volcano in Hawaii. Right: Sulfur dioxide outgassing from the Halemaumau vent in Hawaii.

incorrect, for a couple of reasons. One is that most star- and planet-forming systems are best seen in infrared light, not visible light. The other is that forming systems, while up to a few light years across, are still very tiny on the sky from our vantage point. Suppose we wish to look at a protoplanetary disk 1 light year across at a distance of 500 light years. This works out to be about 1/10 of a degree across. And if we want to see details of a forming solar system, which might be about 100 au across, we are then looking at something that subtends only about 3 arcseconds. It's only within the past few decades that astronomers have had access to instruments capable of handling nonvisible light wavelengths at such small angles.

Another problem with searching for planets around other stars is simply glare. The protostar or star is on the order of a million times brighter or more than any of its planets; stars, after all, emit their own visible light, whereas planets only reflect visible light (the problem is not as striking in infrared light, but is still there). Again, only in recent decades have astronomers developed techniques—such as coronagraphs—that can block out the light from the star and reveal the planets orbiting it. Astronomers have thus tended to use indirect methods for searching for exoplanets.

How have astronomers been searching for exoplanets? Several techniques have yielded results.

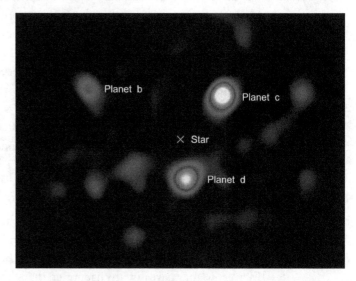

FIGURE 7.10. Three exoplanets orbiting the star HD 8799. The star's light is blocked to remove its glare so the planets are easier to see. The image was taken with the 5.1 meter Hale telescope at Palomar Observatory.

1. Spectroscopy

Stars show spectral absorption lines, wavelengths removed from the overall light of the stars due to the presence of various elements in their atmospheres. Each wavelength is well known from laboratory measurements. If a star is approaching us, that wavelength or spectral line is shifted to smaller wavelengths ("blueshifted") and if the star is receding from us, the spectral line is shifted to longer wavelengths ("redshifted"). While the shifts are typically tiny (often much less than 1%), they are within the scope of our instruments.

Suppose a star has a planet. Recall it is not completely correct to say the planet orbits the star; rather, it is better to state the star and planet mutually orbit a common center of mass (see chapter 4). While the glare of the star will make it difficult, if not impossible, to see the star, the spectral lines from the star can be seen. As the star "wobbles" due to the gravity of its planet, its spectral lines shift back and forth in a distinct, repeatable pattern. Astronomers can therefore infer the presence of the planet from the shifting spectral lines. Furthermore, it is possible in many cases to tell if more than one planet is making the star wobble.

It is helpful to plot the results on a velocity curve. The relative velocity of the star is plotted on the vertical axis and time is plotted on the horizontal axis. The wobble of the star, which implies the presence of an exoplanet, shows up as a repeating curve (see Figure 7.11). If the star has several planets, then the graph shows a mix of several curves, which astronomers can mathematically untangle.

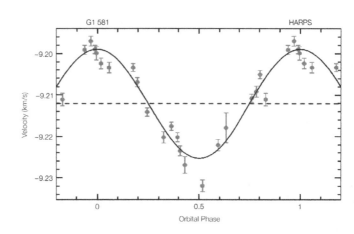

FIGURE 7.11. The velocity curve of the red dwarf star Gleise 581, indicating the presence of an exoplanet with an orbital period of 5.366 days. Courtesy of the European Southern Observatory.

2. Direct Imaging

As earlier discussed, exoplanets (or protoplanets) are several orders of magnitude (i.e., powers of ten) dimmer than the stars (or protostars) they orbit. Protoplanetary disks are also typically outshined by their host stars. These problems are particularly strong in visible light, since stars tend to emit much of their power in visible light, whereas planets and disks only reflect visible light. To directly see the planets and/or disks, we need to either somehow decrease, if not eliminate, the glare from the star, or view the system in a different wavelength regime, or both. It helps further if we can get the best resolution (ability to see tiny details) as possible.

The majority of telescopes are on Earth, unsurprisingly. But the air we breathe also moves and has pockets of differing temperatures, meaning the light we see from stars is not as direct as it could be. To avoid this problem, we can launch telescopes to observe above the Earth's atmosphere. This of course is done—the Hubble Space Telescope is the most famous example—but it is also expensive, telescopes cannot be repaired or serviced in orbit, and space telescopes are more limited in size than ground telescopes. It would be of great use to have some way of adjusting for the air's turbulence while still owning all the advantages of a telescope on the ground. Fortunately, there is such a method.

Adaptive optics (see chapter 5) is a technique used by virtually all large research observatories constructed in the past several decades. A powerful laser is shot into the air near the target. The laser beam reflects off the air and the reflection is captured by the telescope. The reflected image is compared to how the laser should appear without air turbulence.

FIGURE 7.12. Adaptive optics: The deformable secondary mirror of the Very Large Telescope, plus two of the four guide star lasers. Courtesy of the European Southern Observatory.

FIGURE 7.13. The brown dwarf 2M1207 (center) and its exoplanet (lower left) in three wavelength bands of infrared. The composite image was taken by the VLT 8.2-meter telescope, using adaptive optics, at the ESO Paranal Observatory.

This is continuously monitored in order to track turbulence, usually on the order of a hundred times per second. The distortion information is fed into a computer controlling actuators—small motors—that push and pull on the back of the primary and/or secondary mirror. This way, the telescope is effectively behaving as if it were in vacuum.

3. Transits

We earlier in chapter 2 studied various types of eclipses, wherein one object (like the Moon) neatly covers another object (like the Sun) due to their similar angular sizes. Astronomers use different terms if the objects don't match up so well. If a large object (like the Moon) cuts in front of a small object (like a star), we call that an "occultation." If a small object cuts in front of a large object, we call that a *transit*.

The planets Mercury and Venus transit the Sun, since they can cut in between the Earth and the Sun. We see transits of Mercury relatively frequently, from 13–14 times per century, in large part due to Mercury's short orbital period. Transits of Venus across the Sun are much rarer and occur in pairs separated by centuries; the last pair of transits occurred in 2004 and 2012, and the next pair will happen in 2117 and 2125.

In order to see a transit, the plane of the orbit of the planet has to be similar to ours. This is in part why transits by Venus are so rare: Its orbital plane is 3.4° different than ours, which doesn't sound like much but means Venus can be 6 million kilometers too high or too low in order for its shadow to reach the Earth. There is no reason why all other solar systems should be aligned with ours—randomly, a few percent of other systems might line up. But there are so many stars that there ought to be many candidates.

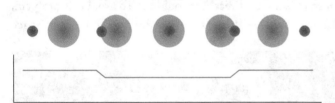

FIGURE 7.14. Top: The orbit of an exoplanet takes it in front of its parent star. Above: The light curve of the star, expressing the brightness of the star as a function of time. Note the characteristic drop in the star's brightness during the exoplanet's transit.

Even if an exoplanet transits its star, we won't be able to see its shadow directly; the glare from the star will just be too much. But the exoplanet's shadow will cut off a small portion of the star's light, often a percent of the total or less. Interestingly, though, modern telescopes with digital cameras are able to measure this—even amateurs with backyard telescopes have been able to image exoplanet transits.

While professionals and amateurs alike have been involved in using transits to search for exoplanets, the most productive project has been the Kepler spacecraft. Kepler was launched in 2009 and placed in orbit about the Sun (not the Earth) to have a better view of the sky. Kepler has a photometer capable of monitoring up to 150,000 stars at once. Data is sent to researchers on the ground for analysis.

The results have been astounding. In its 9 ½ years of operation, Kepler confirmed the existence of over 2500 exoplanets, including several that orbit in their stars' habitable zones (often defined as the distance from a star where water can exist as a liquid). Together with other ground-based work, the number of known exoplanets is nearly 3,800 via all methods by July 2018.

Kepler's mission unfortunately has come to an end. The spacecraft no longer possessed sufficient fuel to continue its mission. Kepler didn't need fuel to maintain its orbit about the Sun; rather, it needed fuel in order to point the telescope toward its targets. The spacecraft was also showing its age, as several components were failing. However, Kepler proved itself and its techniques so well, several other missions are already in action or being prepped to take over, including the European Space Agency's Gaia satellite, the ESA's CHEOPS (Characterizing Exoplanets Satellite), and NASA's TESS (Transiting Exoplanet Survey Satellite).

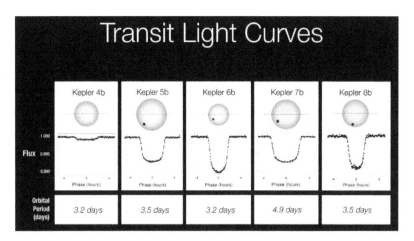

FIGURE 7.15. The first five of the Kepler's exoplanet discoveries by way of transits. Courtesy of NASA/Kepler Mission.

Section 7.4: Earth-Like Exoplanets

Perhaps most interesting is the possibility of finding Earth-like planets—and then, of course, life. What do we know so far?

First, we need to make clear that, as of now, nobody has detected life—even just microbes or simple plants—anywhere besides Earth. While simple organic molecules have been detected in many places in space, nothing we regard as life has been found. What we can do is look at other factors and/or conditions that hint at life. Along with that, we should discuss just what we mean by "Earth-like."

> **Check Your Neighbor**
>
> Make a list of various properties of the Earth that you think are important for the maintenance of life.

One of the more important notions when searching for life is the *habitable zone*, also known as the "Goldilocks zone" after the fairy tale. The most important substance for the maintenance of life—at least here on Earth—is liquid water. Thus, when looking at another solar system, astronomers like to estimate the distance an exoplanet can be from its parent star and be able to maintain water in its liquid state. As in the Goldilocks tale, if an exoplanet is too close to its star, its temperature will be too high for water to remain liquid (Papa Bear's porridge is "too hot") and if an exoplanet is too far from its star, its temperature will be too low (Mama Bear's porridge is "too cold"). But if the exoplanet is at the right distance from its star, its temperature should be "just right."

The type of star affects the size and location of the habitable zone. The Sun is actually a bit larger and brighter than most stars,[3] which means an exoplanet would have to be closer to such a star than we are to our Sun. Some stars are larger and brighter than the Sun, which of course has the opposite effect. Other stars bring other problems; very massive stars just don't live long enough for planets to develop life and very light stars can be unstable, shooting out enormous flares that would cook nearby planets.

This notion of a habitable zone necessarily ignores details about the planet itself. If the planet's gravity is too small, then it won't be able to retain a thick-enough atmosphere. In order for water to remain liquid, it requires a minimum air pressure. Our Moon is within our solar system's habitable zone, but we expect to find no indigenous life there, since it has no air. Other properties of the planet itself may prevent the existence of liquid water; Venus is arguably far enough from the Sun (or, it may have been so in the past) for water to be liquid, but the runaway greenhouse effect of

FIGURE 7.16. A relatively brighter star (top) has its habitable zone (shaded region) further away; a relatively dimmer star (above) has its habitable zone closer in.

---

[3] At least 85% of all stars in the Milky Way are smaller and dimmer than the Sun.

Venus keeps the planet at an average temperature of 750 K (900 °F). If a planet doesn't rotate at a reasonable rate (being tidally locked by the star's gravity, for instance), heat won't be distributed very well across the surface of the planet—again, Mercury is an example, with a solar day about equal to 6 Earth months. The exoplanet might be so volcanically active as to drown potentially life-bearing regions in lava or noxious gases. The exoplanet should probably be rocky (analogous to a terrestrial planet) and not gaseous (like a Jovian planet). The exoplanet might have no magnetic field to shield it from solar winds and cosmic rays (this is the case for Mars), and so on.

Astronomers also look for the presence or absence of oxygen. Oxygen is a highly volatile element—it is key for fire, respiration and even rust—and therefore tends to disappear unless replaced. On Earth, plants handle this task, removing carbon dioxide from the air in the process. It is noteworthy that Venus and Mars, our neighboring worlds, both have atmospheres dominated by carbon dioxide. Should astronomers detect oxygen in the atmosphere of an exoplanet, it is a hint (though not a guarantee) that life is possibly there. But as with the detection of an exoplanet, the glare of the host star and the small size of an Earth-like planet makes it difficult (to say the least) to even determine if an exoplanet has an atmosphere, never mind finding the percentages and composition of said atmosphere. Astronomers are just now (within the past few years) getting together the equipment and techniques to begin searching for exoplanetary atmospheres.

Do we have any candidate Earth-like exoplanets? A few systems have been found, and now that astronomers know how to search for them, their numbers are slowly increasing. The first pair of Earth-sized planets belong to the Kepler-20 system. An artist's impression of these two planets accompanies images of Venus and Earth for comparison (Figure 7.17):

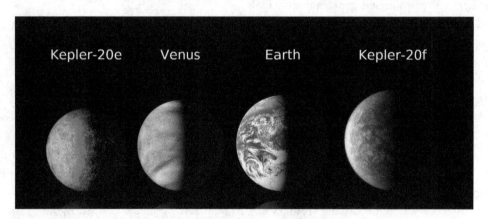

FIGURE 7.17. Two planets from the Kepler-20 system. Kepler-20e has a radius 0.87 times that of Earth, and Kepler-20f a radius 1.03 that of Earth. Courtesy of NASA.

However, Kepler-20e and Kepler-20f are most likely far too close to their star to lie within its habitable zone, with orbital periods of 6.1 and 19.6 days, respectively. The Kepler-20 system has at least three other planets further from its star, but they are probably gas giants. Another system with exoplanets smaller than Earth is Kepler-42, whose three planets include one with a radius estimated as small as 0.17 times that of the Earth. Unfortunately for our discussion, all three of Kepler-42's planets are also too close in order to keep water from evaporating.

Another notion gaining traction is that of the *Super Earth*, a planet which is estimated to be up to a few times the mass of the Earth, but still consisting primarily of rock and metal rather than hydrogen and helium gas. The strength of gravity (i.e., acceleration due to gravity) would be higher than it is here, but we don't really know what, if any, effect that might have on the possibility of life. One example is Tau Ceti, a star only 12 light years (less than 4 parsecs) from us. Out of four possible exoplanets, two appear to be Super Earths, one near the closer edge (Tau Ceti e)

Check Your Neighbor

What physical property would help us decide if an exoplanet is made mostly of rock and metal?

and the other near the furthest edge (Tau Ceti f) of the habitable zone. Tau Ceti as a star is noticeably cooler and dimmer than the Sun and would have a yellow-orange tint to its light. Tau Ceti is surrounded by 10 times more dust than our solar system, which implies a far larger amount of debris in the forms of asteroids and/or comets, which in turn implies a greater risk of impacts for its planets. A far larger rate of impacts would significantly drop the chances of life, but it is still worth exploring.

If we don't have many candidate exoplanets just like the Earth, are there any solar systems like our own? No others are identical, of course, but at least one other star is now known to have at least eight planets. Using a special "machine learning" from Google, NASA astronomers were able to find an eighth planet in the Kepler-90 system, one which orbits its parent star with a blisteringly fast period of only 14.4 days. The system is also noteworthy in that its planets start out small near the star and progressively get larger with increasing distance. However, all the planets are within 1 au of the parent star, making it rather

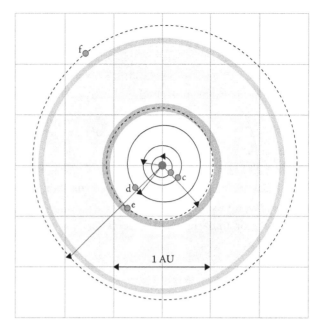

FIGURE 7.18. Orbits of exoplanets about Tau Ceti. The shaded colors refer to potential habitable zones, with green representing the most likely locations for liquid water. Dots are used to indicate the orbits of planets "e" and "f," which are not well known. Credit Icalanise.

crowded! Despite this, the orbits appear stable. The masses of most of the planets of Kepler-90 are uncertain, though all appear to be at least as large as Earth.

The most promising of the recent exoplanet discoveries is TRAPPIST-1. Three exoplanets were first found by Belgian astronomers using the Transiting Planets and Planetesimals Small Telescope (TRAPPIST) at the La Silla Observatory in Chile and the Observatoire de l'Oukaïmedan in Morocco. Four other planets were discovered in 2017 by other astronomers. Even more so than Kepler-90, the TRAPPIST-1 system is packed; all seven exoplanets have orbits smaller than that of Mercury's about the Sun.

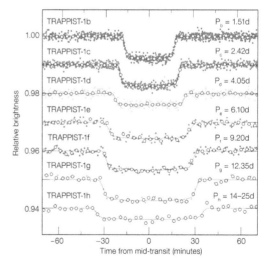

FIGURE 7.19. Left: An artist's comparison of the Sun to TRAPPIST-1. Right: Light curves from the Spitzer Space Telescope showing the transits of the seven exoplanets of TRAPPIST-1. Courtesy of ESO.

Why the interest? TRAPPIST-1 is what astronomers call a red dwarf. Its mass and radius are small, about 8% and 11% that of the Sun, respectively. Even more so, its overall light power output is 0.05% that of the Sun. Therefore, even with its planets residing extremely close to its parent star, up to 6 of them may lie within its habitable zone. Several of the planets appear to be very close to the Earth in terms of mass. Furthermore, observations with the Hubble Space Telescope suggest the presence of liquid water on at least some of them.

TRAPPIST-1, unfortunately, is a type of star that tends to flare occasionally, meaning its planets are exposed to shocks of radiation (such as x-rays) and solar winds that would likely have detrimental effects on any life forms. The planets are also so close to their parent star and each other that they are all in various ratios of orbital resonance, and they may not rotate independently, so that one side of their surfaces may always face the star, not allowing heat to be distributed evenly.

Even if any or all of the above systems turn out to be hostile for life, they do hint at the many possibilities elsewhere in the galaxy.

Summary

In this chapter, we have discussed the following:

▸ Leading hypotheses regarding the formation of the solar system

▸ The physics of planet formation

▸ Modern methods of detection of planets outside the solar system

▸ Current knowledge regarding potential Earth-like planets

Questions

1. As a cloud of gas and dust shrinks, what happens to its
   + temperature?
   + rate of spin?
   + shape?

2. "Spiral nebulae" were once thought to be examples of forming solar systems.
   + What are these, really?
   + Cite a reason why real forming solar systems were so difficult to discover.

3. Two attractive forces, electricity and gravity, are important for forming planets. Which force is responsible for pulling together the following:
   + Dust particles
   + Planetesimals

4. A nebula has an extremely low temperature. What can we say about the average speeds of particles in the nebula?

5. The light curve of the star WASP-19 is shown in Figure 7.20. Answer the following questions:
   + To which property of the star (as seen from Earth) does the dip refer?
   + What is the most likely explanation for the dip?
   + About how much time does this dip last? Hint: The horizontal axis is expressed in days.

6. A direct image of the exoplanet H106906b is shown in Figure 7.21. What can we say about this exoplanet's properties? Specifically,
   + about how long will its orbital period be—a few days? A few years? Thousands of years?

- what type of materials do you expect this exoplanet to mostly consist of—hydrogen and helium? Rock? Metal? Water ice?
- which type of planet from our solar system do you expect this exoplanet to most resemble—a terrestrial (like Mercury)? A water giant (like Uranus)? A gas giant (like Jupiter)?

7. Suppose three exoplanets are discovered orbiting another Sun-like star. Which planet is best suited as a candidate for life?
- An exoplanet whose average temperature is above the boiling point of water
- An exoplanet whose average temperature is above the freezing point of water
- An exoplanet whose average temperature is below the freezing point of water

8. Which star is the best candidate for exoplanets that may harbor life?
- A star like Deneb, which emits copious amounts of ultraviolet light
- A star like alpha Centauri A, which emits copious amounts of visible light
- A star like Barnard's Star, which emits copious amounts of infrared light

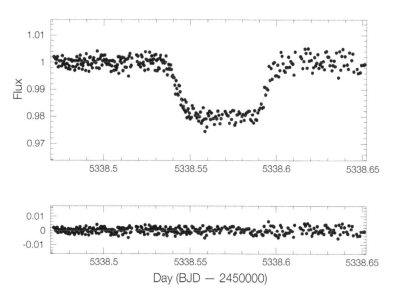

FIGURE 7.20. The light curve of WASP 19-b, from TRAPPIST.

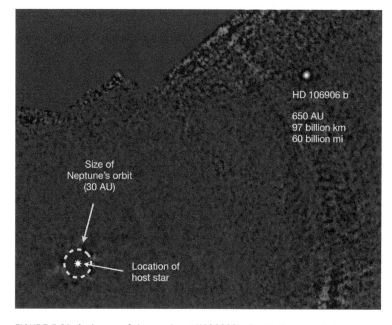

FIGURE 7.21. An image of the exoplanet H106906b. Credit: Vanessa Bailey.

Activities

▸ *Astrophysics activity 7.1*: Measure the masses and volumes of a variety of objects to determine their densities. Observe how liquids arrange themselves according to density. Apply these results to discussions regarding the Earth and other solar system objects.

▸ *Astrophysics activity 7.2*: Use simulations to review various properties regarding the planets and use those to understand how the solar system formed.

▸ *Astrophysics activity 7.3*: Using the home Web page of NASA's Kepler spacecraft, investigate how the spacecraft operates and review its recent findings.

Works Referenced

Graham-Campbell, J. (Ed.). (1994). *Cultural atlas of the Viking world.* Oxford, UK: Andromeda.

The history of the nebular hypothesis is described in:

Kant, I. (1755). *Universal natural history and theory of the heavens.* Translation by Ian Johnston (2012), Richer Resources Publications, Arlington, VA.

Keppler, M. et al. (2018, June 30). Discovery of a planetary-mass companion within the gap of the transition disk around PDS 70. *Astronomy and Astrophysics.* Retrieved from http://www.hq.eso.org/public/archives/releases/sciencepapers/eso1821/eso1821a.pdf

Laplace, P. (1796). *Exposition du systeme du monde.*

Müller, A. (2018, June 30). Orbital and atmospheric characterization of the planet within the gap of the PDS 70 transition disk. *Astronomy and Astrophysics.* Retrieved from http://www.hq.eso.org/public/archives/releases/sciencepapers/eso1821/eso1821b.pdf

Palmquist, S. (1987, September). Kant's cosmogony re-evaluated. *Studies in History and Philosophy of Science 18*(3), 255–269.

Safronov, V. (1969). *Evolution of the protoplanetary cloud and formation of the Earth and planets.* Moscow, Russia: Nokia Press.

Swedenborg, E. (1734). *Philosophical and mineralogical works.*

Woolfson, M. M. (1993). Solar system: Its origin and evolution. *Quarterly Journal of the Royal Astronomical Society 34,* 1–20.

Other exoplanet discoveries are found in the following sources:

Borucki, W. J., Koch, D., Basri, G., Batalha, N., Brown, T., Caldwell, D., & Prsa, A. (2010, February). Kepler planet-detecting mission: Introduction and first results. *Science, 327*(5968), 977–780. doi:10.1126/science.1185402

Mayor, M., & Queloz, D. (1995). A Jupiter-mass companion to a solar-type star. *Nature, 378*(6555), 355–359. doi:10.1038/378355a0

Information about the Kepler-20 system comes from Fressin, Francois, Torres, G., Rowe, J. F., Charbonneau, D., Rogers, L. A., Ballard, S., & Uddin, K. (2011, December 20). Two Earth-sized planets orbiting Kepler-20. *Nature, 482*(7384), 195–198. doi:10.1038/nature10780

Information about the Kepler-42 system comes from NASA. (n.d.). KOI-961: A mini-planetary system. *NASA Ames Research Center Kepler; A Search for Habitable Planets.* https://www.nasa.gov/mission_pages/kepler/main/index.html?FuseAction=ShowNews&NewsID=179

Information about the Tau Ceti system comes from the following sources:

Feng, F., Tuomi, M., Jones, H. R. A., Barnes, J., Anglada-Escudé, G., Vogt, S. S., & Butler, R. P. (2017). Color difference makes a difference: Four planet candidates around Tau Ceti. *Astronomical Journal, 154*(4), 135. doi:10.3847/1538-3881/aa83b4

MacGregor, M. A, Lawler, S. M., Wilner, D. J., Matthews, B. C., Kennedy, G. M., Booth, M., & Francesco, J. D. (2016). ALMA observations of the debris disk of solar analogue Tau Ceti. *Astrophysical Journal, 828*(2), 113. doi:10.3847/0004-637X/828/2/113

Teixeira, T. C., Kjeldson, H., Bedding, T. R., Bouchy, F., Christensen-Dalsgaard, J., Cunha, M. S., ... & Pijpers, F. P. (2009, January). Solar-like oscillations in the G8 V star τ Ceti. *Astronomy and Astrophysics.* 494(1), 237–242. doi:10.1051/0004-6361:200810746

Information about the Kepler-90 system comes from Cabrera, J., Csizmadia, S., Lehmann, H., Dvorak, R., Gandolfi, D., Rauer, H., & Hatzes, A. (2013, December 31). The planetary system to KIC 11442793: A compact analogue to the solar system. *Astrophysical Journal, 781*(1), 18. doi:10.1088/0004-637X/781/1/18

Information about the TRAPPIST-1 system comes from the following sources:

Bourrier, V., de Wit, J., & Jäger, M. (2017, August, 31). Hubble delivers first hints of possible water content of TRAPPIST-1 planets. Retrieved 2019-04-20. https://www.spacetelescope.org/news/heic1713/

Gillon, M., Jehin, E., Lederer, S. M., Delrez, L., De Wit, J., Burdanov, A., … & Queloz, D. (2016). Temperate Earth-sized planets transiting a nearby ultracool dwarf star. *Nature*, 533(7602), 221–224. doi:10.1038/nature17448. PMID 2713592

Specific data (masses, radii, periods etc.) regarding exoplanets can be found at http://exoplanet.eu/catalog/?f=%27KOI-961%27+in+name, http://www.openexoplanetcatalogue.com, and https://exoplanets.nasa.gov/newworldsatlas/

The discovery of the new exoplanet PDS 70b was announced in various news media. The original press release from the European Southern Observatory was given out on 2018-07-02 at http://www.hq.eso.org/public/news/eso1821/

The Kepler spacecraft's main web page is at https://www.nasa.gov/mission_pages/kepler/main/index.html; Updated statistics of Kepler's discoveries is at https://www.nasa.gov/kepler/discoveries

Orbital parameters are taken from:

Tuomi et al. (2012) "Signals embedded in the radial velocity noise. Periodic variations in the tau Ceti velocities" https://arxiv.org/abs/1212.4277

The habitable zone is plotted according to the formulae given in:

Underwood, Jones and Sleep (2003) "The evolution of habitable zones during stellar lifetimes and its implications on the search for extraterrestrial life" https://arxiv.org/abs/astro-ph/0312522

Credits

Fig. III.2: Source: https://www.nasa.gov/image-feature/ames/kepler-90-system-planet-sizes.

Fig. 7.1a: Source: https://commons.wikimedia.org/wiki/File:Immanuel_Kant_2.jpg.

Fig. 7.1b: Source: https://commons.wikimedia.org/wiki/File:Pierre-Simon_Laplace.jpg.

Fig. 7.2: Copyright © by ALMA (ESO/NAOJ/NRAO), NSF (CC BY 4.0) at https://apod.nasa.gov/apod/ap141110.html.

Fig. 7.3: Copyright © by ESO (CC BY 4.0) at http://www.hq.eso.org/public/news/eso1821/.

Fig. 7.4a: Copyright © by Wikibob (CC BY-SA 3.0) at https://commons.wikimedia.org/wiki/File:Pegasus_51_location.png.

Fig. 7.4b: Source: http://www.planetary.org/multimedia/space-images/charts/radial-velocity-graph-51-pegasi.html.

Fig. 7.5: Copyright © by AstroMark (CC BY-SA 3.0) at https://commons.wikimedia.org/wiki/File:Lhborbits.png.

Fig. 7.6a: Copyright © by ESO (CC BY 4.0) at https://www.eso.org/public/images/eso9924a/.

Fig. 7.6b: Copyright © by ESO and Digitized Sky Survey 2 (CC BY 4.0) at https://commons.wikimedia.org/wiki/File:NGC_2023_-_Horsehead_nebula_(crop).jpg.

Fig. 7.7a: Source: https://apod.nasa.gov/apod/ap961017.html.

Fig. 7.7b: Source: https://apod.nasa.gov/apod/ap010502.html.

Fig. 7.9a: Copyright © by Brocken Inaglory (CC BY-SA 3.0) at https://commons.wikimedia.org/wiki/File:P%C4%81hoehoe_and_Aa_flows_at_Hawaii.jpg.

Fig. 7.9b: Copyright © by Brocken Inaglory (CC BY-SA 3.0) at https://commons.wikimedia.org/wiki/File:Sulfur_dioxide_emissions_from_the_Halemaumau_vent_04-08-1_1.jpg.

Fig. 7.10: Source: https://commons.wikimedia.org/wiki/File:444226main_exoplanet20100414-a-full.jpg.

Fig. 7.11: Copyright © by ESO (CC BY 4.0) at https://commons.wikimedia.org/wiki/File:Radial_Velocity_Curve_of_Gliese_581_%28HARPS_3.6m%29.jpg.

Fig. 7.12: Copyright © by ESO/E. Vernet (CC BY 4.0) at https://commons.wikimedia.org/wiki/File:The_VLT%E2%80%99s_new_Deformable_Secondary_Mirror.jpg.

Miranda. Credit: NASA/JPL/Kevin M. Gill

CATASTROPHE!

To review how various catastrophic events have shaped objects in the solar system

OBJECTIVES

- ► To review a recent impact on Earth
- ► To study impacts of asteroids and comets on larger objects
- ► To compare models of the origin of the Moon
- ► To use counts of impact craters to estimate ages of surfaces
- ► To discuss how rings are formed
- ► To discuss other types of catastrophes and their effects

INTRODUCTION

While we have discussed the properties of the solar system and our current understanding of how it formed, there are a few details yet to cover. Specifically, random events—primarily, but not limited to collisions between objects—have sculpted the surfaces of many objects, changed how objects rotate about their axes, and even are arguably responsible for the origin of some of the solar system's major objects, up to and including our Moon.

KEY TERMS

Catastrophe: Used here, an event that causes major damage and/or disruption to the physical and/or motion properties of an object. Sample types of catastrophes include collisions between objects, tearing apart of objects via gravitational tides, and extreme volcanism

Catastrophism: The idea that catastrophes are important in the shaping of the Earth and other objects in the solar system

Crater peak: The result of the rebounding shock-waves in the immediate aftermath of an impact. Debris from the rebounding wave can be sent straight up from ground zero and fall straight back downward

Crater rays: Rays or streaks of fine dust excavated and thrown up by an impact

Elasticity: The tendency of a solid object, when distorted suddenly, to snap or rebound back to its original shape and size

Giant impact hypothesis: The idea that the Moon's origin is due to the collision of another planet with the Earth early in the history of the solar system

Ground zero: The point on the ground or surface where an impactor lands

Impact basin: A rounded, often circular region where an impact was so violent as to melt the surface for hundreds or thousands of miles surrounding ground zero. Impact basins are so large that they follow the curvature of the object, rather than impact craters, which tend to have flat floors

Impact crater: Often a bowl-shaped indentation in the surface of a solid object due to an impact of a smaller object. Impact craters need not be large; microscopic impact craters have been found on bits of glass found in soil samples from the Moon

Impactor: Typically used to describe the smaller of the objects involved in an astronomical collision, such as an asteroid hitting a planet

K-T extinction: The extinction of three-fourths of all life (including dinosaurs) on Earth 66 million years ago, separating the cretaceous and tertiary ages on Earth, thought by many scientists to be due to a giant asteroid impact off the shore of what is now the Yucatan Peninsula in Mexico

Late heavy bombardment (LHB): A period of time, approximately from 4.1 to 3.8 billion years ago, when the rate of asteroid and comet collisions in the inner solar system was 100 times or more than it is today

Number density: The number of objects—such as the number of impact craters—per unit area

Tunguska event: A titanic explosion in the summer of 1908 in central Siberia, thought by most scientists to be due to a piece of an asteroid exploding in the Earth's upper atmosphere

Uniformitarianism: The notion that major changes for objects such as the Earth are due to gradual changes caused by uniform processes

KEY INDIVIDUALS

Alvarez, Walter: An American geologist of the late 20th century who, with his physicist father Luis, proposed the hypothesis that a giant asteroid collision with the Earth was responsible for the extinction of the dinosaurs and other life forms on Earth 66 million years ago

Hartmann, William K.: An American astronomer of the late 20th century who was among the first to suggest the *giant impact hypothesis* for the origin of the Moon. He is also a well-renowned painter of astronomical objects and events

Kulilk, Leonid: An early 20th-century Russian geologist who was the first to survey the site of the Tunguska Event

Levy, David: An American astronomer and author of the late 20th century who collaborated with the Shoemakers on several comet discoveries, including Comet Shoemaker-Levy 9 that collided with Jupiter in 1994

Shoemaker, Carolyn: An American astronomer of the late 20th century who discovered the smudge on a photographic plate that turned out to be Comet Shoemaker-Levy 9

Shoemaker, Eugene: An American geologist of the late 20th century who helped illuminate the notion that catastrophes are important in shaping the solar system; also part of the team that discovered Comet Shoemaker-Levy 9

Section 8.1: Case Study: The Tunguska Event

At breakfast time I was sitting by the house at Vanavara Trading Post, facing north. … I suddenly saw that directly to the north, over Onkoul's Tunguska Road, the sky split in two and fire appeared high and wide over the forest. The split in the sky grew larger, and the entire northern side was covered with fire. At that moment I became so hot that I couldn't bear it as if my shirt was on fire; from the northern side, where the fire was, came strong heat. I wanted to tear off my shirt and throw it down, but then the sky shut closed, and a strong thump sounded, and I was thrown a few meters. I lost my senses for a moment, but then my wife ran out and led me to the house. After that such noise came, as if rocks were falling or cannons were firing, the Earth shook, and when I was on the ground, I pressed my head down, fearing rocks would smash it. When the sky opened up, hot wind raced between the houses, like from cannons, which left traces in the ground like pathways, and it damaged some crops. Later we saw that many windows were shattered, and in the barn, a part of the iron lock snapped. (Vasiliev, 1981)

This is the testimony of S. Semonov, an eyewitness to the Tunguska event, which happened in June 30, 1908. The Tungusk (Evenki) people are a native tribe of the central Siberia. In Evenki lore, the *Agdy* is alternatively described as the lord of thunder, or as thunderbirds, that knowledgeable shaman can call down upon rival clans. The Evenki claimed that after this event only the *Agdy* could survive there. In fact, it was a natural, not supernatural, event, with much to teach us about how the Earth interacts with the solar system.

The Tunguska event centered around a gigantic explosion sent out shockwaves that knocked down trees over about 2,000 square kilometers (770 square miles) and was registered by seismographs around the entire planet. Fortunately, the region is sparsely populated; although there were some injuries—primarily from burns and collapsing structures—there were no confirmed human deaths.[1] Herds of reindeer were not so lucky, nor were structures: Windows were shattered and homes flattened to go with the immense damage to the surrounding forest.

Nearly a thousand papers (not surprisingly, mostly in Russian) have been written about the Tunguska event in the century since it occurred. But the first expedition to examine the damage was not conducted until 1927 by Leonid Kulik (1883–1942), a Soviet geologist with a particular interest in meteorites. Kulik[2] assumed that a large meteor hit the Earth, and he expected to find an impact crater. His expedition never did find a crater, though. Thinking the meteor may have buried itself in the soggy ground, he and his team dug trenches looking for fragments of the meteor, but continually came up with nothing. (Later expeditions in the 1950s and 1960s turned up microscopic metal and silicon spheres in soil samples.) Kulik conducted several comprehensive surveys over several years, with his most important discovery the flattening of trees in a radial pattern from what we now presume is ground zero.

Several ideas have been put forward to explain the event, which testifies as much to the ingenuity of human beings as to actual possibilities, including the following:

+ The collision of a miniature black hole with the Earth
+ A chunk of antimatter that annihilated upon contact with the atmosphere
+ A crash of an extraterrestrial spaceship
+ A natural hydrogen bomb

None of these exotic alternatives have any credible evidence in their favor. The best of the early attempts offered to explain the lack of an impact crater was that a chunk of Comet Encke (a short-period comet that orbits the Sun once every few years) broke loose from the main comet nucleus. The orbit of Comet Encke and the object's trajectory across the skies of Siberia make this highly unlikely, however.

The best explanation currently available suggests the object was a piece of an asteroid. In decades past, astronomers thought that the divisions between

FIGURE 8.1. A picture of trees flattened by the Tunguska explosion, taken by the L. A. Kulik expedition in 1929.

---

[1] One story tells of a man who was working high in the trees and fell to his death after being startled by the explosion. The unconfirmed account may represent the only human fatality.

[2] Kulik tragically died in captivity of typhus during World War II after being captured by the Germans. He had also fought in the Russo-Japanese war in 1905 and during World War I.

comets and asteroids were clear, and that asteroids consist solely of rock and/or metal. We now realize that many asteroids also contain significant amounts of water ice. The plunge of a small asteroid (or meteoroid) into the atmosphere of the Earth creates such friction—the speed of such an uncontrolled descent can exceed 25,000 miles per hour—that the meteoroid's temperature and pressure build until the water explosively evaporates.

Geologists have been able to reasonably reconstruct what happened. The fragment blew up about 8.5 kilometers (5.3 miles) above the surface. Scientists originally estimated its energy output between 10 and 15 megatons of dynamite (for comparison, the atomic bomb that destroyed Hiroshima yielded about 15 kilotons), but downgraded it (if the term applies) to 3–5 megatons once they realized it was headed somewhat toward the ground, shooting much of its force downward. The temperature at the center of the explosion reached 1,700 kelvin, the shockwave traveled outward at about 580 kilometers per hour (360 miles per hour) and measured 5.0 on the Richter earthquake magnitude scale. The shockwave was strong enough to be picked up by seismographs across the world twice (i.e., the shockwave traveled twice around the Earth), and the dust kicked up brightened night skies enough that people could read newspapers at night in London, 10,000 kilometers (6,000 miles) away. No official deaths occurred, but had it hit about 4.5 hours later, the rotation of the Earth would have taken the city of St. Petersburg uncomfortably within range.

A century-plus later, the forest has mostly regrown, although many trees can still be seen on the ground. A small lake, named Cheko, lies about 8 kilometers (5 miles) north-northwest of the estimated epicenter, aligned with the estimated path of the meteoroid, leading geologists to wonder if it is the consequence of a piece of the meteoroid making it to the surface. Explorations of the silt at the bottom of the lake give conflicting ages, one being many thousands of years old, but another around a century. The lake does possess the correct oval shape and orientation to be a result of an impact. Whether Lake Cheko is the result of the meteoroid's collision with Earth is as yet uncertain.

FIGURE 8.2. A trail left by the Chelyabinsk meteor in 2013 (left); damage to a warehouse in Chelyabinsk due to the meteor's shockwave (right).

The Tunguska event is not the only example in recent years of an impact. On February 15, 2013, another rock from space hit Earth, this time near the city of Chelyabinsk in the Ural district of Russia. Again, fortunately, there were no fatalities, but about 1,200 people reported injuries from flying debris, mostly via shattered window glass due to the shockwave caused by the passage of the object through the sky at supersonic speeds. Eventually the remainder of the meteoroid landed in a lake, creating a perfectly circular hole in the ice and leaving a chunk of rock about half the size of an adult, which divers later recovered from the bottom of the lake. These events are also not unusual; we average about one small asteroid explosion (more like Chelyabinsk than Tunguska) in the skies of Earth each year. Military personnel during the Cold War had to learn to distinguish these occurrences from actual nuclear bombs, lest a natural event lead to a nuclear exchange.

Tunguska and Chelyabinsk remind us that we are part of an active solar system, for both good and ill. This chapter is devoted to exploring how impacts and other catastrophic events affect the Earth and other objects in the solar system.

Section 8.2: The Late Heavy Bombardment

As hinted at in chapter 7, collisions between objects helped form the solar system. Small dust grains collided and stuck together via electrostatic forces; planetesimals collided and stuck together via gravity. Friction between the planetary disk and gas giants was responsible for the migration of Jupiter and Saturn inward during the early days of the solar system. Energy released from collisions helped melt rock and metal, sifting materials via density and creating their differentiated structures. In this section, we are interested in how collisions between objects had mostly (otherwise) completed their formation.

The solar system is 4.55 billion years old, which we know by using radiometric dating on meteorites. The formation of the Sun, planets, and other objects made up the first few millions of those years, after which the solar system settled down—temporarily, as it turned out.

Sample rocks brought back by the Apollo astronauts showed that most melting had occurred between 4.1 and 3.8 billion years ago. This is curious for a few reasons. First, this indicates a wave of melting happened well after the Earth and other terrestrial objects formed. Second, the time scale, while long by human standards, is somewhat narrow by solar system terms. Third, the sheer number of impacts during this time must have been a hundred to a thousand times more common than it is today. This period of time is called the *late heavy bombardment* (LHB).

The most ancient rocks on Earth date to about 3.8 billion years old, with a few exceptions. Geologists originally assumed this simply meant the Earth was molten until then. But models of cooling processes indicate the surface of the Earth should have become solid only[3] 100 million years (0.1 billion years) after its formation. The LHB may provide an answer. If impacts happened often enough, they could have re-melted parts of the early Earth's surface and kept melting it until the LHB receded.

How often and how violent were impacts during the LHB on Earth? Extrapolating from observations of lunar craters, researchers find the following:

- 22,000 or more impact craters larger than 20 kilometers (12 miles) across
- About 40 impact basins larger than 1,000 kilometers (600 miles) across
- Several impact basins larger than 5,000 kilometers (3000 miles) across

Assuming this is correct, why did the LHB happen? Or, more to the point, why did it wait for several hundred million years after the initial formation of the solar system? The answer appears to be planetary migration.

We discussed planetary migration at length in chapter 7. Gas giants are difficult, if not impossible, to form relatively close to their parent stars, in part because the temperatures of the planetary disk and star evaporate volatiles such as hydrogen and helium closer in. The idea is that Jupiter and Saturn therefore formed far from the Sun (30 au or further) but wandered or "migrated" inward due to friction between them and the dust of the protoplanetary disk. The thought is that Jupiter and Saturn essentially traded places with Uranus and Neptune, which had originally been closer to the Sun.

The next effect to discuss is how Saturn and especially Jupiter's gravity changed the inner solar system. As Jupiter got closer to the Sun, its gravity sent many objects toward the Sun that previously had orbits several au out. Most of this debris would be swept up by the Sun itself, but occasionally terrestrial objects would be in the way. The Earth thus was not the only planet affected (see Figure 8.3).

> **Check Your Neighbor**
>
> The late heavy bombardment (LHB) period lasted for several hundred million years, but did eventually come to an end. Why?

---

[3] Yes, we are using the word "only" to describe the passage of 100 million years. Welcome to planetary astronomy!

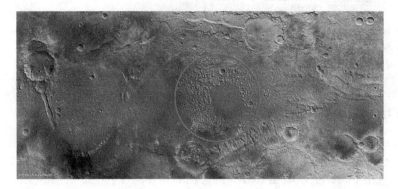

FIGURE 8.3. Eroded "bumps" outline the Atlantis Chaos (outlined in red), an impact basin on Mars thought to be from the Late Heavy Bombardment period. The basin, measuring 170 km by 145 km, may have once been completed covered by water. Courtesy the European Space Agency.

We note that not all geologists are convinced of a specific and/or separate bombardment period. One of the criticisms is that the samples brought back to Earth by the Apollo astronauts all come from the same impact basin of the Moon, which tells us why the samples all tend to have similar ages (they may have come from the same impact event). At the moment, though, the combination of computer modeling of the early solar system, the restrictions on ages of ancient rocks on Earth, and observations of other planetary systems lean toward the LHB model.

A positive consequence of the LHB for Earth may have been its water supply. Oceans cover 71% of the Earth's surface, and we are the only object in the solar system currently with copious amounts of liquid water on its surface, although there are hints that other objects, such as Mars, may also once have had oceans. On the other hand, water is the most common molecule in the solar system after hydrogen (which is restricted to the atmospheres of the gas giants) and is found in ice form in many of the moons of the outer solar system. Water ice makes up much of comets, and astronomers have learned over the past few decades that asteroids, once thought to consist almost entirely of rock, also tend to have a lot of water content.

Water would almost certainly have evaporated and escaped the forming Earth, due to its original high temperatures and lesser gravity, meaning our water needs to have come from somewhere. One possible source is venting from underground, such as volcanoes (which continue to contribute small amounts of water to this day), or "leakage" from rocks with hydrate minerals. But it appears that the most likely source of water on Earth is collisions with asteroids during the LHB.

Check Your Neighbor

Why would the forming Earth have had less gravity (i.e., a smaller acceleration due to gravity on its surface) than it does today?

Comets—at least comets from the Kuiper Belt and/or Oort Cloud—were once speculated to be the primary source of Earth's oceans. But detailed analysis of current comets shows they possess about twice as much deuterium ("heavy" hydrogen) as ocean water.[4] Asteroids, on the other hand, show close to the same amount of deuterium as Earth's water, suggesting they were the primary contributors. The atmosphere of the Earth during the LHB is thought to have been dominated by carbon dioxide and to be thick enough (i.e., exert enough pressure) to keep water liquid on its surface, despite much higher temperatures than the Earth experiences today. Similar situations may have happened for Venus and Mars, and even briefly for the Moon. The case for the asteroidal origin of Earth's oceans has been strengthened by recent observations of other planetary systems from telescopes such as Spitzer, which used infrared light to discover water ice, rock, and simple organic compounds at Eta Corvi (see Figure 8.4).

---

[4] More specifically, the ratio of deuterium to protons in comet versus Earth water. Deuterium, or "heavy" hydrogen, is an isotope with one neutron and one proton in the nucleus of the hydrogen atom.

Section 8.3: The Physics of Impacts

We've already hinted that the striking of a large body (like the Earth) by a smaller object (like an asteroid) is incredibly violent. But how destructive are impacts? And what are the physical processes that govern impacts?

Let's use the Moon as an example. The Moon presents a relatively simple case, since it possesses no atmosphere, oceans, or active geology, which can affect both the collision and how the results of a collision are later viewed. And to do that, we need to learn a little about impact craters.

Figure 8.5 depicts the far side of the Moon, as seen by the Apollo 16 astronauts in 1972. It looks unfamiliar, for

FIGURE 8.4. An artist's depiction of comets bombarding an exoplanet. The Spitzer telescope discovered evidence of water ice and rock in the Eta Corvi system, indicating the presence of comets. Image credit: NASA/JPL-Caltech.

the simple reason that it is; the Moon is tidally locked, meaning it has no independent rotation and therefore always shows the same side to us. The thing that stands out is the lack of lunar "maria" or impact basins where lava flows have covered old craters. One explanation is that the Moon's surface is thicker on the far side and consequently more difficult to melt. What we do see are craters. The far side of the Moon is saturated with them.

FIGURE 8.5. Left: The far side of the Moon, taken by the Apollo 16 astronauts; right, Daedalus (the largest crater in the picture), also on the far side of the Moon, by the Apollo 11 astronauts. The slightly oval shape of Daedalus is due to foreshortening, as the Apollo 11 spaceship was flying over the lunar surface.

The other observation that announces itself is the shape of the craters: Daedalus, a crater near the lunar equator on its far side, is also shown in Figure 8.5. With a few exceptions (and there are some), craters are circular in shape. Closer inspection shows the circles are really walls of solid material, with the middle section or "floor" of the crater smooth and flat. Occasionally (not always) there is a pointed structure or peak at the very center of the crater.

A close-up view of another crater, Aristarchus, lets us see important details. The entire crater itself is 40 kilometers (25 miles) wide and 3 kilometers (2 miles) deep, which is nothing special regarding diameter or depth for a lunar crater. The dark material represents rock that was melted and re-solidified after the impact; the lighter streaks represent rocks and dust excavated during the impact. Boulders up to 100 meters across were thrown about due to the impact that formed Aristarchus.

Finally, let's look at another crater from directly above. Jackson (Figure 8.7) is another crater on the far side of the Moon. What catches the eye here are streaks or "rays" emanating from the crater. These rays show dust—in

FIGURE 8.6. The western wall of Aristarchus, a crater on the near side of the Moon.

FIGURE 8.7. Jackson crater on the far side of the Moon, showing prominent crater rays. From the Clementine mission (NASA).

this case, fine (thin) dust sprayed across the lunar landscape. The dust shows up as streaks because it reflects light much better than the darker, thicker rock it covers. Not all craters show crater rays, but the few ray systems we see can be spectacular.

If we wish to understand impacts, we need to explain how these features—circular crater walls, crater peaks, streaks of dust, etc.—come about. Our task now is to go through the process of an impact, step by step. First, let's review the physics principles involved:

+ **Gravity:** Again, gravity is the most important force of nature for describing impacts. The gravity of a large object (such as the Moon) is what helps draw smaller objects (such as asteroids) toward it in the first place. Gravity also determines in large part the relative speed of the incoming object

+ **Density:** Different asteroids or comets are made of different materials. As we discussed in chapter 6, density is in part a measure of the "toughness" of an object. Since density is also determined by the material of which the object is made, we can use density to help us estimate the mass of an incoming object

+ **Energy:** Recall that kinetic energy is the combination of the mass of a moving object and the square of its speed. The more massive the incoming object, or the faster the speed of the incoming object, the more kinetic energy it brings, and the more violent the impact

+ **Elasticity:** When a solid object feels a force that distorts it, it has a tendency to rebound or snap back to its original shape and size

+ **Melting point:** The temperature at which a particular solid substance melts

+ **Reflectivity (or albedo):** The percentage of light reflected by a substance. A reflectivity of 1 (or 100%) means all light incident upon a substance is reflected, and a reflectivity of 0 (or 0%) means all light incident upon a substance is either transmitted through the substance or is absorbed by it

With these ideas in mind, let's review the steps involved in an impact. While astronomers have had few opportunities to observe impacts happening in "real time," experiments have been conducted—for example, with the equivalent of high-speed bullets—using high-speed cameras and computer modeling to show how impacts work. Again, we will use the Moon as our example. For the following discussion, we will also assume a small asteroid (roughly spherical, about 5 km across, made of rock) will be the object hitting the Moon.

1. A small object (the future impactor) traveling through the solar system heads toward the Moon. It could be originally heading straight toward the Moon. It could also originally have a path that otherwise would make its path a near miss, but the pull of gravity of the Moon alters the impactor's path so that it does indeed head toward the Moon.

2. The impactor's speed increases as it approaches the Moon. It's the reverse of an object's escape speed: An object that ideally is very far away with virtually no initial speed will be traveling at escape speed at the moment the impactor hits the Moon's surface. If the impactor had an initial speed relative to the Moon (which is most likely), the impactor's speed will be greater than the Moon's escape speed. For the Moon, the speed is 1.7 kilometers per second (4,000 miles per hour) or larger.

3. The impactor does not need to come straight down toward the surface of the Moon (Figure 8.8). In fact, it is far more likely that the object is coming in at an angle.

4. At such speeds, a typical asteroid is likely to completely disintegrate in a giant explosion. For a 5-km diameter object made of rock (assume a density of 2,500 kg/m³), we can estimate its kinetic energy to be about 2.7×10^{22} joules. For comparison, this is well over 6 million megatons of TNT. Most of that energy goes into vaporizing the asteroid and flinging debris (both from the impactor and the section of the surface it hit) across the surface of the Moon.

5. Some of the debris is melted during the impact; in some cases, the melting is severe enough to fuse small bits of rock into tiny microscopic beads of glass (soil samples returned by the Apollo astronauts exhibit such beads). Some of the debris consists of shattered rock thrown outward from ground zero. And some of the debris is fine dust dug out from deep under the surface, which also scatters across the surface. The dust forms highly reflective rays emanating from ground zero.

FIGURE 8.8. An asteroid approaches the surface of the Moon. Note the asteroid's path does not have to be straight down. The view is from the side, so we can see not just the surface but a short distance underground.

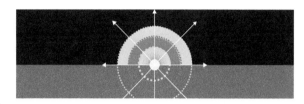

FIGURE 8.9. The asteroid vaporizes upon impact. Shockwaves travel outward from the impact site (ground zero) and into the ground. Debris flies outward above the surface in all directions, including bits of solid rock, molten rock and dust.

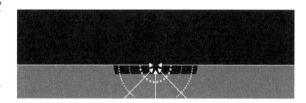

FIGURE 8.10. After the shockwave passes, the ground tries to return to its original shape and size. It doesn't completely succeed, but the rebounding waves focus at ground zero.

6. The impact sends shockwaves into the surface. In the case of the Moon, there are no shockwaves as such sent into the air, since it doesn't have air. If this were the Earth, a supersonic shock wave would indeed travel through the air, followed by a slower (but still quickly moving) shock carrying enormous heat. An explosion of this type on Earth would also create a mushroom cloud, though minus the radiation that accompanies nuclear bomb tests on Earth.

7. The ground tries to "rebound"; that is, it tries to return to its original shape and size, a property of solids we call *elasticity*.[5] This means rebounding shockwaves come back toward ground zero. The focusing of these rebounding shockwaves can throw more debris straight up, which after it lands can form a *crater peak*. Crater peaks are not necessarily trivial; it is common to see lunar crater peaks extending to heights well over a mile or two above the crater floor.

8. Once the impact is complete ("the dust has settled"), we are left with (a) a circular hole, or crater, with a relatively flat floor; (b) a crater peak (though this is not guaranteed); (c) rocky debris—molten and/or solid—scattered equally in all directions from the impact site; and (d) crater rays, also emanating radially from the impact site (again, not guaranteed). Since the walls consist of shattered rock and dust, the walls

---

[5] To show elasticity for yourself, poke your arm gently with a finger. While your finger is in place, you will see a "dent" in your arm. Remove your finger, and your arm quickly reverts back to its normal shape.

tend to slump, so while they are often quite steep, they are not perfectly vertical.

The future of the crater (and scattered debris and crater rays) depends on its environment after this. If the crater is made on the surface of an object like the Moon, it is essentially permanent. Most objects in the solar system have no atmospheres, no running water nor active geologies, and so possess no mechanisms to erode impact craters. Such craters can be altered only by future impacts. We occasionally see one crater overlapping another for this reason. Also, the solar system is not completely a vacuum, and dust can fall on top of a crater and soften its appearance. Solar system dust similarly slowly covers crater rays, though it may take hundreds of thousands of years to cover them completely.

Some other effects are occasionally seen. Debris sent high above the surface during the impact can land far away and make their own craters; these are called "secondary" craters as a consequence. In other cases we observe a string of craters, like a string of beads or pearls, which can be due to an object that breaks apart before impact. In rare cases, impactors come in at extremely shallow angles and leave behind oval (elliptical)-shaped craters rather than circular ones.

How are we sure that craters on the Moon are primarily due to impacts rather than volcanoes or other explosions? The forces that make volcanoes tend to lift material up rather than simply make holes in the ground (consider the Hawaiian Islands, for example) and are not typically as symmetrically round as impact craters. We know of no other processes that might cause large explosions on solid objects in the solar system, but just in case, we can compare craters made from nuclear bomb tests on Earth to impact craters (Figure 8.12).

FIGURE 8.11. The rebounding shockwave can make a crater peak in the very center of the crater. The walls are made of shattered rock and slump downward.

Check Your Neighbor

Two craters are so close that crater A partially lays on top of crater B. Which crater is older?

Check Your Neighbor

Crater C shows prominent crater rays and crater D shows no rays. Which crater is older?

Check Your Neighbor

Which image in Figure 8.12 represents a nuclear bomb test and which an impact? Briefly defend your answer.

FIGURE 8.12. One of these images represents the crater left behind after the "Sedan" U.S. nuclear bomb test in 1962, and the other represents the impact of a small asteroid in the Arizona desert. Can you tell which is which?

This discussion focused on impacts of a size that leave behind craters. Some collisions melt so much rock that lava flows outward for hundreds or thousands of miles from the impact site. The lava covers low-lying features, including craters, and turns dark and opaque when it solidifies. The near side of the Moon famously has several of these impact basins. If you look carefully enough (Figure 8.13), you should be able to tell that the basins, like craters, tend to be circular in shape, even if they overlap each other. You can probably also tell which basins are relatively older and which are younger, and for the same reasons we can estimate relative ages for craters.

The number (or *number density*) of craters on an object depend on several factors. As mentioned earlier, if an object is quiet—no weather, no quakes, no mountain-building, etc.—it is likely to retain its craters in relatively pristine appearances. On the other hand, if an object is active—it has wind, rain, and snow; it moves crustal plates across its surface; it has life—then craters don't tend to survive for long, astro-

FIGURE 8.13. The full Moon on August 7, 2017. Impact basins ("maria") show up as smooth, dark, circular regions.

nomically speaking. Earth is a much larger target than the Moon and is otherwise in the same region of the solar system, so we would expect the Earth to experience far more impacts than the Moon. However, geologists esti-

mate the Earth shows evidence for just a few hundred impacts (Arizona's meteor crater, featured in Figure 8.12, is a rare, well-preserved example), whereas the Moon is saturated with impact craters. Mercury, much of Mars, and various moons and asteroids show evidence of large numbers of collisions.

The environment in which an object resides also affects its number density of craters. The most cratered object in the solar system is one of Jupiter's big moons by the name of Callisto. Interestingly, another of Jupiter's big moons, Io, shows very few impact craters due to its intense volcanic activity (Figure 8.14).

Check Your Neighbor

Callisto, a moon of Jupiter, is about the same size as the planet Mercury. Callisto is even more saturated with craters than Mercury, despite having a significantly smaller pull of gravity due to its much smaller mass. What is different about the environment of Callisto that would encourage it to be hit so often?

FIGURE 8.14. Jupiter's giant moons Callisto (left) and Io (right), as taken by NASA's Galileo space probe.

What if an asteroid or comet collides with an object that isn't solid? We have five potential candidates: the Sun and the Jovian planets. In the case of the Sun, impactors are unlikely to ever "hit" its surface, but instead evaporate or explode long beforehand due to the intense heat. Even if the Sun were hit by a major planet that could make the plunge—suppose something the size of Mercury dove into it—it wouldn't leave a crater, since the Sun consists of extremely hot gas. As for the Jovian planets, while their surfaces (really, upper atmospheres) aren't hot, they too are gaseous, not solid, and we wouldn't expect impacts to leave craters.

This notion has been put to the test. In 1993, the astronomer Carolyn Shoemaker, while hunting through images for comets, found something unusual. Rather than appearing as a slowly moving point of light, like most comet nuclei, or with a tail pointing away from the Sun, as a comet can have when close to the Sun, it looked more like a smudge or smear. Upon checking her discovery, her collaborators, geologist/husband Eugene Shoemaker and their friend David Levy, realized it wasn't simply a comet, but a string of comets (Figure 8.15). Being the ninth comet they discovered as a team, it was subsequently named Comet Shoemaker-Levy 9.[6]

FIGURE 8.15. The "string of pearls": Pieces of Comet Shoemaker-Levy 9, as seen by the Hubble Space Telescope before its collision with Jupiter, May 17, 1994.

After its orbit was calculated, it was determined that Shoemaker-Levy 9 had gotten very close to the planet Jupiter in 1992, and in fact was officially orbiting Jupiter rather than the Sun. The gravitational tides of Jupiter shredded the comet into nearly two dozen pieces, which slowly spread apart but otherwise kept their orbital path. More importantly, its orbit would bring it back around to impact Jupiter over several days in July of 1994.

The individual pieces of Shoemaker-Levy 9 didn't leave any craters, but they did leave their mark, albeit briefly. An individual piece would burrow itself several tens of miles deep within Jupiter's thick atmosphere before exploding due to the intense pressure and heat. In the process, each explosion would send various substances at those depths up toward the top of Jupiter's atmosphere, both from the comet pieces themselves and compounds belonging to Jupiter. The substances appear brownish from a distance, giving the illusion that Jupiter had suffered bruises!

Jupiter eventually "healed," and though the clearing of its bruises took several months, decades later it shows no evidence of ever being hit by a string of comets. Due to the mass of each piece of comet and the high speeds (Jupiter's escape speed is about 60 kilometers per second, or nearly 350,000 miles per hour!), the impacts were enormous. The largest fragment, labeled "G," yielded approximately 6 million megatons of energy, and most other fragments gave similar yields. For comparison, the atomic bomb used in World War II over Nagasaki had a yield of about 20 kilotons.

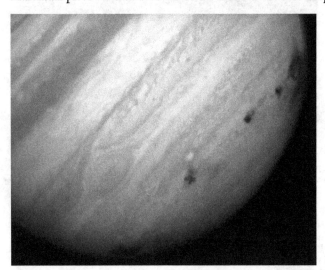

FIGURE 8.16. Impact sites or "bruises" due to pieces of Comet Shoemaker-Levy 9 hitting Jupiter in July of 1994. Courtesy of NASA/ HST Comet Team.

---

[6] Comets are officially named after their discoverers, or in some cases after other important astronomical/historical persons.

The story of Comet Shoemaker-Levy 9 teaches us an important lesson. While Jupiter (and Saturn) likely spurred the period of the late heavy bombardment, Jupiter today acts much like a cosmic vacuum cleaner, sucking in debris that otherwise could endanger Earth and other terrestrial worlds. Jupiter today is impacted by comets and asteroids at a rate estimated between 2,000 and 8,000 times more frequently than the rate we experience here. How much Jupiter protects us otherwise is still open to debate, but we know one thing for sure: A comet that hits Jupiter is one less comet available to hit Earth.

Section 8.4: How Did We Get the Moon?

Before the Apollo missions, astronomers didn't have a clear idea how our Moon formed; or, they tended to assume the Moon formed with the Earth. We now have evidence that this isn't the case. Rather, the Moon is likely the result of a titanic collision between the young Earth and another planet.

To understand why astronomers now favor this idea, we need to evaluate current properties of the Moon and compare them to the Earth:

1. The Earth's density is 5.54 grams per cubic centimeter; Mercury and Venus have similar densities. The density of Mars is significantly less at 3.93 g/cc, and the Moon's is even smaller, at 3.34 g/cc.
2. The plane of the Moon's orbit about the Earth is not really near the plane of the Earth's equator (being over 18° off). Rather, the Moon's orbital plane is only 5° off of the Earth's orbital plane about the Sun.
3. The diameter of the Moon is one-fourth that of the Earth and its mass is over 1% that of Earth.
4. The Moon and the Earth both have similar oxygen isotope percentages. We know this from analysis of lunar soil samples returned by Apollo astronauts.

FIGURE 8.17. Tycho crater on the Moon. Courtesy of NASA.

What do these observations tell us?

1. The Earth and Moon are both made of rock and metal, but the percentages are very different. The mass of the Earth's core, as a fraction of the total mass of the Earth, is much larger than the equivalent fraction for the Moon. Or, the Moon has a very small metal core in comparison to Earth's core.
2. Moons that form with planets share their angular momentum, meaning they tend to orbit their planets in the same plane that the planet rotates. For similar reasons, the planets tend to orbit in the same plane as the Sun's rotation. However, the Moon's orbit about the Earth is closer to the plane of the solar system rather than the Earth's rotational plane.
3. The Moon—both in terms of radius and of mass—is enormous for a natural satellite. While there are larger moons than ours in the solar system, they are much smaller in comparison to their planets than our Moon is to us. For example, Io and the Moon are similar in radius and mass, but Jupiter is over 300 times as massive as the Earth. The only comparable pairing is Pluto and its moon Charon, and the two of them combined are much smaller than our Moon.

4. Objects that formed in different regions of the solar system should have at least somewhat different compositions. But while the Moon's percentage of metal is significantly less than that of the Earth, the Moon and Earth both hold the same isotopes of oxygen. This is interesting, because this says that somehow the Earth and Moon did form in the same region. Any model of the Moon's origin needs to account for these facts.

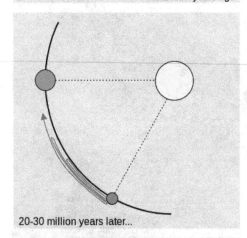

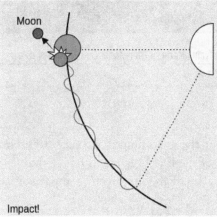

FIGURE 8.18. The great impact hypothesis: The protoplanet Theia forms in virtually the same orbit as the proto-Earth; perturbations change the orbital period of Theia; Theia eventually collides with Earth.

What hypothesis pulls all these facts together? If the Moon formed with the Earth, then it should have the same percentages of metals and its orbit should be in the same plane as that of the Earth's equator. On the other hand, if the Moon formed independently of the Earth and was later captured by the Earth's gravity, then its oxygen isotope percentages should be noticeably different than that of the Earth.

The model most popular at this time is the *giant impact hypothesis*. In the 1960s, the Soviet astronomer V. S. Safronov (see chapter 7) spurred others to think of how planetesimals gathered themselves together out of the original protoplanetary disk. Two American astronomers, William K. Hartmann and Donald R. Davis, ran with this idea and applied it to the case of the Moon, publishing their suggestion in 1974. Important tweaks to the hypothesis were made in the late 1990s by Robin Canup. Further observations in recent years (water in chondrites, isotopes of zinc, etc.) support the findings regarding oxygen isotopes from the Apollo missions. However, the model isn't yet complete, nor is it accepted by all astronomers; for example, a research group in Israel suggests the Moon is the result of not one giant collision but a continuous bombardment of smaller planetesimals on the early Earth that kicked material up into orbit about our planet. Assuming for the moment the giant impact idea has merit, how might it work?

The name of the hypothesized other planet is usually given as Theia.[7] Depending on details of the specific computer model, Theia would have been anywhere from 10% to 90% of the mass of the Earth. Theia formed at a distance from the Sun similar (not identical) as the forming Earth. It may sound at first that this would ensure the two objects would collide rather quickly, but the reverse is true: With very similar orbital periods, it would take many years for them to approach each other. Theia may have in fact spent much of its short life (granted, several tens of millions of years) in one of the Lagrange points of the Earth-Sun combination, keeping its position compared to the Earth very stable. Recall the Trojan asteroids that currently lead and follow Jupiter are in such a position now.

The orbit of Theia would not be permanently linked to Earth, however, as gravitational perturbations eventually did get it to move at a slightly different speed than Earth. Eventually Theia

---

[7] In keeping with the mythological theme for naming planets, Theia is yet another deity from the Greco-Roman tradition—in her case, she was a daughter of Ouranos and Geia (a.k.a. Heaven and Earth), and among her attributes was the representation of the bright blue daylight sky.

would collide with the young Earth, about 20–30 million years after the initial formation of both objects. The collision would need to have been at a glancing angle rather than directly head on. Theia was completely destroyed and a large portion of the upper crust of Earth was vaporized. Much of the metallic core of Theia would have sunk to the center of the Earth (thus enhancing the Earth's total amount of metal) along with much of its other material. About 10% of Theia would have fallen into orbit around the Earth, eventually coalescing to become the Moon.

The new Moon would have been only about 10% as far from the Earth as it is today. The Earth's gravitational pull on the Moon would have been a hundred times stronger, so the Moon would have quickly become tidally locked, and it never has had an independent rotation. Due to tidal friction exerted by the Moon on the Earth, the Moon would have slowly increased its semi-major axis, an effect we can still measure today. The Earth's rotational period would also have been much faster after the collision; the duration of the Earth's day might have been as short as 5 hours. Angular momentum of the new Moon-Earth system would be conserved, the trade-off for the growing orbit of the Moon being the slowing of the Earth's spin.

Whether the great impact hypothesis is correct or not, it appears that collisions between objects in some fashion or another are responsible for our Moon.

Section 8.5: A Sampling of Other Solar System Impacts

Earth isn't the only planet that has experienced major collisions that have altered its destiny. Let's take a brief look at some others.

1. Venus
Venus is unique among the planets in that it rotates retrograde—backward compared to the others—or, equivalently, Venus is upside down. Venus also needs 243 Earth days to rotate once on its axis, easily the slowest of all the planets. It is possible Venus simply formed this way, but it seems unlikely, given the role angular momentum plays in the solar system. Venus may have itself suffered a very intense impact early in its history, which in its case altered its rotation.

2. Mars
Mars possesses an axial tilt and length of day (rotational period) very similar to Earth's. The issue with Mars is its lack of a strong magnetic field. Mars should still be at least partially molten inside, meaning ions should be flowing inside it, meaning it should be generating a magnetic field much more substantial than it actually does. One suggestion put forward is that Mars has suffered a series of large impacts which has shut down the flow (convection) of molten material inside, therefore shutting down its magnetic field. This matters for Mars because the atmosphere of Mars is not protected from the solar wind, and whereas Mars should have enough gravity to hold a substantial atmosphere, most of its air has been lost. Without air, Mars cannot sustain liquid water on its surface, and the possibility of life on Mars is subsequently much less that it might otherwise be.

3. Phobos and Deimos
Mars has two moons, but these are objects so small (each several tens of miles across) that astronomers have long thought them simply to be asteroids captured by the gravity of Mars. However, another thought that has gained traction recently is that the two moons are remnants of large impacts, being debris thrown high above the Martian surface and remaining in orbit.

4. Uranus
Like Venus, the rotation of Uranus is odd. While the rotational period of Uranus is in line for what we see for other gas giants, its tilt is not. The rotational axis of Uranus is inclined by 98°, meaning Uranus rotates on its "side"

compared to the rest of the solar system. A popular suggestion is the collision of Uranus with an Earth-sized world (<u>not</u> Earth itself!) early in its history. Seasons on Uranus are therefore rather strange: At times, the North Pole of Uranus points toward the Sun and the southern half of the planet stays in darkness; at the other side of its orbit, it's the South Pole that has continuous daylight. These winter/summer seasons are separated by spring/autumn seasons where the equator of Uranus points toward the Sun, and essentially all of Uranus has the same day/night cycle. Uranus last passed its (northern) autumnal equinox in 2007 and is scheduled for its next northern winter (southern summer) solstice in 2028.

5. Miranda

The same event that knocked Uranus over may have had consequences for the rest of the Uranus system. After the collision, enormous amounts of debris would have been scattered throughout nearby space, and some of that debris would have impacted the moons of Uranus. The major moons of Uranus (there are five of them) and its rings all ended up orbiting about the equator of Uranus as a consequence. Miranda, the smallest of the moons (it is about 800 kilometers, or 500 miles, across) suffered such a titanic collision that it literally broke apart. The self-gravity of Miranda pulled it back together, but like a puzzle whose pieces were thrown randomly into the air and then reassembled, Miranda's pieces came back together out of order. The Voyager II mission in 1986 (see the image at the beginning of this chapter) shows extremely large and deep features for a moon of its size, and very distinct boundaries between different terrains.

6. Triton

Triton is a case where we are less looking at a past collision and toward a future one. Triton is a relatively large moon orbiting Neptune. But rather than orbiting in the same rotational sense as other Neptunian moons ("prograde," or forward), Triton orbits in the opposite rotational sense ("retrograde," or backward). Because of this, tidal forces between Triton and Neptune, combined with conservation of angular momentum, means that Triton is slowly getting <u>closer</u> to Neptune, not further away as our Moon is doing from us. It is unlikely Triton will eventually crash into Neptune, though. If Triton does not collide with another moon of Neptune, its decreasing orbit will eventually bring it within Neptune's Roche Lobe, where the tides of Neptune will shred it to bits. If you have the patience to wait 3.6 billion years from now (and why not?), you may see a ring system surrounding Neptune to rival Saturn's rings of today.

Section 8.6: Other Catastrophes

For the purposes of this chapter, we can define a *catastrophe* as an event that causes major damage to an object and/or to its motions (rotational or orbital). The impact of a large comet or asteroid on the Earth would definitely qualify. But catastrophes don't need to be impact related, or for that matter happen in short amounts of time. Let's discuss a few examples of non-impact related catastrophes in the solar system.

1. Rings

How do planets acquire rings? The most prevalent method appears to be via gravitational tides. As discussed earlier in the book (see chapter 4), tides are really differences in forces of gravity, due to different locations. The Moon's gravity tides cause our oceans to slosh back and forth twice per day, and over millions of years slow down the Earth's spin, but we of course would not call this a "catastrophe."

However, there are cases where gravity tides are truly destructive. Suppose the orbit of a small, icy moon about its planet is shrinking (Figure 8.19). The gravity tides from the planet increase as the moon gets nearer to it. Eventually, the moon comes within the *Roche Lobe* of the planet, a region within which the strength of the planet's tides exceed the self-gravity of the moon. The moon shreds apart under the external stress, and its pieces can eventually spread themselves out to become planetary rings.

We discussed such an event earlier with Shoemaker-Levy 9, though that was a comet and not a moon. But the type of object is less important than the forces involved. The tidal destruction of an icy moon is a leading hypothesis for the rings of Saturn and that of a rocky moon for the rings of Uranus. Neptune's rings are more properly described as "arcs," meaning the moon was either recently disrupted and its pieces still spreading apart, or in the process of disintegrating. Jupiter also has rings, but they have a different origin, which we will discuss next.

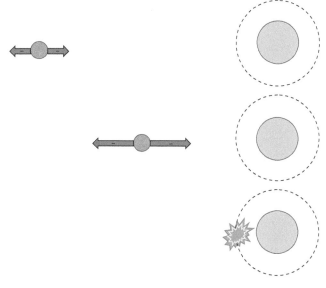

2. Extreme Volcanism

Gravity tides don't just affect moons by tearing them to bits. Gravity tides can also churn up the insides of moons. Tides can flex an object back and forth (we see a little of this with our own ocean tides), and this flexing can generate heat. In rare cases, the heat can be enormous.

The example that stands out most is Io, a moon of Jupiter. Jupiter's tides flex Io's surface up and down by

FIGURE 8.19. (Top) A moon in orbit (left) in orbit about a planet (right) experiences net tidal forces (red arrows) due to the gravity of the planet. The dashed circle represents the Roche Lobe of the planet. As the moon gets closer to the planet (middle above), the tides grow stronger. If the moon gets within the planet's Roche Lobe (above), the tides overcome the self-gravity of the Moon and rip it apart. The objects and distances are not to scale.

FIGURE 8.20. Saturn's rings in visible light (top) and radio light (bottom). Credit: NASA/JPL/Space Science Institute.

about 6 miles (!). The flexing is not restricted to the surface; the interior of Io is warped back and forth so much as to keep its interior molten. The net result is that a moon about the same size as ours is the most volcanically active object in the solar system. It is not uncommon for astronomers to note a dozen volcanoes erupting at the same time across the face of Io, or for ejecta to travel hundreds of kilometers above Io's surface. In fact, much of this material leaves Io to orbit Jupiter itself—Io's volcanoes are the source of Jupiter's rings. This is also not just an interesting visual—since much of the ejecta is ionized, it strengthens Jupiter's magnetic field by a factor of three.

The volcanic activity of Io was discovered by NASA's Voyager I spacecraft in 1977. Eruptions were detected all over its surface. Material could be ejected at speeds over 500 meters per second (1,200 miles per hour), and the temperature of the surface is over 1,000 kelvin, rending any future landing missions unworkable. The volcano shown in Figure 8.21 ejected debris over 160 kilometers (100 miles) above Io's surface, and the diameter of the volcano was about 300 kilometers (200 miles) in diameter, which is comparable in area to a state the size of South Carolina. The surface of Io is unlike any other object in the solar system; its color is primarily

FIGURE 8.21. A volcanic eruption over the limb (edge) of Io, as seen by Voyager I. Credit: NASA/JPL.

yellow, due to sulfur compounds dredged to its surface, and almost no impact craters are visible since the surface is continually renewed by lava.

3. Climate

Some catastrophes aren't sudden—rather, some can take thousands or millions of years to develop. The poster child for a planet-wide long-term catastrophe is the planet Venus.

FIGURE 8.22. Venus in visible light through clear and blue filters, as seen by Mariner 10 in 1974. Credit: NASA/Ricardo Nunes.

Venus is much like the Earth in bulk, with a similar mass, surface gravity, and density, and shows signs of an active geology (Venus has several hundred volcanoes). Some astronomers wonder, during its early history, if Venus had liquid water on its surface. The Sun was noticeably dimmer in its youth, and Venus would have been within the Sun's habitable zone.

However, Venus took a divergent path long ago and now can be described as the closest analog to hell in the solar system. Its upper atmosphere is yellowish from sulfuric acid and other contaminants and has continuous lightning storms. The surface boasts (if that is the correct word) an average temperature of 750 kelvin (900 °F) and an atmospheric pressure 90 times that of Earth, which is the equivalent of the pressure one might feel over half a mile below the surface of the ocean here on Earth. The daytime sky is about as bright as an overcast day on Earth, and it is always overcast on Venus, with clouds tens of miles vertically thick. The night will be as pitch black as can be—no starlight ever penetrates its clouds—and nights last about two Earth months.

The reason for the horrific conditions of Venus is due to a runaway greenhouse effect. We will discuss the science of the greenhouse effect in more detail in a future chapter, but for now we can say that virtually all the carbon dioxide that Venus has is in its atmosphere (the majority of our CO_2 is in other locations on Earth) and creates a super-efficient blanket that holds in the heat of the Sun. As the Sun aged and became brighter, temperatures on Venus slowly climbed and CO_2 that was otherwise trapped leaked into its air. Venus may once have been a world of great promise; now it is a disaster.

Venus is not the only planet to experience severe changes of climate. Geologists estimate the Earth has passed through at least five separate ice ages, the worst of which was the Cryogenian period, from 850 to 630 million years ago, during which the Earth was likely completely encased in ice. The famous "Cambrian explosion," where complex life made its appearance across the globe about 560 million years ago (the "explosion" lasting several tens of millions of years) only happened after the end of the Cryogenian ice age. Discussions of climate change have as their backdrop the notion that we are actually in the middle of the latest ice age (the Quaternary glaciation), which started 2.58 million years ago. We are taking an "interglacial" break of sorts, but ice sheets may make their return in the (for humans) far future. Mars, a planet that shares some of Earth's behaviors, also shows evidence for recurrent ice ages and like Earth has had its polar ice caps grow and shrink over geologic time scales.

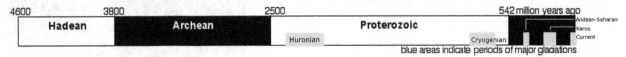

FIGURE 8.23. Ice ages (in blue) over the history of the Earth. Credit: William M. Connolley.

4. Solar Wind

We are fortunate to live with a fairly stable star. Stars much more massive than the Sun emit copious amounts of ultraviolet light, and stars much less massive than the Sun are susceptible to giant flares. Either situation is not conducive to life. But the Sun is mildly active (in comparison), and one of its important actions is the emission of the solar wind.

The solar wind is a streaming of high-velocity charged particles (ions), mostly protons, escaping the surface of the Sun. Such particles carry enormous amounts of energy, individually speaking, and collisions between solar wind particles and (for example) molecules of the atmosphere of a planet could impart enough energy to the air molecules so that they escape the gravity of the planet.

This isn't much of a problem for the Earth, as we have a strong magnetic field that shields us from the solar wind. Mars, on the other hand, lacks a magnetic field, and thus solar wind particles pummel its atmosphere. Mars has plenty of evidence for once having had a much thicker atmosphere made of carbon dioxide—dry river beds argue for ancient running water, for instance—but most of its air is long gone. In fact, recent surveys of Martian CO_2 suggest Mars has lost the majority of its former air to space, and even if its remaining frozen CO_2 were released, it would never return to its former density and pressure.

Section 8.7: How About Those Dinosaurs?

Let's end with a peak at the most famous of all planetary catastrophes: the extinction of the dinosaurs. Approximately 66 million years ago, something happened that wiped out three-fourths of all life on Earth, including what are popularly called dinosaurs, but also many species of birds, mammals, ocean-going species (such as ammonites, mosasaurs and plesiosaurs), and pterosaurs. It wasn't just animals; plant life was also severely affected. Nor was it restricted to one region—life died on land or at sea, in warm or cold climates, and all across the globe. Geologists can't narrow time measurements via the geologic column so much as to see if the extinction was sudden or drawn out over millions of years, but other evidence favors a quick end.

Paleontologists wrangled for decades over various possible causes, including rising seas, global climate change, disease, a nearby supernova, and even the supposedly small brains of dinosaurs. In 1981, the geologist Walter Alvarez and colleagues[8] published research stating how they found highly elevated amounts of the element iridium in the geologic column corresponding to the time of the death of the dinosaurs. Iridium is an element rather rare on Earth but found in larger concentrations in some rocky asteroids. The hypothesis initially garnered ridicule but gained momentum as other geologists found elevated iridium in other parts of the world at the same place in the geologic column.

The hypothesis was given a great boost when petroleum geologists, surveying the ocean floor off the coast of the Yucatan Peninsula in Mexico, discovered a substantially sized impact crater in 1991. About

FIGURE 8.24. The thin Martian atmosphere peaking over the Tharsis volcanic region, as seen by the Mars Express spacecraft. Credit: ESA/DLR/FU Berlin/Justin Cowart.

FIGURE 8.25. An artist's depiction of the asteroid that caused the K-T extinction event. Credit: Don Davis/NASA.

---

8   One of those colleagues was Luis Alvarez, Walter's father and a physicist who had worked for the Manhattan Project during World War II. Luis Alvarez also won the Nobel Prize in physics in 1968 for his work in nuclear physics.

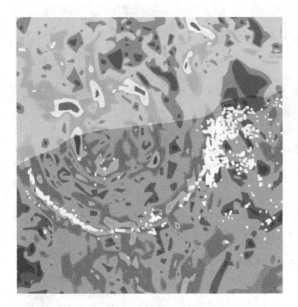

FIGURE 8.26. A map of gravitational anomalies off the coast of the Yucatan Peninsula, Mexico, showing a crater buried deep underground. Credit: Milan Studio.

half of the crater is buried deep under the ocean floor and the other half under land—66 million years gives the Earth plenty of time to cover it up—and it was subsequently named after a nearby village, Chicxulub (pronounced "Chick – zoo – loob").

The Chicxulub crater, despite being completely invisible from the surface, is not small. The crater is about 180 kilometers (110 miles) across, indicating that a rocky asteroid about 10 kilometers (6 miles) across must have been the culprit. The asteroid would have hit the Earth at speeds near 18 kilometers per second (40,000 miles per hour) and released more than two million times the amount of energy of the most powerful nuclear bomb ever detonated. Models suggest the damage would have taken two general forms: First, the initial shock would have triggered fires across the planet and raised the air temperature to broiling; second, the dust blasted into the air would have covered the Sun for months or years, dropping global temperatures to freezing. Creatures not killed by the initial blast would have had difficulty finding food to survive the long winter afterward.

As with many important events that occurred so long ago, the asteroid hypothesis is not agreed to by all. Several paleontologists and geologists think the asteroid impact, even if it happened as described, could not by itself be responsible for a mass extinction. Others point to different causes, one popular contender being volcanic eruptions in what are now called the Deccan Traps in India. The eruptions from the traps could have released

Check Your Neighbor

Was the K-T extinction a good or bad event for life on Earth? (And does it matter whose perspective we use to answer this question?)

poisons into the atmosphere, including sulfuric compounds and copious amounts of carbon dioxide, and dust that could have blocked sunlight, like the asteroid might have done. In either case, or via some yet-unknown mechanism, a catastrophic event killed off the majority of life on Earth 66 million years ago, unwittingly clearing the way for the takeover of the planet by mammals and, eventually, people.

Summary

In this chapter, we have discussed how catastrophic events have shaped objects in the solar system. Catastrophes can happen suddenly (via asteroid impacts) or slowly (via climate change), but in either case we can define catastrophes by the drastic changes they cause. Specifically, we covered the following:

- ▸ The details of an asteroid impact on Earth that occurred in historic times
- ▸ The science of impacts
- ▸ The origin of the Moon
- ▸ Other examples of important impacts in the solar system
- ▸ Other types of catastrophes that shape the solar system
- ▸ A possible astronomical explanation for the extinction of the dinosaurs

Questions

1. A powerful explosion occurs high in the atmosphere. Some observers worry that a rogue nation is testing nuclear weapons. Others suggest the cause of the explosion was a piece of an asteroid or comet entering the Earth's atmosphere. No radiation is seen at the epicenter. Tell which explanation is more likely and briefly defend your answer.

2. A piece of asteroid heads toward Earth. It is expected to impact the Earth with a speed of 12 meters per second. Spectroscopic analysis tells us the asteroid piece is made mostly of rock (density of 2,000 kilograms per cubic meter) and imaging tells us the asteroid piece is roughly spherical with a diameter of 100 meters.

   + Determine the volume of the piece of asteroid. Hint: The formula for the volume of a sphere is

   $$V = \frac{2\pi}{3}R^3$$

   + Determine the mass of the asteroid. Hint: The formula relating mass, volume, and density is
   $$m = \rho V$$

   + What will be the kinetic energy of the asteroid upon impact? Hint: Kinetic energy is given by the formula

   $$K = \frac{1}{2}mv^2$$

   + How much kinetic energy is this in terms of tons of TNT? Hint: The conversion from joules to tons of TNT is

   $$1 \text{ ton of TNT} = 4.184 \times 10^9 \text{ joules}$$

3. Figure 8.27 shows a close-up of the surface of Jupiter's moon Ganymede, taken by the Galileo spacecraft. The figure covers 213 by 97 kilometers (132 by 60 miles) and the resolution (i.e., smallest detail visible) is 121 meters per pixel. Answer the following questions:
   + Sketch or otherwise identify a boundary between two separate sections of the surface.
   + Which section appears older? Briefly defend your reasoning.
   + Which section has the smaller number crater density?

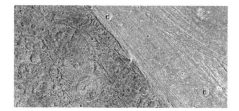

FIGURE 8.27. A close-up of the surface of Ganymede, from the Galileo spacecraft. Credit: NASA/JPL.

4. Figure 8.28 shows a wide-field view of Ganymede, taken by the Galileo spacecraft. Answer the following questions:
   + Which region is likely to be younger: the darker or the lighter patches?
   + The lighter the regions, the more likely the surface contains
     · Hydrogen gas
     · Rock
     · Metal
     · Water ice
   + Which craters are likely to be younger: those with bright white rays surrounding them, or those without the rays?

5. Two new moons are found orbiting a planet. Moon A has a "prograde" orbit, meaning it orbits in the same rotational sense as the planet, and moon B has a "retrograde" orbit, meaning it orbits in the opposite rotational sense as the planet. Which moon likely formed with the planet and which moon likely was captured by the planet?

FIGURE 8.28. A wide-field image of Ganymede, from the Galileo spacecraft. Credit: NASA/JPL/DLR.

6. Two new moons are found orbiting a terrestrial planet. The density of moon C is similar to that of the planet, and the density of moon D is significantly less than that of the planet. Which moon likely formed with the planet, and which moon is likely the result of an ancient collision with the planet?

Activities

▸ *Astrophysics activity 8.1:* Run simulations showing impacts of asteroids of various masses and compositions with the Earth.

▸ *Astrophysics activity 8.2:* Run simulations to show how particles in planetary rings behave and the parameters needed to keep them stable.

▸ *Astrophysics activity 8.3:* Watch "Heaven and Hell" from the original *Cosmos* series and answer questions as directed. The video is available online.

Works Referenced

Gasperini, B., & Longo, X. (2008, June). The Tunguska mystery. *Scientific American*. Retrieved 2019-04-20. https://www.scientificamerican.com/article/the-tunguska-mystery/

Gritzner, C. Human casualties in impact events. *SAO/NASA Astrophysics Data System (ADS)*. Retrieved 2019-04-20. http://adsabs.harvard.edu/full/1997JIMO...25..222G

Kresak, L. (1997). The Tunguska object: A fragment of Comet Encke? *Czechoslovak Academy of Sciences*. Retrieved 2019-04-20. http://adsabs.harvard.edu/abs/1978BAICz..29..129K

Sagan, C. (1980). *Cosmos*. (Chapter 4—"Heaven and Hell"). Random House.

Sekanina, Z. (1983). The Tunguska event: No cometary signature in evidence. Retrieved 2019-04-20. http://adsabs.harvard.edu/abs/1983AJ.....88.1382S

Traynor, C. (1994). Perplexities of the Tunguska meteorite. *NASA Astrophysics Data System*. Retrieved 2019-04-20. http://adsabs.harvard.edu/abs/1994Obs...114..227T

Vasiliev, N. V., et al. (1981). Eyewitness accounts of Tunguska (crash). *Wayback Machine*, 6(4). Retrieved from http://tunguska.tsc.ru/ru/science/1/0

Zlobin, A. (2007). Quasi three-dimensional modeling of Tunguska comet impact (1908) (conference paper). 2007 Planetary Defense Conference. George Washington University, Washington, D.C. Retrieved 2019-04-20. https://www.researchgate.net/publication/237284225_Quasi_Three-dimensional_Modeling_of_Tunguska_Comet_Impact_1908

Information about the period of late heavy bombardment and its consequences for Earth are found in the following sources:

Claeys, P., & Morbidelli, A. (2011). Late heavy bombardment. In M. Gargaud, R. Muriel, J. C. Quintanilla, C. Cernicharo, H. J. Cleaves II, J. Henderson … & V. Michel (Eds.), *Encyclopedia of astrobiology* (pp. 909–912). Berlin, Germany: Springer.

Drake, M. J. (2005). Origin of water in the terrestrial planets. *Meteoritics & Planetary Science*, 40(4), 519–527. doi:10.1111/j.1945-5100.2005.tb00960.x

Gorman, J. (2018, May 15). How asteroids may have brought water to Earth. *New York Times*. Retrieved 2019-04-20. https://www.nytimes.com/2018/05/15/science/asteroids-water-earth.html

Ryder, G. (2000). Heavy bombardment on the Earth at ~3.85 Ga: The search for petrographic and geochemical evidence. In R. M. Canup & K. Righter (Eds.), *Origin of the earth and moon* (pp. 475–492). Tucson, AZ: University of Arizona Press.

Ryder, G. (2002). Mass flux in the ancient Earth-Moon system and benign implications for the origin of life on Earth. *Journal of Geophysical Research: Planets*, 107(E4). Retrieved 2019-04-20. https://agupubs.onlinelibrary.wiley.com/doi/epdf/10.1029/2001JE001583

Sleep, N. H., Zahnle, K., & Neuhoff, P. S. (2001). Inaugural article: Initiation of clement surface conditions on the earliest Earth. *Proceedings of the National Academy of Sciences, 98*(7), 3666. Retrieved 2019-04-20. https://www.pnas.org/content/98/7/3666

Taylor, J. G. (2006, August). Wandering gas giants and lunar bombardment. Retrieved from http://www.psrd.hawaii.edu/Aug06/cataclysmDynamics.html

Terik, D. R., & Schultz, P. H. (2018). The delivery of water by impacts from planetary accretion to present. *Science Advances, 4*(4). doi:10.1126/sciadv.aar2632

A review of the discovery of Comet Shoemaker-Levy 9 is provided in Marsden, B. G. (1993). Comet Shoemaker-Levy (1993e). *IAU Circular, 5727.*

An assessment of Jupiter's influence on asteroid & comet impacts through the inner solar system is given by Nakamura, T. & Kurahashi, H. (1998, February). Collisional probability of periodic comets with the terrestrial planets—an invalid case of analytic formulation. *Astronomical Journal.* 115(2), 848.

Discussions regarding the origin of the Moon are in the following sources:

Hotz, R. H. (2017, January 9). Researchers suggest new theory for the Moon's origin. *Wall Street Journal.* Retrieved 2019-04-20. https://www.wsj.com/articles/researchers-suggest-new-theory-for-the-moons-origin-1483977602

Pahlevan, K., & Stevenson, D. (2007, October). Equilibration in the aftermath of the lunar-forming giant impact. *Earth and Planetary Science Letters, 262*(3–4), 438–449.

Planetary Science Institute. (n.d.). *The origin of the moon.* Retrieved from https://www.psi.edu/epo/moon/moon.html

Wiechert, U., Halliday, A. N., Lee, D. C., Snyder, G. A., Taylor, L. A. & Rumble, D. (2001, October). Oxygen isotopes and the moon-forming giant impact. *Science, 294*(12), 345–348.

The orbit and fate of Triton is discussed in Chyba, C. F., Janikowski, D. G., & Nicholson, P. D. (1989, July). Tidal evolution in the Neptune-Triton system. *Astronomy and Astrophysics, 219*(1–2): L23–L26.

The Cryogenic ice age is discussed in Hyde W. T., Crowley T. J., Baum S. K., & Peltier W. R. (2000, May). Neoproterozoic "snowball Earth" simulations with a coupled climate/ice-sheet model. *Nature, 405*(6785), 425–429.

The K-T extinction event (more famously known as the extinction of the dinosaurs) is discussed in many places, including the following sources:

Alvarez, W. (1997). *T. rex and the crater of doom.* Princeton, NJ: Princeton University Press.

Alvarez, L. W. Alvarez, W., Asaro, F., & Michel, H. V. (1980). Extraterrestrial cause for the Cretaceous–Tertiary extinction. *Science, 208*(4448), 1095–1108. doi:10.1126/science.208.4448.1095

Duncan, R. A, & Pyle, D. G. (1988). Rapid eruption of the Deccan flood basalts at the Cretaceous/Tertiary boundary. *Nature, 333*(6176), 841–843. doi:10.1038/333841a0

Hildebrand, A. R., Penfield, G. T., Kring, D. A., Pilkington, M., Zanoguera, A. C., Jacobsen, S. B., & Boynton, W. V. (1991, September). Chicxulub Crater; a possible Cretaceous/Tertiary boundary impact crater on the Yucatan Peninsula, Mexico. *Geology, 19*(9), 867–871.

History. (n.d.). Why did the dinosaurs die out? Retrieved from https://www.history.com/topics/why-did-the-dinosaurs-die-out

Hofman, C., Féraud, G., & Courtillot, V. (2000). 40Ar/39Ar dating of mineral separates and whole rocks from the Western Ghats lava pile: Further constraints on duration and age of the Deccan traps. *Earth and Planetary Science Letters, 180*(1–2), 13–27. doi:10.1016/S0012-821X(00)00159-X

Robertson, D. S., McKenna, M. C., Toon, O. B., Hope, S., & Lillegraven, J. A. (2003). Survival in the first hours of the Cenozoic. *Geological Society of America Bulletin, 116*(5/6), 760–768. doi:10.1130/B25402.1

Credits

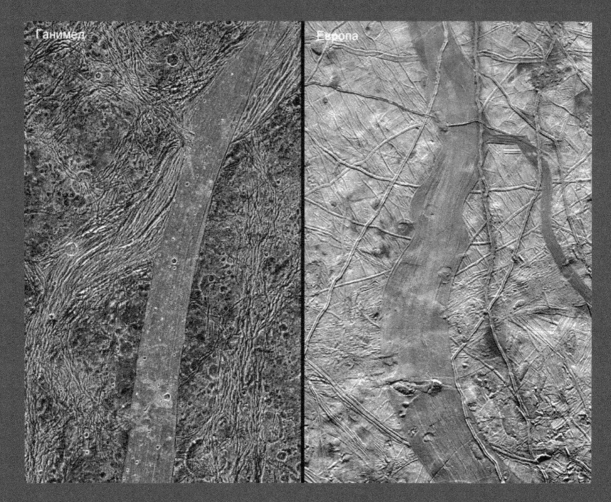

Close-ups of the surfaces of two moons of Jupiter, Ganymede (left) and Europa (right), from the Galileo spacecraft. Credit: NASA/JPL/Brown University.

CHAPTER 9

GEOLOGY IN THE SOLAR SYSTEM

PURPOSE

To review how different uniform geological processes have sculpted objects in the solar system

OBJECTIVES

- To use the Earth as a prototype for geology
- To introduce the notion of uniformitarianism
- To discuss the role of mechanisms in geology and astronomy
- To relate density and flow to how interiors of objects are layered
- To show how the lack of geologic activity shapes objects in the solar system
- To show how high amounts of geologic activity shape objects in the solar system

INTRODUCTION

In our last chapter, we explored how catastrophes—drastic changes driven by external forces—can sculpt the appearances of objects in the solar system. But objects can change themselves via internal forces as well. This chapter is devoted to those objects that possess geologic activity. Since we live on the Earth, we are most familiar with its geology, and we will explore it in some detail. Later, we will compare the Earth to geologic activity (or the lack thereof) for other objects in the solar system. Other properties of solar system objects, such as their atmospheres and magnetic fields, will appear in future chapters.

KEY TERMS

Albedo: The fraction or percentage of light that reflects off the surface of an object. Objects that reflect no light whatsoever have albedos of zero (0%) and objects that reflect all the light incident upon them have albedos of one (100%). Albedo can hint at the overall composition of an object's surface

Catastrophism: The idea that catastrophes are important in the shaping of the Earth and other objects in the solar system

Continental drift: The idea that the continents and oceans "drift" or move across the surface of the Earth over geologic periods of time. A precursor to *plate tectonics*

Convection: The movement of large masses of fluid due to differing temperatures and densities. For example, mantle rock deep inside the Earth slowly wells upward and mantle rock just underneath the Earth's crust slowly sinks. The net effect is to have very slow "bubbles" of mantle rock carry individual crustal plates along the surface of the Earth

Density (specifically mass density): The amount of mass per unit volume of an object. Density tends to be a set value for a specific substance. If an object consists of several different liquid substances, the heavier (higher density) substance tends to sink and the lighter (lower density) substance tends to rise

Differentiation: The process by which an object made of several substances mixed together separates these materials into distinct layers. For the solar system, this implies objects must have been liquid during their formation so that the different-density substances could flow in order to separate into layers

Kelvin-Helmholtz contraction: The notion, put forth separately by Lord Kelvin of England and Friedrich Helmholtz of Germany, that a large enough object (like the Sun) can contract under its own weight, and in the process liberate enormous amounts of light and heat. This is an important step in understanding how stars form

Mechanism: A way for events to progress via natural laws; for example, the convection of molten rock in the Earth's upper mantle is the mechanism that drives *plate tectonics*

Paleomagnetism: The study of magnetic fields associated with deposits of iron in ancient rock. Analysis of paleomagnetic fields on the floor of the Atlantic Ocean was a key piece of evidence in support of plate tectonics

Pangaea (also Pangea): Means "All lands": The notion that the Earth's continents were once united to create a super-continent several hundred million years ago. Earth has actually had several "pangaeas" throughout its history

Plate tectonics: The theory in geology that the Earth's crust is split into several dozen pieces or "plates" that are driven to move across the surface of the Earth by convection of the upper mantle

Radioactivity: The natural splitting apart of atomic nuclei via nuclear forces that releases enormous amounts of energy. Radioactive materials can also be used to determine the ages of some objects, including the Earth

Subduction: The process by which one of Earth's plates can "slip" or "dive" underneath another plate.

Triple point: A combination of temperature and pressure that allows a substance to readily switch between the three major phases of matter of gas, liquid, and solid. Earth is an example of a planet with conditions near the triple point of water

Uniformitarianism: The notion that major changes for objects such as the Earth are due to gradual changes caused by uniform processes

Uranium: The 92nd element on the periodic table, uranium is most famous for its radioactive properties. Uranium is an important component of the Earth's interior, helping to keep much of it molten

KEY INDIVIDUALS

Becquerel, Antoine-Henri: A French physicist of the late 19th/early 20th century who first discovered natural radioactivity. He shared the Nobel Prize in physics in 1903

Hutton, James: A Scottish geologist of the late 18th century who was instrumental in popularizing the idea that major changes on the Earth are due to slow, gradual, natural processes

Kelvin (a.k.a. Thomson, William): An English physicist of the late 19th century who suggested that the Sun generates its light by shrinking according to its own weight. While incorrect for the current Sun, this notion is an important step in understanding how stars form

Lyell, Charles: A Scottish geologist of the early 19th century who, like Hutton, favored the uniformitarian approach to explaining geological questions. His book *Principles of Geology* became the standard text for the following century or so

Ortelius, Abraham: A Dutch geographer of the late 16th/early 17th century who published the first modern atlas and first suggested the continents had once been joined together

Wegener, Alfred: A German geologist of the early 19th century who promoted the notion of "continental drift," which decades after his death was incorporated into the modern theory of plate tectonics

Whewell, William: An English natural philosopher of the mid-19th century who invented many common terms used in modern science, including scientist, physicist, *catastrophism*, *uniformitarianism*, and others

Section 9.1: Case Study: Plate Tectonics

Into the early 20th century, geologists assumed the Earth was globally static. That is, there was plenty of evidence for small-scale changes (the silting of a river delta or the depositing of layers in a sedimentary rock formation), but except for the occasional violent event (a volcanic eruption or massive earthquake), the overall look of the Earth didn't change. Continents and oceans always existed, and always existed in their current locations.

This assumption was first questioned when European explorers began compiling relatively accurate maps of the world. The first person to note that the Earth might have experienced drastic changes was a Dutch cartographer named Abraham Ortelius (1527–1598). His *Theatrum Orbum Terrarum* ("Theatre of the World"), published in 1570, is the first of what we would call an atlas, a map depicting the entire world (Figure 9.1).

FIGURE 9.1. Abraham Ortelius (portrait by Peter Paul Rubens); a global map by Ortelius from his "Theatre of the World" in 1570.

Ortelius's map includes some items that don't exist; for example, while it appears he has drawn the continent of Antarctica at the bottom, in fact Antarctica would not be discovered for a few centuries afterward, and Ortelius was simply following a tradition of assigning lands ("terra incognita") to places that had not yet been explored. On the other hand, his map has some strikingly correct modern features, even if some details are missing. Most of the continents are well represented (details regarding South America's west coast are lagging) and even places like Indonesia, Madagascar, and Greenland are there, although Australia, like Antarctica, is missing since it had yet to be discovered by Europeans.

What is interesting here is that Ortelius noted the northeastern coast of South America and the southwestern coast of Africa match up, like separated puzzle pieces. Similarly, the eastern coast of North America appears to fit with the western coast of Europe and the northwestern coast of Africa. Ortelius is the first person to suggest that these continents were once in the same place and subsequently split apart, by the actions of volcanic eruptions and earthquakes.

With increasing precision, it became easier to see the apparent (literal) connections between the continents, and several others would note this. But few geologists favored the notion, primarily because nobody could offer a convincing mechanism by which continents could move. Contemporary geology assumed the Earth, with some local exceptions, was a solid object, and therefore moving continents made no sense. The idea of splitting continents thus lingered for centuries.

In 1915, the German scientist Alfred Wegener (1880–1930) published his first edition of "The Origin of Continents and Oceans," noting the similarities of the shapes of the coasts of South America and Africa. But more importantly, he put together other lines of evidence. For example, he showed that the two continents shared the same fossils up until a specific point in time, and then the fossil record diverged. Similarly, he found layers of rock

(rock "strata") were similar up to a divergent point of time in, for example, Newfoundland and New Brunswick in North America compared to Ireland and Scotland. Wegener also noted the presence of the mid-Atlantic Ridge was perhaps the location of the diverging.

 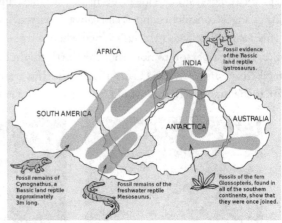

FIGURE 9.2. Alfred Wegener during an expedition in Greenland in 1930 (left); a modern map showing samples of common fossils for Pangaea, based on Wegener's work (right).

Just as with Ortelius centuries before, Wegener's idea, called *continental drift*, didn't gain traction during his lifetime, and for the same reason: There didn't appear to be a way to make it work. Geologists were hard put to imagine a continent plowing its way through solid rock (to be fair, we can't see that happening now!), and, lacking a mechanism, ridiculed Wegener's hypothesis. The fact that Wegener's occupation was as a meteorologist and not as a geologist contributed to the disdain. Wegener died in 1930, unfortunately decades before his (and Ortelius's) idea found vindication from the wider geologist community.

With improving technology, better evidence began rolling in during the 1950s and 1960s. The most striking piece came from *paleomagnetism*, the study of magnetism contained in ancient rocks. The Earth's magnetic field occasionally flips its polarity—currently, the Earth's south magnetic pole is in upper Canada, but it would have been the north magnetic pole several hundred thousand years ago. The flipping isn't on a precise schedule, but it does change about once every 200,000 years or so. Geologists found iron (an element very susceptible to magnetism) aligned itself first in one direction and then another on the floor of the Atlantic Ocean, depending on its distance from the middle of the ocean. Further, the "middle" of the Atlantic Ocean is marked by a ridge of underwater mountains (some occasionally breaching the surface to be islands) that meanders in a pattern suspiciously like the shape of the coastlines of the eastern American continents and the western coastlines of Europe and Africa.

Whether continents were "drifting" or being driven apart in the Atlantic, at some point we might expect they would run into each other on the other side of the globe. Geologists discovered a process called *subduction*, where the edge of one continent would slowly slip under another. Further, they found that it wasn't merely continents; ocean floors also act in a similar fashion. We now talk about the surface of the Earth consisting of individual continental and oceanic plates and the theory has the name *plate tectonics*. But what is the mechanism that drives plates across the globe?

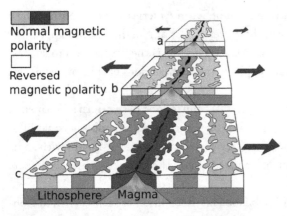

FIGURE 9.3. A model of magnetic "striping" on the floor of the Atlantic Ocean. "a" = 5 million years ago; "b" = about 2.5 million years ago; "c" = today.

We will discuss the internal structure of the Earth (and other large solar system objects) later, but for now the short answer is that the Earth is not solid, at least not all the way through. Large sections of the Earth, including the upper mantle—the section underneath the crust—are liquid, and more importantly, the liquid mantle flows. The plates are consequently carried along by the flowing upper mantle. Plates can split apart or "diverge" (as at the mid-Atlantic Ridge), come together or "converge" (the Indian plate is running into the Eurasian plate to form the Himalayan mountains), or even slide side by side (the Pacific plate and North American plate are an example of such a "transform" plate boundary).

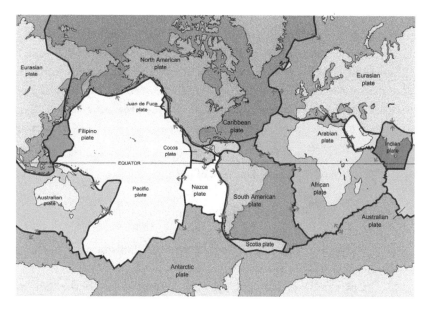

FIGURE 9.4. A color map showing the major tectonic plates of Earth. The arrows indicate their relative directions of movement.

The theory of plate tectonics is now recognized as one of those overarching ideas that ties an entire discipline together, as evolution does for biology or the Big Bang does for cosmology. More to the point for us here, it is an example of how slow, gradual processes can shape the appearances of planets and moons.

Section 9.2: Uniformitarianism versus Catastrophism

By the late 18th century, scientists were confronting the growing evidence that the Earth is not a static object but undergoes profound changes. One group tended to favor *catastrophism*, the notion that large changes must be caused by quick and violent events; the Biblical flood of Noah was commonly cited as a culprit and the de-

struction of the continent of Atlantis[1] is a common theme. Another group, led by geologist James Hutton, thought instead that changes are gradual, coming about by the application of natural laws. Hutton published extensively on his views, his most famous book being *Theory of the Earth*.

The debate would rage for decades. Hutton's biggest advocate was Sir Charles Lyell (1797–1885), from Scotland like Hutton, who also favored *uniformitarianism*, the idea that changes in the Earth—for example, layers of sedimentary rock and the silting of rivers—take place gradually over extremely long periods of time via uniform processes. Lyell's *Principles of Geology*, originally

FIGURE 9.5. Portraits of James Hutton by Henry Raeburn (left) and Charles Lyell by George J. Stodart (right).

---

[1] The destruction of the continent of Atlantis itself was an extremely popular hypothesis throughout the 19th century. Most scholars placed it at the center of the Atlantic Ocean (hence the name), though the Mediterranean Sea was also popular. The idea was that the Atlanteans were an ancient race with secret knowledge beyond our ken who helped found civilization as we know it. The "theory of Atlantis," we now know, is a myth.

published in three volumes from 1830 to 1833 was perhaps the defining text for geology for the following century. The two terms (catastrophism and uniformitarianism) were both coined by the philosopher William Whewell (1794–1866), another philosopher/scientist who also published research in geology. Uniformitarianism became the dominant way of thinking for geology (and other related fields) until just a few decades ago with the recognition of the importance of catastrophic impacts (see the previous chapter).

According to Reijer Hooykaas, a historian of science, Lyell's uniformitarianism can be broken down into four separate statements:

- **Uniformity of law:** The laws of nature are universal and constant (that is, they apply everywhere and at all times)
- **Uniformity of methodology:** The processes (mechanisms) at work today were at play in the same manner (rate) in the past
- **Uniformity of kind:** Not only are the mechanisms of today the same kind as mechanisms in the past, but they produce the same effects
- **Uniformity of degree:** Geological circumstances are the same today as in the past

Note that the four statements can be treated as independent, and geologists are not always in agreement with them. For example, the second assumption is debatable, in that the rates of change today are not necessarily the same as those in the past.

One of the larger hurdles for the uniformitarian approach was the age of the Earth. Geologists began to see that hundreds of thousands, if not millions, of years were needed to make the massive changes they saw in the geologic column. This ran into opposition from two sources. First, many scholars still preferred to reference the Bible, which hints at an age for the Earth of several thousands of years, but not millions. Second, astronomers and physicists were hard put to find mechanisms to account for the enormous times geologists were finding. On the other hand, with Charles Darwin's publication of *Origin of Species*, biologists too were requiring enormous durations of time.

We find ourselves returning to the term *mechanism* when discussing plate tectonics or uniformitarianism. Let's take a moment to discuss why this is important.

By "mechanism," we don't mean a mechanical device. Rather, the idea comes out of how science is applied. Science itself is not merely a body of knowledge or set of facts to memorize, though these are important. Rather, science is a problem-solving process. Different disciplines of science use differing ways of solving their problems, but the basic idea of science being an active rather than a passive learning procedure is critical. Or, as is sometimes said, science is really a verb, not a noun.

A complimentary feature of science is that it deals with nature. For practical reasons, scientists look for ways in which nature operates to effect changes, which we refer to as "mechanisms" for short. If you throw a stick into the air, it falls back down, and the mechanism behind this action is the gravitational force between the stick and the Earth. If you kick a soccer ball so that it rolls across a field, it eventually comes to a halt due to the mechanism of friction between the ball and the blades of grass of the field. This "mechanistic" view of nature came of age with Isaac Newton and, with a few exceptions, governs how scientists apply their craft even today.[2] As mentioned briefly, the mechanism for plate tectonics is convection. Why convection works requires a deeper dive into the Earth (literally and figuratively) to search for even more basic mechanisms, as does the parallel question of the age of the Earth.

Let's examine some possible mechanisms that shed light on the age of the Earth. The first real attempt from physics to put a cap on the age of the Earth approached it indirectly by putting a cap on the age of the Sun. By the late 1800s, physicists knew that a massive object contracting under its own weight will transform much of its gravitational potential energy into heat. The first application of this to the Sun was made public by William

---

[2] This is often termed "methodological naturalism," whereby scientists refer to natural laws to solve scientific questions. "Philosophical naturalism" is the idea that all questions can be solved by appealing to natural causes. The distinction is subtle and beyond the scope of our short discussion here.

Thomson of England, later Lord Kelvin (1824–1907) during a talk given in 1887. The process is called *Kelvin-Helmholtz contraction*, combining Kelvin with the German physicist Helmholtz, and is recognized as a key component of star formation.

In Kelvin's suggestion, the Sun would be slowly shrinking under its own weight. The heat produced by this process would keep the Sun hot enough to glow. If the rate of shrinking was constant (or, more specifically, the rate of transformation of gravitational energy into heat was constant), then the Sun's light output would remain constant. His idea, picturing both the shrinking of the Sun and the appearance of the Earth, is shown in Figure 9.6.

Kelvin worked out two calculations. First, he found that the amount of shrinking of the Sun needed to produce its current luminosity is so slight that people would not have been able to notice it (without modern telescopes) over the entirety of human history. Second, he found the maximum amount of time the Sun could shrink was about 9 million years.

As long as this seems, it is several orders of magnitude too small to account for the time scales required by contemporary biology and geology. But no other

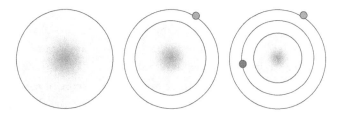

FIGURE 9.6. A 19th-century hypothesis concerning the age of the Earth and Sun. The Sun generates energy by gravitational contraction. As it shrinks, it leaves behind planets. The Earth's age therefore corresponds to its distance from the Sun.

FIGURE 9.7. William Thomson, Lord Kelvin (left); Antoine-Henri Becquerel (right).

known source of energy at that time would last any longer, and Kelvin's calculations were at the time state of the art. Fortunately, scientists would not have much longer to wait.

In 1896, less than a decade later, the French physicist Antoine-Henri Becquerel (1856–1939) noticed that photographic plates left in a drawer (where light could not get at them) were fogged. Eventually he traced the cause to a sample of uranium and realized the uranium was giving off its own energy without any need for a chemical reaction. This phenomenon quickly was dubbed *radioactivity* (as in the "activity" from the source radiates in all directions). Calculations showed that radioactivity releases much more energy, gram for gram, than chemical reactions or gravitational contraction could ever supply for, and scientists realized this could account for the Sun's enormous power output. We now know that the specific kind of radioactivity found by Becquerel is not responsible for the

Sun's output, and that the Sun is sustained instead by nuclear fusion. But the discovery of radioactivity was the first step to discovering the true power source of the Sun several decades later. Radioactivity, in short, supplied the energy to explain the incredibly long ages of the Sun and Earth.

Radioactivity also has much to say about plate tectonics, and in fact is a deeper mechanism for the convection of the upper mantle. Given the Earth's mass and volume, it should have cooled enough by now that it should be mostly solid inside. Instead, the Earth is more akin to a drop of water, being mostly liquid inside with an extremely thin "skin" on its outside. While there is a section of the Earth's core that

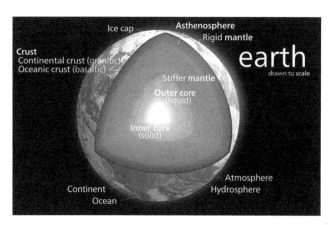

FIGURE 9.8. A scale model of the interior of the Earth, showing its major layers (core, mantle, and crust).

is solid, most of the core and most of the mantle—easily making up the majority of the interior of the Earth—is liquid. It is the presence of a (relatively) large amount of uranium, and its accompanying radioactivity, that supplies the heat to keep the Earth molten inside.

The Earth consists of three major layers: a core of metal (mostly iron and nickel), a mantle of heavy rock (laden with iron and magnesium), and a crust of lighter rock (basalt or granite). Each section can itself be split into two subsections due to differing conditions; for example, the "inner core" is solid and the "outer core" is liquid. The upper mantle—the region of the mantle just underneath the crust—is barely a liquid as we understand it, flowing at rates on the order of just a few centimeters per year. But it does move, and the upper mantle carries the solid pieces of the crust, the "plates" of our plate tectonics, along as it flows. Table 9.1 (from the United States Geological Survey) lists the thickness of each layer, its range of densities, and the substances of which each layer consists.

TABLE 9.1. The Interior Layers of the Earth

Layer	Thickness (km)	Range of Density (g/cm³)	Common substances
Crust	30	2.2–2.9	Silicate rocks, basalt, etc.
Upper mantle	720	3.4–4.4	peridotite, olivine, pyroxene, etc.
Lower mantle	2171	4.4–5.6	magnesium and silicate oxides
Outer core	2259	9.9–12.2	iron + oxygen, sulfur, nickel alloy
Inner core	1221	12.8–13.1	iron + oxygen, sulfur, nickel alloy

Table adapted from information found in *Theory of the Earth* by Don L. Anderson

Let's take a quick look at the details of plate movement. We mentioned earlier how plates can split apart, come together, or move side by side. Figure 9.9 illustrates these three different processes. On the left of Figure 9.9, we see the splitting of a plate, officially occurring at a "divergent" boundary. The convection of the upper mantle is depicted via curling arrows and shows how the upper mantle forces the pieces of the plate apart. Volcanic islands can form from the magma brought through the divergent boundary. In the middle of the figure, we see two plates come together at a "convergent" boundary. Note that the two plates do not simply crash together; rather, one plate slips under the other, which is called "subduction." At the convergent boundary, the edge of the plate on top is pushed up, which forms mountains, and deep inside the Earth where the two boundaries rub against each other, we find a "hot spot" that induces volcanic activity. At right we see two plates passing by each other at a "transform" boundary. Again, earthquakes and volcanoes are encouraged by the relative motions of the plates (plate boundaries are not smooth). Finally, to be complete, there are so-called "hot spots" (not pictured) where magma wells up through thin sections in the middle of a plate. A hot spot can push magma straight up through the plate, forming a volcanic island. As the plate moves over the hot spot, the hot spot can create several volcanoes, which tend to show up in a line or string of volcanic islands.

Check Your Neighbor

Consider famous features on the Earth. List at least one feature for each of the boundaries (including hot spots).

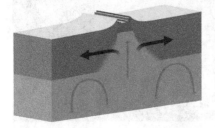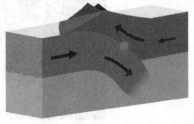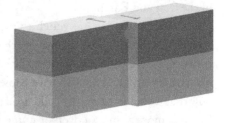

FIGURE 9.9. The various boundaries between tectonic plates on Earth. Divergent boundary (left); convergent boundary (center); transform boundary (right).

We can finally answer our question: What is the mechanism that drives plate tectonics? The Earth is liquid inside—at least, liquid enough to the extent that it sluggishly flows. While the rate of flow is slow, it is relentless. The large masses (momenta) of the upper mantle rock carry the plates along with it. As long as the upper mantle fulfills these conditions, it flows, so that the Earth has moving plates. The consequences of moving plates include not only dramatic events—volcanic eruptions and earthquakes—but also long-term climate change, including changing the latitudes of continents, reshaping continents, creation of islands, and sequestration of materials into the Earth, such as water and carbon dioxide. The convection of the mantle overall, combined with the rotation of the outer core, is responsible for the Earth's magnetic field, which acts to protect the atmosphere.

Our discussion has shown how the Earth's geology is not determined solely by uniform processes or occasional catastrophes. "Uniform" mechanisms are responsible for behaviors such as plate tectonics and magnetic fields. "Catastrophic" mechanisms are responsible for craters (small scale) and the very formation of worlds (large scale). Geologists now recognize that both ideas are important for understanding our planet. Our next task is to apply these ideas to other objects in the solar system.

Section 9.3: The Interiors of Other Worlds

The previous discussion about the Earth's interior hints at how other objects might be structured. The first idea is that the interiors of many astronomical objects <u>are</u> structured, and not just randomly thrown-together bits. This may appear contradictory to what we've recently discussed regarding impacts, which appear random.

Suppose we consider a sizeable object, which we can state for the moment would be several hundreds of kilometers across. For many (not all) such objects, the formation process, which involved an incredible number of smaller colliding objects, energy released in these collisions would go to heating the forming object. Heat would specifically come from gravitational potential energy, kinetic energy (recall kinetic energy comes from the relative speeds of objects), heat from the forming Sun and protoplanetary disk, and (usually later) tidal interactions. If enough heat is released, the object in question can melt.

Our sample object is likely to consist of a variety of substances; in the solar system, the common options are hydrogen, helium, other light gases (such as methane or ammonia), water, assorted rock, and metal with iron and nickel dominating. If the object melts at least partially through, then the different substances can sort themselves out due to their densities. As long as the substances don't react chemically with each other, higher density materials tend to sink while lighter density materials tend to rise.

Figure 9.10 illustrates the point. You've probably heard the phrase "water and oil don't mix." Physically, it simply means that oil molecules electrically repel water molecules and vice versa. Rubbing alcohol is a third substance that maintains its independence from water and oil both. If we pour water, vegetable oil, and rubbing alcohol into a graduated cylinder and shake it up (i.e., we attempt to mix the three substances thoroughly) and wait (it doesn't take but a minute to see results), we will see the alcohol, oil, and water have flowed past each other to seek their own level.

The analogy for astronomy should be clear. If an astronomical object is molten (liquid) all the way through, we should expect to see some filtering of different substances into layers dependent on their relative densities. Such is the case, as we can see from looking at the example of the terrestrial planets (Figure 9.11).

FIGURE 9.10. A graduated cylinder containing layers of rubbing alcohol, vegetable oil, and colored water.

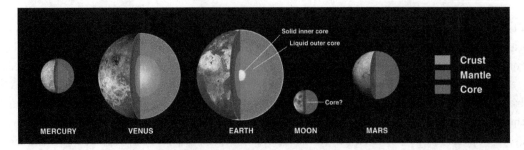

FIGURE 9.11. Interior of the terrestrial worlds, including the Moon, to scale. Credit: NASA.

All the terrestrial worlds (if we include the Moon among them) have the same basic interior structure:

- A core of iron and nickel. Most terrestrials are suspected to have a solid, inner core and a liquid, outer core
- A mantle of heavy rocks. The atoms that form basic rock structures are oxygen and silicon; here, elements like iron and magnesium are mixed in, increasing the density of the rock. The mantle also can come in different sections, one solid, one liquid
- A crust of light rocks. Magma—molten rock, brought up by volcanic action or created by violent impacts—cools into a lighter, almost black rock generally known as basalt. The Earth's ocean floor in the Atlantic Ocean is basalt, for example. We also find an even lighter rock, generally granite related, making up the crusts of terrestrials. On Earth, since the granite is slightly lighter than basalt, it tends to "float" higher and thus makes up most of our continental land

Individual worlds have their own individual layers and layer thicknesses, of course. The Messenger spacecraft, which spent time orbiting Mercury, discovered that perhaps 85% of its interior is taken up by its core. Venus has a similar structure as Earth, but its core is somewhat smaller, which makes sense as Venus overall is somewhat smaller than Earth. The Moon has a noticeably tiny core (recall our discussion about the Moon's origin in chapter 8) and thus a relatively larger mantle. Details of the Martian interior are still up for grabs, but the overall density of Mars also suggests it has a small core and large mantle.

> ### Check Your Neighbor
>
> The overall density of Mercury is 5.4 g/cc and the overall density of Mars is 3.9 g/cc. Which planet consists of a larger percentage of mantle rock?

We live on Earth, so we can be expected to gather detailed information about its interior. But how do we know anything about the interiors of other worlds? Several methods of inquiry are used, but here are a few of the most important:

- Overall density
- Comparison of overall density to the density of substances at the surface
- Determination of specific substances on the surface
- The flattening of the surface (i.e., how close to a perfect sphere is the object)
- The strength of a magnetic field

Overall density gives us some broad brush strokes regarding an object's interior composition. For example, the density of (uncompressed) water ice is 1 gram per cubic centimeter. If our object in question has an overall density of 3 g/cc, then we know the object can't consist solely of water ice. Overall density simply requires we know the mass and the radius of the object, which tend to be relatively easy to determine, at least for objects roughly spherical in shape.

The comparison of the density of substances at the surface to the overall density of the object uses similar logic. If we determine the density of surface rocks of our object is near 2 g/cc, but the overall density of the object is closer to 5 g/cc, then we know the object can't be made solely of the type of rock found at the surface. A subset of this idea is to directly determine the types of substances on the surface. Such science usually requires sophisticated spectroscopy and/or sampling of materials via robot probe.

The flattening of the surface helps us compare the total mass of our object to the "toughness" of its substances. Objects made of very dense substances tend, assuming total masses are the same, to be closer to perfect spheres. Common surface features like volcanoes, mountains, river beds, and canyons are all "imperfections" from the object not being a perfect sphere. If an object has relatively large surface features, it is often a hint that its density is low.

Finally, does our object possess a strong magnetic field? Magnetic fields (we will see them in detail in chapter 11) come about from having moving liquid

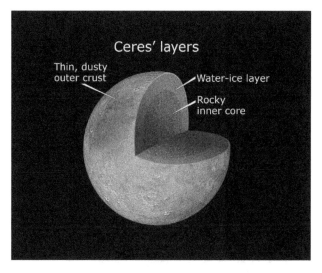

FIGURE 9.12. The interior of the largest of the asteroids, Ceres. Note the lack of a metal core. Credit: NASA/ESA/A. Field (STScI).

metal in a good-sized section of the interior. A lack of a magnetic field tells us our object has little metal, or doesn't spin rapidly, or its metal and/or rocky layers are not liquid. For example, Venus is very near the Earth in terms of mass, radius, and density, and is suspected to have at least some liquid metal and/or rock in its interior. But its slow rotation (its sidereal rotational period is 243 days!) shows us why its magnetic field is virtually nonexistent.

Asteroids generally orbit somewhat further out from the Sun than the terrestrial worlds, and the general trend of decreasing overall density holds for those few asteroids for which we have good data. Ceres, the largest of the asteroids (and part of the asteroid belt) is light enough that it cannot have much, if any, of a metallic core. Rather, it probably has a core of relatively heavy rock and an outer section of water ice. The crust of Ceres is likely a variation of that theme, consisting of dust, rock, and ice mixed together. Ceres is large enough to be spherical, and therefore was probably at least partially molten in its early days. But its location in the solar system tells us it probably never had much in the way of metal (percentage wise) available in the first place. The few other asteroids we have densities for tend to agree with the rock-ice mix hypothesis.

As we get farther and farther from the Sun, we find objects trading heavier materials for lighter ones. Recall (from chapters 6 and 7) why this is so: Objects closer to the forming Sun experienced higher temperatures, and only "tough" materials like metal and rock tended to survive, whereas water evaporated. As we get further out from the Sun, the temperature dropped, and the more popular substances like water had a better chance of survival.

A good example of the interior of a large (and solid) object from the outer solar system is Jupiter's moon Callisto. Callisto is much larger across than our Moon and is on a par with Mercury in terms of diameter. But Callisto's density is much less than that of Mercury. Data from the Galileo space probe hints that the bulk of Callisto is light rock, perhaps mixed with water ice. The crust of Callisto is not granite or basalt as on Earth or the Moon, but rather frozen water ice with a coating of

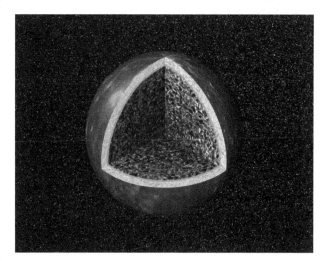

FIGURE 9.13. The interior of Jupiter's moon Callisto, as hinted at by the Galileo spacecraft. Callisto is a mix of rock and ice, with perhaps a thin underground ocean of liquid water and a crust of frozen water ice. Credit: NASA.

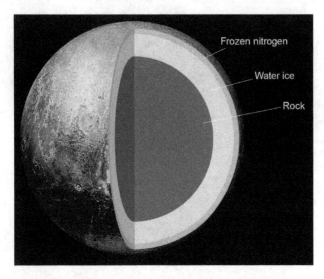

FIGURE 9.14. The interior of Pluto, using data from the New Horizons spacecraft in 2015. Not only does Pluto lack a metal core, but it includes a layer of frozen nitrogen. Credit: NASA/Johns Hopkins University Applied Physics Laboratory/Southwest Research Institute.

dust on the surface. Callisto may, like its sibling moons Europa and Ganymede, have an underground ocean of liquid water beneath the icy crust, which is many tens of kilometers thick.

Even further out is Pluto. Pluto represents a newer class of objects, which among other names we can call "icy dwarfs." The icy dwarfs are so far from the Sun that not only do they possess large amounts of frozen water, but other forms of ice as well. Figure 9.14 shows Pluto has a thick layer of frozen nitrogen, which is amazing—the same element that counts for 4/5 of the atmosphere that you and I breathe is a solid there. Pluto's semi-major axis is 40 au, which means it gets 1/1600 of the intensity of sunlight we enjoy on Earth and allows nitrogen to freeze (which requires temperatures near 40 kelvin, or about −390 °F).

Finally, what about asteroids and comets? These objects are generally too small to have undergone much, if any, differentiation, and thus (with some exceptions) are not expected to have distinct layers. The distinction between the two classes of objects is that asteroids are primarily made of rock (there is a significant subclass that incorporates metal) and comets are primarily made of a variety of ices. In both cases, billions of years of life in the solar system has allowed them to gather interplanetary carbon-based dust; an asteroid or comet nucleus several tens of kilometers long may have a "crust" or skin of dark dust several meters thick. In fact, the few close-up images of comet nuclei show they are among the darkest objects in the solar system—a strange result at first glance, considering how bright comets can be when they approach the Sun.

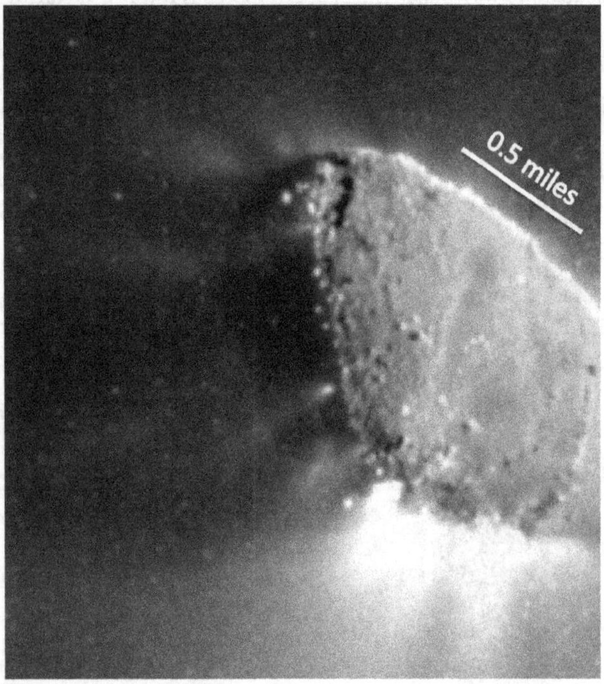

Figure 9.15 exhibits a close-up of the nucleus of Comet Hartley (from NASA's EPOXI mission), which both shows the dark nature of its surface and bright jets emerging from its sun-lit side. The jets are from water and other ices melting below the carbonaceous crust, with the pressures of expanding liquids shooting out of "pores" (weak spots) in the crust. While asteroids have densities similar to common rocks (around 2 grams

Check Your Neighbor

Albedo is a measure of the amount of light reflected by a material, zero (0%) for an object that reflects no light at all and 1 (100%) for an object that reflects all light incident upon it. In which case does a comet have an overall albedo close to zero: when the comet is far from the Sun or when it is close to the Sun?

FIGURE 9.15. A close-up of the nucleus of Comet Hartley. The image shows both its nonreflective surface and jets of water shooting out of weak spots in its crust. Credit: NASA/JPL-Caltech/UMD/EPOXI mission.

0.5 miles

per cubic centimeter) the comet nuclei for which we have reliable data all reveal densities around 0.6 g/cc or less, implying the interiors of comet nuclei are not only ices, but very "fluffy" ices at that.

To sum up: If an astronomical object was large enough to have been at least partly molten during its formation at the beginning of the solar system, it would (a) have a layered ("differentiated") structure, and (b) consist of different mixes of materials, depending on its original distance from the forming Sun. Also, the make-up and conditions of the interiors of objects have consequences for the appearances of their surfaces, a topic we take up next.

Section 9.4: "Dead" Worlds

What happens to an object if it does <u>not</u> possess an active geology? Essentially, it serves as a target from other objects in the solar system.

The label "dead" is a relative term and can change over time. Objects like the Moon and Mercury were active—volcanoes, possible atmospheres, etc.—very early in their histories, but virtually ceased all activity billions of years ago.[3] Some objects are in the process of dying; Mars is an example of this, having apparently ceased volcanism about 250 million years ago and has lost almost all of its atmosphere, limiting its weather. Virtually all asteroids, as long as they are floating through space and not hitting other objects, are completely geologically dead. Comet nuclei are better described as "dormant" rather than dead, since they can become extremely active if they get close enough to the Sun. Being geologically dead (or dormant) does not mean nothing can happen to an object, but that events happen <u>to</u> the object and not due to the object itself.

Possibly the most densely cratered object in all the solar system is Jupiter's moon Callisto. While the Galileo spacecraft's measurements hints at a possible underground ocean, no evidence of running water appears on its surface. Rather, living in the shadow of Jupiter's great gravity, Callisto has spent its existence as a planet-sized target. Callisto is peppered with impact craters and shows no signs of any processes of getting rid of them—no volcanoes, no earthquakes, no running water, no weathering (no atmosphere), and so on.

However, this doesn't mean that Callisto is uninteresting, or that we can't learn anything from it. Its surface is generally very dark (low albedo), likely due to billions of years of travel throughout the solar system gathering carbonaceous dust. But occasionally we see bright—white in color—craters and even some crater rays. The

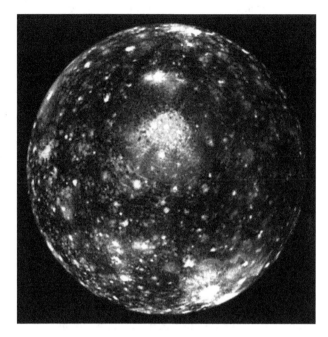

FIGURE 9.16. The surface of Callisto, one of the solar system's most densely cratered objects. Credit: NASA/JPL.

FIGURE 9.17. The north entrance to the Parsons Boulevard subway station entrance in Queens, New York City. Note the snow piled up in front, some of it pristine, some of it covered by soot.

---

[3] Even so, there are indications of slight amounts of outgassing—gasses escaping the rocks and floating off into space—for Mercury and the Moon both.

explanation is that Callisto may be dark on the surface but consists of lighter (in color) snow and ice underneath. When an asteroid or comet hits Callisto, it digs out a lot of bright snow and spills it across the surface. Older craters no longer show the bright snow, which eventually is covered up by the slow accumulation of the solar system's dust. An analogous situation on Earth is the covering of a snowdrift in a city by soot and car exhaust (Figure 9.17): The soot tends to cover just an inch or so of the surface, but plunging one's hand into the snowdrift reveals pristine, clean snow underneath.

Another item we can learn just by looking at the surface of an object is its relative age. Even a geologically "dead" world, which we can expect to have all of it die more or less at the same time, does not need to have the same aged sections of its surface. For example, if an extremely large asteroid hits the surface of the Moon, its impact can melt much of the surface. The lava released can cover the neighboring surface, including any craters that had been there earlier, in effect renewing the surface.

How about objects too small to be round? Phobos, one of the moons of Mars, is either a captured asteroid or a remnant of an ancient enormous impact. Phobos is about 24 kilometers along its longest axis. Figure 9.19 shows that, even though Phobos is an incredibly small object for the solar system, even smaller objects are out there and, given enough time, Phobos shows craters just as much larger objects do. Phobos is far too small to ever have been geologically active or hold an atmosphere, but there are some subtle signs of activity. The thin, straight lines ("striations") are not something Phobos can do on its own. One interesting hypothesis is that the tides of Mars slowly pull boulders across the surface of Phobos, digging shallow channels as they go.

We have seen that even objects that have no mechanisms available to change the appearances themselves can still experience events that change their appearances for them. Our last stop is to view examples of the most active objects in the solar system. Hint: The Earth is <u>not</u> number 1!

Section 9.5: Active Worlds

Earth, by definition has a "geology," but it isn't the only geologically active object in the solar system. It isn't even

FIGURE 9.18. A close-up photograph of the Moon during the Apollo 16 mission in 1972. Each rectangle (A or B) covers approximately the same area. Which rectangle represents a relatively younger surface? Credit: NASA.

Check Your Neighbor

Figure 9.18 was shot on a 70-mm hand-held camera during the Apollo 16 manned Moon mission. Two rectangular regions, labeled A and B, are sketched upon the image. Which rectangle represents a relatively younger surface?

FIGURE 9.19. Phobos, one of the moons of Mars. Each pixel represents about 36 meters on a side. The long axis of Phobos (from lower left to upper right) is 24 kilometers long. Credit: NASA/Mars Global Surveyor.

the most active object. And astronomers, starting with the first planetary space probes in the 1960s, have been constantly surprised by the amount of activity from planets and (especially) moons, regardless of where they are in the solar system or how large they are. Since we've discussed the Earth already, we leave it behind for this section to look at the actions—and possible mechanisms—of other worlds.

Our discussion regarding Earth revealed that having a liquid upper mantle under a solid crust allowed for convection and consequent surface activity. The key point discovered by planetary astronomers these past several decades is not that the mantle and/or crust need to be a specific substance (like rock), but rather that they are in these phases of matter. Several worlds will have mantles (if that is the proper term) of liquid water and crusts of solid water ice. A few will have substances—nitrogen is a prime example—that are gas on the Earth, but can be found in all three major phases. Let's look at a few examples, starting with the most geologically active object we know.

1. Io

Jupiter has four "giant" moons, that is, moons that are approximately as large as our Moon or larger. Io, which is similar to our Moon in radius and mass, is the closest of the four to Jupiter (though not the closest of Jupiter's moons).

Chapter 4 included a brief look at Io during a discussion of gravity tides. To review quickly, here, because the amount of gravitational force depends on the square of the distance from an object (Jupiter, for example), the gravity force will not be the same at different locations (such as the side of Io nearest to Jupiter versus the side of

Io furthest from Jupiter), "tides" being the shorthand term for this effect. Jupiter alone exerts enormous tides on Io, but Io also received periodic contributions from its neighboring moons Europa and Ganymede. The net result is that Io is continually flexed inside back and forth like a bending paper clip. And like the paper clip, the energy used to flex Io turns into enormous heat. The interior of Io is virtually all molten, so much so that it is common for observers to note a dozen or so active volcanoes and to measure a surface temperature near 1,000 K (over 1,300 °F), making it the hottest surface in the solar system besides the Sun.

Io also has the youngest surface of any moon or planet (excepting the Jovians), being estimated at a million years on average. While this is ancient for people, it is quite young for an astronomical object. And this is an average; surfaces near erupting volcanoes will literally be brand new. Very few impact craters are visible, even though Io lives in the same neighborhood as Callisto (see Section 9.4), arguably the most densely cratered object in the solar system. Astronomers sometimes joke that any visitors to Io[4] would need daily geological reports much in the same way we get daily weather reports here.

Check Your Neighbor

Io's surface is extremely young at about 1 million years. About how old do you think Io is as an object in general? Why?

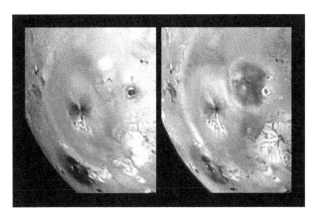

FIGURE 9.20. Close-up images from the Galileo spacecraft of Io. Left: Pillan Patera in April 1997; right: Pillan Patera in September 1997, after a massive volcanic eruption. The "stain" of ejecta is about 400 km (250 miles) in diameter, and the plume rose 120 kilometers (75 miles) above the surface. Credit: NASA/JPL.

---

[4] A trip to Io is not recommended. Not only is Io's surface nearly 1,000 K and subjected to frequent volcanic eruptions, but it also is continually bathed in deadly radiation from Jupiter's intense magnetic field.

2. Europa and Ganymede

Io is the most extreme version of how gravity tides can affect a moon, but it's hardly the only example. In order outward from Jupiter after Io are Europa and Ganymede. While these moons do not "feel" the tides as strongly as Io, the tides do churn up their interiors enough to form oceans of liquid water underneath a thick crust of water ice. Neither Europa nor Ganymede appear to have volcanoes or geysers as such, but they do show some evidence of surface motion. Sections of both moons look like ice floes have broken off and slid across each of their surfaces; for example, photographs from the Voyager missions can be used to reconstruct craters that otherwise appear sliced in half. As with Io, there are few impact craters, indicating that something must be removing or covering them up.

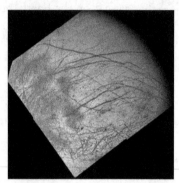 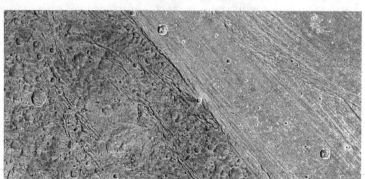

FIGURE 9.21. Other images from the Galileo spacecraft. Left: Dark bands (cracks) in the surface of Europa; right: light and dark terrain with "stripes" on Ganymede. Credit: NASA/JPL.

Europa in particular has caught the eyes of astronomers. The moon appears like nothing else than a crystal ball hit by a hammer, with a network of cracks visible from a distance. As you might expect, a violent impact event can not only leave a crater but shatter the ground all around the crater. For an object like the Moon or Mercury, lava and rock are opaque, and so even if the crust is broken up, we can't see it; for Europa, with an icy crust, we can see through the ice to spot the cracks. Further, matter from below the crust can well up as liquid or be released as gases. The cracks are notable in another way; recent spectroscopic observations of Europa hint at the presence of (very simple) organic molecules where cracks reach the surface. One idea is that organic compounds can form in the underground oceans of Europa and well to the surface through the cracks. NASA is seriously pondering a lander mission to Europa to sample the ice in one of these regions (not a mission to dig down to the oceans; they're too deep for us yet) to confirm the presence of organic matter. We aren't saying there is life in the underground oceans of Europa (yet!) but just studying organic compounds on Europa can give us hints as to how life arose on Earth.

Check Your Neighbor

It takes energy to make organic compounds. Sunlight on Europa is too weak to reach its underground oceans. What might serve as an energy source?

Ganymede has many of the same basic features as Io—cracks in its icy surface, lack of impact craters, etc.— although there is less evidence of these types of activities. This makes sense, as Ganymede is further from Jupiter than Europa and thus the tides felt by Ganymede are not as strong. Ganymede also includes "cantaloupe terrain," areas where the surface is mottled like the skin of a cantaloupe. Such terrain appears on several other objects which also have icy surfaces and geologic activity due to tides, but astronomers are not decided on the mechanism(s) responsible.

3. Enceladus

Enceladus is a moon of Saturn. Being only 500 kilometers (300 miles) across, it is significantly smaller than our moon or other "giant" moons in the solar system, though it is large enough for its gravity to bend it into a round (spherical) shape. Enceladus was thought to be too small to be geologically active, but images from the Cassini mission show that to be close to the opposite of the case.

Enceladus has active geysers. The tides of Saturn keep Enceladus warm inside, and Enceladus joins the list of moons that have icy crusts and underground liquid water. When the underground pressure forces water through weak spots on Enceladus, liquid water sprays in jets that travel several kilometers above the surface. Enceladus is far too small to have its own atmosphere, so as the water emerges into the cold vacuum, the liquid very quickly turns into ice crystals, or what we can call Enceladus's version of snowflakes. The snow drifts back down, not only keeping the surface young, but the covering of fresh

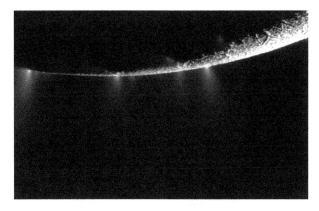

FIGURE 9.22. Geysers erupting from "tiger stripes" near the south pole of Enceladus, as seen by the Cassini spacecraft. Credit: NASA/JPL/SSI.

snow makes Enceladus the brightest, in terms of albedo, object in the solar system. As with Europa, astronomers are currently toying with the idea of sending a lander to analyze the ice in person—or robot, if you will.

4. Triton

Triton is Neptune's largest moon. Being so far from the Sun (Triton receives 1/900th of the intensity of sunlight we get on Earth), it was expected the extreme cold would simply freeze the moon into inactivity. Again, astronomers were surprised. Triton is so cold that nitrogen can exist at the *triple point*—a combination of temperature and pressure where a substance can be in gaseous, liquid, or solid form. Triton has a thin atmosphere of nitrogen, which is only possible because the individual nitrogen molecules are moving at such slow speeds due to its frigid temperatures. Triton also has a thin crust of nitrogen ice and pockets (it's unclear if the liquid nitrogen makes a worldwide underground ocean) of liquid nitrogen. The temperature is so close to absolute zero that slight changes in temperature yield large effects. When the Sun shines on parts of Triton, it can warm the surface enough to encourage liquid nitrogen geysers.

Examination of details of photographs from Voyager II, which visited Triton in 1989, show dark streaks across parts of its southern hemisphere. The streaks were unlike any other feature ever seen in the solar system and posed a mystery until astronomers realized they were the results of geysers. Liquid nitrogen from underneath the crust bursts through the surface, in this case carrying darker matter (dust?) with it. The geysers go straight into the air for several kilometers high until the gentle winds of Triton push the geysers sideways. Eventually the dark material falls on the surface, making streaks pointing in the direction of the local winds.

5. Mars

Mars, one of our neighboring planets, each show indications of, if not current geologic activity, then great bursts of activity in their pasts.

Mars appears to have shut down itself several hundreds of millions of years ago. We will follow up some of the consequences of this for Mars in our chapter on

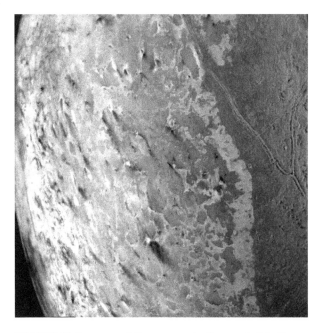

FIGURE 9.23. Geysers on Triton, as seen by Voyager II. Note the geysers trail in the same general direction. Credit: NASA.

magnetic fields, but here we wish to discuss some of its geologic features—features that rank among the largest of their kind in the solar system.

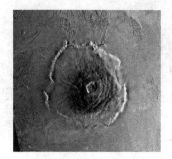

FIGURE 9.24. Left: Olympus Mons from the Viking I orbiter. Right: A comparison between Olympus Mons and other mountains on Earth (the vertical scale is exaggerated compared to the horizontal scale). Credit: NASA.

Mars has about a dozen giant volcanoes. The usage of "giant" here is not hyperbolic. The tallest mountain on Earth is Mount Kilimanjaro, and the tallest volcanic mountain is Mauna Kea, both of them reaching about 8 kilometers (5 miles) above their bases. Olympus Mons of Mars reaches about 2.5 times higher than each; at 24 kilometers (16 miles) high, it is the largest volcano in the solar system. "Mount Olympus" also earns its name in terms of horizontal size; at 600 kilometers (400 miles) across, the entire state of Mississippi would fit inside its caldera.

The other giant feature of Mars makes the Grand Canyon look like a ditch. Valles Marineris (Mariner Valley) is 6000 kilometers long, several hundred kilometers wide (it varies), and 11 kilometers (7 miles) deep. If you line Mariner Valley on top of a map of North America, it would stretch from San Francisco to New York City. The Grand Canyon would be a minor tributary in comparison.

Why does Mars have these giant features? Part of the answer is its low surface gravity. A 200-pound person on Earth would only weigh 76 pounds on Mars. While we don't tend to think of it too much in everyday life, all objects—not just people—have weight, and that includes mountains and volcanoes. Olympus Mons doesn't weigh as much as a comparable feature would here on Earth. Another reason appears to be the lack of convection of the upper mantle rock of Mars. Even when Mars had liquid rock underneath its crust some 250 million years ago (it does not appear to have liquid rock now), it seems that the direction of motion was solely upward, not sideways. Olympus Mons and its sibling volcanoes are the results of "hot spots," where magma pushed upward only, thereby allowing the magma to apply its force continuously for millions of years.

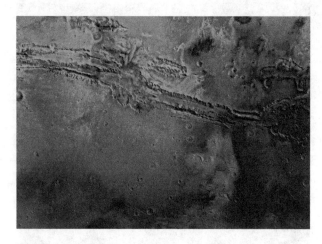

FIGURE 9.25. Valles Marineris on Mars. The image spans 2,500 kilometers (the valley extends even further on either side). Credit: NASA/JPL/USGS.

In the case of Valles Marineris, this is a feature that may go back to very early in Martian history. As Mars cooled, its crust formed first and in one planet-wide continuous piece, the upper mantle followed suit. Many materials—rocks included—shrink as they cool, and the mantle is no different. The shrinking of the upper mantle led to something akin to a planet-wide sinkhole, and the crust buckled and cracked.[5] A map of Mars shows a broad dividing line between its northern and southern hemispheres, the south being several kilometers higher on average (there are exceptions, of course) than the north. Most of the southern hemisphere is saturated with craters, but the north is comparatively clean, which is an indirect bit of evidence for planet-wide oceans (which would wipe out craters) in the Martian past when its atmosphere was much thicker.

---

[5] Mercury experienced something similar to Mars, but in its case it had many individual cracks (called "scarps") running roughly north-south for several hundred kilometers each and several kilometers deep.

Section 9.6: The (Lack of) Geology of the Jovian Planets

We need to say a few words about the Jovian planets—Jupiter, Saturn, Uranus, and Neptune. These objects are gas giants, the term hinting that there is no solid surface for geology in the first place. It is not strictly true that there are no rock or metallic solids for these objects; Jupiter, for example, has a rocky/metallic core 17 times as massive as the Earth. But with Jupiter weighing in total 318 times the mass of the Earth, its core only makes up 5% of Jupiter, a situation more extreme but still similar in kind to the other Jovians. The solid parts of the giant planets are buried so deep under gases and liquids that they are inaccessible.

Figure 9.26 shows the interior structure of Jupiter (Saturn's interior is similar). A large, by Earth standards, mass of various types of rock serves as the core of Jupiter. Whether the core is completely liquid, part liquid/part solid, or completely solid is almost beside the point; how Jupiter behaves is determined by the other 95% of the planet. Surrounding the core is a layer of material seen nowhere else (again, besides Saturn) of metallic hydrogen. Hydrogen is not considered a metal by chemists and cannot take on characteristics of metal under normal circumstances. However, Jupiter and Saturn are not "normal"; or, more precisely, they both possess a unique set of properties. The intense pressures in the interior of Jupiter and Saturn—equivalent to millions of Earth atmospheres—squeeze hydrogen into liquid metal. This metallic state has important consequences for the magnetic fields of both planets, which we will explore further in chapter 11. Note that Uranus and Neptune are too small for this to occur. The Sun is easily large enough to generate the needed pressures, except that it generates energy via nuclear fusion and keeps its interior temperatures far above where metallic hydrogen can survive. Above the layer of liquid metallic hydrogen resides a

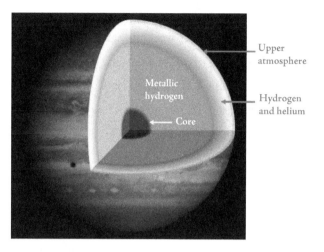

FIGURE 9.26. An artist's depiction of the interior of Jupiter. The dark circle to the left is a shadow of one of Jupiter's moons. Credit: NASA/R. J. Hall.

layer of gases—again, dominated by hydrogen and helium—over which is the upper atmosphere. Jupiter and Saturn thus do not really possess a solid surface for which we can ascribe geology in any meaningful way.

Uranus and Neptune are also gas giants (meaning their composition is dominated by hydrogen and helium gas) but are otherwise distinct from Jupiter and Saturn. Figure 9.27 shows the interior of Uranus (Neptune's interior is similar). We see a large rocky core, probably made from silicate rocks with contributions from iron and nickel. Again, the layer surrounding the core may be unique to these two planets. Lacking the intense pressures needed to squeeze hydrogen into a liquid metal state, Uranus likely possesses a thick layer of water (with contributions from ammonia and methane). The term "ices" is misleading; the intense pressures and temperatures mean the form of water is unlikely to be anything like liquid or solid water here on Earth. This massive slurry, like the metallic hydrogen of Jupiter and Saturn, is responsible for a strong magnetic field, though the

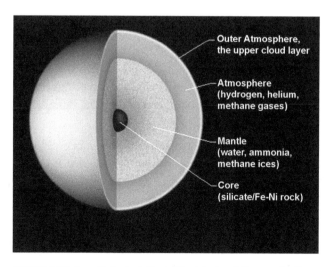

FIGURE 9.27. An artist's depiction of the interior of Uranus. Credit: NASA/S. F. Wolfman.

magnetic fields of Uranus and Neptune are much different than any others we have seen in the solar system. Above the water layer is a thick mix of gases—again dominated by hydrogen and helium, but with a somewhat larger percentage of ammonia and methane than possessed by Jupiter and Saturn. The upper atmospheres of Uranus and Neptune include these larger percentages; since methane tends to absorb red (and infrared) light well, the dominant color left behind is blue.

The Jovian planets, thus, don't have geologies as we understand the term. But they are extremely active planets, and their behaviors are better described in our next chapter on planetary atmospheres.

Summary

In this chapter, we have examined the following:

▸ How plate tectonics work on Earth

▸ A comparison of uniformitarianism versus catastrophism

▸ An investigation of the cores of planets and moons

▸ A description of how surfaces of objects can change even if they are geologically dead or dormant

▸ A description of several examples of objects whose surfaces change due to geologic activity

Questions

1. A continental place moves across the surface of the Earth at 5 centimeters per year. How long does it take to move 100 kilometers?

2. An oceanic plate is in the process of splitting, forcing continental plates in opposite directions. The plates are currently 12,000 kilometers apart and they are separating at 3 centimeters per year. How long ago did they begin separating?

3. The density of Venus is about 5.4 grams per cubic centimeter. The density of rock is 2 g/cc, and iron 8 g/cc. What can we say about the materials making up the interior of Venus?

4. Identify the process (catastrophism vs. uniformitarianism) that best describes the following situations:
   • The splitting of Africa into several plates (they should be visibly separate plates within 10 million years or so)
   • The eruption of Mauna Kea in Hawaii in 2018
   • The making of "Meteor Crater" in Arizona about 20,000 years ago
   • The sliding of the North American plate (relatively southward) next to the Pacific plate (relatively northward)
   • The silting up of a river's delta

5. Three different liquids do not chemically react with one another. Samples of each are poured into a graduated cylinder and given time to separate. Liquid A is in the middle, liquid B is on the top, and liquid C is at the bottom of the cylinder. List in order the liquids in terms of densities, lightest (least dense) to heaviest (most dense).

6. A moon shows few craters and has many regions where the surface appears smooth. Is it most likely to be geologically active or geologically dead?

7. Two moons have diameters similar to that of our Moon. Moon A orbits its planet closer in than Moon B. Which moon is more likely to be geologically active?

8. A moon has very tall mountains and very deep valleys. Which statement is most likely correct: The moon's acceleration due to gravity is relatively strong or relatively weak?

9. Where is a comet most likely to be inactive: when it is closer to the Sun than the Earth or when it is farther from the Sun than the Earth?

10. Geysers of liquid water are spotted on a moon of Saturn. This tells us the moon is geologically active. What is the most likely reason for its activity?

- ⬩ The moon is so large that, on its own, its interior is molten
- ⬩ The moon experiences gravitational tides from Saturn that melt its interior
- ⬩ The moon is made of hydrogen and helium gas inside

Activities

▶ *Astrophysics activity 9.1*: Through video clips, readings, and simulations, examine how the process of convection works in the interior and atmosphere of the Earth, in the interiors for other planets, and for the Sun

Works Referenced

Anderson, D. L. (1989). *Theory of the earth.* Boston, MA: Blackwell.

Cannon, W. F. (1961). The impact of uniformitarianism: Two letters from John Herschel to Charles Lyell, 1836–1837. *Proceedings of the American Philosophical Society, 105*(3), 301–314.

Carey, S. W. (1958). The tectonic approach to continental drift. In S. W. Carey, (Ed.), *Continental drift: A symposium* (pp. 177–363). Hobart, Australia: University of Tasmania.

Casadevall, A., & Fang, F. C. (2016, March 1). Revolutionary science. *MBio, 7*(2), e00158–16. doi:10.1128/mBio.00158-16

Gould, S. J. (1965). Is uniformitarianism necessary? *American Journal of Science, 263*(3), 223–228. doi:10.2475/ajs.263.3.223

Hooykaas, R. (1963). *Natural law and divine miracle: The principle of uniformity in geology, biology, and theology*, Leiden, Netherlands: E. J. Brill.

Hutton, J. (1788). Transactions of the Royal Society of Edinburgh. I: 209-304. The original version was read to the Society in March and April of 1785. See https://www.rcpe.ac.uk/sites/default/files/exlibris_2.pdf

Klous, W. J., & Tilling, R. I. (2001). *This dynamic Earth: The story of plate tectonics* (e-book.). Darby, PA: Diane Publishing Co.

Roberton, E. C. (2011). The interior of the Earth. *United States Geological Survey.* Retrieved from https://pubs.usgs.gov/gip/interior/

Romm, J. (1994, February 3). A new forerunner for continental drift. *Nature, 367*(6462), 407–408, doi:10.1038/367407a0

Runcorn, S. K. (1956). Paleomagnetic comparisons between Europe and North America. *Proceedings, Geological Association of Canada, 8*(1088), 7785. doi:10.1098/rsta.1965.001

Wegener, A. (1929). *Die entstehung der kontinente und ozeane* (4th ed.). Braunschweig, Germany: Friedrich Vieweg & Sohn Akt.

Wikipedia. (n.d.). The principles of geology. Retrieved from https://en.wikipedia.org/wiki/Principles_of_Geology#CITEREFLyell1830

An 1887 lecture by Sir William Thomson (later Lord Kelvin) on the possibility that the Sun generates its energy via shrinking can be found at http://www-history.mcs.st-andrews.ac.uk/Extras/Kelvin_sun_1.html

Credits

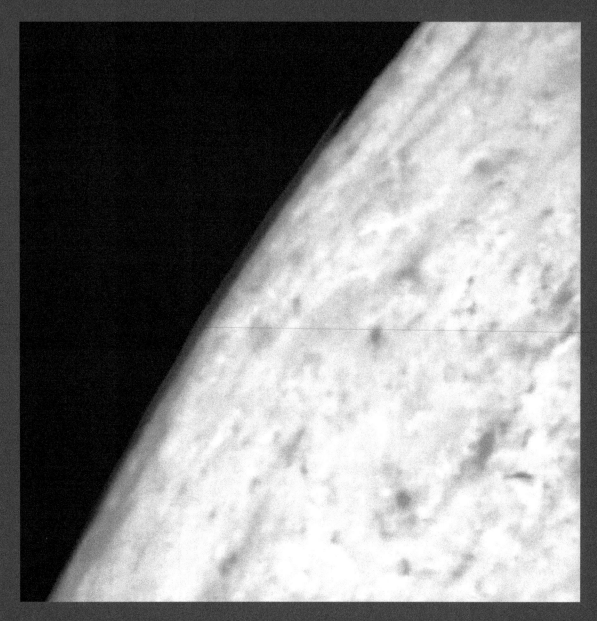

Clouds above Triton as seen from a shallow angle by Voyager II in 1989 (NASA).

PLANETARY ATMOSPHERES

To coordinate all the various reasons why solar system objects may or may not have atmospheres

OBJECTIVES

- To determine the escape speed of an object
- To determine the average (rms) speed of an atom or molecule in an atmosphere
- To discuss secondary effects regarding atmospheres

INTRODUCTION

Why do planets and moons have (or do not have) atmospheres? Further, what determines the various properties of atmospheres—their surface pressure, their temperatures, even their compositions?

In this chapter, we will examine the primary competing effects on planetary atmospheres—gravity and temperature. We will also consider secondary effects such as the availability of substances, rotation rates, chemical reactions and even magnetic fields and will highlight several examples.

KEY TERMS

Boltzmann constant (k_B): A constant of nature, which frequently appears in thermodynamic situations. It has a value of 1.38×10^{-23} J/K

Convection: The movement of masses of fluids of different densities and/or temperatures. Hotter fluids tend to rise and cooler fluids tend to sink

Coriolis effect: An apparent deflection of the motion of a small object due to the rotation of the world to which it belongs. For example, hurricanes in the Northern hemisphere of Earth spin counterclockwise due to the Coriolis effect

Escape speed: The minimum speed a projectile needs in order to escape the gravitational pull of an object

Great red spot: A hurricane, larger than the entire planet Earth, in Jupiter's upper atmosphere that has lasted at least since Galileo spotted it over four centuries ago

Greenhouse effect: A process by which an atmosphere can trap and retain heat from the Sun, raising its temperature

Ideal gas: Not the "best" or "greatest" gas; rather, the simplest way to describe a gas. Even so, the ideal gas approach often does a good job of modeling the properties and behaviors of a gas

kelvin (K): The international standard unit for temperature. The kelvin scale is used to express absolute temperatures, where 0 K refers to (in theory) the coldest possible temperature

Kinetic energy: The energy of motion of an object, dependent upon its mass and speed

Maxwell-Boltzmann distribution: How the number of particles in a gas are distributed according to their speeds

Root-mean-square (rms): A specific type of average value, which accounts for both negative and positive directions of motion

Universal gravitational constant (G): A constant of nature, which describes the relative strength of gravity as a force

Solar wind: A stream of high-energy particles (mostly protons) lost by the Sun

Solubility: The ability of a liquid (such as water) to dissolve a gas (such as carbon dioxide)

Subduction: When one plate (part of the Earth's crust) slowly dives underneath a neighboring plate

Boltzmann, Ludwig: An Austrian physicist of the 19th century who made important contributions to statistical mechanics (a version of thermodynamics)

Maxwell, James Clerk: A Scottish scientist of the 19th century who made important contributions to statistical mechanics, electromagnetism, and other disciplines

Section 10.1: Escape Speed

In chapter 4, we introduced the notion of escape speed as a measure of the strength of gravity on the surface of an object. It will be useful to reintroduce it here:

$$v = \sqrt{\frac{2GM}{R}}$$

where G is the universal gravitational constant, M is the mass of the object, and R is the radius of the object. For example, if we use the Earth's measurements, we find the Earth's escape speed is about 11.2 km/s.

What does this have to do with planetary atmospheres? Consider a particle (an atom or molecule) moving near the top of an atmosphere of a planet, so that it can travel long distances without hitting another particle. If it is (a) moving faster than escape speed and (b) is not pointed at the surface, the particle will leave the planet permanently (i.e., escape the planet's gravity). If enough particles do the same, the atmosphere of the planet will drain away.

Table 10.1 lists escape speeds for the major planets and some selected moons. For simplicity, the masses and radii of the objects are compared to the Earth (i.e., Earth = 1) and the escape speed is listed in kilometers per second:

TABLE 10.1. Escape Speeds for a Sample of Objects in the Solar System

Planet	Mass (Earth = 1)	Radius (Earth = 1)	Escape Speed (km/s)
Mercury	0.055	0.38	4.25
Venus	0.816	0.95	10.4
Earth	1	1	11.2
Moon	0.012	0.27	2.38
Mars	0.108	0.53	5.03
Jupiter	317.8	10.98	60.21
Io	0.015	0.29	2.56
Europa	0.080	0.25	2.03
Ganymede	0.025	0.41	2.74

Planet	Mass (Earth = 1)	Radius (Earth = 1)	Escape Speed (km/s)
Callisto	0.018	0.38	2.44
Saturn	95.219	9.14	36.09
Titan	0.023	0.40	2.64
Uranus	14.545	3.98	21.37
Titania	0.0006	0.12	0.77
Neptune	17.158	3.87	23.56
Triton	0.0036	0.21	1.46
Pluto	0.0022	0.19	1.21
Eris	0.0028	0.18	1.38
Haumea	0.0007	0.13	0.81

FIGURE 10.1. Left: The Earth as seen from Apollo 17. Right: The Moon as seen by the Galileo spacecraft. Why does the Earth have an atmosphere while the Moon does not? Credit: NASA.

Section 10.2: Temperature and Kinetic Energy

The escape speed, or ability of an object to hold onto atmospheric particles, is the first piece we must consider. The second relates to how fast particles can move in atmospheres, which in turn relates to their kinetic energies.

The kinetic energy, or energy of motion, of any object (from molecules to planets and beyond) is given by the formula

Equation 10.1

$$K = \frac{1}{2}mv^2$$

where m represents the mass of the particle and v its speed.

Check Your Neighbor

1. Planet A has more mass than planet B, but both planets have the same radius. Which planet has a higher escape speed, or, perhaps, the speeds are the same?

2. Planet C has a larger radius than planet D, but both planets have the same mass. Which planet has a higher escape speed, or, perhaps, the speeds are the same?

On the other hand, for an *ideal gas*,[1] the average kinetic energy available for particles is given by the formula

Equation 10.2

$$K = \frac{3}{2}k_B T$$

where T is the temperature of the gas and k_B is a constant of nature called the *Boltzmann constant* and has a value of 1.38×10^{-23} J/K.

To find the average speed of a particle in an ideal gas,[2] we set these two formulae equal to each other and solve for the speed. The result is

Equation 10.3

$$v = \sqrt{\frac{3k_B T}{m}}$$

which tells us that the average speed of a gas particle depends on both its own mass and the temperature of the gas.

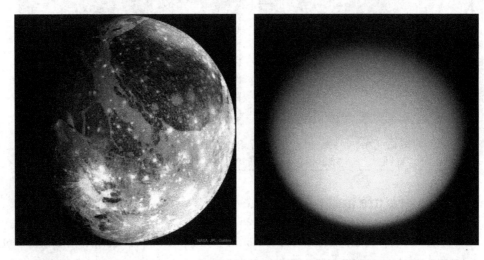

FIGURE 10.2. Left: Ganymede as seen by Galileo. Right: Titan, as seen by Cassini. Ganymede and Titan are similar in terms of radius and mass; why does Titan have a thick atmosphere while Ganymede does not?

Table 10.2 lists average speeds of particles of various substances at a variety of temperatures found in the solar system. Note that while some substances may in actuality be liquids or solids at low-enough temperatures, we nevertheless assume each substance would act as a gas.

One (very) important complication arises from our considerations so far. We have been discussing the speeds of gas particles as *average* speeds. But this implies that some particles have speeds slower than average, and some particles have speeds faster than average.

---

[1] By "ideal," we do not mean the best or first, but rather the simplest. Specifically, an "ideal gas" is one where we can use the simplest possible description of the gas and still get reasonable results.

[2] Officially, this is the "root-mean-square" speed, one of several "average" speeds one can assign to the particles.

TABLE 10.2. Average Speeds (in km/s) of Common Substances at Various Temperatures

T(K)/Substance:	H_2	He	CH_4	NH_3	H_2O	N_2	O_2	CO_2
50	0.78	0.56	0.28	0.27	0.25	0.21	0.20	0.17
100	1.11	0.79	0.39	0.38	0.35	0.30	0.28	0.24
150	1.36	0.96	0.48	0.47	0.43	0.36	0.34	0.29
200	1.57	1.11	0.56	0.54	0.50	0.42	0.39	0.34
250	1.75	1.25	0.62	0.60	0.55	0.47	0.44	0.38
300	1.92	1.36	0.68	0.66	0.61	0.52	0.48	0.41
350	2.07	1.47	0.74	0.71	0.66	0.56	0.52	0.44
400	2.22	1.57	0.79	0.76	0.70	0.60	0.56	0.48
500	2.48	1.76	0.88	0.85	0.78	0.67	0.62	0.53
600	2.71	1.93	0.96	0.94	0.86	0.73	0.68	0.58
700	2.93	2.08	1.04	1.01	0.93	0.79	0.74	0.63
800	3.13	2.23	1.11	1.08	0.99	0.84	0.79	0.67
900	3.32	2.36	1.18	1.15	1.05	0.89	0.84	0.71
1000	3.50	2.49	1.24	1.21	1.11	0.94	0.88	0.75

Check Your Neighbor

1. Particle E has twice the mass of particle F, but both belong to the same gas (i.e., they have the same temperature). Which particle has a faster speed, or, perhaps, the speeds are the same?

2. Planet G has a higher atmospheric temperature than planet H, but both atmospheres contain the same particles. For which planet do the particles have faster speeds, or, perhaps, the speeds are the same?

The exact way in which particles show their individual speeds in an ideal gas was first explained by James Clerk Maxwell (1831–1879)[3] and Ludwig Boltzmann (1844–1906) in the 19th century. We can show how this works via a graph (Figure 10.3) called the *Maxwell-Boltzmann distribution*.

Notice, for example, the average speed of particles in an ideal gas at room temperature (293 K, or 20°C or 68°F) is about 400 m/s (0.4 km/s). But the curve for the 293 K gas shows that particles may be moving so slow as to be close to 0 m/s or beyond 1400 m/s.

Check Your Neighbor

Suppose a planet has an escape speed of 10 km/s and the average speed of a hydrogen (H_2) molecule is 1.11 km/s. Would we expect H_2 to remain in the planet's atmosphere?

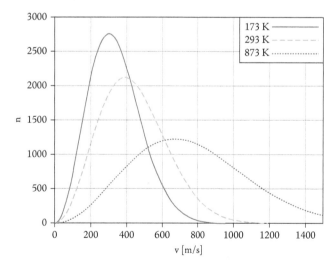

FIGURE 10.3. A graph showing the distribution of the number of particles (vertical) versus the individual speeds of particles (horizontal) in ideal gases at various temperatures.

---

[3] FYI, "Clerk" is pronounced as if it used an "a" rather than an "e," or, in other words, like "Clark."

FIGURE 10.4. James Clerk Maxwell (left); Ludwig Boltzmann (right).

Maxwell-Boltzmann Molecular Speed Distribution for Noble Gases

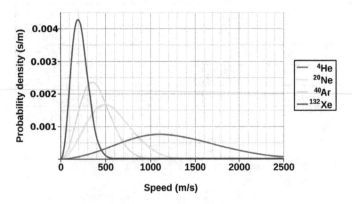

FIGURE 10.5. The Maxwell-Boltzmann distribution for different gases at the same temperature.

Suppose a planet has an escape speed of 1000 m/s. There are many particles in this gas that move faster than 1000 m/s, and therefore would be able to escape the gravity of the planet.

We have more to say. The <u>shape</u> of the curve is the same for a gas at 293 K, regardless of how many gas particles are present. In other words, even if fast-moving particles are removed from the atmosphere, this doesn't mean that only slow-moving particles will remain. Rather, many of the remaining particles will become fast-moving particles too, as long as the temperature is maintained. In the solar system, the source of energy to do this is primarily sunlight.

A good rule-of-thumb is that, in order to keep an atmosphere, a planet or moon needs to have an escape speed six or more times the average speed of the gas particles. With this restriction, so few gas particles can escape that the object may be said to retain its atmosphere permanently.

There are therefore three separate factors that determine whether an object has the ability to hold on to a particular substance. First, the object needs to have enough surface gravity—the larger the surface gravity, the better its chances of holding onto its air. Second, the temperature of the gas in the atmosphere—the higher the temperature, the faster the individual gas particles can move, and thus the lesser the object's chances of holding its air. Finally, the type of gas in the atmosphere—the heavier (more massive) the individual gas particles, the slower the individual particles move, and thus the better the object's chances of holding its air (see figure 10.5 for this comparison).

Section 10.3: Secondary Effects on Atmospheres

1. Availability of Substances

It may be obvious, but it needs to be stated: A planet can't have a particular substance in its atmosphere, regardless of other conditions, if the substance isn't available.

The Earth is a bit of an anomaly when considering the materials present in the solar system. The Earth is made primarily of rock and metal, and elements such as iron, oxygen, and silicon are most popular here. This isn't true for the rest of space, however—both in the solar system, and in space overall, the two most common elements are hydrogen and helium.

It is no coincidence that the four most-massive planets (Jupiter, Saturn, Uranus, and Neptune) are also composed almost entirely of hydrogen and helium, the two most popular elements in the solar system.[4] It is also worth mentioning here that the Sun, too, is composed of these elements, with only a smattering (< 2% by mass) of elements besides hydrogen and helium. Further, in terms of numbers, hydrogen is about ten times more common than helium, but helium atoms are about four times more massive than hydrogen atoms, which makes up the difference in percentages cited in Table 10.3.

---

[4] Also, not coincidentally, the two lightest elements.

TABLE 10.3. Abundances of Chemical Elements (by mass)

Element	Solar System	Earth (overall)	Earth (atmosphere)
Hydrogen	74.9%	<1%	traces
Helium	23.8%	<1%	<0.1%
Carbon	<0.1%	<1%	traces
Nitrogen	<0.1%	<1%	78.1%
Oxygen	<0.1%	30.1%	20.9%
Argon	<0.1%	<1%	0.96%
Calcium	<0.1%	1.5%	<0.1%
Silicon	<0.1%	15.1%	<0.1%
Sulfur	<0.1%	2.9%	<0.1%
Aluminum	<0.1%	1.4%	<0.1%
Magnesium	<0.1%	13.9%	<0.1%
Iron	<0.1%	32.1%	<0.1%
Nickel	<0.1%	1.8%	<0.1%

Data courtesy of "Solar System Abundances and Condensation Temperatures of the Elements," Lodders, K., (July 10 2003). The Astrophysical Journal, 591:1220-1247.

Some elements with which we are very familiar as part of Earth's atmosphere—oxygen, nitrogen, carbon etc.—are actually about a million times less common than hydrogen by number. Even so, these are the next most-common elements in the solar system, and compounds formed from them (often in combination with hydrogen) are relatively popular for objects smaller than the giant planets. Molecules like water, carbon dioxide, nitrogen, methane, and ammonia are thus easily found amongst atmospheric constituents of such objects.

If hydrogen and helium are so popular, why aren't they major players in the Earth's atmosphere? The answer goes back to our first two competing concepts, escape speed and temperature. At Earth's distance from the Sun, hydrogen molecules and helium atoms are moving too fast for the Earth to retain.

2. Planetary Rotation

Another secondary effect that can have large consequences is the rate of rotation for an object. Earth rotates once each 24 hours, allowing all regions to experience sunlight and darkness each in relatively short order, and in effect helping spread the sun's energy across the entire planet.

This is not true for Mercury. The extremely slow rotation of Mercury, combined with its orbital period about the Sun, combine for a day-night cycle of nearly 6 Earth months. Instead of the approximately 400 K we might otherwise expect, the temperature on the day side of Mercury can therefore reach 700 K. It doesn't matter for these purposes that the night temperature of Mercury plunges as low as 100 K; particles on the day side of Mercury have time to gain all the speed they need to leave Mercury behind. Mercury's slow rotation helps guarantee Mercury lacks a substantial atmosphere.

FIGURE 10.6. A close-up of Mercury. Mercury has enough gravity to hold on to an atmosphere but doesn't have one. Why not?

Venus also has an extremely slow rotation rate. However, the escape speed on Venus is fully capable of retaining its atmosphere (primarily carbon dioxide), even at an average temperature of 750 K.

3. Chemical Reactions

Among the more obvious differences between Earth and its neighboring planets Venus and Mars is how its atmosphere is constituted. The atmospheres of Venus and Mars each consist of about 95% carbon dioxide. CO_2 is a small (though important) participant in Earth's atmosphere, much less than 1%, and Earth's air is instead dominated by nitrogen (78%) and oxygen (21%) molecules. The presence of oxygen in copious amounts is even more surprising, since oxygen is an incredibly reactive element and should have been used up long ago. Why?

Earth has, so far as we know, the unique distinction of housing life. Specifically here, Earth has plant life, which produces oxygen by combining carbon dioxide and sunlight via photosynthesis. On other solar system objects, oxygen combines quickly with other elements and is at best a trace constituent in other atmospheres. If astronomers one day discover an extrasolar planet with relatively large amounts of oxygen, a likely conclusion will be that such a planet has its own version of plant life.

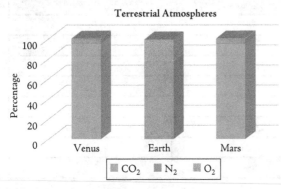

FIGURE 10.7. Percentages of major atmospheric constituents of Venus, Earth, and Mars.

Earth is not the only object where chemistry plays an important role regarding its atmosphere. Titan—Saturn's largest moon—has an atmosphere primarily made of nitrogen, with small amounts of methane (CH_4) and ethane (C_2H_6). Observations from the Atacama Large Millimeter Array (ALMA) during 2014 also discovered more complicated hydrocarbons, such as vinyl cyanide (C_2H_3CN). It is hypothesized that the interaction of sunlight with simpler compounds makes more complicated molecules. Figure 10.8 shows pictures of Titan from space, depicting its smog-like upper atmosphere.

 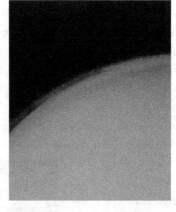

FIGURE 10.8. NASA images of Titan: A crescent Titan from a distance by Cassini (left); a close-up of Titan showing its haze by Voyager I (right). Credit: NASA/JPL/SSI.

4. Magnetic Fields

Planets do not acquire atmospheres with their magnetic fields. Perhaps contrary to popular belief, magnetic fields do not automatically attract everything; in fact, magnetic fields only affect electric current (moving electric charges),[5] and magnetic fields can repel as well as attract. What, then, do magnetic fields contribute to our understanding of planetary atmospheres?

The Sun continually ejects high-energy particles—mainly protons—which we call the solar wind. These particles fly off the Sun's photosphere and stream in all directions into space. It is common for such particles to cover the distance from the Sun to the Earth in just a few days.

---

[5] How then does a bar of iron or a steel paperclip feel a pull from a magnet with no visible electric current? It turns out there is a net motion of electric charges (called "spin") at the subatomic level for certain materials, especially those containing iron.

Suppose such a solar wind particle reaches the Earth's atmosphere and collides with one of the molecules in our air. Collisions like this tend to transfer momentum and energy from the high-energy particle to the low-energy particle; in other words, the Earth's atmospheric molecule is now moving faster than it was before (Figure 10.9). If the molecule has obtained a high-enough speed, it can potentially escape the Earth's gravity.

FIGURE 10.9. At left, a solar wind particle (the small sphere) heads into a collision with a molecule (dumbbell-shaped) in the atmosphere of a planet. At left, the particle and molecule separate after the collision, the molecule now moving faster than it had before the collision.

If this process continues long enough, the solar wind can strip the atmosphere away from a planet. This is especially problematic for objects relatively close to the Sun, such as the terrestrial planets, where the solar wind is strongest. The question is not how a planet can hold onto an atmosphere; rather, the question becomes how is it any planets retain atmospheres? The answer lies with magnetic fields.

Recall that most solar wind particles are protons; that is, they are moving electric charges. This means they can be affected by magnetic fields.

If a planet possesses a strong magnetic field, solar wind particles are diverted around the planet (much like water flowing past a rock in a stream), rather than impacting the planet's atmosphere (Figure 10.10).

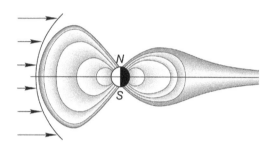

FIGURE 10.10. Left: Water rushes by rocks in a stream. Right: An artist's rendition of how solar wind particles rush by the Earth due to the Earth's magnetic field.

In the solar system, each Jovian planet has a large magnetic field and thus shields itself from the solar wind. Any smaller objects with atmospheres are too far from the Sun for the solar wind to be intense enough to completely strip them of their air. Of the terrestrial planets, only the Earth possesses a sizeable magnetic field, and thus only the Earth can shield itself from the solar wind. Mercury, the Moon, and Mars (Venus is a special case, as we will discuss next) lack large magnetic fields, and none of these objects has much of an atmosphere.

Mars is worth a detailed look. Given the escape speed of Mars (about 5 kilometers per second) and the root-mean-square speed of a carbon dioxide molecule at Mars' location (about 0.4 km/s), we would expect Mars to keep a relatively thick atmosphere. Yet the surface pressure of the Martian atmosphere is about 1% of the Earth's, which is to say that the Martian "air" is a vacuum by Earth standards (see Figure 10.11). What happened to Mars?

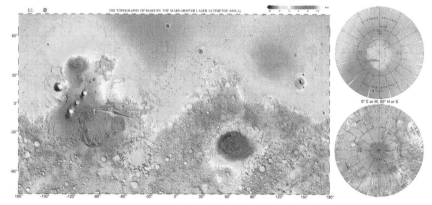

FIGURE 10.11. A topological map of Mars, by the Mars Orbiter Laser Altimeter (MOLA). The more toward the blue, the lower the elevation; the more toward the yellow-white, the higher the elevation. Credit: NASA/JPL/USGS.

FIGURE 10.12. Gusev crater on Mars. What appears to be a dry river bed dissects the crater. Credit: NASA/JPL/USGS.

Mars shows plenty of evidence of having copious amounts of water in the distant past. Figure 10.11 shows a topological (surface elevation) map of Mars from the Mars Orbital Laser Altimeter (MOLA). The flat map covers from 60° north at the top of the figure to 60° south at the bottom; the two circular maps to the side show the northern and southern hemispheres, respectively. The north and south of Mars, to first approximation, have very different appearances. The South, at higher elevations, is peppered with impact craters; the North, at lower elevations, is in contrast very smooth (Note the presence of two large impact basins in the South, and their relative low elevations). Liquid water could have covered up and/or eroded impact craters in these lower-elevation regions. Many other images depict what appear to be shorelines of lakes or dry river beds, and there are even a few that seem to be showing water bursting out of the ground.

Why are we discussing water, specifically, liquid water? Water cannot exist in a liquid state without an external (outside) pressure. On Earth, this external pressure is supplied by the Earth's atmosphere. Liquid water exists elsewhere in the solar system (Europa, Ganymede, and others) but only underground. To have liquid water on the surface of a world, we need air. But liquid water doesn't exist on the Martian surface any more. Since Mars has but an extremely thin atmosphere today, the conclusion is that the air disappeared.

One hypothesis concerning Mars is that it did once have a significant magnetic field, but that it has faded away. Magnetic fields are induced by fast-spinning electric charges, the type of circumstance available for a planet like Mars. Astronomers also know that planetary magnetic fields are further generated by interior convection, which in the case of Mars would be produced by the movement of liquid rock in its mantle.

Convection works best if the temperature differences are great at opposite locations. But the convection of the Martian mantle has shut down—all its volcanoes are dormant and appear to have been so for the past 200 million years. Mars is a large enough world that it should still have much liquid rock inside (there hasn't been enough time for Mars to cool off) but liquid rock, if present, doesn't seem to be moving.

This hypothesis suggests that Mars has undergone repeated major collisions from asteroids over its history, perhaps as many as 20 times or more (again, consult Figure 10.11 for two obvious examples). Each collision raises the temperature of the Martian surface (crust), which means the difference in temperatures between the upper and lower parts of the Martian mantle is decreased, which mutes the convection of the mantle. The repeated collisions have therefore virtually eliminated the Martian magnetic field, which exposed its atmosphere to the solar wind. We will discuss magnetic fields in more detail in the next chapter.

5. Greenhouse Effect

In comparing the terrestrial worlds, the atmosphere of Venus stands out as an anomaly—not because of its composition (Mars also has an atmosphere dominated by carbon dioxide)—but because of its thickness. The surface pressure of the atmosphere of Venus is 90 times that of Earth, and thousands of times that of Mars. How did this happen?

A little less than half of the Sun's radiation is visible light, less than half is infrared light, and a few percent is ultraviolet (other wavelengths are less than 1%). Figure 10.13 shows how different molecules absorb light in the Earth's atmosphere. Most of the Sun's ultraviolet emission is prevented from reaching the ground, and a significant portion of the Sun's infrared emission is absorbed by water vapor and carbon dioxide. Interestingly, most of the Sun's visible light does reach the ground.

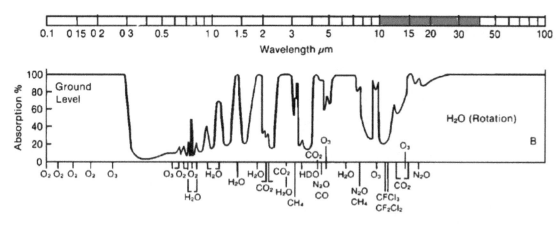

FIGURE 10.13. The efficiency of absorption of light (vertical axis) versus the wavelength of sunlight in microns (horizontal axis). The contributions of various molecules is identified. Most of the sun's light is in the yellow-colored band, and most of the light returned to space is in the blue-colored band. Credit: Jonathan Lawhead.

Some of the Sun's visible light is reflected by the ground (and clouds and ice), but most of it is absorbed by the ground. The ground warms up as a consequence, and reemits infrared light as a result, due to its temperature. This means that CO_2 and H_2O have an opportunity to absorb infrared light from the ground as well as from the Sun. Other molecules (not pictured in the figure), like methane, also contribute to absorption of infrared radiation.

The energy so absorbed helps warm the atmosphere. Given the Earth's distance from the Sun, we would reasonably expect the Earth to be mostly, if not completely, covered with ice. Instead, this absorption of re-radiated infrared radiation—the greenhouse effect—keeps the Earth above the freezing point of water. A moderate greenhouse effect, as the late Carl Sagan once said, is a good thing.

Earth possesses a fair amount of liquid water on its surface. Both Mars and Venus may also have done so once upon a time, but neither does now—why not?

The answer for Mars is relatively easy. Mars is too cold, and its air too thin, to sustain liquid water. While there is evidence for liquid water below the Martian surface, where pressures and temperatures are higher, water quickly evaporates or freezes under the surface conditions of Mars.

Venus, Earth, and Mars all possess copious amounts of carbon dioxide. The Martian atmosphere has mostly been lost, and what little Mars still has tends to congregate in its polar ice caps. Earth's carbon dioxide has been largely replaced by oxygen or stored in other locations—carbon dioxide has dissolved into Earth's oceans or taken into the Earth's mantle by subduction.

Venus has several disadvantages (or advantages, depending on one's feelings) regarding its atmospheric CO_2. Venus is too close to the Sun for carbon dioxide to ever have existed in frozen form. Venus does not have plant life or other photosynthesis-like processes to remove carbon dioxide. If Venus ever had liquid oceans, its temperature has long been too hot for carbon dioxide to remain dissolved in its water. Finally, Venus does not have the equivalent of Earth's plate tectonics, so it cannot carry carbon dioxide away into its interior.

Venus appears to be the victim of a "runaway" greenhouse effect. Let's assume for argument's sake that it once upon a time (millions or billions of years ago) had significant amounts of liquid water on its surface. CO_2 dissolves well into cold water, but not

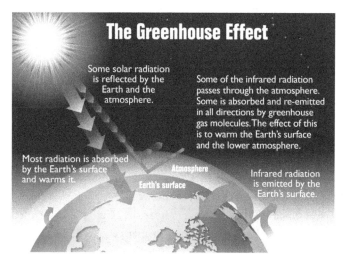

FIGURE 10.14. The Greenhouse effect for Earth. Credit: Environmental Protection Agency (EPA).

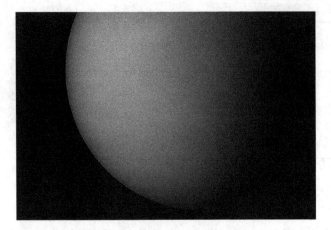

FIGURE 10.15. Venus from space, as seen by the Galileo spacecraft. Clouds tens of miles vertically thick obscure the surface. Credit: NASA/JPL/Galileo/Kevin Gill.

in warm water. If the temperature becomes hotter, carbon dioxide comes out of the water and into the atmosphere. But if there is more CO_2 in the atmosphere, the atmosphere does a better job of absorbing infrared radiation, raising the temperature. As the temperature increases, more CO_2 is released, and the process accelerates ("runs away") until essentially all the available CO_2 is in the atmosphere. While this is a simplified picture, it does hint at how all of Venus's carbon dioxide could end up in its atmosphere, whereas the majority of carbon dioxide on Earth lies (fortunately!) elsewhere.

Check Your Neighbor

Which can of soda—a cold can or a warm can—has more "fizz"? How does that relate to the atmospheres of Venus and Earth?

Venus currently has a surface temperature close to 750 K (900°F) and a surface pressure 90 times that of ours. It is quite evident that Venus has more air than the others both in terms of overall amounts and vertical extent. Even though Venus is close to the Sun, rotates very slowly, and has almost no magnetic field, its runaway greenhouse guarantees its thick atmosphere.

Section 10.4: Special Cases in the Outer Solar System

Planets are not the only objects to possess atmospheres. Some of the objects in the outer solar system have them, and in one case, a thicker atmosphere than ours on Earth. Let's take a peek.

1. Titan

We've already mentioned that Titan has an atmosphere—but why? Titan, Saturn's largest moon, has about the same radius and mass as the two largest moons of Jupiter, Ganymede and Callisto, and about the same radius (though not mass) as Mercury. None of these other objects have substantial atmospheres,[6] but Titan's is thicker than ours. How can Titan keep its air where the others cannot?

Very simply: location, location, location. Titan, belonging to Saturn, is 9.5 au from the Sun. Compare this to Ganymede and Callisto, which are 5.2 au from the Sun, or Mercury, the closest planet to the Sun at a distance of 0.39 au. The heat from the Sun is simply much less at Titan. In fact, the atmosphere on Titan yields a pressure at the surface about 1.5 times that here on Earth. While the surface gravity of Titan is similar to that on Ganymede and Callisto, and notably less than that of Mercury, Titan is the object that can retain its air.

Check Your Neighbor

The vertical extent of Titan's atmosphere (off its surface) is many times higher than Earth's atmosphere, even though the surface pressures are similar. Why does the air go further up for Titan? Hint: How do their surface gravities compare?

Significantly for Titan, it is near the triple-point for methane; that is, the combination of pressures and temperatures at the surface allow for methane to be in gaseous, liquid, or solid form, similar to the role played by

---

[6] Mercury does appear to have a small amount of outgassing—that is, gases from underground leaking through the surface—and is bathed in the solar wind. Neither amounts to much, and the surface of Mercury is better described as existing in a vacuum.

water on Earth. While the intensity of sunlight at Titan is barely 1% of the intensity of sunlight here, it does exist, and the sunlight (and radiation from Saturn's magnetic field) interact with methane and other substances on Titan to create a worldwide haze. Somewhat like Venus, we cannot see the surface of Titan from space due to the opacity of the atmosphere. In the case of Venus, the planet is surrounded by (vertically) tens of kilometers thick clouds; In the case of Titan, the moon is surrounded by its own version of smog.

Titan is one of the few moons in the solar system that has been visited by a lander. The Huygens probe was part of the Cassini mission launched by the European Space Agency (ESA); when Cassini entered the Saturn system, it detached the Huygens probe, which passed through Titan's atmosphere, slowed down its descent via parachute, and landed safely on the surface. During its descent and (while it remained functional) on the surface, Huygens also took several photographs.

Huygens found a tangerine-orange daytime sky, due to the prevalence of methane-dominated smog. The color is so dominant that the rocks on its surface also appear this color. More interestingly, Titan is covered by lakes of liquid methane. This makes it of prime interest in the search for life on other worlds. Water's role on Earth is most often to act as a "solvent"; that is, a liquid that allows other molecules to move around, interact and chemically react, without experiencing much changes itself. Could liquid methane facilitate its own biology? The super-cold temperatures on Titan suggest no, but astronomers, as we have seen, have been surprised quite often by the large amounts of activity in the outer solar system before, and perhaps there are chemical reactions that best act when temperatures are frigid.

FIGURE 10.16. An image from the surface of Titan by the Huygens probe of the European Space Agency. Credit: ESA/NASA/JPL/University of Arizona.

2. Triton

The other moon in the solar system with an atmosphere worth noting is Triton, of Neptune. Triton is yet another level of cold, so to speak, compared to Titan.[7] For Triton, being 30 au from the Sun and thus receiving about 0.1% of the sunlight we get (and 1/10 of the sunlight at Titan), making temperatures near 40 kelvin (−390°F). Instead of water or methane, nitrogen is the substance at the triple point. We have already mentioned the geysers of Triton in the previous chapter; Triton also possesses a thin atmosphere (see the figure at the beginning of this chapter). Like Titan, Triton's atmosphere extends for many tens of kilometers above its surface, and much for the same reason.

3. Pluto

Pluto is one of the latest objects to enjoy a visit from a spacecraft. New Horizons performed a flyby in the summer of 2015, after a 9-year voyage, and astronomers are still processing what they found. But the early indications make out Pluto to be yet another world that is both active and frigid.

Pluto, even more so than Triton, is dominated by nitrogen ice. Methane and water ices make up most of the rest of its surface. Solid can turn to gas directly, instead of passing through the liquid phase, a process called *sublimation*. Even at Pluto's great distance from the Sun (semi-major axis of 40 au) and bitter cold, Pluto's gravity is still

---

[7] "Titan" and "Triton" are similar-sounding words. A few ways to keep them straight: "Titan" is usually understood to refer to a large person or object, and the moon Titan is much larger than Triton. Also, in Greek myth, the term "Titan" refers to a class of deities rather than an individual—Saturn being the chief Titan—whereas "Triton" is an individual deity, a god of the sea that worked for Neptune.

so weak as to make it difficult to hold onto much of an atmosphere. The average air pressure on Pluto is about 1 pascal; to put that into perspective, Earth's average air pressure is a little over 100,000 pascals. Pluto does exhibit seasonal changes even so; its highly elliptical orbit can take it to 30 au from the Sun,[8] during which the slight increase in temperature releases gas into its atmosphere and more

FIGURE 10.17. Left: Pluto from a distance. Right: A close-up of Pluto. Both images are from the New Horizon spacecraft. Credit: NASA/JHUAPL/SwRI.

than doubling its surface pressure. In times when Pluto is further from the Sun, the process reverses and air settles out of the atmosphere.

Section 10.5: The Jovian Planets

We've saved the best—or at least the largest—for last. In a sense, the Jovian planets are almost nothing but atmosphere. The masses of each of them is so large that all gases can be held by their gravities. Since hydrogen and helium

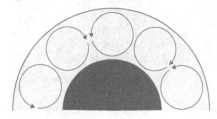

FIGURE 10.18. A cut-out showing convection in the lower atmosphere of a gas giant. Relatively hotter gas from deeper within the planet attempts to rise (i.e., away from the center) and relatively cooler gas attempts to sink (i.e., move toward the center).

are the most popular elements in space overall, they are the most popular substances making up the Jovians. Other common substances—methane and ammonia are popular—are also present. Even so, Jupiter and Saturn are distinct from Uranus and Neptune, and it could be argued these two pairings make up their own sub-sub-classes of planets (see chapter 9).

Regardless of their differences, their similarities are more important for the moment. All the gas giants have a thin upper atmosphere, replete with ice-crystal clouds, over a much thicker layer of gas. Each gas giant emits more energy than it receives from the Sun even now, billions of years after their formations.[9] On Earth, our weather is driven by sunlight. The Sun's light is so weak, even at Jupiter, that their weather systems are driven by the convection of this thick gas. In an odd way, the weather of the Jovian planets resemble the plate tectonics of Earth.

Convection is a physical process by which fluids flow due to differing densities (or, equivalently, different temperatures). We encountered it previously when discussing plate tectonics on Earth, where the motion of magma in the upper mantle, via convection, was the mechanism that drove crustal plates across the Earth. Convection also affects the Earth's atmosphere—the pockets of relatively higher and lower densities of air so familiar from weather forecasts are examples. Heat travels via convection from the depths to the upper atmospheres of the gas giants.

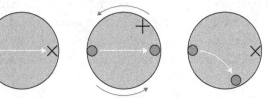

FIGURE 10.19. The Coriolis Effect as displayed by throwing a ball straight across a merry-go-round. Left: If the merry-go-round does not rotate, the ball travels straight to its target. Center: If the merry-go-round rotates, the ball still travels straight, but the target moves out of the way. Right: From the point of view of the merry-go-round, it appears that the ball curves away from the target.

---

[8] In fact, Pluto was closer to the Sun than Neptune, whose semi-major axis is 30 au, from 1979 to 1999.

[9] In a sense, this is also true of the Earth: The energy it contains in its interior is far more than the energy it receives via sunlight. But, with some exceptions, the interior energy is contained underneath a solid rocky crust.

A further twist to our story, literally, comes from the rotations of the planets. Imagine sitting at the edge of a merry-go-round and playing catch with a friend at the opposite side. If the merry-go-round isn't moving, you simply throw the ball straight to your friend. But if the merry-go-round is rotating, aiming your throw straight across will lead you to miss your friend. From both you and your friend's vantage point, it looks like the ball swerves. In reality, it is simply following one of Newton's laws: "An object in motion tends to stay in motion"; that is, the object tends to go in a straight line. It doesn't look straight because, while the ball is in the air, the merry-go-round (and you and your friend) are moving underneath it.

The same turns out to be true for the Earth. When artillery became capable of launching projectiles with ranges of several miles or more, sailors noted their aim was significantly off if they didn't account for the Earth's spin. Hurricanes and cyclones have characteristic spiral shapes and circular winds due to the Coriolis effect. At the largest of scales, the Earth has "zones" of winds that tend to travel along east-west directions,[10] separated by regions ("doldrums") where winds are nearly nonexistent.

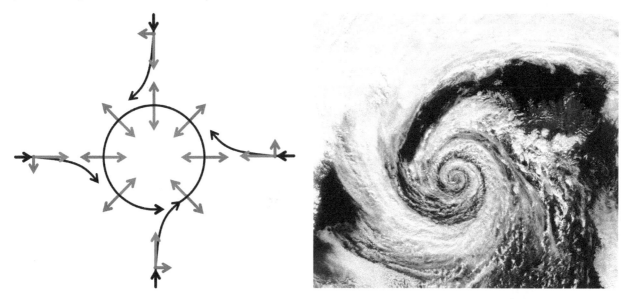

FIGURE 10.20. Left: A schematic of a low-pressure weather system created by the Coriolis effect. The black arrows represent wind velocity, the blue arrows pressure, and the red arrows the Coriolis force. Right: A low-pressure system over Iceland in 2003 (Courtesy of NASA/Aqua-MODIS satellite).

The gas giants are not immune to the Coriolis effect; indeed, they are if anything more susceptible to it. All the Jovians show "bands" and "zones," straight east-west regions of high winds, with neighboring bands moving in opposite directions. In some cases (Jupiter's Great Red Spot is the most famous example), great hurricanes show up at the boundaries of the bands. Each Jovian's rotational speed is incredibly fast—Uranus, the slowest-rotating of the four gas giants, has an equatorial speed of 2.6 kilometers per second (5,800 miles per hour). Compare this to the speed of the equator of the Earth as it rotates—0.46 km/s (1040 mph)—and we can see that the upper atmospheres of the gas giants are well stirred. The combination of rising gases from the interior plus the twisting from the Coriolis effect yields the banded structure for the upper atmospheres for all the Jovians.

Jupiter's bands are the most visible, so we'll use them as an example. Figure 10.21 shows a picture of a "full" Jupiter taken by the Hubble Space Telescope in 2016. The colors have been digitally enhanced to exaggerate its features; to the naked eye, we tend to see white, yellow, orange, and brown; this enhanced image brings out red as well. The bands move relative to each other, east versus west (note that north is at the top of this figure and south at the bottom, as is customary). The bands are not smooth—some of them show a great deal of turbulence (the swirls

---

[10] For example, if you live in the continental United States, the prevailing winds tend to be from west to east.

FIGURE 10.21. Jupiter, as seen by the Hubble Space Telescope. Credit: NASA/ESA/Hubble/Opal Program/STScI/Karol Masztalerz.

are reminiscent of smoke)—and boundaries between neighboring bands are not distinct. To some extent, the colors are indicators of depth: White refers to clouds of ammonia crystals that float relatively high, whereas brown refers to regions with complex hydrocarbons that tend to stay at lower depths. Phenomena such as lightning and aurora have also been observed.

Jupiter possesses several oval-shaped features, the largest of which is the famous *Great Red Spot*. The Great Red Spot, at left on Figure 10.21, was first seen by Galileo in 1609, and given his description was probably redder and larger than it is today. This, the largest storm in the solar system (excepting those on the Sun), sits at the boundary between two opposing bands, with the upper (more northerly) band moving relatively to the west and the lower (more southerly) band moving relatively to the east, supplying a counterclockwise twist or torque. The Great Red Spot "rotates" about once every 6 days, yielding wind speeds at the edges of nearly 1 kilometer per second (over 2,000 miles per hour!). Comparing observations over time suggest the Great Red Spot has shrunk in area by about one third over the past 150 years. We of course do not know how long the Great Red Spot has existed, but it has lasted at least 4 centuries, and possibly much longer; compare this to the largest hurricanes of Earth, which may last for a month or so before blowing themselves out.

FIGURE 10.22. Images of Uranus taken by the Voyager II spacecraft in 1986. Left: Uranus in true color (more or less). Right: A computer-enhanced image of Uranus, showing its atmospheric bands are tilted with the rest of the planet. Credit: NASA.

Uranus, by contrast, is perhaps the blandest object in the solar system. To the naked eye, Uranus is a featureless, pale blue disk. An odd behavior of Uranus is its axial tilt, 98° to the plane of the solar system. Both the rings of Uranus and its moons also orbit the planet at that angle. Whether the weather (sorry!) of Uranus was also tilted in like fashion was a question for astronomers prior to the 1986 Voyager II flyby. Or, which is more important for driving the weather on Uranus: the light and heat it receives from the Sun, or its own internal heat and spin.

Computer-enhanced images of Uranus (Figure 10.22) reveal that (a) Uranus has a band structure, like Jupiter and Saturn (and Neptune, which was confirmed by Voyager II in 1989), and (b) the bands wrap themselves around in the same direction as Uranus's spin. The bands of Uranus, though obviously not as clear as the

Check Your Neighbor

Why do you think Uranus's weather is driven by itself and not the Sun, as weather is on Earth?

other Jovians, also move in east-west directions, as determined by the rotational axis of the planet and not its orbit about the Sun.

The Jovian planets are virtually nothing but atmosphere, in a sense. Studying how they behave gives us insight as to how Earth's atmosphere behaves.

Summary

In this chapter, we discussed how the presence and properties of an object's atmosphere depends on the following:

- Gravity
- Temperature
- Composition
- Rotation
- Magnetic fields
- Convection

Questions

1. Two moons each possess thin atmospheres. The atmosphere of moon A extends about 100 kilometers above the surface and the atmosphere of moon B extends about 50 kilometers above the surface. Which moon has a stronger acceleration due to gravity?

2. Show the algebraic steps to solve for the average speed of a gas particle, given equations 10.1 and 10.2.

3. How fast is the Earth's escape speed in units of miles per hour? Hint: 1 mile is approximately equal to 1.609 kilometers, and 1 hour equals 3,600 seconds.

4. Venus and Mars both have atmospheres primarily composed of carbon dioxide. For which planet is the average speed the slowest? Hint: What are their relative distances from the Sun?

5. Given the escape speed on the surface of Saturn's moon Titan, would you expect Titan to be capable of retaining methane (CH_4) in its atmosphere? Briefly express your reasoning.

6. Among the most intriguing discoveries since the mid-1990s is that of "hot Jupiters," Jupiter-sized (or "massed") planets that orbit their stars much closer than Mercury does the Sun. A famous example is 51 Pegasi b. 51 Peg b orbits its star with a semi-major axis of 0.05 au, suggesting a surface temperature of about 1,000 K. Supposing 51 Peg b is as massive as Jupiter, would we expect 51 Peg b to have originally formed so close to its star? Briefly defend your answer.

7. Mercury's escape speed (see Table 10.1) is 4.25 km/s. How does this compare to the average speed of CO_2 at (a) 400 K, the average temperature we expect Mercury should have, and (b) 700 K, the actual daytime temperature of Mercury? (c) If Mercury was always at its nighttime temperature of approximately 100 K, what would Mercury's atmosphere look like then?

8. The axial tilt of planets like the Earth ensure that its temperature at its equator is consistently higher than that at its poles. Is this spread of temperatures (164 K to 331 K) on Earth extreme enough to imply that it will lose some of its current atmospheric constituents (N_2, O_2) during higher temperatures that it would retain at lower temperatures?

9. Titan and Earth have similar surface atmospheric pressures (i.e., the air "weighs" about the same on the ground). Which atmosphere extends further into space, that of Titan or that of Earth? Hint: See their respective escape speeds from Table 10.1.

Activities

▶ Consider the Earth's atmosphere:

- ◆ Referring to Tables 10.1 and 10.2, determine which gases Earth is capable (via its escape speed) of retaining in its atmosphere, assuming a temperature of 300 K.
- ◆ Look up the atmospheric constituents actually present in the Earth's atmosphere. Briefly discuss why a given substance from Table 10.2 is missing or present in low quantities, even if the Earth is capable of retaining it.

▶ Under which conditions would it be possible for a <u>person</u> to retain an atmosphere? Specifically, do the following:

- ◆ Find the escape speed for a person with a mass of 75 kilograms and a "radius" of 0.10 meters (aka 10 centimeters)
- ◆ Find the equivalent temperature for a gas with an rms speed equal to our hypothetical person's escape speed
- ◆ Compare your temperature to the coldest temperatures currently achieved in laboratories (on the order of one billionth of a kelvin)

▶ *Astrophysics activity 10.1:* First, use a thermometer to show how a light bulb raises the temperature of the air near it. Second, show how gases and solids dissolve into water and how the ability to dissolve ("solubility") changes with changing temperatures. Finally, compare these results to the atmospheres of Venus and Earth.

Works Referenced

Lodders, K. (2003). Solar System abundances and condensation temperatures of the elements. *Astrophysical Journal*, 591(2), 1220–1247.

Jupiter's upper atmosphere, including the Great Red Spot, is briefly described in https://apod.nasa.gov/apod/ap180425.html

Credits

Fig. III-5: Source: https://commons.wikimedia.org/wiki/File:Tritoncloud.jpg.

Fig. 10.1a: Source: https://commons.wikimedia.org/wiki/File:The_Earth_seen_from_Apollo_17.jpg.

Fig. 10.1b: Source: https://commons.wikimedia.org/wiki/File:Full_moon.jpeg.

Fig. 10.2a: Source: https://apod.nasa.gov/apod/ap170514.html.

Fig. 10.2b: Source: https://commons.wikimedia.org/wiki/File:Titan_Visible.jpg.

Fig. 10.3: Copyright © by Superborsuk (CC BY-SA 3.0) at https://commons.wikimedia.org/wiki/File:Maxwell-Boltzmann_distribution_1.png.

Table 10.3: Source: https://iopscience.iop.org/article/10.1086/375492.

Fig. 10.4a: Source: https://commons.wikimedia.org/wiki/File:James_Clerk_Maxwell_big.jpg.

Fig. 10.4b: Source: https://commons.wikimedia.org/wiki/File:Boltzmann-Ludwig.jpg.

Fig. 10.5: Source: https://commons.wikimedia.org/wiki/File:MaxwellBoltzmann-en.svg.

Fig. 10.6: Source: https://commons.wikimedia.org/wiki/File:EW1027346412Gnomap.png.

Fig. 10.8a: Source: https://commons.wikimedia.org/wiki/File:Titan_Crescent.jpg.

Fig. 10.8b: Source: https://commons.wikimedia.org/wiki/File:Titan%27s_thick_haze_layer-picture_from_voyager1.jpg.

Fig. 10.10a: Copyright © by Eric Richards (CC BY-SA 3.0) at https://commons.wikimedia.org/wiki/File:Shallow_Stream_in_Rock_Hill%2C_NY.jpg.

Fig. 10.10b: Source: https://commons.wikimedia.org/wiki/File:Solar_Wind_and_Earth%27s_magnetic_field_-_SVGu1.1.svg.

Fig. 10.11: Source: https://commons.wikimedia.org/wiki/File:Mars_topography_%28MOLA_dataset%29_with_poles_HiRes.jpg.

Fig. 10.12: Source: https://commons.wikimedia.org/wiki/File:Gusev_-_PIA00183-MC-23-AeolisRegion-19980605_%28cropped%29.jpg.

Fig. 10.13: Source: https://commons.wikimedia.org/wiki/File:Absorption_efficiency_graph_from_Lightning_in_a_Bottle.png.

Fig. 10.14: Source: https://commons.wikimedia.org/wiki/File:Earth%27s_greenhouse_effect_%28US_EPA%2C_2012%29.png.

Fig. 10.15: Copyright © by Kevin Gill (CC BY-SA 2.0) at https://commons.wikimedia.org/wiki/File:Venus_-_February_1990_(16355043031).jpg.

Fig. 10.16: Source: https://commons.wikimedia.org/wiki/File:Huygens_surface_color.jpg.

Fig. 10.17a: Source: https://commons.wikimedia.org/wiki/File:Pluto-enhanced-color-new-horizons.png.

Fig. 10.17b: Source: https://commons.wikimedia.org/wiki/File:15-152-Pluto-NewHorizons-HighResolution-20150714-IFV.jpg.

Fig. 10.20a: Copyright © by Cleontuni (CC BY-SA 3.0) at https://commons.wikimedia.org/wiki/File:Coriolis_effect10.svg.

Fig. 10.20b: Source: https://commons.wikimedia.org/wiki/File:Low_pressure_system_over_Iceland.jpg.

Fig. 10.21: Source: https://apod.nasa.gov/apod/image/1804/JupiterOpal_HubbleMasztalerz_1880.jpg.

Fig. 10.22a: Copyright © by Kevin Gill (CC BY 2.0) at https://commons.wikimedia.org/wiki/File:Uranus_-_January_17_1986_%2840346713492%29.jpg.

Fig. 10.22b: Source: https://commons.wikimedia.org/wiki/File:Uranus_-_GPN-2000-000440.jpg.

Aurorae on the North and South poles of Saturn, from the Hubble Space Telescope.

CHAPTER II

PLANETARY MAGNETIC FIELDS

To understand the role of magnetism in planetary astronomy

OBJECTIVES

- ▸ To demonstrate the origins of magnetic fields
- ▸ To witness effects of Earth's magnetic field
- ▸ To review the effect of a lack of magnetic field on planets
- ▸ To review how magnetic fields can be enhanced for planets
- ▸ To discuss the interactions between planetary magnetic fields and their environments
- ▸ To preview the relation of the magnetic field of the Sun to the solar cycle

INTRODUCTION

As we discussed in chapter 4, gravity is the most important fundamental force we need to consider when describing how planets behave and interact. But another fundamental force with large effects on planets is electromagnetism, a combination (as its name suggests) of electricity and magnetism. While electric fields are usually irrelevant when studying planets, magnetic fields can have dramatic consequences for planets, especially when discussing planetary atmospheres.

In this chapter, we will first examine basic properties of magnetic fields, including how they are generated. We will first look at the Earth's magnetic field, and then review several planetary case studies, in particular, why Jupiter has a larger magnetic field than expected, and how a lack of a Martian magnetic field has substantially altered its atmosphere.

KEY TERMS

Aurora: Light emitted by molecules in a planet's atmosphere, specifically due to the interaction of the planet's magnetic field and the solar wind

Conductor (also electrical conductor): A material that easily allows electric charges to flow within it

Differential rotation: When different sections (latitudes) of an object rotate with different periods. Restricted to gaseous objects in practice; solid objects like the Earth cannot do this

Dynamo effect: A combination of rotation (i.e., Coriolis effect) and convection that, by stirring up the interior of a planet, is responsible for its magnetic field

Electric charge: The basic quantity responsible for electric fields. Particles that carry electric charges include electrons and protons

Electric current (or current): Electric charge(s) moving relative to the object in question

Electric field: A change in space due to the presence of electric charges. Electric fields can exert either attractive or repulsive forces on other electric charges

Field: A change of space due to the presence of an object. For example, masses emit gravitational fields, which in turn exert attractive forces on other masses

Magnetic field: A change of space due to the presence of moving electric charges (current). Magnetic fields can exert either attractive or repulsive forces on other moving charges

Magnetic pole: A magnet always comes with a pair of magnetic poles. Magnetic field lines curve in loops, by convention starting at the North magnetic pole and going toward the South magnetic pole

Magnetosphere: The region surrounding an object where its magnetic field interacts with its environment (such as a planet's magnetic field interacting with the solar wind)

Plasma: A variation of gas as a state or phase of matter. The term "gas" usually is restricted to electrically neutral particles; "plasma" refers to gas where a significant fraction is ionized

Scalar (or scalar quantity): A quantity that can be represented as just an amount. Examples include distance, speed, mass, or even money

Solar cycle: An 11-year cycle driven by the rising and falling of the Sun's magnetic field

Solar flare (also just flare): An explosion on the surface of the Sun that can send a large number of high-energy particles out into the solar wind. Flares have been known to damage electrical grids and satellites

Solar irradiance: The total amount of power from the Sun received (per unit area) at the location of the Earth

Solar wind: Charged particles escaping from the Sun, primarily protons

Sunspot: A region of intense magnetic field on the surface of the Sun. A sunspot appears dark because its temperature is several thousands of degrees lower than its surroundings

Temperature gradient: The difference in temperatures at different locations

Vector (or vector quantity): A quantity that is represented by both an amount and a direction. Examples include velocities, forces, and magnetic fields

Section 11.1: Properties of Magnetic Fields

Magnetism as a force of nature has been known since antiquity. Ironically, given the subject of this textbook, most magnetic materials found on the surface of the Earth originated in space, having fallen to Earth as meteors. Iron-rich meteorites can sometimes possess their own magnetic fields, the rock of the Earth's mantle contains iron, and the core of the Earth itself is a blend of iron and nickel. We focus on iron rather than other elements because (a) it is often very responsive to magnetic fields and (b) it is one of the most popular elements inside the Earth.

How are magnetic fields generated (or "induced," as is said in physics)? First, let's back up and discuss the notion of a *field*. A field is simply the representation of how an object can alter space around it. For example, we all live on the Earth due to its gravitational field (see chapter 4). Many fields are invisible, but some are not; for example, you perceive certain types of electromagnetic fields all the time, something we normally call visible light. In the case of gravity, a gravitational field can exert attractive forces on a mass, which is why a stick falls down after you throw it up into the air. In the case of light, electromagnetic fields can induce chemical or electrical changes, which is why you see colors or your cell phone receives a text.

Magnetic fields affect moving electric charges. Suppose a proton flies off the surface of the Sun and heads toward Earth. Earth's magnetic field can exert a force on that proton, (typically) deflecting it around the Earth. It's even more intricate than that: Magnetic fields themselves are created when electric charges move. So there is a great deal of back-and-forth ("symmetry") at work here.

Physicists tend to separate different quantities into two broad categories. A *scalar* is a quantity that is just represented by an amount. For example, a ten dollar bill in your wallet is a scalar, or the mass of the Earth is a scalar. In contrast, all fields are *vector* quantities. A vector is a combination of an amount and a direction—for example, driving in a car at 25 miles per hour is a scalar, but 25 miles per hour heading north is a vector. We can represent a vector in a figure or sketch with an arrow. Magnetic fields, like gravitational fields, are vectors.

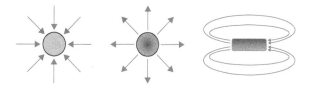

FIGURE 11.1. Field lines for different forces. Left: Gravitational lines always point toward the object. Center: Electric lines can point toward or away; here, lines point away from a positive charge. Right: Magnetic "lines" are always loops, going from North to South poles.

Figure 11.1 shows several examples of field lines. An object like the Earth, which is close to being a perfect sphere, can be depicted as having gravitational field lines pointing straight toward it. This implies the Earth's gravity acts equally well in all directions and tries to pull other objects toward it. An object that has a positive electric charge can also be depicted with radially symmetric electric field lines. Since electric charges come in two kinds—positive and negative—we can draw field lines either approaching or receding from a charged object. The convention is that positive charges have electric field lines pointing away, for example. By contrast with the straight field lines we see for gravity and electricity, magnetic field lines[1] always appear in loops or curves (note that the bar magnet in Figure 11.1 keeps us from seeing some of the lines or loops).

We can cite some simple equations to support our sketches. The weight of an object w, that is, the gravitational force acting on the object, on the Earth can be expressed as simply the product of its mass m times the acceleration due to gravity g (Equation 11.1a). Similarly, the electric force F_E acting on an electrically charged particle is equal to the particle's charge q multiplied by the strength of the electric field E (Equation 11.1b). But again magnetism is more complicated. Not only do we need to include the particle's charge q and the strength of the magnetic field B[2], but also the relative speed at which the particle is moving compared to the magnetic field v and the angle θ between the direction of motion of the particle compared to that of the magnetic field (Equation 11.1c):

Equation 11.1a

$$w = mg$$

Equation 11.1b

$$F_E = qE$$

Equation 11.1c

$$F_B = qvB\sin\theta$$

Something else pops out from this discussion. Since gravity is solely an attractive force, mass is considered to always be (mathematically) positive; there is no such thing as a "negative" mass. Electric charges, on the other hand, can be positive or negative. Again, magnetism is more complicated. There are no individual magnetic "masses" or "charges"; rather, magnets always come with North and South *magnetic poles*. Further, nature is apparently constructed so that magnets always come with both the North and South poles—nobody has ever seen an individual North or individual South magnetic pole.

---

[1] Note that physicists still call these "lines" even though they aren't lines according to mathematicians.

[2] Why "B" for magnetic field strength? "M" is already used to represent mass. Physics equations often have this issue—there are so many quantities that we need to use other letters. Even Greek letters like θ ("theta") are often brought in.

FIGURE 11.2. A refrigerator magnet versus the Earth.

Yet another property to note about magnetic (and electric) fields: they can be very strong. Consider something as simple as a refrigerator magnet or sticky note. The magnetic force acting on the magnet, and the electric forces acting as the "glue" of the sticky note, are so strong they can defy the gravity of the entire planet Earth trying to pull them down. Even so, magnetic and electric forces are usually secondary effects in astronomy, whereas gravity is the most important. Here, gravity does only one thing: It attempts to pull objects together. Magnetism and electricity can repel as well as attract. At the large scales of astronomy, the repulsion and attraction of these forces tend to cancel themselves out, whereas there is no canceling gravity.

Section 11.2: Earth's Magnetic Field

Planets can also have magnetic fields. The origins of planetary magnetic fields are complex and not yet fully understood, but we know that (a) the interior of the planet must possess materials capable of conducting *electric current*, and (b) this material must be moving. Electric current—that is, moving electric charges—can be conducted by several types of materials, but in planets available materials tend to be various types of metals or exotic forms of water.

We can simulate the behavior of a planetary magnetic field by pretending it has gigantic bar magnets inside (Figure 11.3). It is important to realize that planets do not possess gigantic bar magnets, but it is a good starting point for discussion. In the case of the Earth, our south magnetic pole is currently near our north rotational pole (what we usually consider to be the "North Pole") and vice versa.

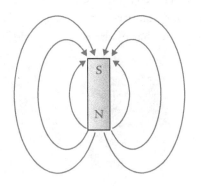

FIGURE 11.3. Left: A bar magnet and its magnetic field lines, with the magnet's South Pole at the top. Right: The Earth and its magnetic field lines.

TABLE 11.1. Relative Strengths of Planetary Magnetic Fields

Planet	Rotational Period	Relative Magnetic Field Strength (Earth = 1)
Mercury	58.81 days	0.006
Venus	−243.69 days	0.00
Earth	23.9345 hours	1
Mars	24.623 hours	0.025
Jupiter	9.925 hours	19,519
Saturn	10.50 hours	578
Uranus	17.24 hours	47.9
Neptune	16.11 hours	27.0

Data courtesy the National Space Science Data Center and the Planetary Society.

The Earth's core consists of two sections, both a mix of iron and nickel (see Figure 11.4). The "inner" core at the very center is solid, and does not contribute to the Earth's magnetic field. The "outer" core is liquid, and is our magnetic field's primary source. The inner core is not "primordial"; that is, it did not always exist. Rather, the inner core started solidifying anytime 0.5 to 2 billion years after the formation of the Earth itself. The inner core continues to grow, albeit slowly, as it (very) slowly cools. Also, the inner and outer core do not rotate at exactly the same rate; seismologists estimate the inner core rotates about one extra angular degree per year. Finally, the inner core does not appear to be uniform—that is, smooth and consisting of exactly the same materials everywhere—but rather has several layers and features of its own.

The liquid core is electrically conductive and rotates about as fast as the rest of the Earth, allowing electricity to flow. But the liquid core also is extremely turbulent. Convection of the liquid metal, in conjunction with its rotation, act to create the equivalent of gigantic whirlpools. This combination of motions, called the *dynamo effect* has been studied extensively both via scaled-down experiments and computer simulations. One major consequence is that the Earth's magnetic field is not completely stable. Instead, it varies somewhat in strength and the location of its magnetic poles alters with time. For a few centuries, the Earth's South magnetic pole appeared to be shifting to the South; since 1900, it has been wandering back toward the Earth's North rotational pole (Figure 11.5). A similar shifting has been taking place for the Earth's North magnetic pole with respect to its south rotational pole.

The Earth's magnetic field does not exist in isolation. It interacts with the *solar wind*, particles (primarily protons) escaping from the surface of the Sun. The solar wind, which would otherwise hit the Earth's atmosphere, is almost entirely diverted around the Earth (Figure 11.6) instead. The relatively few solar wind particles that do hit the Earth are mostly diverted toward the Earth's magnetic poles, which are located near the Earth's North and South rotational poles. When these particles hit the upper atmosphere, the energy they carry excites the

Check Your Neighbor

Figure 11.3 shows both a bar magnet and the magnetic field lines of the Earth. The North rotational pole of the Earth is at the top of the figure and its south rotational pole is at the bottom. About where would we find the North and South magnetic poles of the Earth?

Check Your Neighbor

In general, is there a relationship between the rotational period of a planet and the strength of its magnetic field? If so, what is it?

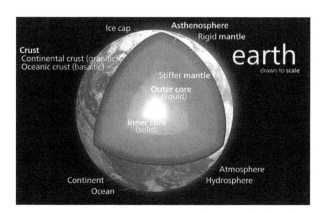

FIGURE 11.4. A cutout showing the interior of the Earth, to scale. The Earth's magnetic field starts with the outer core.

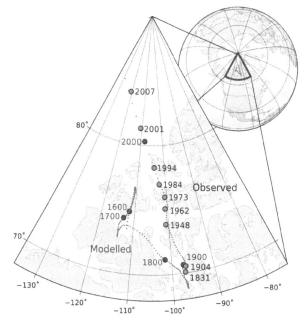

FIGURE 11.5. The wandering of the Earth's South magnetic pole over the past several centuries.

FIGURE 11.6. An artist's rendition of the solar wind interacting with the Earth's magnetosphere. The image is not to scale. Credit: NASA.

atmosphere, which then emits light we perceive as *aurorae* (see Figure 11.7). Green is the most vivid color (there are sometimes others), resulting from how the solar wind particles impact oxygen molecules in our upper atmosphere.

Besides making pretty lights, how does the solar wind—and its interactions with Earth's magnetic field—impact us? You've probably heard from time to time how solar flares affect satellite communications, or are dangerous for astronauts, or even cause electricity blackouts. But these are relatively recent developments, related to our usage of modern electrical technology.

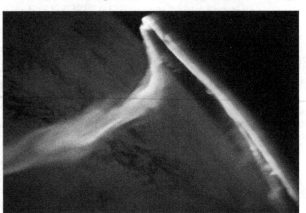

FIGURE 11.7. Left: An aurora seen from the ground in Sweden (Credit: Pavel Shyshkouski). Right: An aurora seen above the Earth (Credit: International Space Station).

The interaction of the solar wind and the Earth's magnetic field (or *magnetosphere*) is more of a long-term project than you may realize. The Earth's magnetic field turns out to be very important, and perhaps vital, for life on Earth.

Solar wind particles, again, primarily protons, can reach the Earth from the Sun in only a few days—which is to say, they are often moving at several tens of millions of miles per hour. This is an order of magnitude (i.e., power of ten) larger than the speeds of the particles in our atmosphere. If a proton collides with (say) an oxygen molecule, it will likely impart much of its energy to the oxygen molecule, meaning that the oxygen molecule will be moving faster than it was before. As we saw in the previous chapter on planetary atmospheres, a particle with a high enough speed can potentially escape the gravitational pull of its planet. The net result is that, if the solar wind is allowed unimpeded access to our atmosphere, it will bleed our atmosphere away.

Fortunately for Earth, we do possess a relatively strong magnetic field. Our magnetic field shields us from the solar wind and other high-speed particles from space that would drain away our atmosphere.[3] Most of the solar wind is diverted around the Earth's magnetosphere, much like water flows around a rock in a stream. Not all of the solar wind is shunted away; some particles are trapped in the magnetosphere and bounce back and forth (the "Van Allen" belts), and others do manage to reach the atmosphere, giving rise to aurorae as noted. But these are minor effects, and the Earth's magnetic field has protected our air fairly well over its long life.

---

[3] We need to be careful not to give the impression that the Earth's magnetosphere is actually like a hollow sphere. Rather, much like Earth's gravitational field, it is strong at the Earth's surface and declines with increasing altitude. Like the Earth's gravitational field, you and I live within the Earth's magnetosphere all the time.

Could our magnetic field ever shut down? With 4.5 billion years or so history behind it, it seems unlikely. Earth's outer core—the spinning liquid metal portion of our interior—is slowly cooling, but at a rate currently estimated to be only a drop of 100 Celsius degrees per billion years. In other words, the outer core will stay liquid far beyond when the Sun itself will come to an end (and then we, or our descendants, would have more pressing problems anyway!). And while the Moon's tides do indeed act to slow the Earth's rotation, this also is a very gradual thing, and again the Earth can be expected to rotate quickly enough to maintain a strong magnetosphere well into the Sun's obsolescence. In short, unless a dramatic event, or series of events, occurs, our planet's magnetic field can be expected to always be there for us.

However, this does not mean the Earth's magnetic field doesn't experience dramatic changes or perturbations. We have already noted that the Earth's South magnetic pole is slowly wandering about upper Canada. Plenty of evidence exists showing the Earth's magnetic field has "flipped" many times throughout geologic history.

The Earth's crust is splitting along the mid-Atlantic Ridge, an idea we explored in chapter 9.

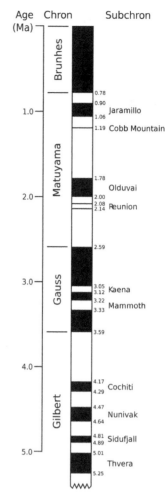

FIGURE 11.8. Top: A "black smoker" at the mid-Atlantic Ridge, a mix of superheated steam and minerals escaping into the ocean through a crack in the Earth's crust (Credit: NOAA/P. Rona). Right: The changes in magnetic polarity of the mid-Atlantic Ridge over the past 5 million years. Black is "normal" and white is "reversed" polarity (Credit: USGS).

As convection brings molten rock from the upper mantle up to the surface, it also acts to drive the ocean (and several continents) apart. But mantle rock has a significant amount of iron in it. While the rock is molten, iron atoms tend to align themselves with the magnetic field of the Earth, meaning the rock itself becomes partly magnetic. Once the magma cools, however, the iron atoms are locked in place, essentially freezing their magnetic poles in place as well.

This interesting phenomenon wouldn't gather so much attention, except for the behavior of Earth's magnetic field over time. If the Earth's magnetic field always pointed the same way—if, for example, the Earth's South magnetic pole was always near the Earth's North rotational pole—iron in the rocks of the mid-Atlantic Ridge would always orient themselves accordingly. But geologists have found that the orientation of the magnetic fields of the rocks of the ridge have flipped back and forth several times. The average time flip is about 200,000 years, though this is by no means a reliable periodic behavior.

In other words, the Earth's magnetic poles themselves appear to "flip" on geologic time scales. Geologists speculate if this means the strength of the Earth's magnetic field, and therefore its protective shielding, significantly declines during these episodes. It is not completely clear how this might affect life on Earth (the flipping is not abrupt, compared to the lifespans of living organisms) and there is no clear-cut evidence for mass extinctions at these boundaries. Nevertheless, it does hint that our planet is still a dynamic and ever-changing place.

Check Your Neighbor

One section of rock on the floor of the Atlantic Ocean is 1,000 kilometers from the center of the mid-Atlantic Ridge and another section is 500 kilometers from the center of the ridge. Which section is older?

Section 11.3: Mars

In many ways, the planet most like Earth is our neighbor, Mars. Mars has a 24-hour day (more or less), and with its axial tilt of 24° experiences seasons. Mars has polar ice caps, volcanoes, canyons and dry river beds, hints of a time when Mars was a warmer and wetter place. The highest temperatures of Martian summers can reach a comfortable 70°F,[4] though its winters are cold, far more bitter than the worst Antarctica has to offer. Several landers have made successful trips to Mars and still today explore its surface; a probe even spotted the wheel tracks made in the Martian sand by one of them! With Venus being such a horrible place with its intense runaway greenhouse effect, Mars is the planet most discussed when people suggest living on other worlds or even terraforming it to make it look more like Earth.

FIGURE 11.9. A trail on Mars left behind by water flowing down a hillside before freezing, as seen by the Mars Pathfinder robotic rover. Credit: NASA/JPL/MGS/MSSS.

Mars has one major restriction for potential visits by humans: Its air is next to nonexistent. It's not merely made of the "wrong" stuff for people, with 95% of the Martian atmosphere being carbon dioxide and next to none of it consisting of oxygen. Rather, the air pressure at the surface of Mars is only 1% of the air pressure at sea level on Earth. This is effectively a vacuum as far as people are concerned. The lack of air on Mars makes for important consequences; Mars has wild swings in its day/night temperatures, Mars has few clouds and no rain; and most importantly, liquid water cannot survive exposure on the Martian surface. While there is evidence that liquid water might lurk beneath the surface in isolated spots, if liquid water breaks through to the surface, it quickly evaporates and/or freezes. Yet Mars is covered with features—dry river beds, shoreline of ancient lakes etc.—that suggest it once was covered in water. This would only have been possible if the Martian atmosphere was much thicker than it is today. So the question becomes, where did the Martian air go? Some recent theories involve the Martian magnetosphere.

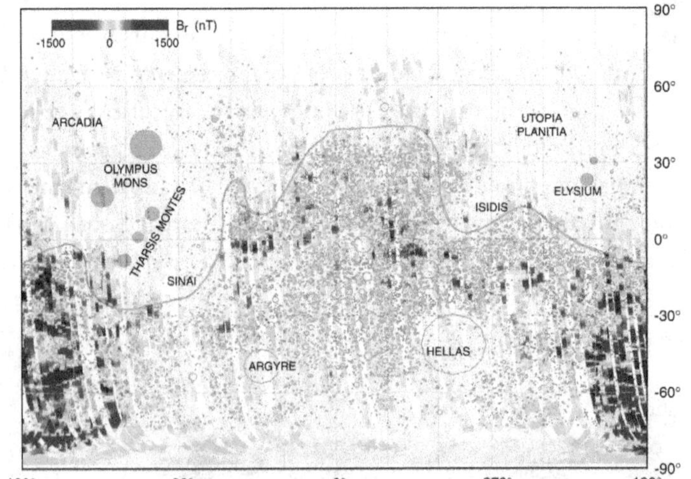

Despite being much smaller than the Earth in both mass and radius, Mars has a large-enough escape speed that it should be able to hold onto air; that, combined with its distance from the Sun suggests that heavier molecules like carbon dioxide, nitrogen, oxygen and the like should be held by Mars, though not hydrogen or helium (see chapter 10). Mars almost certainly had plenty of air earlier in its history, given the prevalence of evidence for

FIGURE 11.10. A global map of magnetic anomalies on Mars by the Mars Global Surveyor. Compare to the global elevation map of Mars (Figure 10.11). Credit: NASA/JPL/GSFCNASA.

---

[4] Unfortunately, the super thin air of Mars means this temperature only extends about an inch above the surface. For any visitor standing up, the temperature at one's head would be around a hundred degrees below zero Fahrenheit.

previously watered terrain and clues of underground liquid pools of water even today. The culprit appears to be the Martian magnetic field—or, more properly, the lack of one.

Mars is a planet whose surface is more or less cut in half. The northern hemisphere of Mars is at lower elevations, by 6 to 8 kilometers, than its southern hemisphere (the border is not exactly at the Martian equator, and there are important exceptions), the Martian north looking a little like the relatively thinner oceanic crust on Earth and the Martian south a little like the relatively thicker continental crust of Earth. There are noticeably fewer craters in the northern hemisphere of Mars than in the south. More recently, via measurements from the Mars Global Surveyor probe, the magnetic field in the northern hemisphere of Mars (and other low-lying areas) is next to zero, and what little magnetic field Mars has is concentrated in the rocks of the crust of the south. Mars must have had a dynamo effect early in its history in order to set up a magnetic field of any kind, but the dynamo shut down long ago. The remnants of the original Martian magnetic field in its southern hemisphere are about 40 times weaker on its surface than its equivalent strength for Earth.

How can a planet's magnetic dynamo be altered substantially? Convection, combined with the Coriolis effect, drives the dynamo effect. If either (or both) is shut down, the dynamo will shut down. Convection specifically depends on a *temperature gradient* (a fancy term for temperature differences at different locations), as heat naturally flows from relatively hot to relatively cool regions. But convection bubbles will not flow if the temperatures at different locations are nearly the same.

Here are two ideas regarding the demise of the Martian magnetosphere, both involving asteroid impacts.

1. Early Giant Impact

The Mars Global Surveyor spacecraft first noticed the Martian "dichotomy" between its northern and southern hemispheres in 1985. The most striking connection was that the split shows up in terms of elevation, thickness of crust, and magnetic fields. The astronomer Sabine Stanley and her collaborators suggested in 2008 that Mars had undergone an enormous, though glancing, asteroid (or protoplanet) impact very early in its history. The impact was sufficient to melt the crust of only the northern half of the planet. Computer modeling by Sabine's group indicates this led to (a) the northern crust of Mars being notably thinner than the crust of the southern half of Mars and (b) raised the temperature of the northern hemisphere's crust to be nearly the same as that of the mantle beneath it. The southern hemisphere, more or less left alone, did not experience either effect. This meant that convection came to a halt in the northern hemisphere of Mars much faster than it did for the southern hemisphere.

The lack of a magnetic field for the northern hemisphere of Mars exposed the north to the solar wind, which stripped the atmosphere in the north of its air molecules. But air moves very easily around a planet (i.e., air particles distribute themselves very well), meaning that some particles from the southern hemisphere would move around to the north, in their turn to be lost to space thanks to the solar wind. The lack of a magnetic shield around just a significantly large section of Mars would eventually guarantee the loss of its atmosphere.

2. Repeated Impacts

As a variation on this theme, instead of (or in conjunction with) Mars being hit by an enormous object early in its history, it was hit repeatedly (perhaps as often as 20 times) by relatively large impacts. One of those potential impact sites is the Hellas impact basin, the oval-shaped region in the southern hemisphere of Mars. The Hellas impact basin, or Hellas Planitia, is up to 2,100 kilometers (1,300 miles) across and 9 kilometers (6 miles) deep. The basin is further surrounded by a ring of debris stretching 4,000 kilometers (2,500 miles) out from the center of the basin, and the ring of debris adds an extra 2 kilometers (1.2 miles) of height to the surroundings.

Hellas Planitia is perhaps representative of not one gigantic impact, but a succession of smaller ones that also disrupted the Martian magnetic dynamo. Picture Mars being hit by one large asteroid, whose impact subsequently raises the temperature of the local crust. The crust and upper mantle now being, at least temporarily, at similar temperatures, the convection in that section of Mars comes to a halt. Eventually the crust would cool and the convection resume, but not as robustly as before. A series of such impacts would land body blows upon Mars, until

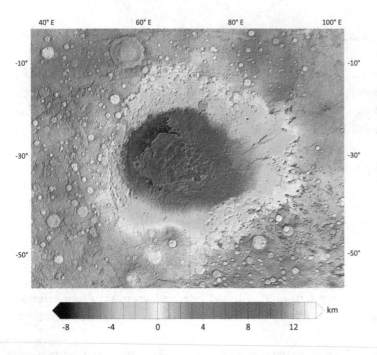

FIGURE 11.11. A false-color close-up of the Hellas impact basin by the Mars Global Surveyor. The blue end of the spectrum represents lower depths and the red end higher elevations. Credit: NASA/JPL-Caltech/Arizona State University.

eventually the convection shut down altogether and permanently. Again, the resulting lack of a strong magnetic field would expose the Martian atmosphere to the solar wind.

One last question regarding Mars: Could we one day terraform it? That is, could we one day bring the Martian atmosphere back? The molecules that escaped the Martian atmosphere are completely lost, but could Mars have somehow stored air particles in other places? The most popular molecule in the Martian atmosphere is carbon dioxide, so this is where we should start.

Unfortunately, there appear to be several arguments against this. Much of Earth's "carbon cycle," the processes that maintain a relatively stable amount of carbon dioxide in our air, involves subduction. Subduction (see chapter 9) is the process by which one crustal plate dips underneath, or "subducts," another plate. Much of the Earth's carbon dioxide is sequestered, or removed, by this mechanism. Conversely, this implies Earth has a large amount of CO_2 stored in the upper mantle. Mars, however, does not appear to ever have had as active a geology as Earth, including plate tectonics, and thus doesn't have a lot of CO_2 stored deep underground.

Another potential location is in the Martian surface. Carbon dioxide can theoretically be taken in (the specific term is "adsorbed") by surface rocks. However, NASA's Curiosity rover has analyzed the chemistry of the surface in its area of exploration and found few carbonate rocks. If Curiosity's findings are representative of the Martian surface, then there won't be nearly enough CO_2 to make a difference. Finally, while there might be lots of CO_2 stored in specific locations such as volcanoes, this isn't enough either.

It may be that humans will one day be able to terraform Mars. But given our current knowledge and technology, terraforming would realistically be in the very far future.

Check Your Neighbor

Venus, our other neighbor, also lacks any real magnetic field. Offer at least two possible reasons why this is so.

Section 11.4: Jupiter and Saturn

The largest planetary magnetic field in the solar system, not surprisingly, belongs to Jupiter. Jupiter's mass alone tells us this should be the case. But Jupiter has a unique approach to generating its magnetic field.

The terrestrial worlds generate (or generated) their magnetic fields via the same basic approach: convection of molten matter containing iron, setting up a dynamo effect. The Earth—the largest of such objects—also has the strongest magnetic field, but it is not the only object to have one. Mercury, for example, has a larger magnetic field than either Venus or Mars, likely because it also has the larger percentage of iron and other metals in its interior. The Moon has a tiny magnetic field, apparently frozen in place, since its metal core is relatively small and almost completely solid.

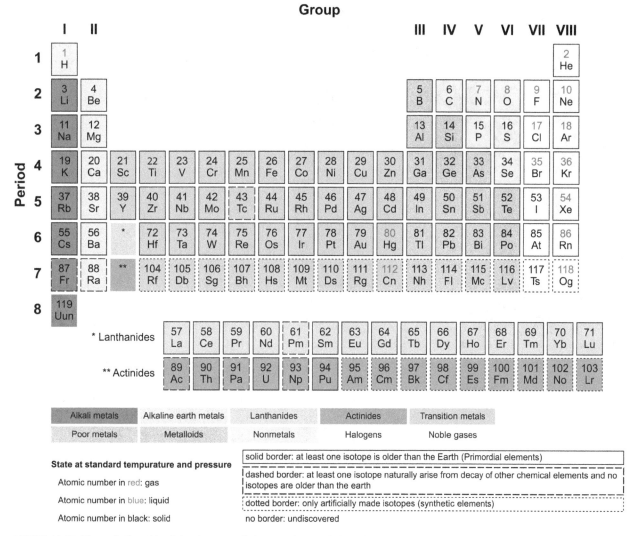

FIGURE 11.12. The periodic table of the elements. Hydrogen, element 1, is at the top of the column of alkali metals, though it is not normally itself considered a metal.

Jupiter does have a solid rocky/metal core, but it only counts for 5% of Jupiter's mass. Jupiter is famous as the largest of the "gas giants," but this region is also not instrumental for Jupiter's magnetism. Jupiter has a layer of metallic hydrogen that does the trick.

Hydrogen is not considered a metal by chemists—and for good reason, as it never shows metallic behavior. Normally, hydrogen atoms bond to each other to form diatomic molecules (H_2) and stays as a gas over a very wide range of conditions. It does not form a solid or liquid except under extreme cold, and its gaseous phase does not act like a conductor of electricity. However, hydrogen sits atop the column of alkali metals, which includes elements such as sodium and potassium, because it has one "extra" electron in its outermost (valence) shell. But hydrogen only acts like a metal under extreme circumstances.

In 1935, the physicists Eugene Wigner and Hillard Bell Huntington predicted that hydrogen molecules would split apart under enormous pressures, currently thought to be near 4 million times the air pressure at the surface of the Earth (In fact, the pressure is so high that researchers have had trouble making this happen in the laboratory). Under these extreme conditions, the hydrogen nuclei would be forced into a lattice (grid-like) arrangement and the individual electrons would be spread throughout, which would behave like the solid metals with which we are familiar. A few researchers, such as the solid-state British physicist Neil Ashcroft, argue that a liquid phase of metallic hydrogen could exist given the proper combination of low temperatures and high pressures. Giant planets like

FIGURE 11.13. Aurora at the north pole of Jupiter, as seen by the Hubble Space Telescope. The aurora were captured by the HST's Imaging Spectrograph and the visible disk of Jupiter in visible light. Credit: NASA/ESA/J. Nichols (University of Leicester).

Jupiter and Saturn, with thousands of kilometers of gas available to exert such pressures, are expected to contain thick layers of metallic hydrogen.

Jupiter's magnetic field acts much like a bar magnet, similar to the Earth's, except that its north and south magnetic poles are nearly aligned with its north and south rotational poles, respectively.[5] The strength of Jupiter's magnetic field is about 20 times that of Earth's at its surface (keeping in mind we really mean the top of Jupiter's atmosphere), but Jupiter's magnetosphere is much larger and differently shaped than that of Earth. "Jupiter's magnetosphere extends about 7 million kilometers toward the Sun and tails hundreds of millions of kilometers away from the Sun in a teardrop shape, well past the orbit of Saturn. The magnetic "moment" of Jupiter, a better indicator of overall strength, is close to 20,000 times that of Earth. Aurora on Jupiter (Figure 11.13) are virtually permanent and are made not so much by interactions with the solar wind—in fact, the stronger the solar

wind at Jupiter, the weaker its aurorae—but rather its interactions with its large moons, especially Io, as we shall see. The aurorae emit electromagnetic radiation in nearly all wavelengths, with their intensity strongest in infrared and ultraviolet. As there is almost no nitrogen or oxygen in Jupiter's atmosphere, the interactions of electric currents and hydrogen gas is responsible for the aurorae.

Jupiter's magnetosphere would be immense if it were generated solely by the planet itself. But it has an assistant: its moon Io. Recall that Io is the most geologically active object in the solar system, exhibiting almost continuous volcanic eruptions (see chapter 9). About 1,000 kilograms of material is ejected from Io every second and enters into a doughnut-shaped region (called a "torus") in orbit about Jupiter. Most of this material is sulfur dioxide, which is broken apart into its constituent sulfur and oxygen ions by the solar wind, which makes the torus a plasma. The swirling ions of the Ionian plasma extend and strengthen Jupiter's magnetic field up to a factor of three times as strong as it would be without Io's contributions. Further, Jupiter's magnetosphere is flat compared to that of Earth, thanks to Io's rotating plasma torus.

Jupiter's magnetosphere also affects the behavior of its other moons. Europa and Ganymede (and perhaps Callisto) have underground oceans of liquid water, protected by thick icy crusts. The water in these oceans,

Check Your Neighbor

Suppose Jupiter's magnetosphere were visible to the naked eye. How would it compare to the size of the full Moon? Hint: Jupiter is 4.2 astronomical units (630 million kilometers) at closest approach to Earth, there are 360° in a full circle, and the full Moon is 1/2° across.

---

[5] As this chapter was being written, preliminary results from the Juno spacecraft currently orbiting Jupiter suggests the planet may actually have two separate South magnetic poles. If so, this could drastically alter our perceptions of how Jupiter's magnetic field is generated inside the planet.

somewhat like Earth's, have significant amounts of salt. Salt water is far more electrically conductive than fresh water, and the Galilean moons as a consequence react to the presence of Jupiter's magnetic field. Further, the Galilean moons do possess the thinnest of atmospheres (a billion or more times less pressure than that of sea level on Earth), which include ionized particles that are traded back and forth with Jupiter's magnetosphere. Ganymede, in particular, has its own magnetic field, weak of course in comparison to that of Jupiter but strong enough to create its own small cavity (magnetosphere) inside its environment.

What does this all mean? For starters, the environment around Jupiter is a deadly place. Radiation kicked up by Jupiter's magnetic field

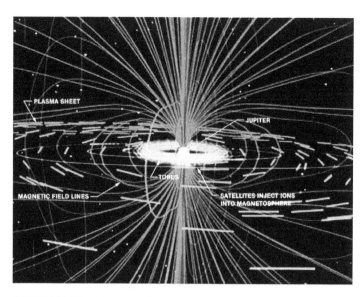

FIGURE 11.14. In this artist's depiction, plasma from Io (in yellow) extends and reshapes Jupiter's magnetic field. Credit: NASA/JPL.

saturates the Jovian system. The first space probe to visit Jupiter was Pioneer 10 in 1973; when it arrived, NASA scientists realized Jupiter was emitting ten times more radiation than they had expected. Pioneer 10 fortunately avoided the most intense regions of Jupiter's magnetosphere (recall the magnetosphere is somewhat flat), but its sibling spacecraft Pioneer 11 did not. Pioneer 11 got too close to Jupiter and its magnetic field, causing serious electrical interference that cost NASA most of its pictures of Io. The Voyager I and II missions required serious upgrades to shield them properly when they made their visits in 1979–1980. Four other spacecraft have measured Jupiter's magnetosphere up close: Ulysses, Galileo, Cassini, and currently Juno. Ulysses was actually tasked with observing the Sun from a great distance, and Cassini's ultimate destination was Saturn. Galileo and Juno were/ are orbiter missions, with Juno reaching Jupiter in July 2016, and a large part of Juno's mission is to investigate the details of the Jovian magnetosphere. Oddly enough, the energy delivered from Jupiter's magnetosphere may help produce complex molecules on the surfaces of Europa and Ganymede, and some of that material could slowly work its way into the deep oceans, perhaps contributing raw materials and energy useful for life.

Could humans explore the Jupiter system? It's probably not a good idea. Our current rocket technology could theoretically get explorers to the Jupiter system, but not retain enough energy to leave it, even if we're merely intending to land on one of Jupiter's moons. The other major problem with personal exploration is the radiation. In 2003, NASA commissioned a study of the possibility and reached the conclusion that the ionizing radiation present in the Jovian system would quickly kill any astronauts who landed on Io (which already has its own issues as a destination), Europa or Ganymede. Callisto, the furthest of the Galilean moons from Jupiter and the least interesting (so far) of the four, is the only place astronauts could safely explore.

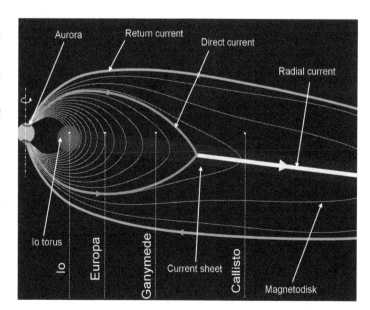

FIGURE 11.15. An artist's depiction of the various electric currents and Galilean moons embedded in Jupiter's magnetosphere. Credit: Ruslik0.

How about Saturn, Jupiter's smaller sibling? Saturn reproduces most of the features of Jupiter's magnetic field, albeit slightly smaller and less energetically. Saturn also has a teardrop shape to its magnetosphere, again oriented with its tail pointing away from the Sun. Saturn's magnetism also interacts with its own moons, even including a contribution to plasma in orbit about Saturn from Enceladus at the rate of 1,000 kilograms per second, the difference between Enceladus and Io being that Enceladus ejects water vapor from geysers as opposed to Io's ejection of sulfur dioxide from volcanic eruptions. Saturn's radiation from its magnetosphere also requires extensive shielding on any spacecraft that visit its environs, and it too is inimical to human life.

Section 11.5: Uranus and Neptune

In considering the magnetic fields of Uranus and Neptune, it may help to review their origins and bulk properties. Current theories of planetary formation suggest that Uranus and Neptune formed closer to the Sun than Jupiter and Saturn, but were pushed outward by the gravities of their larger siblings when Jupiter and Saturn migrated inward during the early years of the solar system. As a consequence, Uranus and Neptune are not only smaller in terms of mass, but are also different from Jupiter and Saturn in their internal compositions (compare Figures 9.26 and 9.27 from chapter 9). Uranus and Neptune are thought to be mostly made of water, ammonia, and some methane; depending on the models applied, Uranus may be anywhere from 64% to 93% of these materials, with a relatively small rocky core and atmosphere of hydrogen and helium. Some astronomers therefore tend to refer to Uranus and Neptune as "icy giants," although this is very misleading, as the mix of water-ammonia-methane is not solid ice as we experience, but rather a slurry reaching temperatures in the thousands of kelvins. The ammonia-water mix is highly ionized, which combined with rapid planetary rotation and convection results in a dynamo effect producing a strong magnetic field.

Astronomers could only speculate about the magnetic fields of Uranus and Neptune prior to the flybys by the Voyager II spacecraft in 1986 and 1989, respectively, but most expected the fields would be similar to those of Jupiter and Saturn. Uranus provided them with their first shock.

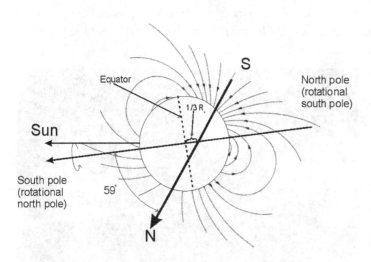

FIGURE 11.16. The magnetosphere of Uranus. Note how it is neither centered at the center of the planet nor is it aligned with the rotational center of the planet. Credit: NASA.

The magnetic field of Uranus is not centered on the center of the planet (Figure 11.16). Rather, it is offset by about 8,000 kilometers, 1/3 of the radius of the planet. Furthermore, the magnetic field is not aligned with the rotational axis of Uranus; instead, it is tilted by 59°. By way of comparison, the Earth's magnetic field is tilted by 11° relative to its axis of rotation, and the field is essentially centered at the center of the Earth.

This makes for some strange consequences for Uranus. The strength of its magnetic field ranges from 1.1 gauss[6] in the northern hemisphere of Uranus down to 0.1 gauss in its southern hemisphere. This allows the solar wind to penetrate to the upper atmosphere of Uranus once per day (a day for Uranus, not the Earth), though the gravitational pull of Uranus and the distance from the Sun to Uranus limits

[6] The gauss is a unit that expresses the strength of a magnetic field. For comparison, the Earth's average magnetic field strength at its surface is 0.5 gauss.

the amount of gas particles Uranus might lose. Uranus, like Jupiter and Saturn, experiences aurorae and its magnetic field interacts with its moons. The sideways rotation of Uranus—recall its rotational axis is tilted 98° relative to the plane of the solar system—means its magnetic tail has a corkscrew rather than a teardrop shape.

Why is the magnetic field of Uranus so odd? A popular suggestion involved the odd tilt of its rotational axis. It is thought that Uranus was struck a glancing blow by an Earth-size protoplanet early in its history, knocking it over. The weird nature of its magnetic field seemed to be explained by this ancient event. Only three years after Voyager II, that explanation no longer appeared tenable.

The reason is that, when Voyager II flew by Neptune in 1989, it found yet again an oddly arranged magnetic field. Neptune's axis of rotation is similar to that of Earth and Saturn, so astronomers anticipated its magnetic field would be aligned with its axis and centered on the center of the planet. Again, they were surprised to find that Neptune's magnetic field is tilted by 47° relative to its axis of rotation and is centered 13,500 kilometers (55% of the radius of Neptune!) from the center of Neptune. Neptune does not give evidence of having undergone a cataclysmic impact as Uranus does, yet its magnetic field is off-axis and off-center, like that of Uranus.

The current leading hypothesis is that, unlike the deeper sources of magnetic fields generated by the Earth or Jupiter and Saturn, the magnetic fields of Uranus and Neptune are generated primarily by the ammonia-water layer, which is much closer to their surfaces. Another thought involves the possibility that Uranus and Neptune form diamonds (liquid and solid both) that interfere with the normal generation of their magnetic fields. Unfortunately, there are no space probes scheduled to revisit either Uranus or Neptune, and our information is limited to that gathered by Voyager II or long-distance observations via instruments like the Hubble Space Telescope.

Section 11.6: The Sun

While this chapter's focus is on the magnetic fields of planets, this is a good place to introduce the magnetic field of the Sun. Not surprisingly, the object containing 99.9% of the solar system's mass has a magnetic field that virtually envelops the solar system. Despite this, we still don't know a great deal about the Sun's magnetic field.

The Sun is both a simpler and more complicated object than a typical planet. The Sun is simple in that it is gas (plasma, specifically) all the way through. The Sun is also simple in that it has three primary interior layers (the core, radiative zone, and conductive zone), which are defined not so much by what they consist of, but rather how they behave. But the Sun is more complicated for a similar reason: With no solids or liquids anywhere, with the Sun being an object that generates its own heat, and with the Sun's interior temperature ranging from several thousand to several millions of kelvins, the Sun is an incredibly turbulent object.

Figure 11.17 shows the appearance of the magnetic field lines from the Sun at two different dates, January 1 of 2011 and July 16 of 2014. First, these close-up images show the incredible complexity of the Sun's magnetic field

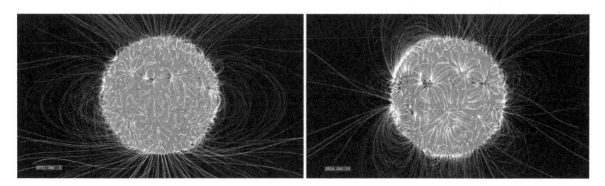

FIGURE 11.17. Magnetic field lines of the Sun from January 2011 (left) and July 2014 (right). Credit: NASA/Goddard Space Flight Center/Bridgman.

FIGURE 11.18. The effects of differential rotation on the Sun. All the sunspots are lined up at the same longitude at the beginning of the cycle, and the red line represents a portion of a magnetic field line (left). The sunspots closest to the equator move faster than those nearest the poles, distorting the magnetic field line (middle). As time continues, the magnetic field line, once extending along a north-south direction, becomes wrapped up so that it more closely follows an east-west direction (right).

locally. Second, the Sun's field has noticeably changed in just 3.5 years. The 2011 image (at left) looks more like the bar-magnet model we have been showing for the magnetic fields of the planets; when we get to 2014 (right), the field lines are much more tangled.

This shows up in a pattern of behavior we call the *solar cycle*. We shall discuss this further in the next chapter, but for now we can lay out what we understand regarding its mechanism. The Sun exhibits what astronomers call *differential rotation*; that is, different latitudes of the Sun rotate at different rates. In this case, the Sun's equator rotates with a period of 25 days, but the rotational period increases with changing latitude, so that the Sun rotates with a period of 35 days near its poles. Further, this is not merely a surface effect; differential rotation seems to persist deep into the Sun.

Figure 11.18 shows how differential rotation can work to distort a magnetic field. Suppose we have several sunspots, all lined up at the same solar longitude (at left). A magnetic field line is represented in red. As the Sun rotates, its equator moves faster than other latitudes, and its poles move more slowly. The sunspots quickly move away from having the same solar longitude (middle) and the magnetic field line becomes stretched and distorted. If we wait long enough, the spots nearer the equator have lapped the spots near the poles, and the corresponding magnetic field line becomes wrapped up around the Sun (right).

The Sun's differential rotation is not thought to extend all the way to the center of the Sun. The Sun has three interior layers: the core, where energy is generated; the radiative zone, where energy is transported by radiation (light); and the conductive zone, where energy is transported by convection. The transition between the radiative and convective zones is relatively sharp and has the term "tachocline." Below the tachocline, in the radiative zone and core, the Sun rotates uniformly; above the tachocline, in the convective zone, the Sun exhibits differential rotation. With this "shear," or sliding of layers horizontally in the tachocline, lies the beginnings of the Sun's magnetic field.

Combine differential rotation with convection, and the Sun's magnetic field lines tangle into knots. Concentrated field lines represent stronger fields than relatively smooth field lines, meaning the knots are locations of extremely strong magnetism. Recall that magnetic fields exert forces on moving charges (section 11.1), and we can see that the knots act to move particles away from them. Subtracting the charges—or, more precisely, their energy—lowers the temperature at the locations of the knots. Where a knot breaks out at the surface of the Sun, its temperature is several thousand kelvins (typically 4,000 K instead of 6,000 K) lower than its immediate surroundings, and the knot appears dark in comparison, thus the term *sunspot*.

Figure 11.19 shows a close-up picture of a pair of sunspots from the Solar Optical Telescope. In describing the appearance of a sunspot, we use similar lingo to that used for eclipses, thus the darkest (central) part of a sunspot is its "umbra" and the lighter, surrounding section of the sunspot is its "penumbra." The reason is that the strength of the

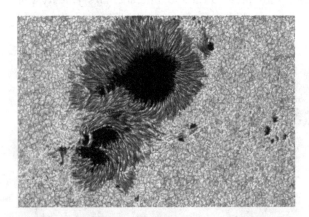

FIGURE 11.19. A close-up of sunspots in the photosphere of the Sun, as seen by the Solar Optical Telescope. A solar flare was observed later the same day. Credit: NASA/JAXA.

Check Your Neighbor

Which section of a sunspot—the penumbra or the umbra—has a lower temperature?

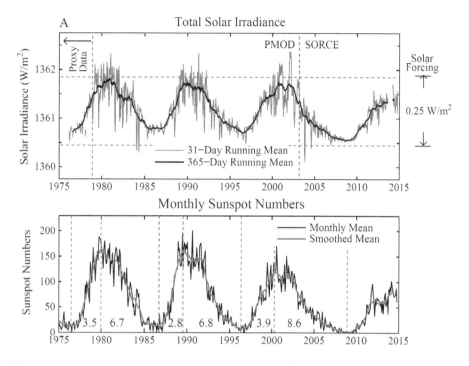

FIGURE 11.20. Two graphs showing changes in the Sun from 1975 to 2015. Top: The solar irradiance (brightness). Above: The number of sunspots. Credit: Hansen et al.

magnetic field of the sunspot, or knot, decreases with distance away from its center. Even so, sunspots are often surprisingly well defined. Sunspots "live" anytime from several days to several weeks, until the knots break apart.

The wrapping of the Sun's magnetic field, from the mechanism of differential rotation, increases the tangling and number of knots with passing time. This doesn't last forever; the Sun eventually reaches a tipping point where the tangling becomes undone and fewer knots form. The number of sunspots, the most obvious marker of this activity, starts at a minimum, increases to a maximum, then decreases to a minimum and restarts the process. This *solar cycle* lasts an average of 11 years, though it has been recorded as short as 7 and as long as 19 years.

How does this affect Earth, if at all? While the Sun is a stable star by any reasonable measure, it does have its quirks. The total amount of power emitted from the Sun's surface, as received by the Earth (the *solar irradiance*) follows a periodic pattern much like the total number of sunspots. This isn't what you would think is a huge effect—the Sun's brightness rises and drops less than a tenth of a percent—but even this small amount of change can affect

weather on Earth. More pertinent for modern society is the proclivity of the Sun to have explosions on its surface during solar maxima. These explosions, commonly called *solar flares*, can damage satellites in near-Earth orbit and threaten the health of astronauts. The most extreme versions of solar flares, called coronal mass ejections (CMEs), can cause blackouts on Earth if the CME heads our way. A famous case occurred in 1989, where a CME shorted out the electrical grid in Québec, Canada. A CME was observed to leave the Sun on March 9 of 1989; 3.5 days later, it arrived at Earth. Aurorae could be seen as far south as Texas and Florida. Several satellites suffered damage, and

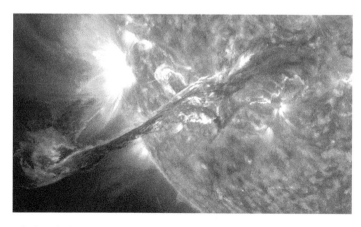

FIGURE 11.21. A coronal mass ejection (CME) from the Sun on August 31, 2012, as seen by the Solar Dynamics Observatory. Fortunately this CME did not head directly toward Earth. Credit: NASA Goddard Space Flight Center.

the Space Shuttle Discovery noted a problem with one of its fuel cells, the problem disappearing only when the solar wind abated. The energy from the CME overloaded the Hydro-Québec power grid, and residents lost power for 9 hours. Electric power companies and governments responded by implementing procedures to avoid such blackouts, and the United States now continuously monitors solar "weather."

One last comment: Much like how the Earth's magnetic field acts to shield us from the solar wind, the Sun's magnetic field acts to shield the entire solar system from extrasolar (i.e., from outside the solar system) *cosmic rays*. Typically this isn't a big deal, as Earth's magnetic field would protect us, but some hypotheses have been proposed that cosmic rays from nearby supernovae have sparked extinction events on Earth. We will continue to discuss the Sun's magnetic field and solar cycle in relation to the rest of the Sun's behaviors and properties in the next chapter.

Summary

In this chapter, we did the following:

▶ Reviewed properties of magnetic fields, including how they are produced

▶ Covered details of the Earth's magnetic field

▶ Discussed a case study of the disappearance of the Martian magnetic field

▶ Laid out the benefits and drawbacks of planetary magnetic fields

▶ Compared the magnetic fields of the gas giants (Jupiter and Saturn) versus the icy giants (Uranus and Neptune)

▶ Introduced the magnetic field of the Sun

Questions

1. Compare the atmospheres of Earth and Mars. Both have the proper conditions otherwise (surface gravity, average temperature, types of molecules available) to possess relatively thick atmospheres. Yet Earth has a relative thick atmosphere and the atmosphere of Mars is close to a vacuum. Briefly describe the potential role of their respective magnetic fields regarding the presence or absence of an atmosphere.

2. The Earth's magnetic field (from the outside) looks like the field from a bar magnet. Is there a bar magnet inside the Earth? If not, why does the field look that way?

3. Venus is suspected to have at least a partially molten mantle, like the Earth. Yet Venus has no appreciable magnetic field, whereas the Earth has a relatively strong magnetic field. What factor (for generating magnetic fields) is missing for Venus compared to the Earth? Hint: It is <u>not</u> the runaway greenhouse effect.

4. Mars spins at virtually the same (angular) rate as the Earth. Yet Mars has an extremely weak magnetic field, whereas the Earth has a relatively strong magnetic field. What factor (for generating magnetic fields) is missing for Mars compared to the Earth?

5. Mercury is thought to be solid nearly throughout the entirety of its interior, yet its magnetic field is much stronger than either that of Venus or Mars. Suggest a reason for this. Hint: Can a solid object possess a strong magnetic field?

6. Salt water is partially ionized; that is, some of the salt (NaCl) dissolves into separate positive sodium (Na^+) ions and negative chlorine (Cl^-) ions. Europa's underground oceans appear to respond to the magnetic field of Jupiter. Relate these two statements together.

7. High above the Earth's surface are the Van Allen belts, two coiled sections of space surrounding the Earth within which high-energy ions are trapped. Spacecraft (and astronauts) need to be shielded if they pass through the belts. With what is the Earth's magnetic field interacting to make the Van Allen belts?

8. The Earth's magnetic field "flips" polarity on average every 200,000 years, but the Sun's flips polarity on average every 11 years.
   * What is responsible for the Earth's flipping of its field?
   * What is responsible for the Sun's flipping of its field?
   * Why does the Sun flip its field so much quicker than the Earth? (Hint: It's not the difference in the strengths of the fields)

9. The Earth's magnetosphere protects the rest of the Earth from the solar wind. Where does the solar wind go after it encounters the Earth?

Activities

▸ *Astrophysics activity 11.1:* Explore various properties of magnetism (with the instructor's assistance) by using (a) bar magnets and iron filings and (b) a coil of wire, a power supply, light bulbs, and miniature magnetic compasses. Relate these findings to what we know about the magnetic field of the Earth.

▸ Use pictures of sunspots over a month's worth of time to demonstrate the differential rotation of the Sun.

Works Referenced

Facts about planets from the National Space Science Data Center (NSSDC): https://nssdc.gsfc.nasa.gov/planetary/factsheet/

The Earth's magnetic field is discussed in https://www.nasa.gov/

Aaurno, J. M., Brito, D., & Olson, P. L. (1996). Mechanics of inner core super-rotation. *Geophysical Research Letters, 23*(23), 3401–3404. doi:10.1029/96GL03258

Jacobs, J. A. (1953). The Earth's inner core. *Nature, 172*(4372), 297–298. doi:10.1038/172297a0

Jephcoat, A., & Refson, K. (2001, September 6). Earth science: Core beliefs. *Nature, 413*(6851), 27–30. doi:10.1038/35092650. PMID 11544508

Labrosse, S., Poirier, J., Le Mouël, J. (2001, August 15). The age of the inner core. *Earth and Planetary Science Letters, 190*(3–4), 111–123. doi:10.1016/S0012-821X(01)00387-9

Facts and hypotheses concerning Mars, its magnetic field, and its effects on Martian conditions come from the following sources:

Brooks, M. (2008, September 26). Giant impact explains Mars' wonky magnetic field. *New Scientist.* Retrieved from https://www.newscientist.com/article/dn14827-giant-impact-explains-marss-wonky-magnetic-field/

Lakdawalla, E. (2008, October, 24). Why is only half of Mars magnetized? *The Planetary Society.* Retrieved from http://www.planetary.org/blogs/emily-lakdawalla/2008/1710.html

Stanley, S., Elkins-Tanton, L. T., Zuber, M. T., & Parmentier, E. M. (2008). Mars' paleomagnetic field as the result of a single-hemisphere dynamo. *Science, 321*(5897), 1822–1825.

Wenz, J. (2018, July 31). "No seriously, Elon. You can't just nuke Mars (we asked)". *Discover Magazine.* Retrieved from http://blogs.discovermagazine.com/d-brief/2018/07/31/no-you-cant-just-nuke-mars/#.W4Six85KjIU

Jupiter's magnetic field, including theories concerning liquid metallic hydrogen, are discussed in the following sources:

Azadi, S., Monserrat, B., Foulkes, W. M. C., & Needs, R. J. (2014). Dissociation of high-pressure solid molecular hydrogen: A quantum Monte Carlo and anharmonic vibrational study. *Physical Review Letters, 112*(16), 165501. doi:10.1103/PhysRevLett.112.165501

Cooper, J. F., Johnson, R. E., et al. (2001). Energetic ion and electron irradiation of the icy Galilean satellites. *Icarus, 139*(1), 133–159. doi:10.1006/icar.2000.6498

Cowley, S. W. H., & Bunce, E. J. (2001). Origin of the main auroral oval in Jupiter's coupled magnetosphere–ionosphere system. *Planetary and Space Sciences, 49*(10–11), 1067–1088. doi:10.1016/S0032-0633(00)00167-7

Edwards, T. M., Bunce, E. J., Cowley, S. W. H. (2001). A note on the vector potential of Connerney et al.'s model of the equatorial current sheet in Jupiter's magnetosphere. *Planetary and Space Science 49*(10–11), 1115–1123. doi:10.1016/S0032-0633(00)00164-1

Guillot, T., Stevenson, D. J., Hubbard, W. B., & Saumon, D. (2004). The interior of Jupiter. In F. Bagenal, T. E. Dowling, & W. B. McKinnon, *Jupiter: The planet, satellites and magnetosphere* (pp. 35–57). Cambridge, UK: Cambridge University Press. Also see https://www.researchgate.net/publication/260964214_Jupiter_the_planet_satellites_and_magnetosphere Retrieved 2019-04-20

Khurana, K. K., Kivelson, M. G., et al. (2004). The configuration of Jupiter's magnetosphere. In F. Bagenal, T. E. Dowling, & W. B. McKinnon, *Jupiter: The planet, satellites and magnetosphere.* (pp. 593–616) Cambridge, UK: Cambridge University Press. Also available as a separate article through the University of Iowa at http://www-pw.physics.uiowa.edu/~dag/publications/2004_TheConfigurationOfJupitersMagnetosphere_JPSM.pdf Retrieved 2019-04-20.

Kivelson, M. G., Bagenal, F.; et al. (2004). Magnetospheric interactions with satellites. In F. Bagenal, T. E. Dowling, & W. B. McKinnon, *Jupiter: The planet, satellites and magnetosphere* (pp. 513–536. Cambridge, UK: Cambridge University Press.

Krupp, N., Vasyliunas, V. M., et al. (2004). Dynamics of the Jovian magnetosphere. In F. Bagenal, T. E. Dowling, & W. B. McKinnon, *Jupiter: The planet, satellites and magnetosphere* (pp. 617–638). Cambridge, UK: Cambridge University Press.

McMinis, J., Clay, R. C., Lee, D., & Morales, M. A. (2015). Molecular to atomic phase transition in hydrogen under high pressure. *Physical Review Letters, 114*(10), 105305. doi:10.1103/PhysRevLett.114.105305

Russell, C. T. (1993). Planetary magnetospheres. *Reports on Progress in Physics, 56*(6), 687–732. doi:10.1088/0034-4885/56/6/001

Wigner, E., & Huntington, H. B. (1935). On the possibility of a metallic modification of hydrogen. *Journal of Chemical Physics, 3*(12), 764. doi:10.1063/1.174959

The magnetospheres of Uranus and Neptune are discussed in the following sources:

Faure, G., & Mensing, T. (2007). Uranus: What happened here? In F. Gunter & T. M. Mensing, *Introduction to planetary science* (pp. 369–370). New York, NY: Springer.

Ness, N. F., Acuña, M. H., Behannon, K. W., Burlaga, L. F., Connerney, J. E. P., Lepping, R. P., & Neubauer, F. M. (1986, July). Magnetic fields at Uranus. *Science, 233*(4759), 85–89. doi:10.1126/science.233.4759.85

Podolak, M., Weizman, A., & Marley, M. (1995, December). Comparative models of Uranus and Neptune. *Planetary and Space Science, 43*(12), 1517–1522. doi:10.1016/0032-0633(95)00061-5

Russell, C. T. (1993). Planetary magnetospheres. *Reports on Progress in Physics, 56*(6), 687–732. doi:10.1088/0034-4885/56/6/001

Stanley, S., & Bloxham, J. (2004, March 11). Convective-region geometry as the cause of Uranus' and Neptune's unusual magnetic fields. *Nature, 428*(6979), 151–153. doi:10.1038/nature02376. PMID 15014493.

The Sun's magnetic field and its effects are discussed in the following sources:

American Geophysical Union. (1997, March). *Geomagnetic storms can threaten electric power grid Earth in space, 9*(7), 9–11.

Hydro-Québec. (1989, March). *Understanding electricity.* http://www.hydroquebec.com/learning/notions-de-base/tempete-mars-1989.html Retrieved 2019-04-20.

NASA/Marshall Space Flight Center (2015). *The solar interior.* Retrieved 2019-04-20. https://solarscience.msfc.nasa.gov/interior.shtml

Solar Storms. *A conflagration of storms.* Retrieved from http://www.solarstorms.org/SWChapter1.html

Credits

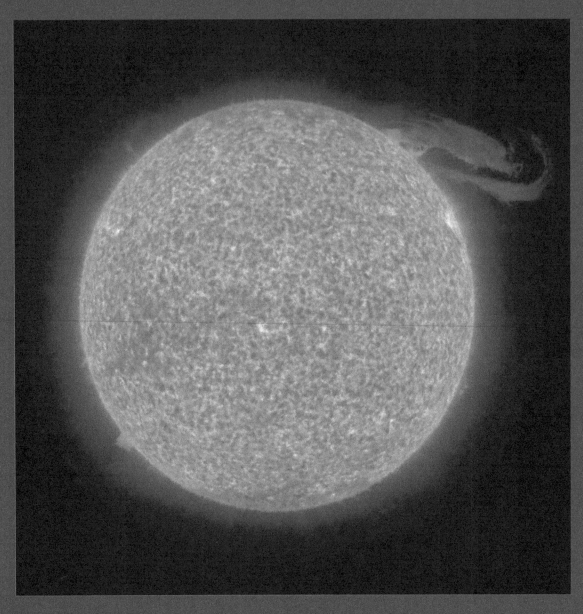

A solar prominence (upper right) erupts from the surface of the Sun on September 29, 2008, as seen by the STEREO spacecraft. Credit: NASA.

THE SUN

To study the Sun in detail

OBJECTIVES

- To distinguish the Sun from all other solar system objects
- To relate random collisions of particles to macroscopic properties
- To list the interior layers of the Sun
- To list the exterior layers of the Sun
- To outline the future of the Sun

INTRODUCTION

We have saved the best—or at least, the biggest—for last in our tour of the solar system. The very term "solar" system gives it away; "sol" is simply the Latin word for the Sun. The Sun not only represents the majority of the solar system's mass but belongs to a completely different class of object, a star, than anything else in our solar system. As such, we need to introduce different ways of speaking when discussing the Sun.

Even so, the Sun is nothing special compared to other stars. It is neither the brightest nor dimmest; the largest nor smallest; the hottest nor coolest; the longest lived nor shortest lived, and so on. The Sun is close enough to being an average star that astronomers use it as their basis of comparison with all other stars. Therefore, not only do we wish to learn about the Sun for its own sake, but also in order to compare it with other stars.

In this chapter, we review all the basic layers, properties and behaviors of the Sun. Future chapters will go further in developing how stars are born, live and die.

KEY TERMS

Alfvén waves: Low-frequency shock waves generated by magnetic fields that can carry energy from one location to another

Black body: An object that absorbs all light incident upon it and emits light according to its surface temperature. The Sun is an approximate black body. The term refers to the absorption part of its definition, not its emission

Chromosphere: The section of the Sun's atmosphere where the temperature is hotter than the underlying layers, and thus where we see spectral emission lines

Convective zone: The region of the Sun's interior where energy is transported primarily by convection

Core: The innermost region of the Sun, where nuclear fusion supplies the energy to support the Sun against its own weight

Corona: The outermost region of the Sun, where the Sun's atmosphere becomes extremely thin but also extremely hot, and a region that does not have a specific shape

Coronal mass ejections (CMEs): An extreme version of a solar *flare*, where a large amount of material is blown off the surface of the Sun and escapes into space

Differential rotation: When different sections (latitudes) of an object rotate with different periods. Restricted to gaseous objects in practice; solid objects like the Earth cannot do this

Granules/supergranules: The tops of convection cells (granules) or combinations of convection cells (supergranules) in the photosphere of the Sun. The overall effect is called *granulation*

Heliopause: About 50 au from the Sun, where the solar wind and interstellar medium collide

Heliosphere: Extending from the solar corona to the heliopause, the region in the solar system where the solar wind flows outward from the Sun

Hydrostatic equilibrium: In general, the balance of forces (or pressures) that individually try to alter the size and shape of an object. In the Sun, the balance is between gas pressure (pushing outward) versus gravity (pulling inward)

Irradiance: (also solar irradiance): The amount of power (via radiation) per unit area received from the Sun

Limb: A term that means the edge of the Sun, as seen from a distance

Luminosity: A term used to describe the total power emitted by a star in the form of electromagnetic waves (light)

Magnetosphere: The region of space surrounding the Sun dominated by its magnetic field

Maunder minimum: A section of several decades during the 17th century where the solar cycle seemed to shut down, causing a "little ice age" on Earth

Opacity: The ability of matter to block the passage of light. This can be either via absorption or via reflection

Plasma: A state of matter much like gas, except that the individual particles are at least partially ionized

Photosphere: The region of the Sun that we see from a distance. The *opacity* of the Sun drops enough that visible light photons can escape from the Sun

Prominence: A tendril of gas erupting off the surface of the Sun and forced to go in a loop due to locally strong magnetic fields

Radiative zone: The region of the Sun's interior where energy is transported primarily via radiation (photons)

Random walk: A nickname for the process by which particles move due to random collisions with their neighbors

Solar constant: The intensity of sunlight (power per unit area) from the Sun as received at 1 au (the average distance of the Earth from the Sun). The solar constant has a value of 1368 W/m^2

Solar filter: A device used to block the majority of light from the Sun so that it may be seen safely

Solar sail: A type of experimental spacecraft that uses gigantic Mylar-like sheets to act as sails to catch the solar wind for propulsion

Solar wind: The stream of particles, mostly protons, which completely escape the Sun's gravity

Star: An object (the Sun is an example) that naturally uses nuclear fusion to support itself against its own weight

Tachocline: A sharply defined boundary between the radiative and convective zones

Section 12.1: The Sun Compared to the Solar System

The phrase "99.9%" is often thrown about in common speech when we wish to exaggerate the importance of something or someone compared to all others. In the case of the Sun, we can take the phrase literally: The Sun contains 99.9% of the mass of the entire solar system. To put this number into perspective, recall that Jupiter, at 318 times the mass of the Earth, holds more mass than all the other planets, moons, asteroids, comets, and assorted dust particles in the solar system. The Sun, at a whopping 330,000 times the mass of the Earth, is well over 1,000 times the mass of Jupiter. In terms of sheer size, there is simply no comparison (Figure 12.1).

The Sun is enormous in other ways. The Sun's radius is 696,000 kilometers, placing it more than 100 times larger across than the Earth, which has a radius of 6,378 kilometers, and making it nearly 10 times larger across than Jupiter, which has a radius of 71,492 kilometers. Even more impressive is its volume; since volume scales as the cube of the radius, this means the Sun is 1.3 million times the volume of the Earth; or, more poetically, 1.3 million Earths could fit inside the Sun.

FIGURE 12.1. The Sun and major planets to scale. Credit: Lsmpascal.

The Sun is made of hydrogen and helium gas, a little like Jupiter and Saturn, but instead of a layer of metallic hydrogen or a rocky core, the Sun is gaseous all the way through. This shows up partly in its density, which is 1.4 grams per cubic centimeter, much less than the 5.54 g/cc of the Earth. Most of the Sun's gases are in the ratios of 90% (by number) hydrogen and 9% (by number) helium, with all other elements combining to make up the remaining 1%. Only the core of the Sun is different, a fact we will discuss later in this chapter.

TABLE 12.1. Basic Properties of the Sun Compared to the Earth

Property	The Earth	The Sun
Mass	5.97×10^{24} kg	1.99×10^{30} kg
Radius	6378 km	696,000 km
Density	5.54 g/cc	1.41 g/cc
Surface Temperature	164–331 K	5780 K
Rotational period	23 hours 57 minutes	25–35 days
Escape speed	11.2 km/s	618 km/s
Luminosity	—	3.96×10^{26} watts

But the Sun is not merely quantitatively different than the planets. It is also qualitatively different; that is, it is not merely a much larger planet. Rather, it belongs to a completely separate class of objects we call *stars*. Much of the rest of this textbook deals with stars, so we will give a brief review of their properties here, as exemplified by the Sun. In short, stars are objects so large that their own weight—their own self-gravitational pull—will collapse them to a point unless gas pressure, sustained by interior nuclear fusion, holds them up in response.

This constant battle between gravity and nuclear fusion is the defining characteristic of a star, and the Sun is no exception. As long as the Sun has fuel to keep its nuclear fusion going in its core, it will sustain itself against its own weight. As the Sun burns up its fuel, it undergoes subtle changes, and when it completely runs out, it will change quite dramatically. Again, we will cover the details later in this book, but we do wish to give a preview here.

The most obvious fact about the Sun is that it is extremely bright. This is another property of the Sun: It is the only object in the solar system that generates visible light.[1] All other objects are seen via reflected light. Even as bright as the Moon can be—the full Moon can cast shadows on a clear night—it is nowhere close to the brightness of the Sun, whose light is in itself blinding, but also lights up the entire daytime sky. Astronomers call this property *luminosity*, which describes the power output of the Sun in terms of the visible light it emits (and, to be complete, any other wavelengths) due to the high temperature of its surface. The luminous "surface" of the Sun is not a solid surface; in fact, the average temperature of the visible part of the Sun is nearly 6,000 kelvin (or 11,000°F), far too hot for any solid to exist there. And at that, this is the coolest region the Sun has to offer.

---

[1] Strictly speaking, this is not true. Several planets exhibit lightning and aurora that emit visible light. However, these contributions are incredibly tiny compared to the planets themselves and the light they reflect from the Sun.

Since the Sun is entirely gaseous—its interior temperatures are far too hot for any solids or liquid to exist—it exhibits *differential rotation*. This was noticed by Galileo, who appears to be the first person to track the motion of sunspots. Correctly guessing that sunspots are on the surface of the Sun, he noted not only that they show how fast the surface rotates, but that different latitudes of the Sun rotate at different rates, from the combination of Coriolis effect and convection. Like the Jovian planets, the Sun rotates fastest at its equator, with a period of 25 days; near its poles, the Sun's rotation slows to a period of 34 days. Compared to the rotational speeds of most of the planets, the Earth at 24 hours, Jupiter at less than 10 hours, and so on, this is a bit surprising. The Sun possesses much less "spin" (angular momentum) than we might otherwise expect. Nor is it always true of other stars; bright stars such as Vega and Altair spin much faster than the Sun. The explanation for the relatively slow spin of the Sun is likely bound up in how the Sun and solar system formed together nearly 5 billion years ago. In fact, the Sun's self-gravity is so strong, and its rotation so slow, that its equatorial diameter and polar diameter differ only by about 10 kilometers (6 miles). Scaled to the size of a beach ball, the difference works out to be about the width of a human hair, making the Sun's shape virtually a perfect sphere.

Section 12.2: The Interior of the Sun

The Sun is powered by nuclear fusion, specifically, hydrogen fusion. Four hydrogen nuclei (i.e., protons) are converted through a three-step process into a helium nucleus and energy, mostly in the form of gamma rays. The Sun devours a lot of hydrogen this way: 600 million tons of hydrogen is converted into helium every second. Even with that rate of usage, the Sun is in no danger of running low of hydrogen anytime soon; its estimated remaining life is about 5 more billion years. Only seven tenths of a percent of the mass of the hydrogen nuclei becomes energy, which sounds like a very small amount until we realize that it is approximately a million times more efficient than the burning of gasoline. The gamma rays produced collide with other particles, imparting their energy and keeping them moving at high speeds. As we saw in chapter 10, high average speeds correspond to high temperatures and pressures; the high gas pressure acts overall to push the Sun outward, counteracting the self-gravity of the Sun trying to pull itself inward. This balance of gas pressure versus gravity is called *hydrostatic equilibrium* by astronomers.

The interior has three basic regions: the core, the radiative zone, and the convective zone. Let us discuss each in turn:

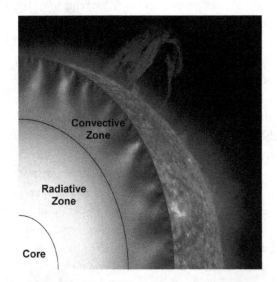

FIGURE 12.2. An artist's depiction of the various layers of the Sun, to scale. Credit: NASA/Marshall Space Flight Center.

1. The Core

The region in which nuclear fusion generates the energy to sustain the Sun is called the *core*. The core makes up the inner 10% of the mass of the Sun, though due to its incredibly high temperatures (and therefore high pressures), it extends outward from the very center to cover the inner 24% of the Sun by radius. The temperature at the very center of the Sun is close to 16 million kelvin, though this drops off to 7 million kelvin at the edge of the core. Similarly, the density of the core is very high—about 160 grams per cubic centimeter at the very center, though also declining, to about 19 g/cc, at the edge of the core. Outside of the core, the temperature and density drop so low that protons have difficulty inducing nuclear reactions. Ninety-nine percent of the Sun's fusion occurs within the first 24% of the radius of the Sun; by the time we reach a distance of 30% of the radius of the Sun from the core, nuclear fusion has ceased completely. Strangely enough, the Sun does not produce a lot of energy per unit volume; it creates about

280 watts per cubic meter, about the same as a compost pile.[2] The reason for this poor production rate is that it takes, on average, about 5 billion years for a pair of colliding protons to force a nuclear reaction. The Sun's energy output is enormous because the Sun itself is enormous, not because it is efficient.

How does this "hydrostatic equilibrium" concept work? Couldn't we imagine altering the Sun's interior—squeezing it together even more, for example—and therefore changing it? Suppose we somehow did this. Squeezing the core would increase the rate of collisions between particles (after all, now they are closer together), which translates into an increase in outward pressure. But the increased outward pressure would then make the core larger, which negates the attempted squeeze. All this means that the Sun is an incredibly stable object, given that nuclear explosions are occurring inside it constantly. Hydrostatic equilibrium is like a thermostat, except that it kicks in when the temperature either goes too high or too low.

The only change that sticks for the Sun is a long-term process. As the Sun turns hydrogen into helium, it does deplete the hydrogen fuel supply. At the Sun's formation about 4.5 billion years ago, 90% of the particles (by number) in the core were hydrogen and 9% helium, the same as the surface of the Sun shows today. But the interior of the Sun is now roughly 50–50 between hydrogen and helium today. Models of how the Sun uses its fuel suggests the Sun has another 5 billion years remaining before the hydrogen is completely depleted in its core. This won't be the end of the Sun's story (we will discuss this more fully later), but its effective "working adult" life will have come to an end.

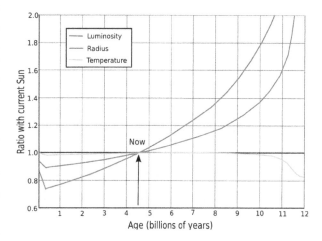

FIGURE 12.3. The development of the Sun over its 10 billion-year lifespan. While the surface temperature of the Sun remains relatively constant, its luminosity and radius change dramatically. Credit: R. J. Hall.

A consequence of this slow change is that the Sun's interior is slowly becoming hotter. As the richness of hydrogen fuel in the core drops, higher temperatures are required to keep nuclear fusion going. Therefore the core today is hotter than it was originally, and the Sun overall is about twice as bright as it was during its formation. Among other effects, the habitable zone of the Sun is slowly crawling outward. We have perhaps another 250 million years or so left for the Earth to remain in this zone, after which the Sun will have become so hot that water can no longer remain liquid. Fortunately, 250 million years is a long time!

2. The Radiative Zone

At the edge of the core, energy is no longer manufactured by nuclear fusion. But energy still moves from the inside to the outside of the Sun, albeit slowly. The in-between layer of the interior, where the dominant method of moving energy occurs via light, is called the *radiative zone*.

The radiative zone extends from 0.24 (24%) of the Sun's radius to 0.70 (70%) of the Sun's radius. In this section, the temperature continues to drop, from 7 million K to 2 million K. The density also continues its smooth decline, from about the density of gold (close to 20 g/cc) to a small fraction of that of liquid water (about 0.2 g/cc).

---

[2] Or, for another comparison, an average adult human emits about 100 watts. Given that grown humans take up much less space than a cubic meter, an average adult generates more power per unit area than the Sun.

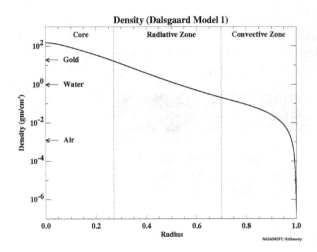

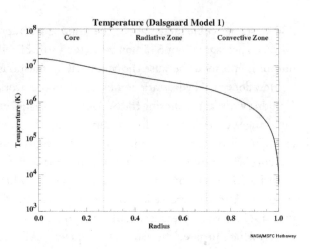

FIGURE 12.4. Mathematical models of the densities (left) and temperatures (right) of the interior of the Sun. Credit: NASA/MSFC Hathaway.

FIGURE 12.5. A simulated random walk of a photon inside the radiative zone of the Sun.

Photons, regardless of their wavelengths or frequencies, all travel at the speed of light. The amount of time for a photon to escape from the surface of the Sun averages close to a million years. This doesn't make sense at first glance; light from the surface of the Sun requires only a little over 8 minutes to make it the 150 million-kilometer distance to the Earth, so why the delay inside the Sun? To understand why, we need to discuss the notion of a *random walk*.

The Sun has, of course, a lot of particles inside it—mostly protons (i.e., hydrogen nuclei), helium nuclei, traces of other nuclei, and electrons that are unattached to nuclei in the radiative zone. Strangely enough, though electrons are thought to be point particles (particles with no discernable size), they interact very well with photons, and thus are easily the most likely particles with which photons will collide. A photon flies for about a centimeter, on average, before smacking into an electron (or, on very rare occasions, a different particle). The photon tends to have more energy than the electron; photons in the radiative zone are still in the gamma ray/x-ray range and are likely to give up some of their energy to the electron. Because photon wavelengths and frequencies depend on their individual energies, a decreased energy means a longer wavelength and lower frequency for the resultant photon; in other words, we have a different photon after the collision. By the time a photon reaches the surface of the Sun, the visible light photon has about 1 millionth of the energy of the original gamma ray, the rest of the energy having gone into supporting the Sun.

Another effect of the random walk is that the photons tend to migrate outward from the core to the surface of the Sun. Each individual collision is random in that it has an equal opportunity of going left versus going right, up versus down, forward versus back, or, between going toward the center of the Sun and toward the outside of the Sun. But there is only one center of the Sun, and many different ways to go away from the Sun. On average, a photon will wander away from the center and toward the surface. All this means hundreds of thousands to millions of years can go by before the remnant of an original photon escapes the Sun.

Check Your Neighbor

The Sun's radius is 696,000 kilometers and the speed of light is 300,000 kilometers per second. If a photon generated at the very center of the Sun could travel unimpeded, about how long would it take for it to reach the surface of the Sun?

3. The Convective Zone

At 70% of the radius of the Sun, the temperature drops to 2 million kelvin. While it sounds odd to say this is a low temperature, here some larger nuclei (carbon, oxygen, iron, etc.) can actually hold onto some electrons, making them partially rather than completely ionized. Partially ionized atoms are far more able to absorb photons than completely ionized atoms, so the photons now have difficulty getting through the gas at all. This property of matter, where light is not allowed to pass, is called *opacity*. The gas as a consequence traps heat and begins to form bubbles with temperatures higher than their surroundings. The bubbles rise toward the surface, beginning the process of convection. The

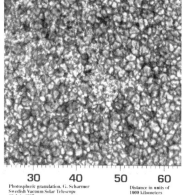

FIGURE 12.6. Left: A pot of boiling water. Right: Granules on the surface of the Sun, from the Swedish Vacuum Solar Telescope.

bubbles expand and cool as they rise, until they reach the surface, where the temperature has dropped to 5,800 kelvin. The density has also dropped dramatically, from 0.2 g/cc to 0.000 000 2 g/cc, or about 1/10,000 of the density of air at sea level on the Earth. The bubbles (or convection "cells") become visible when they break at the Sun's surface, where they are called *granules* or *supergranules* (and the overall effect is termed *granulation*).

In recent years, astronomers have become more aware of a sharp distinction between the radiative and convective zones. Not only is there a hard change from radiative to convective transport of energy, but also a change in how the Sun rotates. The radiative zone (and core) rotates much as a solid object, at the same rate. The convective zone, all the way to the surface, exhibits differential rotation. The boundary between the radiative and convective zones is called the *tachocline* and is also thought to be the location inside the Sun where its magnetic field originates (see chapter 11 for further information).

Section 12.3: The Exterior of the Sun

The exterior of the Sun begins when photons are (relatively) free to escape from the inside of the Sun and make their way to space. The "surface," which we will now call the photosphere, includes many features, but we have several other layers further out to consider. In a sense, we live well inside the Sun's influence, if you consider the Earth is bathed in the solar wind and lies well within the Sun's magnetosphere. The purpose of this section is to briefly review the different sections and important features of the outer parts of the Sun.

1. The Photosphere

The Sun does not possess a solid surface, or even a liquid surface. Officially, the Sun consists of *plasma*, a state of matter like gas in that its particles are free to move individually, but different in that the particles in a plasma are stripped of at least some of their electrons. The temperature and density are low enough that 97% of the hydrogen atoms here are atoms, not ions, though many other elements are still partially ionized. The transition from ionized hydrogen to atomic hydrogen makes it possible for photons to escape from the Sun, and the number density of particles has dropped to 0.37% of the particle density of our atmosphere at sea level. This transition layer is about 200 kilometers (120 miles) thick, which compared to the overall diameter of the Sun (nearly a million miles across) appears thin from a distance. Thus, the Sun appears to have a sharp edge from a distance, and since we see visible light coming from it, we call it the *photosphere*, or "light-sphere."

The Sun is commonly known as a "yellow" star. While it is true that the Sun emits a large portion of its spectrum in yellow, it also emits a lot of green and other visible light wavelengths. Nearly 50% of all the radiative power from the Sun is visible light, with 47% being infrared, 3% ultraviolet, and only traces of other wavelengths. The Sun approximates what physicists term a *black body*, an object that, among other properties, emits light according to

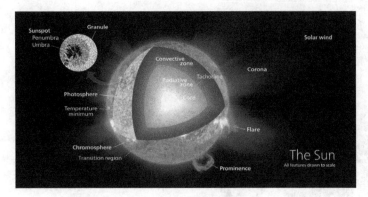

FIGURE 12.7. An artist's depiction of the Sun's exterior (and interior) layers, along with important types of features. Credit: Kelvinsong.

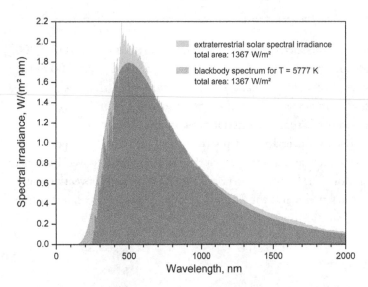

FIGURE 12.8. A graph showing intensity of sunlight versus wavelength. The smooth curve is a theoretical fit to the more jagged data. The surface temperature of the Sun is thus approximately 5,800 K.

its surface temperature. When astronomers attempt to "fit" a black body curve to the Sun's actual output, the temperature of the Sun works out best to be 5,777 kelvin (about 5,800 K). The true irradiance of the Sun is partly affected by absorption of light (from just underneath the photosphere) due to the various different kinds of elements in the solar atmosphere, thus the jagged lines that appear in the spectrum of the Sun (Figure 12.8).

The Sun's photosphere is also where we see its most important individual features. We have already mentioned granules, the tops of convection cells originating deeper inside the Sun. Sunspots, too, make their appearances in the photosphere, showing up as dark compared to the photosphere due to their lower temperatures. Sunspots are the results of locally intense magnetic fields, but they are not the only solar features related to the Sun's magnetism. Another interesting example of the interaction of the plasma of the photosphere and the Sun's magnetic field is the *prominence*. Eruptions of plasma from the Sun often are constrained in their motions by these local magnetic fields to travel in loops (from outside, the most easily seen loops are vertical). If the eruption is powerful enough or located in a region with less-powerful magnetism, the plasma shoots off straight away from the Sun, and is then termed a solar *flare*. In the most extreme explosions, the large chunks

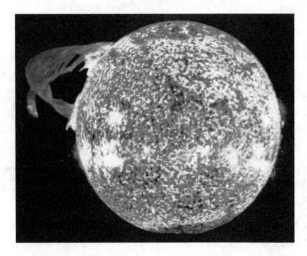
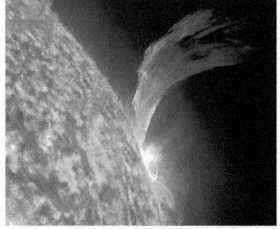

FIGURE 12.9. Left: A gigantic solar prominence captured by Skylab during its 1973 mission. Right: A gigantic solar flare seen in 2010. Credit: NASA/SDO.

of ejected plasma are called *coronal mass ejections*, or CMEs. One CME that flew toward Earth is thought to be responsible for a large electricity blackout in Quebec in 1989 (see chapter 11).

But the most curious of all the surface (photospheric) phenomena are the sunspots. We already discussed their origins in the section on the Sun's magnetic field in chapter 11, so here we focus on their relationship to the solar cycle. The number of sunspots rises and falls over an 11-year (on average) cycle, due to the distortions caused in the Sun's magnetic field from differential rotation plus convection. Not only do the magnetic poles of the Sun flip once each 11 years, but knots in the local magnetic field steal energy from the photosphere, turning these regions dark, thus, sunspots. As the solar cycle progresses from minimum to maximum, the distortions not only increase, but also wander slowly from the poles to the equator of the Sun (see Figure 11.18). Plotted on a graph, the locations of the sunspots over time produces a "butterfly" diagram (Figure 12.10):

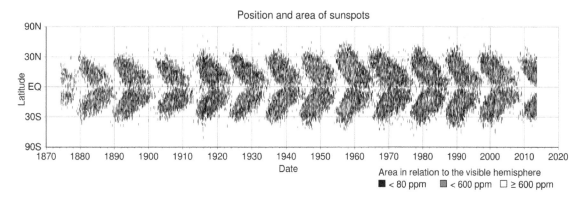

FIGURE 12.10. The areas and locations of sunspots plotted from the late 19th century to the early 21st century. The "butter-fly" pattern results as sunspots slowly graduate from higher to lower latitudes.

Sunspot numbers—and the solar cycle overall—also trend with other features and behaviors of the Sun. During a solar maximum, we also tend to find more prominences, flares, and coronal mass ejections. Also during a solar maximum, the Sun's *irradiance* (amount of power received from the Sun per unit area) also increases, though by less than 1%.[3]

The sunspot cycle is "quasi-periodic"; that is, its pattern repeats in general, but not by the same exact amount—cycles have been observed as short as 7 years and as long as 19. But it also appears that the solar cycle can occasionally shut down altogether. The 17th century experienced a decades-long solar event astronomers term the *Maunder Minimum*, when sunspots—and, we suspect, other associated solar phenomena—simply shut down. The

> ## Check Your Neighbor
>
> If the Sun takes 11 years on average to flip its north and south magnetic poles, how long does it take to return to its original configuration?

Sun cooled enough, and stayed cooler long enough, that the Earth experienced a section of time nicknamed the "Little Ice Age" by geologists. Further, this vanishing of the solar cycle has likely happened several times throughout history, as evidenced by studies of tree rings. Why this happens is still a mystery.

2. The Chromosphere

The temperature of the gas continues to decline 500 kilometers (300 miles) above the official beginning of the photosphere, until the temperature bottoms out at 4,100 kelvin. In this section, the temperature is actually low enough that common-day molecules, such as carbon monoxide and water, are able to form. After this, however, the temperature begins to rise again.

---

[3] This is strictly for visible light; the solar irradiance in ultraviolet has been known to vary by as much as 3%.

FIGURE 12.11. A series of stack images produced this picture of the total solar eclipse of 2017. Note the ring of light around the Moon, the occasional patches of pink of the chromosphere, and the streamers of the corona. Credit: Michael S. Adler.

During a total solar eclipse, patches of color (primarily pink) can sometimes be seen in a ring around the edge of the Moon. These colors do not come from the photosphere, but from this region immediately above it. Atoms at high-enough temperatures will emit, rather than absorb, spectral lines, though the wavelengths and frequencies of the lines remain the same. Hydrogen atoms tend to emit specific red, blue-green and violet lines in the visible part of the spectrum, and taken together give the appearance of pinkish-purple. Since hydrogen atoms make up 90% of the Sun, their pinkish glow is the most prominent. Since we see individual colors from this section of the Sun's atmosphere, it is called the *chromosphere*, or "color sphere."

3. The Corona

The chromosphere blends into the next section of the Sun's upper atmosphere, the solar *corona*. The corona is the first region of the Sun for us that does not have a spherical shape. Rather, the corona shifts shape and size constantly, due to the particles blown off the Sun's surface by flares and interactions with the Sun's magnetic field. The corona can extend several millions of kilometers from the photosphere and is as bright as the full Moon. The reason we don't see the corona each day is simply because the photosphere is about a million times brighter, and therefore washes it out. But both the solar chromosphere and corona can be seen during a total solar eclipse.

The temperature of the Sun's outer atmosphere climbs rather than falls as we move further from the photosphere, reaching 20,000 K at the upper edge of the chromosphere and topping out at an incredibly high 2,000,000 K in the corona. How this happens requires some subtle treatment, since of course the further from the Sun's core, the less energetic the photons and thus the less energy any remaining particles should be receiving. The answer for the rising temperatures, which continue for quite a way, involves a phenomenon called *Alfvén waves.*

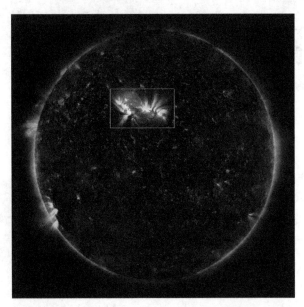

FIGURE 12.12. Spicules (jets of gas) spray outward from the Sun in this image from NASA's Solar Dynamics Observatory (SDO). The spicules sway back and forth due to the influence of Alfvén waves. Credit: NASA/SDO/AIA.

In short, Alfvén waves are low-frequency shock waves generated by magnetic fields in a thin plasma. The waves transmit energy to the ions, shaking them faster, which translates to higher temperatures. In thicker gas (or plasma), particles have the opportunity to collide with each other, meaning they share their energies, and in turn inducing the particles to emit light. This is in fact what happens in the photosphere. But the chromosphere, and even more so the corona, are too thin for this. With fewer and fewer partner particles to collide with, the magnetic waves can transmit energy to these ions, but the ions have difficulty bleeding off this excess energy via collisions. Thus the temperature rises. The specifics of how Alfvén waves accomplish this feat has been under debate since Hannes Alfvén proposed the notion in 1942, but recent work in 2017–2018 appears to confirm Alfvén waves as the main culprit in the heating of the chromosphere, corona, and solar wind.

4. The Solar Wind

At about 20 times the Sun's radius (about 1/10 of an astronomical unit), particles ejected by solar flares become able to flow freely away from the Sun. This region, called the *heliosphere*, represents the outer atmosphere of the Sun escaping into interplanetary space. The specific flow of this material is called the *solar wind*. If by "wind" we mean a flow of gas particles, then the solar wind qualifies, though it is made mostly of protons (hydrogen nuclei) rather than the combination of nitrogen and oxygen molecules that makes up our air on Earth. Another difference between the solar wind and Earthly winds is that the solar wind always flows away from the Sun—at least, inside the solar system—whereas wind directions change constantly here. One of the more interesting designs for future space probes is the notion of the *solar sail*, which would catch the solar wind and propel a spacecraft throughout the solar system. Astron-

FIGURE 12.13. A model of the ICAROS spacecraft displayed at the 2010 meeting of the International Astronomical Union in Prague. Credit: Pavel Hrdlička.

omers have known about the solar wind's potential since they noticed its effects on the MESSENGER spacecraft that visited Mercury. The first functioning spacecraft using solar sails was ICAROS,[4] launched in 2010 by the Japanese Aerospace Exploration Agency (JAXA). ICAROS spent 6 months heading toward Venus, then left to explore the far side of the Sun.

The solar wind does not travel forever. At some point, it runs into the interstellar medium, literally the material (medium) between the stars, which is the accumulation of all the other solar or stellar winds from all the other stars of the Milky Way, along with many other moving particles from a variety of sources. This boundary is called the *heliopause*. The furthest any spacecraft has traveled yet is Voyager I, which swung toward the north of the solar system after its encounter with Saturn in 1980. Voyager I (and Voyager II) is still monitored in order to learn about the outer reaches of the solar system. In 2004, Voyager I passed through a shock front thought to be part of the heliopause, and in 2012, at a distance near 50 au, noted an increase in cosmic rays and a decrease in low-energy solar wind particles, meaning that (in one sense) Voyager I may have reached the edge of the solar system.

Section 12.4: The Present and Future Sun

In our discussion about the core of the Sun (section 12.1), we covered how the interior of the Sun has changed over its 4.5 billion-year life and some of how we expect it to change in the future. What we need to do now is talk about the exterior of the Sun and its effects on the Earth and other planets. Let's review the current situation before we proceed.

The Sun is a normal star (a "dwarf" or "main sequence star" in astronomical parlance) and a fairly stable one. Its visible light output changes less than a percent over its solar cycle, which is smaller than the changes we feel from having a slightly elliptical orbit. In recent geologic history (i.e., the past several hundred thousand years), dramatic changes in climate—such as ice ages—have more to do with the Earth's motions than anything the Sun does.

The Sun as a red giant
(diameter ≈ 2 AU)

The Sun as a main-sequence star
(diameter ≈ 0.01 AU)

FIGURE 12.14. The Sun as a normal ("main sequence") star today, compared to its future as a red giant. Credit: Oona Räisänen.

---

[4] "Interplanetary kite-craft accelerated by radiation of the sun."

The amount of light that gets to the Earth from the Sun, 1,368 watts per square meter, is nicknamed the *solar constant*. What we see on the ground is a little less (close to 1,000 W/m²), because of the season, time of day, latitude, and the absorption and/or reflection of sunlight back to space by clouds and air. The Sun's color is also perceived differently on the ground than in space; the bundle of wavelengths emitted by the Sun place it as a white star, but again atmospheric effects are at play. We're all familiar with the Earth's blue sky during daytime; this is because molecules in the atmosphere do a good job of scattering blue light better than most other colors. The Sun thus looks to some people as if it has a tinge of yellow. The effect is more pronounced during sunrise or sunset, when the Sun's light is trying to get through the thickest part of the Earth's atmosphere, and then we can all see that the Sun can even look red to the naked eye, which it most definitely is not.

What will happen to the Sun—and us—when it finally runs out of hydrogen fuel, 5 billion years into the future? We will cover the details of how stars react to this situation in a future chapter, but the short story is that the outside of the Sun will expand enormously. By how much? Theoretical models are certain that the Sun will engulf the planets Mercury and Venus, and likely reach out past the Earth's orbit as well (more extreme versions even go out past the orbit of Mars). While this happens, the photosphere's temperature will drop, and the Sun will turn an obvious orange-red color from the outside. The cooler temperature of the Sun will not, however, compensate for the Sun's new size. Even if the Earth is not swallowed up, the Sun's heat will evaporate all water and destroy all life that might still remain. Astronomers, for a change being literal, call this the "giant" phase of the Sun's life.

The giant phase for the Sun will last perhaps around a hundred million years, relatively long even by astronomy standards, but it too comes to an end. The Sun is sustained in this phase of its life not by hydrogen fusion in its core, but by helium fusing into carbon, the "ashes" of the first portion of its life becoming the fuel for the succeeding one. Some hydrogen, bordering the core in a concentric "shell," will also be fusing into helium. More massive stars than the Sun can in their turn use carbon for fuel in their cores and so on, but this will not be possible for the Sun, not having enough gravity to squeeze the carbon together forcefully enough to make that happen.

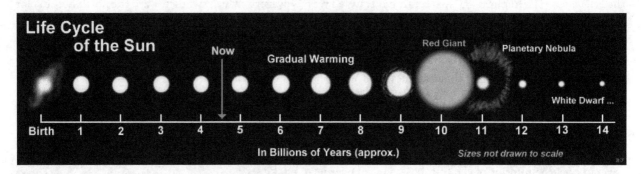

FIGURE 12.15. An artist's depiction of the life stages of the Sun, from birth to death.

The last stages of the Sun's life take little time, astronomically speaking. When the helium fuel runs out in the Sun's core, it becomes unstable. Shell burning (fusing) of helium and hydrogen continues for a short while (10,000 years, perhaps) and during this period, the Sun will slowly grow and shrink on a periodic basis. Stars that pulsate in this manner are called "variable" stars, though the specific types of variations depend on the specific circumstances (primarily mass, but also chemical composition) of the star. At the end of its variable phase, the Sun will eject large portions of itself back into space, looking (perhaps) like gigantic colorful soap bubbles from many light years away. This loss of mass is not trivial; about half of the Sun's original mass will be lost in this fashion. Any remaining planets—the Jovians at least—will have much of their outer atmospheres stripped away, and any possibility of life existing in the solar system in any location will cease. Finally, the remaining piece of the Sun, mostly its core, can no longer sustain itself via nuclear fusion and shrinks dramatically. At the end, it becomes a "white dwarf," a hot but tiny remnant of the former Sun.

The fate of the Sun is preordained. But we can take solace in knowing that the Sun has many billions of years before it comes to an end.

Summary

In this chapter, we did the following:

▶ Introduced the Sun as a different class of object from other objects in the solar system

▶ Went over in detail how its interior functions

▶ Discussed many of its "surface" (photospheric) features

▶ Went over in detail its exterior

▶ Laid out its present circumstances and its future

Questions

1. List at least three differences between the Sun and the major planets that emphasize the Sun belongs to a different class of object.

2. Suppose we somehow can exert a temporary force to make the core of the Sun expand slightly (but enough to notice), and then let it go. What will happen?
   + What will immediately happen to the temperature of the core?
   + What will immediately happen to the size of the core?
   + Will the Sun return to a stable output of energy, or will it continue to noticeably change?

3. Hydrogen fusion—where hydrogen is converted into helium—yields more energy than any other fusion process per reaction. Suppose the Sun tried to run helium fusion, turning helium into carbon. In order to hold the Sun's core up against its own weight, what must happen to the rate of nuclear reactions with helium compared to what is was with hydrogen? Does it need to slow down, remain the same, or speed up?

4. Recall that 600 million tons of hydrogen is converted into helium each second. Assume this rate is constant over the Sun's lifetime. Answer the following:
   + How many kilograms of hydrogen is used each second? Hint: 1 ton ("metric ton") of hydrogen is the same as 1,000 kilograms of hydrogen.
   + Only 0.7% of hydrogen is converted into helium via nuclear fusion. How many kilograms of hydrogen is thus converted into energy per second?
   + The mass of the Sun is 1.99×10^{30} kilograms. What is the percentage (or fraction) of the Sun that is converted into energy each second?
   + Only the inner 10% of the Sun (i.e., the core) actually participates in nuclear fusion. How many seconds will it take to convert all the core's hydrogen into energy?
   + How many years will it take to convert all the core's hydrogen into energy?

5. Sunspots are dark compared to their surroundings in the photosphere.
   + How do the temperatures of sunspots compare to the temperatures of their surroundings?
   + Suppose you could "scoop" a sunspot out of the Sun and place it in empty space. Would it still appear dark? Why or why not?

6. The most dominant color in the chromosphere is a pinkish-purple (though only visible during a total solar eclipse). Which element is responsible for this color?

7. The corona reaches temperatures as high as 2 million K. Yet, if you could be placed only inside the corona (and be shielded from the rest of the Sun), you would likely freeze. What other property of the corona keeps you from receiving enough energy to keep you warm?

8. A CME (coronal mass ejection) can traverse the space between the Sun and Earth in 3 days. Assuming its speed is constant, how fast is a CME moving? Hints: What is the average distance between the Earth and the Sun? Also, you need to convert some units.

9. The solar constant is 1,378 watts per square meter just outside the Earth's atmosphere. Would the solar constant be larger, the same amount or smaller at
   + Jupiter?
   + Mercury?
   + The Moon?
   + Pluto?
   + Venus?

Activities

▸ *Astrophysics activity 12.1:* Perform several experiments relating to random walks. First, flip a pair of coins and track how they land on "heads" or "tails" via plotting their positions. Second, use food coloring to watch random walks ("diffusion") in liquid water. Finally, relate this knowledge to the case of photons in the core of the Sun.

▸ Play the "random walk" simulator (find it at https://commons.wikimedia.org/wiki/File:Random_Walk_Simulator.gif). A particle starts at the beginning of a two-dimensional grid and takes several random steps, using colored line segments to track its progress. Then the particle restarts its journey with a different color. The simulator runs five separate times. Briefly answer the following:
   + Compare the paths to each other. Does the particle ever repeat a path?
   + Does the particle end up back at the center after a random walk?

▸ Search out a video showing convection cells (or, for that matter, boil some water!). Look at a close-up image of the photosphere of the Sun highlighting granulation. Discuss the differences and similarities between the two situations.

▸ The number of sunspots goes up and down over a period averaging 11 years. List at least three other phenomena or behaviors of the Sun that also change over the same period.

▸ *Astrophysics activity 12.2:* Watch the video "A Star is Born" from the *Solar Empire* series. Answer questions about the Sun as directed.

Works Referenced

Abhyankar, K. D. (1977). A survey of the solar atmospheric models. *Bulletin of the Astronomical Society of India, 5,* 40–44.

Alfvén, H. (1942). Existence of electromagnetic-hydrodynamic waves. *Nature, 150*(3805), 405–406. doi:10.1038/150405a0

Anderson, R.W. (2015). *The cosmic compendium: Interstellar Travel.* Published by Lulu.com.

Beer, J., McCracken, K., & von Steiger, R. (2012). *Cosmogenic radionuclides: Theory and applications in the terrestrial and space environments.* New York, NY: Springer.

Dr. Karl. (2012, April). Lazy Sun is less energetic than compost. *ABC Science.* Retrieved from http://www.abc.net.au/science/articles/2012/04/17/3478276.htm

European Space Agency. (2005). *The distortion of the heliosphere: Our interstellar magnetic compass* [Press release]. http://sci.esa.int/soho/36805-the-distortion-of-the-heliosphere/ Retrieved 2019-04-20.

Gibson, E. G. (1973). *The quiet Sun.* Washington, DC: NASA.

Grant, S. D. T., Jess, D. B., Zaqarashvili, T. V., Beck, C., Socas-Navarro, H., Aschwanden, M. J., ... & Hewitt, R. L. (2018). Alfvén wave dissipation in the solar chromosphere. *Nature Physics, 14,* 480–483. doi:10.1038/s41567-018-0058-3

Jones, G. (2012, August 16). Sun is the most perfect sphere ever observed in nature. *The Guardian.* https://www.theguardian.com/science/2012/aug/16/sun-perfect-sphere-nature Retrieved 2019-04-20.

Lean, J. (1989, April 14). Contribution of ultraviolet irradiance variations to changes in the Sun's total irradiance. *Science, 244*(4901), 197–200.

Lean, J., Skumanich, A., & White, O. (1992). Estimating the Sun's radiative output during the Maunder Minimum. *Geophysical Research Letters*, 19(15), 1591–1594. doi:10.1029/92GL01578

Mackay, R. M., & Khalil, M. A. K (2000). Greenhouse gases and global warming. In S. N. Singh (Ed.), *Trace gas missions and plants* (pp. 1–28). New York, NY: Springer.

McCurry, J. (2010, May 17). Space yacht Ikaros ready to cast off for far side of the Sun. *The Guardian*. https://www.theguardian.com/world/2010/may/17/space-yacht-ikaros-japan-venus Retrieved 2019-04-20.

NASA/Marshall Space Flight Center. (2015). The solar interior. Retrieved from https://solarscience.msfc.nasa.gov/interior.shtml

Phillips, K. J. H. (1995). *Guide to the Sun*. Cambridge, UK: Cambridge University Press.

Rast, M., Nordlund, Å., Stein, R., & Toomre, J. (1993). Ionization effects in three-dimensional solar granulation simulations. *Astrophysical Journal Letters*, 408(1): L53–L56. doi:10.1086/186829

Ribas, I. (2010). Solar and stellar variability: Impact on Earth and planets. Proceedings of the International Astronomical Union, IAU Symposium, 5(S264), 3–18.

Solanki, S. K., Livingston, W., & Ayres, T. (1994). New light on the heart of darkness of the solar Chromosphere. *Science*, 263(5143), 64–66. doi:10.1126/science.263.5143.64. PMID 17748350

Shu, F. H. (1982). *The physical universe: An introduction to astronomy*. University Science Books, Mill Valley, CA.

Shu, F. H. (1991). *The physics of astrophysics*. University Science Books, Mill Valley, CA.

Srivastava, A. K., Shetye, J., Murawski, K., Doyle, J. G., Stangalini, M., Scullion, E., … & Bhola, N. (2017, March 3). High-frequency torsional Alfvén waves as an energy source for coronal heating. *Scientific Reports*, 7(1). doi:10.1038/srep43147. ISSN 2045-2322.

Willson, R. C., & Hudson, H. S. (1991). The Sun's luminosity over a complete solar cycle. *Nature*, 351(6321), 42–44.

Zirker, J. B. (2002). *Journey from the center of the Sun*. Princeton, NJ: Princeton University Press.

A simple 2-dimensional random walk simulator is at https://commons.wikimedia.org/wiki/File:Random_Walk_Simulator.gif

Credits

STELLAR ASTRONOMY

Six separate images from the Hubble Space Telescope's Advanced Camera for Surveys were combined to create this picture of the Sombrero Galaxy in 2003. Credit: NASA/ESA and the Hubble Heritage Team (STScI/AURA).

CHAPTER 13

THE BIRTH OF MODERN ASTRONOMY II

The Stars

PURPOSE

To describe the history leading up to our modern understanding of stars and galaxies

OBJECTIVES

- To show motions of stars through space
- To introduce trigonometric parallax
- To discuss the discovery of double star systems
- To reinterpret the meaning of the term "galaxy"
- To discuss the importance of variable stars

INTRODUCTION

In pre-modern times, people knew very little about the solar system. But they knew even less about the stars. At best, the stars were regarded as little lights occasionally making interesting patterns on a fixed sphere. How did we go from ignorance to knowledge regarding the stars?

This chapter tells of the birth of modern astronomy, with the emphasis on the discovery of the motions of stars and of extrasolar objects besides stars. We will add more historical background in further chapters as we delve into the details of the science of stellar astronomy.

KEY TERMS

Astrolabe: A device much like an ornate protractor, used to measure the altitude of celestial objects

Astrometric binary: A binary system where the gravitational attraction of an unseen companion makes the position of the seen companion "wobble" in space

Binary: A system where two stars are held in orbit about each other by their mutual gravitational attraction

Cepheid: A specific type of variable star, used by astronomers to determine distances to galaxies

Constellations: Literally a "group of stars"; official patterns recognized by modern astronomers

Eclipsing binary: A binary system where the constituent stars take turns eclipsing each other

Galaxy: A large grouping of stars—about a billion, minimum—held together by their mutual gravity

Milky Way: The fuzzy white band across the sky seen in dark skies; the galaxy to which the solar system belongs

Nebula: A "cloud" of gas and dust in interstellar space

Optical double: Two stars that appear to be close enough to be in a binary system, but in fact are separate from each other

Parsec: The distance for an object subtending a parallax angle of one arcsecond. It is equivalent to 3.26 light years, or a bit less than 20 trillion miles

Period-luminosity relationship: For Cepheids and like stars, the average brightness of the star is directly related to the time (period) needed for it to go through a complete cycle of variation

Planetary nebula: The expelled gas from a dying star, emitting colors due to high temperatures. Despite the name, planetary nebulae have nothing to do with planets

Proper motion: The apparent motion of a star perpendicular to our line of sight

Radial velocity: The motion of a star either directly toward or away from us

Space velocity: The actual three-dimensional velocity of a star through space

Spectroscopic binary: A binary system where the spectral lines of at least one of the stars shifts back and forth

Stellar cluster: A large group of stars, anywhere from hundreds to hundreds of thousands, held together by their mutual gravitational attraction

Supernova remnant: The gas expelled by the explosion of a supergiant star

Transverse velocity: The velocity of a star across (perpendicular to) our line of sight

Trigonometric parallax (either trig parallax or just parallax for short): A method of using trigonometry and the orbit of the Earth about the Sun to estimate distances to nearby stars

Visual binary: A binary system where both companion stars can be seen through a telescope

KEY INDIVIDUALS

Bessel, Friedrich Wilhelm: An astronomer from 19th-century Prussia (Germany), who was the first to measure the trigonometric parallax of star

Halley, Edmond: An astronomer from 18th-century England, who showed conclusively that stars move through space

Hershel, John: An astronomer in early 19th-century England, who made a detailed catalog of binary star systems; also the son of William Hershel

Hershel, William: An astronomer from late 18th/early 19th-century England, who discovered double stars, cataloged nebulae and galaxies, and made the first map of the Milky Way

Hipparchus: An ancient Greek astronomer and historian, responsible for precision star charts

Hubble, Edwin: An American astronomer in the early 20th century who helped establish the independent nature of galaxies, devised the first classification scheme for galaxies, and found that the recessional speed of galaxies is directly related to their distance from us

Leavitt, Henrietta Swan: An American astronomer in the early 20th century who found an important relationship between average brightness and period of variation for Cepheids

Messier, Charles: A French astronomer in the late 18th century who, while looking for comets, compiled a now-famous list of 110 objects which include various nebulae, stellar clusters, and galaxies

Michell, John: The first person to suggest that stars could be held together in groups of two or more by their mutual gravitational attraction

Shapley, Harlow: An American astronomer in the early 20th century who determined that the Sun is not at the center of the Milky Way

Section 13.1: Impermanent Constellations

In chapter 1, we assumed for simplicity that the stars were fixed on a "celestial sphere" and, while we worked with various angular measurements in order to locate stars, we ignored their physical distances. Here we discuss the three-dimensional nature of stars in space and address the time-dependent nature of constellations. Later, we will show how distances to nearby stars are determined.

Figure 13.1 shows seven stars of the Big Dipper asterism, as we could see it in the night sky. But because stars are points of light on a black background, we don't have a sense of depth perception for them. To address this, Figure 13.1 also shows what happens when we include the distances of the stars. Imagine traveling through space about a hundred light years to the "side" of the Big Dipper. The stars no longer form a recognizable pattern. Or, in other words, our familiar patterns of the stars we put into constellations depends on our vantage point in space.[1] This, by the way, is a separate effect from precession (chapter 2), where the direction of the Earth's axis changes over long periods of time.

But it's not just space that matters. Not only do stars exist in three-dimensional space, but since stars move, the constellations look different at different times in astronomical history. Stars are so far away, and their speeds so slow in comparison, you will not notice a difference in your lifetime. However, subtle differences have been noticed by naked-eye observers separated by many centuries. Figure 13.2 shows the projected appearance of the Big Dipper both 100,000 years in the past and 100,000 years into the future.[2]

The point is that constellations are not permanent features. Rather, as time goes by and/or the Earth moves through space (i.e., as it is pulled along with the Sun as the Sun moves through the galaxy), constellations change.

We need to make a few more comments to wrap up. First, even under the best conditions (perfectly dark skies, away from city lights, etc.), we can only see a few thousand stars with the naked eye. But our home galaxy, the Milky Way, has several hundred billion stars, and there may be as many as several hundred billion galaxies in the observable universe (Figure 13.3). So we only get to see but the tiniest part of the sky.

Second, stars themselves aren't permanent objects. Stars can be born (or formed) and die, and although the time scales are much longer than human lifespans, there are so many stars that we can see such events play out. This image of the Eagle Nebula (Figure 13.4) by the Hubble Space Telescope (a.k.a. the "Pillars of Creation") shows an example of these processes at work. Protostars, stars in the process of formation, are hidden in the "tips" of the pillars by relatively thick clouds of dust. Light from different elements—green for hydrogen, red for sulfur, and blue for oxygen—was combined to make this visible-light image. Thousands of stars and protostars are estimated to be hiding in the nebula.

FIGURE 13.1. The Big Dipper as seen from Earth (left); as seen from about 100 light years to the "side" (right).

FIGURE 13.2. The Big Dipper at different moments in history: 100,000 years ago (left) vs. 100,000 years into the future (right).

FIGURE 13.3. The "Extreme Deep Field" from the Hubble Space Telescope, 2012. Credit: NASA/ESA.

Check Your Neighbor

Suppose we were able to fly through space to the opposite "side" of the Big Dipper. What would it look like? Hint: Use Figure 13.1 for reference.

---

[1] Distances to stars are so far that differences only become apparent outside the solar system. Astronauts would see the exact same constellations on Mars, for example, as we see on Earth.

[2] 100,000 years is about the lower limit to the age of the human species; in other words, this would have been the appearance of the Big Dipper as seen by the first human beings.

Section 13.2: Proper Motion

1. Hipparchus

Hipparchus (c. 190–c. 120 BCE) was an astronomer from Nicaea, at that time part of the ancient Greek world but now the town of Iznik in modern-day Turkey. We explored his discovery of the precession of the equinoxes earlier (chapter 2), but did not then consider other of his important contributions.

While the telescope wouldn't be invented for nearly two millennia after Hipparchus, he did use several instruments for astronomy and may have invented or developed some of them himself. Of importance for this discussion is the astrolabe, especially useful for determining the altitude of celestial objects, and the armillary sphere, which Hipparchus used to plot the positions of up to 850 stars. Hipparchus also constructed a celestial sphere (which unfortunately does not survive), a globe showing the locations of the constellations of his day.

Hipparchus created a detailed catalog of stars which also no longer exists but was incorporated into the work of Ptolemy (chapter 3). Ptolemy noted 48 constellations, most of which survive amongst the 88 modern constellations. The work of Hipparchus would not be improved until Tycho Brahe in the 16th century, and Edmund Halley would refer to Hipparchus's work to show that stars move independently through space some 1850 years afterward.

Hipparchus also introduced the notion of ranking stars according to their brightnesses, an idea put into a numerical scale by Ptolemy and eventually on a strict mathematical basis by the English astronomer Norman Pogson in 1856.

FIGURE 13.4. "Pillars of Creation," part of the Eagle Nebula as seen by the Hubble Space Telescope. Credit: NASA, Jeff Hester, and Paul Scowen (Arizona State University).

FIGURE 13.5. Details from "The School of Athens" by Raphael (1509–1510). Hipparchus faces us holding a celestial sphere; Ptolemy, holding a globe of the Earth, has his back to us.

2. Halley

Edmond Halley (1656–1742) was an English astronomer and a contemporary of Isaac Newton (we encountered Halley earlier in the book when discussing gravity in chapter 4). He is most famous for showing that the same comet was passing by the Earth on a regular schedule, which we now call Halley's Comet.

Halley was a great systematizer of knowledge and avid historian of science; his work spanned such topics as prevailing wind charts for ocean travel, mortality tables (inspiring future actuarial tables used by insurance companies), global measurements of magnetic field directions, and the first telescopic survey of star positions in the southern hemisphere. He also attempted to use a transit of Venus to procure an improvement of the distance from the Earth to the Sun.

By comparing ancient star charts (primarily of Ptolemy, and therefore Hipparchus) with contemporary observations, he was able to show that three stars, Sirius, Arcturus, and Aldebaran had slightly shifted their positions relative to other nearby stars. Observations such as these only indicate motion perpendicular to our line of sight, and for historical reasons are called *proper motions*[3] (Figure 13.6). Proper motions are long-term projects; even the fastest-moving stars only cover on the order of a few arcseconds per century.

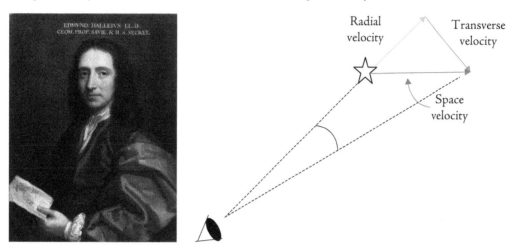

FIGURE 13.6. Edmund Halley (left); proper motion and velocities of stars (right).

Stars move through three-dimensional space (see section 13.1), so they are usually moving at an angle. We can, however, break the actual motion of a star (its *space velocity*) into two separate motions, one directly toward or away from our line of sight (i.e., *radial velocity*) and one perpendicular (its proper motion, represented by its *transverse velocity*). Halley discovered proper motion only; determinations of radial velocity had to wait until the advent of spectroscopy in the 19th century.

Check Your Neighbor

Some historians argue that Hipparchus also knew about proper motion. What does that say about the age of any records to which Hipparchus may have had access?

Section 13.3: Trig Parallax

Trig (or *trigonometric*) *parallax* applies the notion of depth perception to the sky. If we look at a nearby object from different positions, we see an apparent shift in the position of the object compared to a distant background (Figure 13.7).

In astronomy, instead of using our eyes, we use the orbit of the Earth itself. Imagine looking at a nearby star in January, comparing its apparent position to its neighboring stars, then looking at the same star in July, 6 months later. The star hasn't moved,[4] but has *appeared* to move (Figure 13.8).

---

[3] "Proper" here as in "property," or "belonging to"; that is, proper motion belongs to the star itself, and is not a result of the various motions of the Earth.

[4] Recall that proper motion, even for the fastest moving stars, is on the order of milliarcseconds per century and is next to impossible to detect over the course of just half a year.

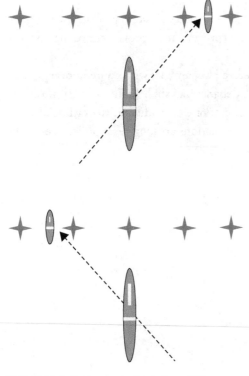

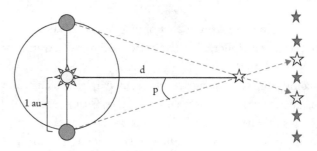

FIGURE 13.8. Using the orbit of the Earth to measure the apparent angular shift in position of a nearby star compared to a far background. The distance from the Earth to the Sun (*1 au*) and the parallax angle (*p*) are used to calculate the distance to the nearby star (*d*).

FIGURE 13.7. Hold a pen in front of you. With your left eye, the pen appears to be in one position compared to a distant background (upper figure). With your right eye, the pen appears to have shifted, even though the pen did not move (lower figure).

Ironically, trig parallax, or rather, the lack thereof, was used as proof against the notion that the Earth orbits the Sun. If the Earth did orbit the Sun, then nearby stars should show trig parallax. But trig parallax wasn't measured for stars until the 19th century. Trig parallax was also used by Tycho Brahe to show that (a) a comet belonged to the solar system and (b) a supernova belonged to the celestial sphere (see chapter 4 for details).

The answer turns out to be both simple and profound. Stars are simply too far away for any of them to show trig parallax with the naked eye. Even the closest known star, Proxima Centauri, shows a parallax less than one arcsecond. The first person to definitively determine the parallax of a star was the German astronomy Friedrich Bessel (1784–1846), who measured it for 61 Cygni in 1838.

Bessel measured the parallax of 61 Cygni to be 0.314 arcseconds, implying a distance to 61 Cygni of 10.3 light years (the modern measurement is 11.4 light years). He was not the only astronomer working on the problem at the time; in fact, it was somewhat of a race for astronomers of the day, and others (such as Friedrich von Struve and Thomas Henderson) determined parallaxes for other stars soon afterward.

Trig parallax is also used by astronomers to define a unit of distance, the *parsec*. Astronomers tend to prefer the parsec to other units such as the light year, since (a) the parsec is a natural outgrowth of other astronomical measurements, such as the astronomical unit, (b) because the system used to compare brightnesses of stars to each other ("magnitudes") is based on the parsec, and (c) having the trig parallax of a star makes it trivial to find its distance in parsecs.

As an example, let's look at the distance to and the proper motion of a famous star (to astronomers, anyway), Barnard's Star.

Barnard's Star has a parallax of 0.54831 arcseconds, a proper motion

FIGURE 13.9. Friedrich Wilhelm Bessel (left); Konigsburg Observatory (right), where the first stellar parallax was measured.

of 10.32812 arcseconds per year, and a radial velocity of –110.51 kilometers per second[5] (we will discuss how this is determined in chapter 15). Let's find (a) the distance to Barnard's Star, (b) its transverse or perpendicular velocity, and (c) its speed through space.

By definition, if the Earth's orbit is used as a baseline (i.e., the distance from one side of the Earth's orbit to the other) and the trig parallax is expressed in arcseconds, then the distance from Earth to the object in question is just

Equation 13.1

$$d = \frac{1}{p}$$

where d is expressed in parsecs. The term itself is a giveaway; a parsec is the distance to a star showing a <u>parallax</u> angle of one arc<u>second</u>. One parsec is 3.2616 light years, or a little short of 20 trillion miles.

Thus, the distance to Barnard's Star is

$$d = \frac{1}{p} = \frac{1}{0.54831} = 1.8238 \text{ pc}$$

If we want to find its distance in terms of light years, multiply by 3.26:

$$d = 1.8238 \text{ pc} \times 3.2616 \frac{ly}{pc} = 5.9484 \text{ ly}$$

The transverse (i.e., perpendicular) velocity is a little more difficult to calculate, primarily because our measurements of proper motion mix in units of years (or centuries), kilometers, and seconds as well as arcseconds. But it can be and is done. The formula to find the speed of a star moving across our line of sight depends both on how fast it appears to move and how far away it is:

Equation 13.2

$$v_t = 4.74 \frac{\propto}{p}$$

where μ (the Greek letter mu, pronounced "myoo") is the astronomer's symbol for proper motion, expressed in arcseconds per year. By also keeping the units of the parallax angle in arcseconds, this formula yields the transverse velocity in units of kilometers per second. Let's apply this to the case of Barnard's Star:

$$v_t = 4.74 \left(\frac{10.32812}{0.54381} \right) = 90.023 \text{ km/s}$$

Finally, the space velocity (or speed) is really the hypotenuse of a right triangle (refer back to chapter 0 for details), with the radial and transverse velocities being the legs of the triangle. The negative sign on the radial velocity means that Barnard's Star is heading (in part) toward us. Using the Pythagorean theorem, the space velocity is

$$v = \sqrt{v_r^2 + v_t^2} = \sqrt{(-110.51)^2 + (90.023)^2} = 142.54 \text{ km/s}$$

---

[5] By the way, the reason we have precision to so many digits is because this is data taken from the Hipparcos spacecraft, which was specifically constructed for this task.

Section 13.4: Binary Systems, Part I

While the first double star system was seen as early as 1617, the first person to suggest the possibility that stars might belong to each other (via their mutual gravitational attraction) was the English natural philosopher John Michell (1724–1793). Michell applied the (then new) science of statistics in 1767 to argue that many more stars appeared next to each other than should be the case. Mitchell extended this idea to include multiple-star systems (more than two stars at a time) and even clusters of stars.

Soon after, William Herschel (we encountered him first in chapter 4) began cataloging double stars, eventually recording hundreds of examples. His detailed observations led him to conclude in 1803 that, as several sets of double stars had subtly changed their positions, the stars must be orbiting each other.

William Herschel's work was continued by his son, John Fredrick William Herschel (1792–1871). John Herschel first began collaborating with his father in 1816, constructing his own telescope, and in 1820 the Herschels (father and son) helped found the Royal Astronomical Society. By 1821, he (with a collaborator named James South) was reevaluating his father's catalog of double stars, and John's final catalog of over 10,000 double stars was published after his death.[6]

The first mutual orbit of a binary system was calculated by the French astronomer Felix Savory (1797–1841), for the star ζ ("zeta") Ursae Majoris, more commonly known as Mizar. Currently, the Washington Double Star Catalog (compiled by the U.S. Naval Observatory) has a catalog of over 140,000 double stars (as of 2018), though only a few thousand have had orbits determined.

FIGURE 13.10. John Herschel (left); the very first photograph ever recorded on a glass plate, of Herschel's telescope (right).

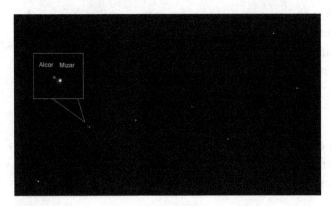

FIGURE 13.11. A photo of the Big Dipper. The optical double of Mizar and Alcor is shown in the inset. Credit: Shawn E. Gano.

Binary stars are distinguished by the capital letters "A" and "B," for example, Alberio A and Alberio B. A third star separate from the others would be called "C," and so on; in some cases, stars are distinguished as "Aa" and "Ab," and so on.

1. Optical Doubles versus Binary Systems

Two stars look like they are right next to each other through a telescope. Can we assume this is actually true? It turns out that we need to be careful before leaping to this conclusion.

Perhaps the most famous example of a pair of stars that at first glance appeared to be a binary are Mizar and Alcor, in the constellation of Ursa Major. The Big Dipper, officially an asterism, makes up the back end of Ursa Major; Mizar and Alcor represent the dot at the bend of the Big Dipper's handle (Figure 13.11). Although at first glance this appears to be a single star, in fact the two stars can be separated with the naked eye under good seeing conditions.

Despite their apparent nearness, trigonometric parallax measurements of Mizar and Alcor show that they are about a parsec away from each other. The reason they look close together is very simple: Alcor is essentially behind Mizar. Remember, stars are points of light on a black background, and so just looking at stars doesn't really give us a sense of depth perception.

---

[6] John Herschel was also one of the early inventors of photography, and in fact coined the term.

Ironically, both Mizar and Alcor appear to be multiple-star systems; Alcor consists of two stars and Mizar has four! Perhaps 1/3 of all stellar systems are multiples of some sort—estimates of the fraction of stars in multiple systems vary widely.

2. Importance of Binary Systems

More to the point, why are binary systems important? It's related to an idea we've encountered before in this book: How can we determine the mass of an astronomical object?

Our previous discussion regarding gravity (chapter 4) showed that the only way we can "weigh" objects of astronomical mass is by watching how smaller objects orbit them. For example, if we want to know the mass of Jupiter, we measure the periods and semi-major axes of its moons. A modified version of this idea can be applied to stars in binary systems.

Suppose we have two stars, one of mass M_1 and the other having mass M_2. An equation that can be used to find the individual masses is

Equation 13.3

$$\frac{T^2}{a^3} = \frac{4\pi^2}{G(M_1 + M_2)}$$

where T is the mutual period of the orbit and a is the distance between the stars. Using this equation is unfortunately more difficult than it appears, for many reasons. First, only one of the stars may even be visible (see the following section). Second, the period may be so long that we haven't seen the stars complete a full orbit, or even a significant fraction of one. Third, the plane of the orbits of the stars may be tilted, and without additional information, we cannot be sure of the distance between the stars. Finally, the orbits are most likely not circular, and again it may be impossible to determine their eccentricities. Any or all of these issues often ensure we can only set limits on the individual masses of the stars involved.

In recent years, the search for extrasolar planets, particularly by the Kepler spacecraft (which ended its mission in 2018), has managed to estimate star masses by observing the orbits of their planets, so the push to search for useful binary systems (for determinations of stellar masses, at least) is not as pressing as it was before.

Section 13.5: Binary Systems, Part II

How can we tell if a system is a binary (or some other type of multiple) system? Astronomers have four separate methods of discovering binaries.

1. Visual Binaries

This is the most obvious way to discover binaries: simply see them. But stars are so far away, and so close together (if in a binary), that we can only determine they are binary systems by using telescopes.

Stars in binary systems do not need to be the same color, mass, or even type. Figure 13.12 shows an example. The Albireo system belongs to the constellation of Cygnus the Swan, marking its head. Using a telescope reveals the Albireo system consists of two stars: one orange, one blue. It turns out the blue star is a massive main sequence star (like the Sun, but more massive and

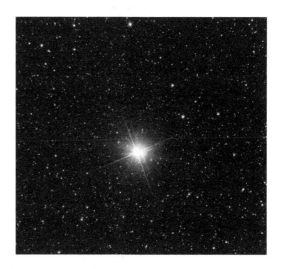

FIGURE 13.12. A photo of the Albireo binary system in the constellation of Cygnus. The spikes are artifacts of the image and thus are not real. Credit: Henryk Kowalewski.

therefore hotter), whereas the orange star is a giant (a star that no longer uses hydrogen as its fuel source, as the Sun does). It is also a bit of an open question whether the two stars, "components," of the Albireo system are in fact a true binary system or an optical double like Mizar and Alcor. Again just because two stars appear next to each other does not guarantee a true physical relationship between them.

The majority of known binaries are not visual, however, which begs the question: How do we know two stars are present if we can't see both of them? Astronomers use several indirect methods of discovery.

2. Spectroscopic Binaries

If we pass white light through a prism or diffraction grating, we can split it into its constituent colors. Further, extremely hot, thin gases emit specific narrow bands or lines of color, distinguishable to astronomers. We will examine spectroscopy further in the next chapter, but for now we can discuss a specific use of spectral lines.

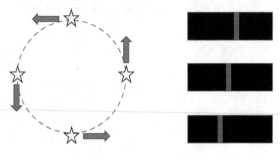

FIGURE 13.13. At left, a star at several points in its orbit in a binary system (its companion is not shown). At right, the shifting of a spectral line due to the motion of the star.

When a star approaches us, its spectral lines are shifted toward smaller wavelengths (or higher frequencies); when a star moves away from us, its spectral lines are shifted toward longer wavelengths (Figure 13.13). A star moving perfectly perpendicular to our line of sight will not show any shift in its spectra. The amount of shifting can be used to calculate the speed of the star in its orbit, which can further be used to determine other parameters of the orbit. In some cases, spectral lines (and their corresponding shifts) can be seen.

An example of a spectroscopic system is Mizar. It appears to have been the very first double star ever seen through a telescope (by Galileo and a collaborator) in 1617, though its nature was not understood for over a century. Mizar is therefore a visual binary, each individual star being about 2.5 times the mass of our Sun. But spectroscopic observations by Antonia Maury led to the publication of the orbit of an unseen companion to Mizar A in 1897, and Mizar B's unseen companion discovery was published by Maury in 1908.

This, by the way, means that the categories for discovering binaries are not exclusive; a system can contain both visual and spectroscopic stars, since these are just our descriptions of how we can tell the stars are there. To tell these newer companions apart, we further label the stars Mizar Aa, Mizar Ab, Mizar Ba, and Mizar Bb—think of it as the astronomy way of naming siblings in the same family, where everybody has the same surname but different personal (first) names.

3. Eclipsing Binaries

Spectroscopic binaries can be potentially found as long as the motions of the stars are at least partially toward or away from us. But without additional information, we can only set limits on the masses of the individual stars. One of the advances in recent years is the hunt for eclipsing binaries (and transiting exoplanets), which helps narrow down the values of those masses.

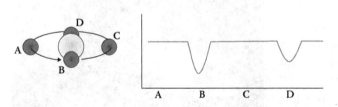

FIGURE 13.14. At left, a small star is shown orbiting a larger star (for simplicity, the larger star is kept stationary). At point B, the smaller star eclipses the larger star; at point D, the larger star eclipses the smaller star. At right, a light curve showing the total amount of light from the system as a function of time.

Recall we defined an eclipse as when an astronomical object covers or shadows another astronomical object of similar angular size. There are no shadows as such, of course, when a star moves in front of another, but we still call it an eclipse because we can't see part or all of the further star (Figure 13.14).

A light curve is simply a graph of the total amount of light coming from a star system as a function of time. While many stars vary their light output on their own (see section 13.7), the dips in the light output for an eclipsing system are relatively easy to distinguish. Because the stars must be lined up so that they pass in front of each other, astronomers can get a handle on the inclination of their orbits (which will be near zero degrees), and therefore get better estimates of the masses of each star.

Only about 5% of all binaries are eclipsing. Statistics on stellar masses have thus been relatively difficult to gather until recently. With the advent of the Kepler space probe in 2009, which used the same general idea to search for exoplanets, and with thousands of exoplanets now confirmed, we now have the opportunity to greatly improve our knowledge of stellar masses.

A famous eclipsing binary system amongst astronomers is the Algol system in the constellation of Perseus (a third star, labeled Algol C, is suspected but has not been confirmed to belong to the system). Components A and B show mutual eclipses with a period just shy of 3 days. The changes in brightness from the system are large enough to be seen with the

FIGURE 13.15. An interferometric image of the three-star Algol system, from the CHARA satellite. Algol A and B are so close to each other that the shape of Algol B is distorted by the gravity of A. The shape of Algol C is an artifact of the observation.

naked eye, and there is some tenuous evidence suggesting the ancient Egyptians knew about it, though its explanation as an eclipsing binary wasn't completely accepted until near the end of the 19th century.

As an added bonus of sorts, the two major components are close enough to each other that the gravitational attraction of Algol A is actually pulling gas off the surface of Algol B. We will revisit such "semi-detached" systems in a future chapter.

4. Astrometric Binaries

Finally, another method of determining the presence of a binary system is by measuring the positions of one or both stars in the system. The term for precision position measuring is called astrometry, and therefore these are astrometric binaries. Only a very few astrometric binaries are known, and those were discovered by other means. Another look at the Sirius system relays how this can be useful.

Figure 13.16 shows various astrometric observations made of the Sirius system were made with the Hubble Space Telescope, holding Sirius A still in the camera in order to focus attention on the motion of Sirius B. Those measurements, combined with historical observations going back to the 1800s, reveals that the common orbital period of the stars is 50.1824 years, the semi-major axis is 7.4957 arcseconds, and the eccentricity is 0.59142. These numbers allowed astronomers to estimate the masses of the individual stars: Sirius A has a mass of 2.063 ($\pm$ 0.023) $M_\odot$ and Sirius B has a mass of 1.018 ($\pm$ 0.011) $M_\odot$.

Section 13.6: Nebulae

We start our discussion of non-stellar objects with an astronomer who was not that interested in them. Charles Messier (1730–1817)

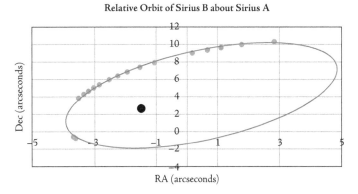

FIGURE 13.16. The motion of Sirius B (blue dots) about Sirius A (large black dot) from 2010–2016, from Hubble Space Telescope observations. The ellipse is the approximate orbit of Sirius B around Sirius A as seen from Earth.

FIGURE 13.17. Charles Messier (c. 1770) at left; M55, a globular cluster, seen in visible light.

was a French astronomer with a passion for comets. Unfortunately for him, he kept encountering objects that would, at first glance, appear to be comets, but upon later examination turn out to be something else. He therefore developed a list of such objects so that he could avoid them in the future.

A preliminary version of his catalog of non-comets was made public in 1771 and published in 1774 with 45 items.

Messier eventually counted 103 objects; historians of astronomy, going through his detailed notes, have since expanded it to 110. The "Messier Catalog" is perhaps the most famous catalog of objects amongst astronomers. Because Messier was only concerned that these objects were not comets, he didn't discriminate amongst them, and thus we find there various nebulae, stellar clusters and even a few galaxies.

In 1782, William Herschel conducted in-depth surveys of non-stellar objects, which were termed "nebulae" (singular *nebula*) for short. Eventually he discovered over 2,400 separate nebulae, which were published in a series of catalogs over two decades. His sister Caroline and son John also contributed, and a larger collection, the *General Catalogue of Nebulae and Clusters*, was published in 1864.

Check Your Neighbor

Do you find anything ironic about the title of the "New General Catalogue"?

Further supplemented by later astronomers—notably by John Dreyer and Caroline and John—the New General Catalogue (NGC), containing over 7,000 objects, was published in 1888 and still serves as the most commonly used method for identifying non-stellar objects.

"Nebula" in this usage is rather vague and includes a wide variety of types of objects, from planetary nebulae to stellar clusters to galaxies. Both the Messier ("M") Catalog and the NGC are still in use today.

We will explore all these different types of objects in future chapters. Here is a quick preview. In no particular order:

1. Planetary Nebulae

William Herschel was the first person to discover a new planet (Uranus), and set out to search for others. While he never did find another planet, he did make observations of objects that were both colorful (like planets) and roughly round in shape. Not knowing what they were, but able to tell they weren't planets, he termed them *planetary nebulae*.

We now know, ironically, that planetary nebulae have nothing to do with planets. Rather, they originate from dying stars expelling their outer layers of gas back into space. Many (not all) do so more or less in all directions, and therefore tend to look round from a distance. The gas is hot enough that it emits spectral radiation. Eventually planetary nebulae dissipate into the interstellar medium but can be visible for tens of thousands of years before spreading out too much to be seen (Figure 13.18). One often finds a small, white dot at the center of a planetary nebula; this is a white dwarf, the leftover core of the former star.

2. Supernova Remnants

Another common nebula found by early modern astronomers we now recognize are the remnants of supernovae. Whereas a small, dying star will (relatively) slowly push its outer layers of gas back into space to form planetary nebulae, a much larger star can end its life via an explosion that completely destroys itself. These events are called supernovae, and their debris are called *supernovae remnants* (Figure 13.18). As with planetary nebulae, sometimes a small fragment remains behind, though these are not observable in visible light and can either be neutron stars or black holes.

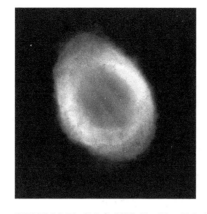 

FIGURE 13.18. At left, M57, the Ring Nebula, an example of a planetary nebula (Credit: AURA/STScI/NASA); at right, M1, the Crab Nebula, an example of a supernova remnant (Credit: NASA/ESA/J. Hester and A. Loll).

3. Star-Forming Regions

Both of the previous nebulae are examples of dying stars. At the other end, time wise, are a variety of nebulae where stars are born. In such nebulae, the gas would not be hot enough to be visible, except that it is heated by a new, bright star (or stars); in other cases, we can infer the presence of such nebulae because they block light from other objects behind them. Depending on how we see them and/or their physical properties, they can have names ranging from molecular clouds to HI or HII regions (Figure 13.19).

As with other nebulae, early modern astronomers had little knowledge of the processes occurring in these objects and were only able to catalog their positions and appearances. In fact, star formation is still an area of active research, and much less is known about how stars form than how stars die.

4. Stellar Clusters

Another basic type of object found by astronomers like Messier and Herschel is a stellar cluster (Figure 13.19). Stars are born in groups of thousands to hundreds of thousands; in some cases, the individual stars break away; in others, they remain inside the cluster for their entire lives. They look fuzzy through small telescopes, leading them to be thought of as nebula, and while some are occasionally associated with nebulae, clusters themselves are not.

5. Galaxies

Once again, we go back to William Herschel. In 1781, he made a survey of

FIGURE 13.19. At left, the Orion Nebula, an example of a star-forming region (Credit: NASA/ESA/M. Robberto). At right, the Pleiades, a cluster of stars (Credit: NASA/ESA/AURA/CalTech/Palomar Observatory). Both images were taken in visible light from the Hubble Space Telescope.

several hundred stars in order to make a three-dimensional map of the sky. He was not able to determine distances to stars via trig parallax (refer back to section 13.3), so he made an interesting assumption: Supposing each star is equally bright intrinsically, he could estimate relative distances using the inverse square law. Given that he was estimating star brightnesses without modern equipment (no photographs or digital detectors), and that stars do not in fact all possess the same intrinsic brightness, he did remarkably well.

Herschel discovered that stars are not randomly distributed across the sky. Instead, we seem to be in the middle of a large disk of stars (Figure 13.20), somewhat thicker in the middle and tapering off at the ends. This in general

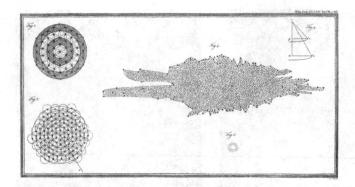

FIGURE 13.20. William Herschel's map of the Milky Way; the Sun (not depicted) is at the center of the sketch. From this he concluded that stars are not randomly distributed through the sky, but rather concentrated in a flattened region.

FIGURE 13.21. Photographs of Harlow Shapley (left) and Edwin Hubble (right).

is correct. We live in the disk of the Milky Way, and the central section of the Milky Way is indeed somewhat thicker (we now call it the "bulge").

Further, among Herschel's "nebulae" were objects that, rather than seeming to be gaseous, appeared themselves to be made of individual stars. We now know these to be individual galaxies, much like the Milky Way but extremely far away.

In the decade of the 1910s, the American astronomer Harlow Shapley (1885–1972) used RR Lyrae stars (a class of variable star) to reevaluate the structure of the Milky Way. He realized that, contrary to what everybody had been assuming, the Sun is not at the center of the Milky Way, but rather off center tens of thousands of light years. Shapley had this correct; however, Shapley also thought that the various star-laden spiral-shaped nebulae belonged to the Milky Way, whereas other astronomers were beginning to think that they might be separate "island universes" outside of the Milky Way.

The deciding factor in the question regarding spiral nebulae—are they part of the Milky Way or separate?—was found by another American astronomer, Edwin Hubble (1889–1953), working at Mount Wilson Observatory in California.

Hubble (with the assistance of Milton Humason and additional data from Vesto Slipher) found that the further away a galaxy, the greater its redshift of its spectral lines, due to the Doppler effect.

This implies that the further away a galaxy, the faster it is moving away from us. Astronomers now recognize this as a consequence of what has been nicknamed the "Big Bang," the expansion of the universe itself. (It is worth noting that Hubble himself was ambivalent about this interpretation.)

Section 13.7: Variable Stars

We need to backtrack in order to discuss our next topic. Stars appear to be constant and unchanging. But people may have known that some stars vary their output long before modern astronomy. There are some hints that 3,200 years ago, Egyptian calendars noted variations in the brightness of the Algol system. Supernovae have been observed by people for thousands of years; records of the Crab supernova (i.e., the event that created the Crab Nebula) were recorded by peoples in 1054 CE as far apart as China and the deserts of North America. But few periodic (repeating) variables were detected before the invention of the telescope. For example, Polaris is a variable star, but since its variations only take a few days and are barely noticeable to the naked eye, its nature wasn't appreciated until recently.

The first variable star to be recognized as such was Omicron Ceti (later named Mira, or "wonderful") by Johannes Holwadra in 1638, with a period of about 11 months. Algol was soon discovered, or perhaps rediscovered, as a variable in 1669 by Geminiano Montanari. The first astronomer to suggest a plausible physical mechanism for

Algol's variability was John Goodricke in 1784. The numbers of variables remained small until the advent of astrophotography in the late 19th century; now several tens of thousands of variables are known and several thousand more suspected.

Possibly the single most important astronomer in the history of variable star studies was Henrietta Swan Leavitt (1868–1921). A graduate of Radcliff College in Massachusetts, she was hired by Harvard College Observatory in 1893 to work as a "computer," a person who was tasked to make tedious calculations, observations, and measurements before the days of electronic calculators. She was part of Edward Pickering's team of female computers working on the Henry Draper catalog,[7] which also included Annie Jump Cannon, Williamina Fleming, and Antonia Maury, all who did not receive the accolades due them in their lifetimes but who are recognized now as fundamentally important contributors to astronomy. Leavitt never officially earned the doctoral degree for which she originally enrolled; her health was often poor, leading to deafness as she grew older. In 1921, as head of the observatory, Harlow Shapley named her as head of stellar photometry, but she died soon after.[8]

Leavitt made two major contributions to stellar astronomy. First, she helped refine the astronomical magnitude (brightness) system developed at Harvard Observatory. Second, she discovered a mathematical relation for certain types of variables, which have had enormous consequences for our understanding of the universe.

FIGURE 13.22. Annie Jump Cannon (left) and Henrietta Swan Leavitt (right) outside of Harvard Observatory in 1913.

From observations of *Cepheid* variables (so called because the first star of this type known is delta Cephei, from the constellation of Cepheus) in the Large and Small Magellanic Clouds,[9] she noted that the brighter a Cepheid, the longer its period of variation. "Leavitt's law," more commonly known as the *period-luminosity relationship*, was first published in 1908 with a follow-up study in 1912.

We know currently of several types of variables, but the Cepheids have turned out to be the most useful to astronomers. The Dutch astronomer Enjar Hertzsprung independently determined distances to Cepheids within the Milky Way, allowing astronomers to use them as a distance scale, and Edwin Hubble later found Cepheids in the Andromeda Galaxy, a stepping stone to the identification of galaxies as separate from the Milky Way and the notion of the expansion of the universe. Hubble and others often stated they thought Leavitt should have won a Nobel Prize for her work; unfortunately, she had died of cancer by the time she was seriously being considered for the award, and the Nobel is only awarded to living candidates.

Cepheids are still objects of study today, both for themselves and because they can be used to determine distances to far-away galaxies. One of the first large research efforts of the Hubble Space Telescope was to study Cepheids in distant galaxies in order to narrow the range of values for the Hubble Constant, which sets the scale of the universe itself.

Check Your Neighbor

Estimate the period of variation of Mira from Figure 13.23.

---

[7] Henry Draper was an astronomer at Harvard in the late 19th century who began a photographic catalog of stars; after his death, his widow, Mary Anne Palmer Draper, donated his estate to Harvard to continue the work. The Henry Draper (HD) catalog remains one of the most cited sources for stars today.

[8] A play titled "Silent Sky" by Lauren Gunderson was recently produced at the University of Southern Mississippi about Leavitt's life as an astronomer.

[9] Both the Large and Small Magellanic Clouds are today recognized as satellite galaxies of the Milky Way.

There is one more item to discuss: Variables come in two basic types:

- ♦ "Extrinsic" variables: A star appears to vary its light output due to external influences, almost always due to eclipses between companions in a binary system. An example we discussed earlier is Algol.
- ♦ "Intrinsic" variables: A star varies its light output because of something the star itself is doing. Common versions are periodic variables (such as Cepheids), where the variability repeats over time, and catastrophic variables (such as the Crab supernova), where the variability is due to an enormous explosion.

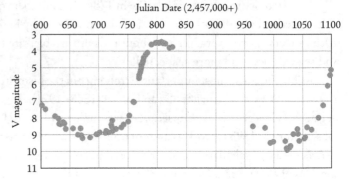

FIGURE 13.23. The light curve of Mira, using data from the American Association of Variable Star Observers (AASVO).

Summary

In this chapter, we discussed the following:

- ▸ How constellations are not ultimately permanent, but vary their appearances over large distances and/or times
- ▸ The discovery of "proper motion," the motion of stars across the sky
- ▸ The application of trigonometric parallax to measuring distances to nearby stars
- ▸ The discovery, cataloging, and classification of binary star systems
- ▸ The discovery, cataloging, and classification of nebulae
- ▸ The discovery and usefulness of variable stars

Questions

1. A light year is the distance a beam of light travels in one year. The speed of light is 3.00×10^8 m/s.
   - ♦ How many seconds are in a year? Assume there are 365 ¼ days per year, 24 hours per day, 60 minutes per hour, and 60 seconds per minute
   - ♦ How far is a light year in kilometers?
   - ♦ How far is a light year in miles? Hint: 1 mile = 1.6 kilometers
   - ♦ How far is a light year in astronomical units? Hint: 1 au = 1.50×10^8 km

2. A parsec equals 3.26 light years.
   - ♦ How far is a parsec in kilometers?
   - ♦ How far is a parsec in miles?
   - ♦ How far is a parsec in astronomical units?

3. The Voyager II spacecraft, the fastest moving space probe in history, recently passed a distance of 100 au from the Sun, taking about 40 years to do this.
   - ♦ In our region of the galaxy, the distance from one star to another is about a parsec. In your opinion, does Voyager II still belong to the solar system, or is it so far away as to belong to another star system?
   - ♦ How many years will it take for Voyager II to travel to Barnard's Star (assuming it is traveling straight toward Barnard's Star, which it isn't), if Barnard's Star is 1.8 parsecs from us?

4. Sirius has a proper motion of 1.34 arcseconds per year, a radial velocity of – 5.50 km/s, and a trig parallax of 0.379 arcseconds. Find the following:
   - The distance to Sirius in units of parsecs
   - The distance to Sirius in units of light years
   - The transverse velocity of Sirius
   - The space velocity of Sirius

5. The brightest star in Canis Minor, Procyon, is actually a visual binary. The mutual period of their orbits is 40.82 years, the two components are separated by 4.3 arcseconds, and their parallax is 0.285 arcseconds
   - How far away is the Procyon system from Earth, in units of parsecs?
   - How far away is the Procyon system from Earth, in units of light years?
   - What is the total mass of the Procyon system?

6. Only about 5% of all binary systems are discovered and/or known via mutual eclipses. Why is the number so low?

7. Leavitt assumed it was fair to compare the brightnesses of Cepheids in the LMC to each other. Why? Hint: The LMC is about 50,000 parsecs from Earth and the average distance between stars in the LMC is about a parsec.

Activities

▸ *Astrophysics activity 13.1:* Carefully observe how trig parallax works for the naked eye(s) and relate your results to stellar astronomy.

▸ *Astrophysics activity 13.2:* Investigate how astronomers name stars and other types of objects.

▸ *Astrophysics activity 13.3:* Use computer simulations to explore how astronomers determine masses of stars from eclipsing binaries.

▸ Use free software (see Works Referenced) to chart the appearance of the stars of a famous group of stars (the Big Dipper, Orion, or the Pleiades are examples) over time. Start at 250,000 BCE and, working at intervals of 50,000 years, continue until 250,000 CE. Either plot the positions of the main stars on sheets of graph paper, or make copies of the images from the software.

▸ Place an object about 50 feet away. Measure its distance using a tape measure. Next, view the object's position compared to a distant background from two separate angles, with a baseline of about 6 feet. Use trigonometry to calculate the distance to the object. Finally, compare the two results. Note: This activity works best outside or in a very long hallway.

▸ Go to the home page of the American Association of Variable Star Observers (AASVO), aasvo.org. Plot a light curve for Mira from January 1 of 2016, to the present, using a "V" (visible light) filter. Print out the plot; from the plot, determine (a) the period of variation for Mira and (b) a rough estimate of its range of brightness variations in terms of magnitudes. Also, why are there blank spots in the data? Hint: Mira is in the constellation of Ceti the Whale, most of which is south of the Celestial Equator.

Works Referenced

Discussions regarding the positions of stars in space and time can be found in the following sources:

Bessel, F. W. (1838). Determination of the distance to 61 Cygni. *Astronomische Nachrichten, 16*(365–366), 65–96. doi:10.1002/asna.18390160502

Eggen, O. J. (2017, October 18). Edmond Halley: British scientist. *Encyclopedia Britannica.* Retrieved from https://www.britannica.com/biography/Edmond-Halley/

Sirola, C. (2017), March). Depth perception. *The Physics Teacher, 55*(3), 78–79.

van Leeuwen, F. (2007), Validation of the new Hipparcos reduction. *Astronomy and Astrophysics, 474*(2), 653–664. doi:10.1051/0004-6361:20078357

Free software exists that shows the proper motions of stars with time; for example, orbitsimulator.com/gravitySimulator-Cloud/properMotionHome.html

Data for Barnard's Star from SIMBAD, as of January 13, 2018: simbad.u-strasbg.fr/simbad/

Binary systems are discussed in Hershel, W. (1803). Account of the changes that have happened, during the last twenty-five years, in the relative situation of double-stars, with an investigation of the cause to which they are owing, *Philosophical Transactions of the Royal Society of London, 93*(1803), 339–382.

A popular review of the properties of the optical double of Mizar and Alcor is found in Christoforou, P. (2017, September 7). *Star facts: Mizar and Alcor.* Retrieved from https://www.astronomytrek.com/star-facts-mizar-and-alcor/

Antonia Maury's discovery of the binary orbit of Mizar A was part of a larger study: Maury, A. (1897). Spectra of bright stars photographed with the 11-inch Draper telescope as part of the Henry Draper Memorial. *Annals of the Astronomical Observatory of Harvard College, 28,* 1–128.

The Washington Double Star catalog (or WDS) is at https://www.usno.navy.mil/USNO/astrometry/optical-IR-prod/wds/WDS

Some biographical information about John Herschel can be found at someinterestingfacts.net/who-is-sir-john-herschel/

Bond, H. E., Schaefer, G. H., Gilliland, R. L., Holberg, J. B., Mason, B. D., Lindenblad, I. W., ... & Gudehus, D. (2017, May 10). The Sirius System and its astrophysical puzzles: Hubble Space Telescope and ground-based astrometry. *The Astrophysical Journal, 840*(70), 1–17. doi:10.3847/1538-4357/aa6af8

A timeline for some major astronomical discoveries, such as William Herschel's mapping of the Milky Way, can be found at https://cosmology.carnegiescience.edu/timeline/1781

Herschel, W. (1785). On the construction of the heavens. *Philosophical Transactions of the Royal Society of London, 75,* 213–266.

Shapley, H., & Curtis, H. D. (1921). The scale of the universe. *Bulletin of the National Research Council, 2*(169), 171–217.

(1929). A relation between distance and radial velocity among extra-galactic nebulae. *Proceedings of the National Academy of Sciences, 15*(3), 168–173.

Hubble's ambivalent attitude toward the expansion of the universe was expressed in a letter he sent to the Dutch cosmologist Willem de Sitter; discussed in Kirschner, R. P. (2004). "Hubble's diagram and cosmic expansion." *Proceedings of the National Academy of Sciences.* 101 pp. 8–13.

Variable stars are discussed in the following sources:

Porceddu et al. (2015). Shifting milestones of natural science: The ancient Egyptian's discovery of Algol's Period confirmed. *PLoS ONE, 10*(12), e0144140.

Samus, N. N., Kazarovets, E. V., & Durlevich, O. V. (2001). General catalogue of variable stars. *Odessa Astronomical Publications, 14,* 266.

Data concerning variable stars can be obtained (and contributions made to!) the American Association of Variable Star Observers (AAVSO) at aavso.org. The data used to create the light curve of Mira can be found at https://www.aavso.org/LCGv2/

Leavitt, H. S. (1908). 1777 variables in the Magellanic clouds. *Annals of Harvard College Observatory, 60*(4), 87–110.

Pickering, E. C. (1912). Periods of 25 variable stars in the small Magellanic cloud. *Harvard College Observatory Circular 173,* 1–3.

The stage play about Leavitt's life, "Silent Sky," was written by Lauren Gunderson in 2015. Information about the play (including permission requirements for conducting performances) can be found at https://www.stageplays.com/PDF/silent_sky.pdf

A review of how Cepheids were used for cosmology is described by W. L. Freedman in "The Key Project to Measure the Hubble Constant." Retrieved from www.stsci.edu/stsci/meetings/shst2/freedmanw.html

Credits

Alpha Centauri, courtesy of the Digitized Sky Survey 2. The size of Alpha Centauri represents its brightness, not its actual size.

LIGHT II

To discuss properties of light which are important for stellar astronomy

- To compare wave and particle models of light
- To discuss various uses of the Doppler effect
- To determine surface temperatures and fluxes for black body objects
- To describe a working model of electron behavior in atoms
- To determine energies and wavelengths of spectral lines

Stars, even more so than planets, are incredibly distant—so distant that personal voyages to them are likely to always remain the stuff of science fiction. Moreover, stars appear to us as points of light, with no visible shapes whatsoever. How, then, do astronomers study stars?

With rare exceptions, our information about stars comes solely from the light they send us. This means, in order to understand stars, we must first understand light: how it behaves and how we interpret our observations of it.

⊙: The symbol for the Sun

Absorption: When an object or substance keeps (absorbs) the light incident upon it

Black body radiation (also thermal radiation): Light emitted by the surface of an opaque object due to its surface temperature

Doppler effect: How observed wavelengths change due to the relative motions between a source and an observer

Double-slit experiment: Sending laser light through two adjacent narrow slits gives rise to a complex pattern of dots on a screen, only explainable if light behaves as a wave

Emission: When an object or substance gives off light

Flux: The power or luminosity of a light source per unit area. Also called "intensity"

Inverse square law: The emitted intensity from a point source decreases with the square of the distance

Luminosity: The power or intrinsic brightness of a light source

Planck's constant: A universal constant expressing the "graininess" of quantum phenomena

Photoelectric effect: Shining light on certain materials can generate electricity. The specifics of the effect can only be explained if we assume light behaves as particles

Photon: A particle (or "wave packet") of light

Quantum mechanics: The branch of physics that tends to deal with very small phenomena such as atoms and elementary particles. The term *quantum* (plural *quanta*) is simply Latin for "number" or "amount" and refers to the idea that concepts like energy come in set amounts

Spectral radiation: Light emitted or absorbed due to the elemental and/or molecular constituents of the object or substance

Speed of light: A universal constant expressing the fastest speed any signal can travel through in a vacuum

Stefan-Boltzmann law: A mathematical relationship between the surface temperature of an object and the flux (light intensity) emitted by it due to black body radiation

Wein's law: A mathematical relationship between the surface temperature of an object and the peak wavelength of the light emitted

KEY INDIVIDUALS

Bohr, Neils: A Danish physicist of the early 20th century who (among other discoveries) put forth the first working model of atoms that addressed spectral lines

Bunsen, Robert: A German physicist of the mid-19th century who coinvented the Bunsen burner and collaborated with Gustav Kirchhoff in spectroscopy

Einstein, Albert: A German physicist who invented the concept of the photon in 1905 (among other discoveries) to explain the photoelectric effect and black body radiation

Huygens, Christiaan: A Dutch physicist of the late 17th century and contemporary of Newton who advocated for a wave model of light

Kirchhoff, Robert: A German physicist of the mid-19th century who discovered three "laws" for spectroscopy and coined the term "black body" for thermal absorbers

Newton, Isaac: An English scientist of the late 17th century who (among many other things!) advocated for a particle model of light

Planck, Max: A German physicist who found an expression in 1901 for the behavior of flux (intensity) of light from a black body object dependent on wavelength

Rutherford, Ernest: A citizen of the British Empire of the late 19th/earth 20th century—originally born in New Zealand but spending his working career in England—whose experiments discovered the smallness of the atomic nucleus

Young, Thomas: An English scientist who conducted a series of experiments around 1800 that showed light behaves as a wave

Section 14.1: Wave/Particle Duality

Once scientists (called "natural philosophers" prior to 1800) began studying light as a phenomenon, they puzzled over its substance. Two major choices emerged: light consists of tiny little particles, or light consists of waves. In both cases, the individual parts—the size across of the particles, or the wavelengths of the visible light waves—are too small to see. This led at first to wild speculation, then to ingenious experiments leading to one option, then to even more subtle and ingenious experiments leading to the other. Today, we live with a situation where we can describe light very well mathematically and manipulate it in incomparable ways, but our language still struggles to properly describe it.

1. Newton versus Huygens

Christiaan Huygens was a Dutch scientist (1629–1695) who in some ways can be thought of as a bridge between Galileo and Newton. He invented the pendulum clock (in the process discovering the mathematical formula for what physicists today call the simple pendulum),[1] which remained the standard in precision time keeping until

---

[1] In modern notation, the period of a simple pendulum is given by $T = 2\pi\sqrt{l\,/\,g}$, where l is the length of the pendulum and g is the acceleration due to gravity on the surface of the Earth.

the early 20th century, and accurately described centripetal acceleration,[2] both being outgrowths of work begun by Galileo. He ground lenses and constructed his own telescopes, and among his discoveries were the giant moon of Saturn called Titan, that Saturn's rings surround but nowhere touch the planet, the first

FIGURE 14.1. A portrait of Christiaan Huygens (left); ocean waves reflecting off a pier (right).

individual features on Mars, and the rotational period of Mars (thereby showing that other planets also rotate). But our purpose here is to review his ideas concerning the nature of light.

Huygens proposed a theory that light consists of longitudinal waves (longitudinal waves shake back and forth along the direction they travel in) in 1678 and formally published his theory in 1690. He also assumed that the speed of light is finite (it is not clear if he was aware of the first precise measurement in 1679, performed by Olaus Roemer). Huygen's concern was primarily geometric optics, that is, how light travels from one location to another in order to form images. His theory had some success in explaining how waves reflect off of and bend around barriers (Figure 14.1), but his longitudinal waves could not explain the effect of birefringence in certain crystals and was therefore usually dismissed.

Later physicists would determine that light waves are transverse, not longitudinal, and the objection to birefringence turns out not to be relevant. Examples of longitudinal waves in nature include sound; examples of other transverse waves include water waves.

Isaac Newton's work with light led him in another direction from Huygens. In one of his most famous experiments, Newton allowed sunlight through a small opening into an otherwise dark room (chapter 5). The beam of sunlight went through a prism, which separated the white light into a rainbow of color. This shows that white light is not itself a fundamental color, but rather a mixture of other colors. Newton then took the further step of sending the rainbow into another prism, oriented in the opposite direction from the first prism, and showed how the rainbow recombined into white light. From this (and other arguments), Newton concluded that individual colors consists of tiny particles (or "corpuscles"), which were elastic, rigid, and weightless.

Newton's reputation was such that other scientists tended to accept his version of light over Huygens's, regardless of the arguments or evidence. This was unfortunate, for it tended to hinder investigations into light for over a century. Eventually, both men turned out to be partially correct.

2. Light as Waves

Newton's views held sway throughout the 18th century. But in 1801, an English natural philosopher named Thomas Young conducted experiments that flipped the script.

Thomas Young (1773–1829) was another of the many people in our histories who made contributions in several fields. He was a medical doctor and was the first to suggest that three separate nerve fibers are responsible for color vision in people. He helped develop the property of solids, useful for engineering, which describes a material's

---

[2] Huygens accurately derived the formula $F = mv^2/r$ for centripetal force in 1673, where m is the mass of the moving object, v is its speed, and r is the radius of the circle it moves in. This helps describe phenomena as varied as whirling a rock with a string, driving a car through a sharp turn, or a planet orbiting the Sun.

strength under stress and strain, and which is now called Young's modulus. He studied how surface tension of a liquid gives rise to capillary action; trees make use of this property to get liquid from their roots to their leaves. And he made contributions to the decipherment of Egyptian hieroglyphics, work completed by the French linguist Jean-François Champollion.

The *double-slit experiment* associated with Young[3] is simple in principle but difficult in practice to pull off without the use of lasers. Imagine shining a beam of light through a set of small rectangular openings, or slits (Figure 14.2). If light consists of particles (corpuscles), then it should make two slit-like patterns on a distant screen. This is <u>not</u> what happens (Figure 14.3):

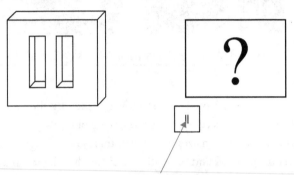

FIGURE 14.2. A close-up of a double-slit apparatus, with relative widths exaggerated for clarity (left); a laser beam directed through the slits onto a distant screen (right).

The resulting pattern can only be explained if light consists of waves. In this experiment, the laser beam goes through two narrow rectangular openings. If light was made of tiny particles, then the beam should show two narrow rectangular shapes on a distant screen. Instead, we get a complex pattern of dots, brightest in the middle, fading toward the edges, with other less-obvious patterns superimposed. This pattern of dots can only come about if the laser beams coming through the slits act as waves.

Other experiments in the 1800s subsequently supported the wave notion. Here's one you can try for yourself: Lift one arm up so that it points at a relatively bright light, such as a florescent light you might have in a classroom. Bring your thumb and forefinger close together, but not so they touch, and watch the light coming through between the two fingers. As they come closer, you should see dark lines forming. This is due to light waves trying to fit through a narrow space and interfering with each other.

3. Light as Particles

The physics community took to describing light as a wave phenomenon for about a century. But starting around 1900, new experiments showed behaviors that couldn't be explained by the wave model. Let's look at one of those now.

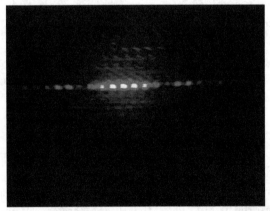

FIGURE 14.3. A portrait of Thomas Young (left); a series of bright dots or "fringes" when red laser light is sent through two narrow slits (right).

---

[3] It appears that Young held individual cards, with sharp edges, one at a time in order to show the wave nature of light. But the double-slit arrangement is a natural outgrowth of such work, nonetheless.

The 19th century was the time in which electricity and magnetism became well understood, culminating with the work of James Clerk Maxwell (1831–1879), who showed that the combination of electrical and magnetic waves was light (now "electromagnetic waves") and used this to derive the value of the speed of light. But toward the end of the 19th century, experimenters discovered a new phenomenon, the *photoelectric effect*.

Suppose we connect a certain type of solid material—platinum, for example—to an electrical circuit and shine light on the material. It is possible to generate electricity in this way, such as is done with solar panels. But the effect didn't make a lot of sense at first.

Electrons, a brand new idea back then, are tiny negatively charged particles. Electrons are attached to atoms by attractive forces from the positively charged protons in the nuclei of the atoms. But if an electron is given enough energy, then it can escape from its atom. Instead of finding a home with another atom, the electron can travel through the circuit, thereby becoming part of an electric current.

Researchers first thought that the best way to explain the photoelectric effect was by shining light waves on the electrons in the material. The waves would bring energy to the electrons, building up until the electrons had stored enough energy to make their escapes. There would be a short delay in time between starting to shine the light and the beginning of the current, as the energy would need to build up, and it was thought that any wave would do the trick, if we were willing to wait long enough.

These expectations were distinctly not met. First, there seemed to be no time delay—as soon as the light was shining, electricity was flowing. Second, not all colors of light worked; there was a critical wavelength (color) at work; shorter waves would be fine, but longer waves than the critical wavelength wouldn't do anything. Electricity generated by the photoelectric effect was therefore all or nothing—it either worked or it did not—and when it worked, the current was immediate (Figure 14.4):

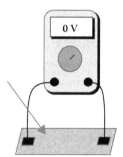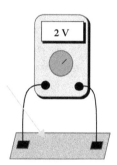

FIGURE 14.4. A solid material is connected to an electric circuit with a multimeter. When red light shines on the surface of the material, there is no voltage generated (left). When blue light shines, there is a voltage generated (right).

The person to explain this was none other than Albert Einstein. Einstein (1879–1953) proposed that instead of light consisting of waves, light consists of tiny particles, which later came to be called *photons*. Each photon carries a set amount of energy defined by its wavelength—longer wavelength photons carry less energy than do shorter wavelength photons. Each material susceptible to this behavior holds its electrons to its atoms with a set amount of energy. If a photon "hits" an electron but doesn't have enough energy, it won't knock the electron off its atom, and no current flows. But if a photon does carry enough energy, it will knock the electron off its atom, and we get electric current. Einstein published his explanation for the photoelectric effect in 1905.

Einstein didn't win the Nobel Prize for his work on relativity, either special or general,[4] or any of the other discoveries he made during his amazing career. Instead, he won it for the photoelectric effect. The ability to turn light into electricity, or electricity into light, is a major feature of modern times—think of your average cell phone—and you'll probably agree it is worth the recognition.

---

[4] We will discuss Einstein's work in both special and general relativity later in this textbook.

So, what's the answer: Is light a wave or is light a particle? The answer is perhaps unsatisfying, but nature isn't obligated to attend to our feelings. It depends. If you perform an experiment that looks for wave-like behavior, you'll find wave-like behavior. If you perform an experiment that looks for particle-like behavior, you'll find particle-like behavior. This is called wave-particle duality, for lack of a more succinct term. An analogy here may be helpful: Think of the two sides of a coin. Each side—heads or tails—shows a different picture. Only one side can be seen at a time, but it's always the same coin.

Check Your Neighbor

How does Einstein's proposal (the photon) also explain why the effect is instantaneous? Hint: Compare this situation to that of two billiard balls colliding on a pool table.

Section 14.2: The Inverse Square Law of Light

Here's something we've all noticed: The farther away we are from a source of light, the dimmer the light gets. And, of course, the closer we are to the source, the brighter the light gets.

This behavior isn't limited to light. Any point source of waves does the same thing, whether it is the height of water waves in a puddle from a drip, or the loudness of an astronomy professor's voice in a lecture hall.

The amount of light coming from the point source doesn't change—a 100-watt light bulb emits 100 watts, regardless of whether you're close to it or far away from it. But the intensity of the waves—their perceived, or as we say in astronomy, apparent—brightness drops with distance (Figure 14.5).

Astronomers therefore distinguish between the "real"—better yet, "intrinsic" or "absolute"—brightness and the perceived or "apparent" brightness. The intrinsic or absolute brightness of an object is its *luminosity*.[5] Contrast that with the apparent brightness, which physicists call intensity and astronomers call *flux*.

Since waves from a point source spread out equally in all directions, they behave as spherical shells of light, and the luminosity is spread out over the surface area of these shells. The surface area of a sphere is $4\pi r^2$, and thus the flux of an object is

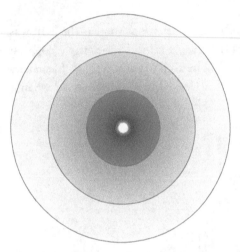

FIGURE 14.5. Waves from a central point source spread out in spherical shells. As the waves spread, their intensity drops as the square of the distance.

Equation 14.1

$$F = \frac{L}{A} = \frac{L}{4\pi r^2}$$

where L is the luminosity and r is the radial (straight-line) distance from the source. This is true for astronomy as much as it is true for light bulbs. We will use this notion in the next chapter to help determine distances to the stars.

Check Your Neighbor

A 50-watt light bulb is seen by two students. Student A is 1 meter from the light bulb and student B is 5 meters from the light bulb. For which student does the light bulb emit a higher luminosity; or, perhaps, is the luminosity the same for both of them? For which student does the light bulb emit a larger amount of flux; or, perhaps, is the flux the same for both of them?

---

[5] Real stars emit much of their power in other wavelengths, primarily ultraviolet and infrared, as well as visible light. The term astronomers use to account for all possible light from a star is *bolometric* luminosity.

Turn this notion around, and we can solve for the luminosity of a star, if we know the flux emitted from the star at its surface and the distance to the star. We will pursue this notion more fully in chapter 15.

Section 14.3: The Doppler Effect

Another experience many of us have had: Stand on the corner of a busy street. Listen carefully to the pitch of the sound of an approaching car. At the moment the car passes by, there is a brief transition. As the car moves away, you notice the pitch has noticeably dropped.

This is called the *Doppler effect*, and it applies to all waves. Suppose, for simplicity, we assume a point source sends out waves of constant wavelength, and therefore frequency (Figure 14.6). No matter where an outside observer is located, that observer will perceive the same wavelength.

On the other hand, consider now the same source, emitting the same wavelength, but moving toward the right (Figure 14.7). An observer to the right is located such that the object is coming toward the observer; an observer to the left is located such that the source is moving away from the observer. We also show an observer that is being passed by. We can use the Doppler effect to learn a variety of important facts about stars.

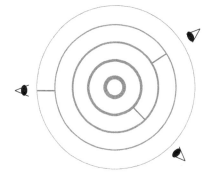

FIGURE 14.6. Waves emitted from a stationary point source. The distance from one wave crest to the next—the wavelength, depicted here in red line segments—is the same for any observer, at any distance, at any location.

1. Radial Velocity

Because waves travel at finite speed (remember this is true even of light waves) the object is catching up to the waves, so they appear crushed together where the source is approaching the observer. The opposite is true where the source is moving away from the observer; the waves appear stretched out. Only for the case of the observer being passed by does the wavelength appear to be at its original length.

How do we apply this to astronomy? If the waves from a star appear stretched out, we can presume the star is moving away from us; if the waves appear condensed, it is moving toward us; this is termed the star's *radial velocity*. A star's motion perpendicular to our line of sight can't be found using the Doppler effect; that is called "proper motion" *or transverse velocity*, something we discussed in chapter 13, and which has to be found via other methods.

Stars tend to give off a blend of waves: the Sun is famous for being a yellow star, but it also emits the full rainbow of colors. Even more, the Sun also emits lots of infrared and some ultraviolet light. So, astronomers need something more specific to follow.

Thin gases in the upper atmospheres of stars show spectral lines. We will investigate spectroscopy in more detail in section 14.5, but for now, we note that different gases in stars emit and/or absorb specific lines of color.

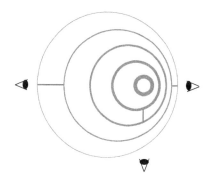

FIGURE 14.7. Waves emitted from a moving point source (in this case, to the right). The perceived wavelength depends on one's location relative to the motion of the source.

Hydrogen, besides being the simplest element, is also the most common in stars. One popular line of color from hydrogen occurs at 656 nanometers,[6] or 656 billionths of a meter, which we perceive as red. Suppose we have a device in a lab that makes hydrogen emit this line. Since we are sitting still compared to the device, we see it at 656 nm. Now consider a star in space moving toward us. Its line won't occur at 656 nm, but smaller than 656 nm. Another star that is moving away from us will have its line occur at a larger wavelength than 656 nm (Figure 15.10).

---

[6] Astronomers often use a unit of length called the Ångstrom. One Ångstrom is one 10-billionth of a meter, or 10 Ångstroms is the same as 1 nanometer. We will stick with nanometers in this book.

How much does a line of color shift due to its motion along our line of sight? With c representing the speed of light, we find to first approximation the velocity of the source relative to us is

Equation 14.2

$$v = \left(\frac{\lambda - \lambda_0}{\lambda_0}\right)c$$

where λ ("lambda") represents the wavelength we perceive and λ_0 the original wavelength from the source. If the answer is positive, then the object is moving away from us; if negative, then the object is moving toward us.

Sample Calculation

Suppose a particular spectral line is observed at 600.0 nm in the lab. When observing a star, the same spectral line is seen at 600.2 nm. How fast is the star moving along our line of sight, and is it moving toward us or away from us?

The wavelength from the source is that seen in the lab, so λ_0 equals 600.0 nm, and the wavelength from the star is that of the moving object, so λ equals 600.2 nm. The speed of light is 3.00×10^5 km/s. Therefore,

$$v = \left(\frac{\lambda - \lambda_0}{\lambda_0}\right)c = \left(\frac{600.2 \text{ nm} - 600.0 \text{ nm}}{600.0 \text{ nm}}\right)\left(3.00 \times 10^5 \frac{\text{km}}{\text{s}}\right) = \left(\frac{0.2 \text{ nm}}{600.0 \text{ nm}}\right)\left(3.00 \times 10^5 \frac{\text{km}}{\text{s}}\right)$$

$$= \left(\frac{1}{300}\right)\left(3.00 \times 10^5 \frac{\text{km}}{\text{s}}\right) = 100 \text{ km/s}.$$

Also, since the velocity is positive, the star is moving <u>away</u> from us.

The Doppler effect may also be used to discuss the thickness of the gas in the upper atmosphere of a star (which is useful for identifying the type of star), the rotational period of a star, and the temperature of the star. These are subtle effects, but still measurable in some cases. How might that look?

2. Doppler Effect and Thickness of Gas

We get one photon (particle of light) at a time when atoms change energy levels (again, look to section 14.5). We get (ideally) just one wavelength for that photon. If the atom is standing still—not completely true, granted—then that wavelength should exhibit no Doppler effect.

On the other hand, if we have a large number of photons coming from a large number of atoms, say, from a gas, the situation changes. Atoms will be moving more or less in random directions inside the gas, some coming toward us and some moving away from us. Most atoms will not have all their speeds either directly toward or away, so there will be a spread (range) of motions. The net effect is to make an otherwise very narrow spectral line and spread it out (Figure 14.8).

3. Doppler Effect and Temperature

In a similar vein, the faster individual atoms move in a star's atmosphere, the wider the spectral lines should be.

The actual situation is more complicated. To make the atoms move faster (in general), we need higher temperatures (recall the discussion on the Maxwell-Boltzmann distribution in chapter 10, "Planetary Atmospheres"). Higher

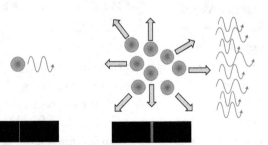

FIGURE 14.8. A relatively stationary atom emits a very narrow spectral line (left). If we have many atoms moving randomly, the net effect is to widen the spectral line (right).

temperatures also make collisions between atoms more energetic. But spectral lines only show up well over relatively narrow ranges of energies and temperatures—a spectral line that is prominent at 5,000 K will be virtually absent at 10,000 K, and so on. So, while otherwise changing the temperature should change the width of a spectral line, for stars this is actually a minor effect.

4. Doppler Effect and Rotation

The Doppler effect can also give us information as to the rate of spin (rotation) of a star. Again, from earlier, we know that atoms moving away from us will increase the observed wavelengths of their spectral lines, and atoms moving toward us will decrease the wavelengths. Compare two otherwise identical stars, one with no rotation and one with a very rapid rotation (Figure 14.9). For the non-spinning star, the width of the spectral line depends primarily on the thickness of the gas. But for the rapidly spinning star, the width of the line can include the Doppler effect from different sections of the star. The part of the star turning toward us acts like an object moving toward us, and the part of the star turning away from us acts like an object moving away from us. The result is that spinning stars have wider spectral lines than non-spinning stars.

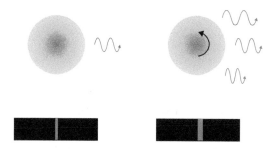

FIGURE 14.9. A star with little or no rotation has relatively narrow spectral lines (left). A rapidly spinning star has relatively wide spectral lines (right).

Like moving objects, the star's rotational axis can be tilted so that we don't see the full contribution of the Doppler effect. Also, most stars do not exhibit rapid spin; our Sun's rotational period is about 1 month on average. However, there are some stars that do rotate rapidly; Vega is an example, with a rotational period a little over 6 days long. Other stellar objects, such as neutron stars, are known to rotate hundreds of times per second; in those cases, we use other methods besides Doppler effect to study them.

Section 14.4: Black Body Radiation

We have talked much about light in this textbook, but we haven't yet discussed how light is made. In this section and the next, we look at the two most important processes in astronomy for generating light. In this section, we consider *black body* (also known as *thermal*) radiation.

Material objects (by "objects" we include thin gases as well as solids and liquids) can manipulate light in four basic ways: reflection (a.k.a. scattering), refraction (a.k.a. transmission), absorption, and emission. We discussed reflection and refraction in our first chapter about light (chapter 5), so we will not revisit them here.

Objects also emit and absorb light. If an object is able to absorb all the light that hits it (or is "incident upon" it), we label that object a "black body"; such objects also emit light in a characteristic manner according to their temperatures. This process was first extensively studied by Balfour Stewart (1828–1897) in 1858, and Gustav Kirchhoff (1824–1887) coined the term "black body" in 1862 (we will meet him again in section 14.5). A working theoretical model for black body radiation was not developed until Max Planck (1858–1947) did so in 1901, with follow-up by physicists such as Einstein.

Max Planck was born the sixth child of a family living in the duchy of Holstein, soon to be incorporated into the growing nation of Prussia, itself becoming the most important state of the new German nation in 1871. He attended a school in Munich as a teenager, where he acquired his interest in physics, and began studying physics as an undergraduate at the University of Munich in 1874. Ironically, his mentor, Phillip von Jolly, told him to avoid physics because "in this field, almost everything is discovered, and all that remains is to fill a few holes." He was appointed associate professor in theoretical physics at the University of Kiel in 1885 and moved to Berlin in 1889 as a full professor at the Friedrich-Wilhelm University. Most of his career was spent on the subjects of heat, radiation, and thermodynamics.

It was in this area that he made the breakthrough that separated what we call "classical" mechanics from quantum mechanics, though he never felt truly comfortable with many of the new theory's consequences.

Physicists up until Planck thought that light could be emitted by a thermal object at essentially any possible wavelength. Planck hit on the (then) daring notion that the wavelengths are instead restricted, introducing a new universal constant of nature he labeled "h" but we now call *Planck's constant*. This new number represents the idea that light comes in lumps or amounts of energy, which Planck labeled *quanta* (singular *quantum*).

Figure 14.11 shows the intensity (flux) of light emitted by a black body per unit wavelength. As we might expect, the taller the curve, the more light emitted. But not all wavelengths show up; there are virtually no waves emitted at very short wavelengths. The curve is not symmetric; there is a slow decrease in waves emitted at longer wavelengths. Finally, we note that the curve peaks at one particular wavelength depending on the temperature of the black body.

FIGURE 14.10. Photographs of Max Planck, c. 1930 (left); Albert Einstein, 1921 (right).

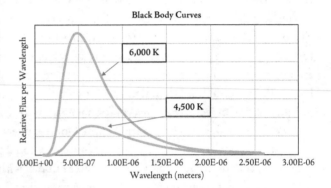

FIGURE 14.11. Black body curves for 6,000 K (taller curve) and 4,500 K (smaller curve).

Check Your Neighbor

At which temperature do we see more flux: for a black body at 4,500 K, or for a black body at 6,000 K?

Check Your Neighbor

At which temperature are we more likely to see emitting predominantly orange light: for a black body at 4,500 K, or for a black body at 6,000 K?

Planck's formula for a black body's emitted flux is fairly complicated, so we won't concern ourselves with it here (see the "Lagniappe" in the appendix if you're curious). But there are two other formulae that come in handy when describing black body objects:

1. Stefan-Boltzmann Law

The higher the surface temperature, the more energetic the light emitted by a black body. While this makes sense, the specifics were not discovered until the late 1800s by Josef Stefan (1835–1893) and Ludwig Boltzmann (1844–1906). Stefan used his work to get the first accurate estimate for the surface temperature of the Sun. A common way to express the law for astronomers is via the *Stefan-Boltzmann law*:

Equation 14.3

$$F = \sigma T^4$$

where F is the total flux emitted by the black body, T is the temperature, and σ is the "Stefan-Boltzmann constant."[7] In our calculations, we will always be interested in comparing objects to each other, and the constant will not be needed.

---

[7] The value of the Stefan-Boltzmann constant in standard physics units is $5.67 \times 10^{-8}\ \mathrm{W \cdot m^2/K^4}$.

Let's use two famous stars from the constellation of Orion to illustrate how this works. Rigel has a surface temperature of just over 12,000 K, and Betelgeuse has a surface temperature a little over 3,000 K. Assuming these numbers, how much more flux does Rigel emit compared to Betelgeuse?

Sample Calculation

In such problems, the best strategy is to take a ratio (refer to chapter 0). Note we also use subscripts liberally; for example, "F_R" can be read as the "flux emitted by Rigel" and "F_B" the "flux emitted by Betelgeuse":

$$\frac{F_R}{F_B} = \frac{\sigma T_R^4}{\sigma T_B^4} = \left(\frac{T_R}{T_B}\right)^4 = \left(\frac{12{,}000 \text{ K}}{3000 \text{ K}}\right)^4 = (4)^4 = 256$$

A small difference of temperature makes a large difference in emitted flux. Although Rigel is only four times hotter, each square patch of Rigel emits 256 times more light than an otherwise equal patch of Betelgeuse!

Check Your Neighbor

Why don't we need to use the Stefan-Boltzmann constant when comparing the fluxes of stars?

2. Wien's Law

It also makes sense that the individual waves (photons) of light carry more energy when the temperature is higher. Planck showed that while there is a spread or range of wavelengths emitted for any black body, there is also a specific wavelength, which is most common (brightest) for any specific temperature. This occurs at the top or "peak" of Planck's black body curve, so we will call this the peak wavelength. As this was discovered by Wilhelm Wien in 1893, it is commonly known as *Wien's law*:

Equation 14.4

$$\lambda_{\text{peak}} T = b$$

where T is again temperature and b is called Wien's displacement constant. We are often interested in the numerical temperature of a star, so we do use this constant in calculations; b has a value of 0.002898 m·K.

Again, an example may help. Let's continue our comparison of Rigel and Betelguese. In this case, we want to know the peak wavelength for each star. To do this, we rearrange Wien's law to solve for the wavelength:

$$\lambda_{\text{peak}} = \frac{b}{T}$$

Check Your Neighbor

In which region of the electromagnetic spectrum will we find the peak wavelength for Rigel? For Betelgeuse?

Sample Calculation

The peak wavelength for Rigel is therefore

$$\lambda_{\text{peak}} = \frac{0.002898 \text{ m·K}}{12{,}000 \text{ K}} = 2.42 \times 10^{-7} \text{ m} = 242 \text{ nm}$$

We leave it to you to show that the peak wavelength for Betelgeuse is 966 nm.

In practice, astronomers actually use spectroscopy to determine the peak wavelength of light coming from a star and use that to estimate the star's surface temperature.

3. Intrinsic Luminosity

Finally, how can we use this to describe the amount of light actually emitted by a star? We discussed the notion of luminosity earlier (section 14.2), but that was how we determine luminosity, given the flux (intensity) we receive from a star and its distance. What are the physical behaviors or properties of the star that determine its luminosity in the first place?

First, astronomers tend to assume stars are spherical in shape, due to their weight (self-gravity). This isn't always true—stars like Vega and Altair are examples showing important deviations—but it usually is, and we can adjust for those deviations on a case-by-case basis. Second, we assume the stars are black body (thermal) emitters. Again, this isn't strictly true, but also again often serves as a good first approximation.

Then the luminosity of a star depends on the emitted flux from a star—due to its surface temperature—and its surface area:

Equation 14.5

$$L = F*A = \sigma T^4 * 4\pi R^2$$

Where R is the radius of the star, and the other symbols remain as previously defined.

We can compare other stars to the Sun. The Sun's radius is 6.96×10^8 m and its surface temperature is 5,760 K. Let's try this for two famous stars: Sirius and Proxima Centauri. Note that astronomers often use the symbol "$\odot$" to stand for the Sun.

Sample Calculation

Sirius has a radius of 1.19×10^9 m, or 1.711 times the radius of the Sun, and a surface temperature of 9,940 K. What is the luminosity of Sirius compared to the Sun?

Set up the problem as the ratio of the luminosity of Sirius to the luminosity of the Sun:

$$\frac{L_S}{L_\odot} = \frac{\sigma T_S^4}{\sigma T_\odot^4} \frac{4\pi R_S^2}{4\pi R_\odot^2} = \left(\frac{T_S^4}{T_\odot^4}\right)\left(\frac{R_S^2}{R_\odot^2}\right) = \left(\frac{T_S}{T_\odot}\right)^4 \left(\frac{R_S}{R_\odot}\right)^2 = \left(\frac{9940K}{5760K}\right)^4 \left(\frac{1.711R_\odot}{R_\odot}\right)^2 \approx 26$$

or Sirius is about 26 times as luminous as the Sun. More detailed research shows that Sirius is a little bit less than that, being 25.4 solar luminosities.

Sample Calculation

In practice, stars are so far away that we can't measure their diameters directly, but instead need to calculate diameters and radii from other information. Proxima Centauri has a luminosity of $0.0017\ L_\odot$ and a temperature of 3,042 K. What is its radius, compared to that of the Sun?

To solve for the radius of Proxima, we need to rearrange the luminosity formula:

$$R = \sqrt{\frac{L}{4\pi\sigma T^4}}$$

With that, and shortening a few steps, we get

$$\frac{R_P}{R_\odot} = \sqrt{\frac{L_P}{L_\odot}\frac{4\pi\sigma T_\odot^4}{4\pi\sigma T_P^4}} = \sqrt{\frac{L_P}{L_\odot}\left(\frac{T_\odot}{T_P}\right)^4} = \sqrt{\left(\frac{0.0017}{1}\right)\left(\frac{5760}{3042}\right)^4} \approx 0.15$$

or Proxima has a radius about 15% that of the Sun. Again, more careful research shows that Proxima's radius is $0.1542\ R_\odot$.

Section 14.5: Spectral Emission and Absorption

Objects can be modeled as black body (thermal) emitters if their constituent particles are close enough together to interact with each other—that is, for objects that are solids, liquids, and/or thick gases. Examples in everyday life include hot coals, incandescent light bulbs (more specifically, the wires inside them), and even people. But what if the material is very thin, and the particles in the material are too far apart for collisions to occur between them very often? Then we can have *spectral emission* or *spectral absorption*.

The first spectroscope was invented in 1814 by Joseph von Fraunhofer (1787–1826), a German scientist. Fraunhofer was orphaned at age 11 and was apprenticed to work for a glass manufacturer. In 1801, the workshop in which he was working collapsed. The rescue was coordinated by the local prince, who thereafter took Fraunhofer under his wing, allowing him time to study. Further contacts with wealthy individuals led to his employment in a glassmaking institute in Bavaria, where he made a career of producing high-quality glass for lenses.

He turned his new instrument to the Sun and discovered hundreds of dark lines across its otherwise continuous spectrum. These are now called "Fraunhofer lines" in his honor. Modern astronomers recognize literally millions of these lines, and they are extremely useful in studying the Sun and other stars.

While Fraunhofer noted in detail spectral lines from the Sun, he had no real understanding of their origins. The rules regarding emission and absorption were developed by Gustav Kirchhoff (1824–1887), a German physicist who in collaboration with Robert Bunsen (1811–1899) discovered the elements cesium and rubidium in 1861 and brought the science of spectroscopy to new levels. One night, so the story goes, they were working in their lab when they spotted through a window a house on fire in the distance.

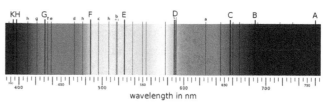

FIGURE 14.12. Fraunhofer demonstrating his spectroscope (top); absorption lines ("Fraunhofer lines") from the spectrum of the Sun (bottom).

FIGURE 14.13. Gustav Robert Kirchhoff (left) and Robert Bunsen (right).

They realized if they could orient their equipment toward the light from the fire that they could identify the substances in the fire. Then they further realized this could be done for the Sun and stars. It was Bunsen and Kirchhoff who realized Fraunhofer's dark lines in the spectrum of the Sun are due to the process of absorption.

Kirchhoff formulated three rules for spectroscopy. In modern language, they are as follows:

1. An object with a sufficiently high density will emit a continuous spectrum.
2. A low-density gas at high temperatures will emit only specific wavelengths (a "line" spectrum) dependent on the composition of the gas.

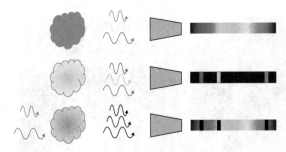

3. Sending white light through a low-density gas will produce a line absorption spectrum, also dependent on the composition of the gas.

FIGURE 14.14. Kirchhoff's rules: Sending the light from a relatively dense gas through a spectroscope produces a continuous spectrum (top); a relative thin, hot gas produces an emission spectrum (middle); light passed through a relatively thin, cool gas produces an absorption spectrum (bottom).

The usefulness of spectra cannot be overestimated in astronomy. We cannot travel to any but the closest of astronomical objects, and stars (despite science fiction) are out of reach. How then can we tell what stars are made from? Since each substance (both atoms and molecules) has its own unique sets of spectral lines, detecting these lines allows us to remotely determine the compositions of astronomical objects.

Even unknown substances can be found. Various astronomers recorded a heretofore-unknown yellow line in the spectrum of the Sun in 1868; subsequent review suggested it was a new element (not to be found on Earth until 1895), which gained the name helium, after the ancient Greek god of the Sun.

One problem remained: Why? Why does a relatively thin gas (hot or cold) show spectral lines? More generally, what is the structure of the atom, and how does it relate to spectroscopy? This mystery wasn't solved until the early 20th century.

Ernest Rutherford (1871–1937) was born in New Zealand. As part of the British Empire, Rutherford was a citizen of Great Britain and ended up at Cambridge University working in the Cavendish[8] laboratory on problems related to atomic structure. Prevailing hypotheses of the day supposed the atom to consist of a cloud of positive charge into which individual electrons were embedded (nicknamed the "plum pudding" model). Rutherford showed that the positive charges of atoms needed instead to be concentrated into an incredibly tiny space, which we now call the atomic nucleus. Rutherford's updated model then supposed the negatively charged electrons should orbit the positive nucleus, much like planets orbit the Sun.

FIGURE 14.15. Ernest Rutherford (left); Niels Bohr (right).

But another difficulty showed itself. Any accelerating electric charge—and an electron moving in an orbit certainly qualifies—emits electromagnetic radiation. The energy to create the EM waves doesn't come from nowhere; it has to come from the orbit itself. In other words, the electron should spiral into the nucleus. Calculations showed this ought to occur in about one-hundred thousandth of a second. If Rutherford was right, then atoms shouldn't be stable.

Rutherford proposed his updated model for the atom in 1911.[9] The next step in understanding atomic structure was proposed by a young Danish physicist, Niels Bohr (1885–1962). Bohr made a radical suggestion: Rather than allowing electrons to occupy any distance from the atomic nucleus, they were instead restricted to set orbital distances. Although his hypothesis did not fully explain why

---

[8] Named after Henry Cavendish, whose experiments in the late 18th century determined the value of the universal gravitational constant long described by Newton.

[9] Rutherford either conducted his own experiments or referred to the work of able assistants. Rutherford won the Nobel Prize in 1908 for his work in radioactivity (including his discovery of the concept of the half-life), and many of his former assistants won Nobel Prizes of their own.

this restriction should work, further studies by physicists such as Louie de Broglie and Erwin Schrödinger put them on solid ground.

In Bohr's model, each electron orbits the nucleus at specific "energy levels." If the electron is given more than this amount of energy, the electron escapes from its atom and the atom is ionized. Otherwise, for an electron to change its orbit, it either needs to lose or gain the exact amount of energy represented by the difference (subtraction) between the levels in question.

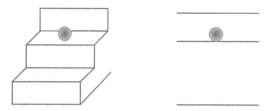

FIGURE 14.16. A ball on a step on a staircase (left). An electron at a specific energy level in an atom (right).

Bohr's specific model worked best for hydrogen and other situations that involved just one electron at a time; models for multiple numbers of electrons were in the future. The Bohr model of the hydrogen atom is best known, and in part looks like this:

Equation 14.6

$$E_n = -\frac{13.6\,\text{eV}}{n^2}$$

Equation 14.7

$$\Delta E = E_f - E_i$$

where E_n represents the energy of an electron at level n and ΔE is the change in the energy of an electron moving from initial level E_i to final level E_f. The number n can be any integer, starting at 1; the "eV" is a unit of energy called the electron-volt, and is often used for individual atoms.

Sample Calculation

Let's look at an example. Suppose an electron is at level #3 and "drops" down to level #2. What happens?

First, we find the energies of each level:

$$E_3 = -\frac{13.6\,\text{eV}}{3^2} = -1.51\,\text{eV}$$

$$E_n = -\frac{13.6\,\text{eV}}{2^2} = -3.40\,\text{eV}$$

Then subtract the two energies:

$$\Delta E = E_2 - E_3 = -3.40\,\text{eV} - (-1.51\,\text{eV}) = -1.89\,\text{eV}$$

What does this all mean?

• The negative sign implies that the electron needs to lose energy in order to drop to a lower level.

• The electron may be at a higher energy level due to this fact. But electrons aren't stable at higher levels and tend to drop down to lower levels.

• In order to shed the energy needed to drop down to a lower level, the electron emits a single photon. Electrons cannot emit two or more photons to make this happen.

• The energy difference ultimately refers to the wavelength of the photon.

Let's carry the example further by finding the wavelength of the photon emitted when an electron jumps down from level #3 to level #2. One electron-volt is equivalent to 1.6×10^{-19} joules of energy.[10] Further, Einstein found the formula describing the relationship between energy of a photon and its wavelength:

Equation 14.8

$$E = \frac{hc}{\lambda}$$

Sample Calculation

Convert the energy of the photon from electron-volts to joules:

$$1.89 \text{ eV} * \frac{1.6 \times 10^{-19} \text{ joules}}{\text{eV}} = 3.03 \times 10^{-19} \text{ J}$$

Next, rearrange the formula for the energy of a photon to solve for its wavelength:

$$\lambda = \frac{hc}{E} = \frac{(6.63 \times 10^{-34} \text{ J} \cdot \text{s})(3.00 \times 10^{8} \text{ m/s})}{3.03 \times 10^{-19} \text{ J}} = 6.56 \times 10^{-7} \text{ m} = 656 \text{ nm}$$

This wavelength is near the red end of the visible light spectrum. It turns out that several visible emission lines arise when electrons in hydrogen jump down from higher levels to level #2. Jumps to level #1 yield ultraviolet lines, and jumps to level #3 yield infrared lines.

Bohr's model also has rules for electrons jumping up levels:

+ Electrons need to gain energy in order to jump up levels.
+ Similar to downward jumps, the electron needs to gain exactly the difference in energy between the levels in question.
+ Also similarly, the electron can only absorb one photon; it cannot absorb multiple photons.
+ Finally, the energy difference again represents the wavelength of the photon.

This means that spectral lines occur at the same wavelengths for a substance, regardless of whether it is emission or absorption at work (see Figure 14.14).

How does this work for stars? Typically, light from deeper within a star passes through surrounding gas that is relatively cooler, so most spectra observed from stars show continuous spectra with absorption lines superimposed on them. Linking the absorption (or emission) lines to the amounts of a substance present in a star is a more complicated story—and one that needs to wait for another chapter.

An interesting postscript regarding Bohr: Next to Einstein, Bohr was the most famous physicist in the world in the days leading up to World War II. When the Nazis threatened to invade Denmark, Bohr had to leave quickly or be captured. After a harrowing crossing of the North Sea to neutral Sweden, Bohr boarded a British bomber for the journey to safety. Bohr hid in the bombardier's bubble on the bottom of the plane. The plane soared so high that the crew needed to don oxygen masks. However, the bubble was separate from the rest of the plane, meaning that once sealed, the crew couldn't communicate with him. Nor could Bohr put on his communication headset, for the simple reason that his head was too large! Bohr passed out from lack of oxygen, but fortunately revived quickly upon landing.

---

[10] To put the joule in perspective, one food calorie is equivalent to about 4200 joules.

Summary

In this chapter, we did the following:

- Reviewed evidence showing light behaves as a wave
- Reviewed evidence showing light behaves as a particle
- Investigated the inverse square law behavior of light intensity (flux)
- Displayed the Doppler effect and discussed several uses of it
- Introduced black body radiation and discussed several aspects of it
- Described how spectral lines are made
- Reviewed the Bohr model of the atom

Questions

1. The Sirius system has a radial velocity of –5.50 km/s (this is typical of neighboring stars). Assume we observe its red emission line from hydrogen, which occurs at 656 nm in the lab. How much of a change in wavelength will we see?

2. A special class of stars, called "hypervelocity stars," has been discovered in recent years that have extremely fast speeds. Star SDSS J09075.0+024507 shows a change of wavelength of 1.55 nm (i.e., the wavelength becomes larger) for an emission line of hydrogen compared to the same emission line in the lab. How fast is this star moving?

3. Given the surface temperature of Betelgeuse is about 3,000 K, estimate its peak wavelength.

4. The peak wavelength seen from the Sun is approximately at 500 nm. What is the approximate surface temperature of the Sun?

5. Earlier in this chapter, we looked at the luminosity of Sirius. Sirius is actually a binary system, and our calculations were for the brighter of the two objects, called Sirius A. Its companion, Sirius B, is a class of object called a white dwarf, and it has a temperature of 25,000 K and a radius of 0.0084 $R_\odot$. Find the luminosity of Sirius B compared to that of the Sun.

6. A giant star and a dwarf star have the same surface temperature, but the giant has a luminosity 10,000 times that of the dwarf star. How much larger in radius is the giant (as a ratio) compared to the dwarf?

7. Find the energy and wavelength for a transition of an electron from level #2 to level #1 in a hydrogen atom. What part of the electromagnetic spectrum is this?

8. Find the energy and wavelength for a transition of an electron from level #4 to level #3 in a hydrogen atom. What part of the electromagnetic spectrum is this?

Activities

- *Astrophysics activity 14.1:* Examine selected wave properties of light through demonstrations and simulations.
- *Astrophysics activity 14.2:* Witness how light is generated via simulations.
- *Astrophysics activity 14.3:* Examine selected particle properties of light through demonstrations and simulations.
- Reproduce Olaus Roemer's measurement of the speed of light using the moons of Jupiter. This is a project that would require several months.

Works Referenced

Discussions regarding the wave nature of light are found in the following sources:

Aufdenberg J. P., Coude de Foreseto, E., Di Folco, E., Ridgway, S. T., Brummelaar, T. A, Sturmann, J. ... & Sturmann, L. (2006). First results from the CHARA Array. VII: Long-baseline interferometric measurements of Vega consistent with a pole-on, rapidly-rotating star? *Astrophysical Journal*, 645(1), 664–675. doi:10.1086/504149

Huygens, C. (1690/2005). *Treatise on light* [E-book]. http://www.gutenberg.org/ebooks/14725

Newton, I., Sir. (1704/2010). *Opticks, or a treatise of the reflections, refractions, inflections and colours of light* [E-book]. https://www.gutenberg.org/files/33504/33504-h/33504-h.htm

Discussions regarding the particle nature of light are found in the following sources:

Mehra, J., & Rechenberg, H. (1982). *The historical development of quantum theory*. New York, NY: Springer.

Planck, M. (1914). *The theory of heat radiation*. http://www.gutenberg.org/ebooks/40030

Stefan, J. (n.d.). On the relationship between thermal radiation and temperature. *Proceedings of the Imperial Philosophical Society [of Vienna]: Mathematical and Scientific Class (in German)*. 79: 391-428. https://babel.hathitrust.org/cgi/pt?id=hvd.32044093294874;view=1up;seq=419

Stewart, B. (1858), An account of some experiments on radiant heat. *Transactions of the Royal Society of Edinburgh*, 22(1), 1–20.

Data for individual stars comes from the following sources:

Adelman, S. J. (2005, March 2). The physical properties of normal A stars. *Proceedings of the International Astronomical Union*. doi:10.1017/S1743921304004314

Doyle, J. G., & Butler, C. J. (1990). Optical and infrared photometry of dwarf M and K stars. *Astronomy & Astrophysics*, 235(1–2), 335–339.

Liebert, J., Young, P. A., Arnett, D., Holberg, J. B., & Williams, K. A. (2005). The age and progenitor mass of Sirius B. *Astrophysical Journal*, 630(1), L69–L72. doi:10.1086/462419

Kervella, P., Thévenin, F., & Lovis, C. (2017). Proxima's orbit around α Centauri. *Astronomy & Astrophysics*, 598(L7). doi:10.1051/0004-6361/201629930

Ségransan, D., Kervella, P., Forveille, TT., & Queloz, D. (2003). First radius measurements of very low mass stars with the VLTI. *Astronomy & Astrophysics*, 397(3), L5–L8. doi:10.1051/0004-6361:20021714

Applications of spectroscopy are discussed in the following sources:

Jensen, W. B. (2005). The origin of the Bunsen burner. *Journal of Chemical Education*, 82(4), 518.

NobelPrize.org. (n.d.). *Ernest Rutherford: Biography*. https://www.nobelprize.org/prizes/chemistry/1908/summary/

Rines, G. E. (Ed.). (1920). Fraunhofer, Joseph von. *Encyclopedia Americana*. https://en.wikisource.org/wiki/The_Encyclopedia_Americana_(1920)/Fraunhofer,_Joseph_von

Credits

Fig. 14.12a: Source: https://commons.wikimedia.org/wiki/File:Fraunhofer_spectroscope.JPG.

Fig. 14.12b: Source: https://commons.wikimedia.org/wiki/File:Fraunhofer_lines.svg.

Fig. 14.13: Source: https://commons.wikimedia.org/wiki/File:Bunsen-Kirchhoff.jpg.

Fig. 14.14: Source: https://commons.wikimedia.org/wiki/File:Spectral-lines-continuous.svg.

Fig. 14.15a: Source: https://commons.wikimedia.org/wiki/File:Ernest_Rutherford_LOC.jpg.

Fig. 14.15b: Source: https://commons.wikimedia.org/wiki/File:Niels_Bohr.jpg.

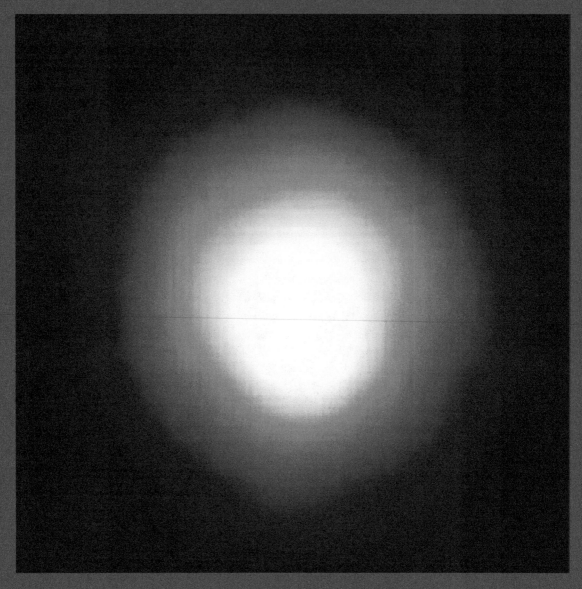

A close-up view of Betelgeuse from the Hubble Space Telescope. Betelgeuse is one of the few stars for which we can directly image its shape. Credit: HST/NASA.

CHAPTER 15

INTRODUCTION TO STARS

To review observational properties of stars

OBJECTIVES

- To introduce the astronomical magnitude system
- To describe spectral types
- To use the HR diagram to analyze star properties
- To review luminosity classes
- To review classes of variable stars
- To compare galactic with globular clusters
- To briefly describe binary systems

INTRODUCTION

Stars appear to be points of light on a distant smooth background. What can we learn from points of light?

Plenty, it turns out. We have already looked at how we can estimate items such as their distances, velocities, temperatures, and compositions, for starters. Here, we begin reviewing what astronomers have discovered and how they organize their findings.

KEY TERMS

Absolute magnitude: How bright a star really is. Related to a star's luminosity

Apparent magnitude: How bright a star appears. Related to a star's observed flux

Astronomical unit (or au): The average distance from the Earth to the Sun. Set at a specific number in 2012

Binary system: A system where two stars are in mutual orbit about each other

Cepheid variable: The most useful class of variable star for determining distances to galaxies

Cluster (also **stellar cluster**): A large grouping of stars (anywhere from hundreds to tens of thousands) that were formed at approximately the same time

Color index: The comparison of a star's apparent magnitude in different colored filters, the most common being blue and yellow (visible)

Color-magnitude diagram: A version of the HR diagram that uses color index instead of temperature on its horizontal axis

Contact binary: A binary system where the two stars mutually exchange material

Detached binary: A binary system where the two stars are far enough apart that they do not exchange material

Galactic (or open) cluster: A grouping of stars, usually several hundred to several thousand. Also relatively young and living in the disk of the galaxy

Globular cluster: A grouping of stars, usually tens to hundreds of thousands. Also relatively old and living in the halo of the galaxy

Flux (observed or received): The amount of power per unit area observed

HR diagram (or Hertzsprung-Russell diagram): A graph of surface temperatures versus luminosities, used to organize and categorize stars

Luminosity: The amount of power emitted by a star

Luminosity class: Primarily the different stages of stellar life cycles

Roche limit: The closest point a small object can get to a larger object before the gravity tides of the larger object tear it apart

Roche lobe: A volume of space surrounding a large mass that is dominated by its gravity. Usually discussed in relation to binary stars

Semi-detached binary: A binary system where one star spills over its Roche lobe into that of its companion and material is pulled from it to its companion

Spectral type: Sorting stars by surface temperatures, according to their spectral lines

Spectroscopic parallax: A method whereby astronomers use the spectral types and luminosity classes of stars to estimate their distances

Zero-Age main sequence (or ZAMS): The diagonal formed on the HR diagram by stars when they first achieve sustained hydrogen fusion upon forming

KEY INDIVIDUALS

Cannon, Annie Jump: An American astronomer from the late 19th/early 20th century who helped devise spectral types

Draper, Henry: An American astronomer who began the process of categorizing stars in the late 19th century

Hertzsprung, Ejnar: A Danish astronomer who, along with Henry Norris Russell, conceived in the early 20th century the HR diagram, a graph that helps astronomers classify stars

Hipparchus: An ancient Greek astronomer who (among many other discoveries) suggested a scheme for relating star brightnesses to each other

Leavitt, Henrietta Swan: An American astronomer from the early 20th century who found the period-luminosity relationship for Cepheid variables

Payne-Gaposhkin (nee Payne), Cecilia: An English-American astronomer from the early 20th century who determined the composition of stars

Pickering, Edward: An American astronomer who conducted the project that cataloged stars according to their spectra in the late 19th/early 20th century

Pogson, Norman: A British astronomer from the mid-19th century who put the magnitude system on a firm mathematical basis

Roche, Edouard: A French astronomer of the mid-18th century who worked on celestial mechanics and the effects of gravity between stars in binary systems

Russell, Henry Norris: An American astronomer who, along with Ejnar Hertzsprung, conceived in the early 20th century the HR diagram, a graph that helps astronomers classify stars

Section 15.1: Stellar Magnitudes

Stars appear to us as points of light of varying brightnesses. How do astronomers express star brightnesses?

The first person to suggest a system of comparing stars to each other in this way (so far as we can tell) was Hipparchus. It seems that he ranked stars according to their relative brightnesses—the brightest nighttime stars were of the first rank, or "magnitude,"[1] stars noticeably dimmer but still relatively

---

[1] The word "magnitude" shares the same root as "magnificent," meaning kingly.

bright otherwise were of the second magnitude, and so on down to sixth magnitude, which were the dimmest stars of all. However, without modern recording equipment, star brightnesses were largely a matter of opinion.

In 1856, the English astronomer Norman Pogson advocated placing the magnitude system on a solid mathematical basis. His suggestions were as follows:

- Extend the magnitude numbers. Positive numbers larger than 6 refer to stars too dim to see with the naked eye. Stars with negative numbers refer to brighter stars (Figure 15.1)
- Vega, one of the brightest stars in the night sky, marks "zero" magnitude. This obviously doesn't mean Vega has no brightness; rather, it acts to anchor the magnitude numbers, much like 0 °C as the freezing point of water acts in the Celsius temperature scale
- Comparing magnitudes is done by subtracting their numbers
- A difference (subtraction) of 5 magnitudes is exactly equivalent to a factor (multiplicative) of 100 in brightness. Other differences in magnitudes can be interpolated (see Table 15.1)

Check Your Neighbor

Star A has a magnitude of +2 and Star B has a magnitude of –2. Which star is brighter?

Check Your Neighbor

Star C has a magnitude of +1 and Star D has a magnitude of +6. Which star is brighter, and by how much in terms of ratios?

Consider this: Two stars appear to be identical in terms of brightness. Are they both really the same brightness? For the moment, the answer is that we can't tell. It could be true; more likely, one star really is brighter than the other, but it is also farther away.

Astronomers therefore separate magnitudes into two categories. One type refers to the received flux (or received intensity) and is called *apparent magnitude*: how bright the star appears to be. But apparent magnitude depends on the distance to the star—the farther the star, the dimmer it will appear. Astronomers are more interested in the "real" or actual or intrinsic brightness of a star, which astronomers call luminosity or *absolute magnitude.*

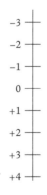

FIGURE 15.1. The astronomical magnitude system, arranged like a number line. Note that negative numbers are at the top, reflecting the idea that the more negative a magnitude, the brighter the star.

TABLE 15.1. Meanings of Magnitudes

Difference of Magnitudes	Brightness Factor
1	2.5
2	6.25
3	16
4	40
5	100
6	?

How do astronomers then compare apparent and absolute magnitudes? We make use of the parsec. Suppose we could move a star until it is exactly 10 parsecs away (chapter 13 discusses the origin of the parsec as a unit of distance). By definition, the apparent magnitude of a star at 10 pc is the same as its absolute magnitude.

Sample Calculation

Elnath is the second-brightest star in the constellation of Taurus the Bull. It has an apparent magnitude of about +1.7 and an absolute magnitude of about –1.3. How far away is Elnath?

We can solve this in a series of steps:

1. Find the difference in magnitudes
2. Find the brightness factor
3. Take the square root of the brightness factor[2]
4. Multiply the result by 10 pc

For Elnath, we have the following:

1. Difference in magnitudes = 1.7 – (–1.3) = **3.0**
2. From Table 16.1, we see the brightness factor for 3 magnitudes is **16**
3. The square root of 16 is **4**
4. 4 times 10 pc equals 40 pc

Most numbers for magnitudes don't work out so cleanly. Astronomers have a formula for relating apparent magnitudes, absolute magnitudes, and distances:

Equation 15.1

$$d(\text{pc}) = 10^{\frac{1}{5}(m-M+5)}$$

where m represents the apparent magnitude and M the absolute magnitude.

Sample Calculation

Let's find the distance to Elnath again, using the distance formula:

$$d = 10^{\frac{1}{5}(1.7-[-1.3]+5)} = 10^{\frac{1}{5}(8)} = 10^{1.6} \approx 40 \text{ pc}$$

---

[2] Recall the inverse square law behavior of light from a point source (see chapter 14).

What if we have the distance to a star (perhaps measured by trig parallax) and its apparent magnitude and now wish to find its absolute magnitude? We can either reverse-engineer the process or use the distance formula. The following passages show an example:

Sample Calculation

Acrux is the brightest star in the constellation of Crux, aka the Southern Cross. It has an apparent magnitude approximately of +0.8 and is about 100 pc away. What is its absolute magnitude?

Reverse-engineer the steps used earlier:

1. Divide the distance by 10 pc
2. Square the result to get the brightness factor
3. Get the difference in magnitudes from the brightness factor
4. Add or subtract the difference (as needed) to get the absolute magnitude

In the case of Acrux, we have the following:

1. 100 pc/10 pc = 10
2. The square of 10 is 100
3. A brightness factor of 100 is equivalent to a difference of 5 magnitudes
4. Acrux is farther away than 10 pc, so subtract the difference: +8 − 5.0 = −4.2

We can also rearrange the distance formula to solve for the absolute magnitude:

Equation 15.2

$$M = m + 5 - 5\log(d)$$

where $\log(d)$ is the base-10 logarithm of the distance expressed in parsecs.

Sample Calculation

Find the absolute magnitude of Acrux using the absolute magnitude formula:

$$M = +0.8 + 5 - 5\log(100) = +0.8 + 5 - 5(2) = +0.8 + 5 - 10 = +0.8 - 5 = -4.2$$

Section 15.2: Spectral Types

Stars not only can be identified by their brightnesses, but also their colors (recall we discussed both blackbody [thermal] radiation and spectral radiation in chapter 14). Each star shows both a general spectrum due to its temperature and (mostly) absorption lines due to the presence of various elements in its upper atmosphere. Astronomers categorize stars today due to both of these features.

The story of the modern astronomical system for classifying stars according to spectral lines started with an American astronomer named Henry Draper (1837–1882), who we briefly introduced in chapter 14. Draper had several interests, and worked as a medical doctor initially, but gave up his position at New York University in

1873 to pursue astronomy full time. Draper was one of the pioneers in astrophotography, recording both images of objects and spectra of stars, accomplishing this first in 1872.

Draper unfortunately died young from double-pleurisy. His widow and collaborator, Mary Anna, came from a wealthy family and donated funds for a medal (given out roughly every 4 years by the U.S. National Academy of Sciences) for excellence in astrophysics, and for a project centered at Harvard University for the cataloging of stars. This work ultimately formed the Henry Draper catalog, and many stars are still known to astronomers by their HD catalog numbers.

FIGURE 15.2. Henry Draper (left); Mary Anna Palmer Draper (center); Edward Charles Pickering (right).

The head of the project at Harvard Observatory was Edward Charles Pickering (1846–1919). He took over the operation of the observatory in 1877 until his death in 1919. His largest personal contribution was to devise a method for photographing many stellar spectra simultaneously, greatly shortening the time and effort required to record them. With Carl Vogel, he was the first to detect binary star systems via spectroscopy (see chapter 14). He also had communications with physicists that helped Niels Bohr develop his ideas regarding atomic structure.

But his most important work was the heading of the Draper project, and to that effect he gathered a pool of impressive astronomers. In the days before computers and digital photography, astronomers needed ways to make detailed observations and calculations regarding the wealth of spectroscopic data pouring in. Often, young women who otherwise were shut out of the field of astronomy due to their gender were hired as human computers to do the detail work necessary. They received much less than their due at the time, but we know recognize the incredible work they did:

- Williamina Fleming, Antonia Maury, and Annie Jump Cannon: They helped devise the modern system of spectral types. Cannon was particularly renowned for her abilities to analyze a spectrum; she identified about 350,000 stars during her career.
- Henrietta Swan Leavitt: She discovered a relationship for Cepheid variable stars (introduced in chapter 13) between their average luminosities and their periods of variation.
- Cecilia Payne-Gaposchkin (whose work was published after Pickering's death): She put the spectral type system on a physical basis, using the then-new science of atomic physics developed by Bohr, and showed that stars are primarily made out of hydrogen and helium.

Women were rarely, if ever, allowed to earn Ph.D. degrees or hold important positions in astronomy at the time, and the "computers" were paid far less than male counterparts.[3] In fact, women were not allowed to handle telescopes or like equipment, and were instead relegated to data analysis. Research papers tended to be published

---

[3] To give a flavor of attitudes of the time, the "computers" were also referred to as "Pickering's Harem."

under the names of Pickering or other male astronomers at Harvard Observatory. Today, though, we are better aware of their contributions, and it could be argued that many of them deserved Nobel Prizes for their efforts.[4]

Initially, stars were typed according to the strength of their hydrogen spectra. Hydrogen is the simplest element, and its spectral accordingly is also relatively simple. The computers found hydrogen spectra in virtually every star, though the relative strengths of the hydrogen lines[5] differed enormously from star to star. Stars were thus labeled type "A" if they showed the strongest hydrogen lines, type "B" if the lines were still very strong but not quite as strong as type "A" stars, and so on down the alphabet.

Upon learning that the lines double as a temperature scale of sorts, Cannon eliminated most of the letters as repetitious and reorganized them in the order which we use today: O, B, A, F, G, K, and M. Modern astronomers have updated and extended the letters, but the basic system remains in use.

Annie Jump Cannon's story is worth a moment. Cannon (1863–1941) was the daughter of Wilson Cannon, a shipbuilder and state senator in Delaware, and his second wife, Mary Jump. Mary encouraged Annie's interest in astronomy and pushed her to attend college—first at Wilmington Conference Academy (now Wesley College) and then Wellesley College. At some point in childhood or early adulthood, Cannon lost most of her hearing (scarlet fever is suspected, but not confirmed), which appears to have limited her socially; rather than marrying and raising children, she instead devoted herself to her work.

FIGURE 15.3. The Harvard "computers," outside of Building C at Harvard College Observatory, in 1913.

FIGURE 15.4. Annie Jump Cannon in 1922 (left); the most common mnemonic used to remember the sequence of spectral types (right).

Upon her mother's death in 1894, Cannon reconnected with her mentor at Wellesley, Sarah Frances Whiting, one of the few women physicists of the day, and became a junior physics teacher (what we might call an "adjunct instructor" today). This led to Cannon taking graduate-level courses in astronomy at Wellesley and later Radcliff College. Male professors from nearby Harvard would give lectures to the female students at Radcliff, and Cannon was hired by Pickering to be an assistant at Harvard Observatory in 1896. Cannon later earned a master's degree from Wellesley in 1907 and was awarded multiple honorary doctorates during her life. Cannon published a catalog of stellar spectra in 1901, and her system of stellar classification was adopted by the International Astronomical Union in

[4] To be fair, astronomy was not considered part of physics in the early decades of the Nobel Prize, and no prizes were awarded for primarily astronomical discoveries until Hans Bethe in 1967 for fusion processes in stars.

[5] Specifically, the hydrogen lines seen in the visible portion of the electromagnetic spectrum, also known as the Balmer lines or Balmer series.

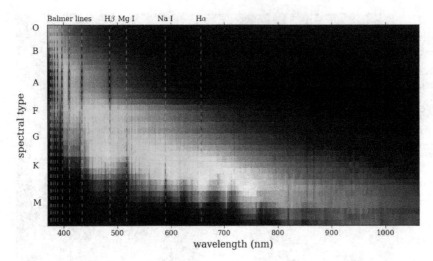

FIGURE 15.5. A sample of spectral types, O through M (other letters used for special cases are not shown). The dark lines in type A are due to hydrogen; note how they become fainter as one gets further from the letter A.

1922 with only minor changes. The American Astronomical Society annually presents the Annie Jump Cannon award each year to female astronomers for distinguished work in astronomy.

What did Cannon find? The Harvard classification system is actually a temperature scale, starting with the hottest stars at letter O and moving downward in temperature until reaching the coolest stars at letter M. It is worth noting that this (a) refers specifically to surface temperatures, not that of interiors of stars and that (b) even an M star is hot by our standards—around 3,000 K, or close to 6,000°F.

Astronomers further subdivide each spectral type letter for finer categorization. For example, B stars range from B0 (the hottest among B stars) to B9 (the coolest). The numbers then roll over; the next spectral type after B9 is not B10, but rather A0.

Different spectral lines are prominent for different types. As already stated, hydrogen is most prevalent in type A and B stars, but type O stars show helium instead and type M stars are cool enough to have molecules in their upper atmospheres. Table 15.2 shows approximate temperatures for various spectral types.

TABLE 15.2. Properties of Spectral Types

Color Index	Spectral Type	Temperature (K)	Color
−0.29	B0	33,000	Blue
0.00	A0	10,000	White
+0.31	F0	7,500	White
+0.59	G0	6,000	Yellow
+0.82	K0	5,200	Orange
+1.41	M0	3,700	Red

You may notice quickly that the table includes a number called "color index." Astronomers, for various reasons, often use colored filters to take images of objects. Common filters are labeled "V" (for visible light, centered more or less on yellow), "B" for blue, "R" for red, and so on. Filters are even used for the near ultraviolet ("U") and infrared ("I"). The apparent magnitude of a star can be measured in different filters. Because the filters let astronomers observe light in different sections of their black body spectrum, comparing the magnitudes from different filters gives us another method of expressing a star's temperature. The most commonly used comparison is blue versus visible, and since magnitudes are logarithmic, the comparisons are done via subtraction: "B − V," for example. This comparison is called the star's color index.

Check Your Neighbor

We stated that apparent magnitudes are used to compute color indexes. Would it make any difference if we used absolute magnitudes? Why or why not?

Section 15.3: The HR Diagram and Luminosity Classes

By the beginning of the 20th century, astrophotography had been in use for several decades, and astronomers had gathered large amounts of data for stars on quantities such as distances, luminosities and temperatures. Attempts were being made to make sense out of it all (like spectral types in the previous section). The next breakthrough came about from two astronomers working separately in different countries.

In 1905, a Danish astronomer named Ejnar Hertzsprung (1873–1967) published a tabulation of star luminosities and temperatures, indicating a link between them for most (not all) of the stars. By 1910, working independently, the American astronomer Henry Norris Russell at Princeton University began graphing these two variables for stars. Today, we credit both men by titling the result the Hertzsprung-Russell diagram, or *HR Diagram* for short (Figure 15.7):

FIGURE 15.6. Left: Karl Schwarzschild and Ejnar Hertzsprung; right: Henry Norris Russell.

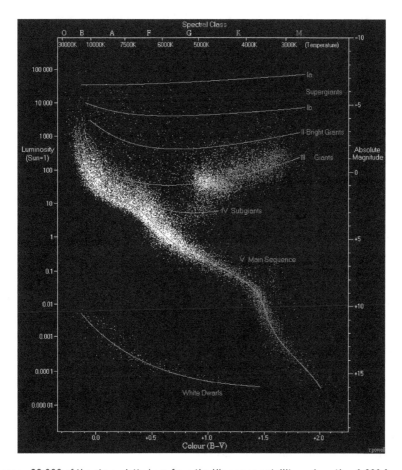

FIGURE 15.7. The HR Diagram. 22,000 of the stars plotted are from the Hipparcos satellite and another 1,000 from the Gliese Catalog of Nearby Stars. Luminosity is on the vertical axis, increasing going up, and temperature is on the horizontal axis, increasing going left.

The first item that should jump out is that stars are not randomly arranged on the graph. The vast majority of stars in our galaxy, 90%, are on the section labeled "Main Sequence." Most of the rest are in the section labeled "Giants," with a few in the "Supergiants" or "White Dwarfs" regions. The main sequence, of particular interest since most stars "live" there, forms a diagonal, more or less, from the upper left to the lower right of the diagram. There is a thin bridge between the main sequence and the giants (called, though not labeled on the diagram, "Sub-Giants"), and astronomers often refer to the region containing giants as the "giant branch."

For the main sequence stars, at least, it is relatively easy, in hindsight, to see why they should behave this way. The more mass a star has, the higher the temperature it needs in order to support itself against its own weight; furthermore, the more massive a star, the larger across it will be. Recall a star's luminosity depends on both its temperature and radius (see chapter 14).

Equation 15.3

$$L = \sigma T^4 4\pi R^2$$

With both effects in play, the higher the mass, the more toward the upper left a star will be on the main sequence; conversely, the lower the mass, the more toward the lower right a star will be. Other types of stars behave differently, so they are not along the diagonal. Telling the stories for all the various types of stars will be our task for the next several chapters.

More items of note about the HR diagram:

+ Both axes are logarithmic; that is, they go as powers of ten. It's more obvious on the vertical scale in Figure 15.7, where one side explicitly shows this; it's perhaps not as easy to see on the horizontal axis, since the range of temperatures is much less than the range of luminosities, but powers of ten are also in use there.
+ Luminosity increases going up the vertical scale.
+ Temperature increases going to the <u>left</u> on the horizontal scale. This is opposite how most graphs are presented, so it takes time to get used to it.
+ Instead of luminosity, absolute magnitude is sometimes used on the vertical scale. Apparent magnitude is not used unless the stars are at the same distance from us, as happens for clusters of stars.
+ Instead of temperature, spectral type is often used on the horizontal scale. Since O stars are the hottest and M the coolest, the traditional order (see the previous section) is retained. Color index is also used, since it is an equivalent for temperature and spectral type. When magnitudes and color indexes are used together, astronomers often refer to that as a color-magnitude diagram.
+ The "Main Sequence" is not an actual sequence; stars, for example, do not move up or down along the diagonal during their lives. The name has historical roots, and is just one of those terms (like "planetary nebula") that is still in use even though the bare words do not convey the proper meaning.
+ On the other hand, "Giants" are actually gigantic (it is common for a giant to be 100 or more times larger across than the Sun), "Supergiants" are actually super gigantic, and white dwarfs are both white in color to the naked eye and small in radius.

This last point is worth a longer discussion. Titles such as "Giants" and "Main Sequence" are separate from spectral types. Spectral types are ultimately an expression of the effective surface temperatures of stars. But stars in different sections of the HR diagram can have the same temperatures. Another way to classify stars is needed to express these differences, which primarily reflect different life stages for stars. Since these stages tend to manifest as differing luminosities, we call them *luminosity classes*.

Luminosity classes are from the Yerkes spectral classification scheme, named for the observatory where it was devised, or the MKK scheme, after its authors (William Wilson Morgan, Phillip C. Keenan, and Edith

Kellman). The original version was proposed in 1943, revised in 1953, and essentially remains the same today.

Different luminosity classes tend to represent different life stages of stars; a "normal" star is a part of the main sequence and is labeled a "Dwarf," whereas sub-giants and giants are older stars. Super-giants are their own category, due to their excessive masses (about 10 $M_{\odot}$ or more); a rare category of older stars is labeled sub-dwarfs (they have different mixes of elements than other stars); and white dwarfs are no longer really stars, but represent the remnants of dead stars. Each luminosity class comes with a Roman numeral (see Table 15.3), and astronomers combine both spectral types and luminosity classes when discussing stars.

TABLE 15.3. Properties of Luminosity Classes

Luminosity class	Description
0 (or 1a+)	hypergiants
1a	luminous supergiants
1ab	intermediate-size luminous supergiants
1b	less luminous supergiants
II	bright giants
III	giants
IV	sub-giants
V	main sequence stars, a.k.a. dwarfs
VI	sub-dwarfs
wd (or D or VII)	white dwarfs

We can take a second look at the HR diagram now (Figure 15.8), identifying the various luminosity classes.

Section 15.4: Abundances of the Elements

By the 1910s, spectral lines had been used to categorize stars by temperature for years, and the new HR diagram was helping further organize them by luminosity. But despite the known connection between spectroscopy and substance (i.e., atom or molecule), the abundances of the elements in stars was an open question. This issue was to be settled by Cecilia Payne.

Cecilia Payne (1900–1979) was one of three children born to a Prussian mother and an English father, who unfortunately died when she was only 4 years old. She won a scholarship to Newnham College, Cambridge University, in 1919, where she studied various sciences. During her time at Cambridge, she attended a lecture by the famous astronomer Arthur Eddington regarding his observations of the total solar eclipse of 1919 that provided evidence for Einstein's general theory of relativity. This inspired her to pursue astronomy; however,

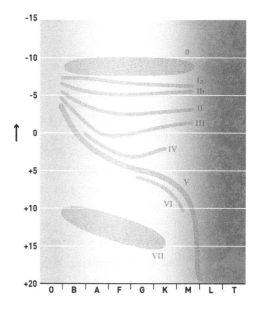

FIGURE 15.8. Another version of the HR diagram, showing luminosity classes. Refer to Table 15.3 for the meanings of the Roman numerals.

Cambridge did not award degrees to women at the time (they would only begin to do so in 1948), so she immigrated to the United States in 1923 on a fellowship provided by Harvard College Observatory. There she entered a newly created graduate degree program under the supervision of the new observatory director, Harlow Shapley.

FIGURE 15.9. Cecilia Payne (later Payne-Gaposhkin) c. 1920.

Shapley encouraged Payne to pursue a Ph.D. Payne applied the then-new findings regarding ionization[6] by the Indian physicist Meghnad Saha to the study of absorption lines in stars. She was able to account for how the wide variety of spectral lines were produced; more importantly, she found that hydrogen and helium are easily the two most popular elements in stars—and, by implication, the entire universe. The discovery was so unexpected that Henry Norris Russell suggested she downplay the result in her Ph.D. Russell later retracted this 4 years later when it became apparent that the result was real.

Payne earned her Ph.D. in 1925 but was still considered merely a "technical assistant" until Shapley convinced Harvard to give her the title of "astronomer" in 1938. Cecilia Payne became a U.S. citizen in 1931 and met her future husband, Sergei Gaposchkin, on a European tour in 1933. Together they (and their assistants) cataloged millions of variable stars in both the Milky Way and its satellite galaxies, the Large and Small Magellanic Clouds. Payne-Gaposchkin won the status of full professor at Harvard in 1956, the first woman to be so titled at Harvard, and eventually was appointed to the chair of the Department of Astronomy at Harvard, also a first for a woman.

What is the importance of her research? It is now a commonplace teaching in astronomy that the universe consists of 99% hydrogen and helium by number, with all other elements making up approximately 1% of all matter. This was shocking to the establishment in 1925. Like Annie Jump Cannon, had she lived in our era, it is likely she would have been awarded a Nobel Prize for her work.

Section 15.5: Uses of the HR Diagram

Astronomers view the HR diagram similarly to how chemists view the periodic table—as a diagram or picture or graph that helps us organize our knowledge. Knowing the spectral type and luminosity class of a star, or looking at the HR diagram of a cluster of stars, will tell us all sorts of general properties, including distances or even the ages of stars.

1. The Zero-Age Main Sequence (ZAMS)

Upon completing their formation process, a star settles on a specific position on the HR diagram. As time goes by, the star will change slightly due to its using up of its supply of hydrogen fuel in its core, and so it will (very slowly and slightly) shift away from its original position. A large number of stars with a variety of masses will land on different positions, all together making up a main sequence. While we will explore these changes more fully in future chapters, for now we can refer to this as the original, or "zero-age," main sequence. The zero-age main sequence, or ZAMS, graph, is a theoretical construct based on what astronomers know concerning how stars form and generate energy.

---

[6] "Ionization" is the process by which one or more electrons are stripped off a neutral atom. This is easy to produce when temperatures are very high, as is the case for the upper atmospheres of stars.

How is the ZAMS generated? Astronomers combine observations with models of how efficiently stars produce energy according to their masses. By and large, the more massive a star, the harder it has to work to hold itself up (via gas pressure) against its own weight. The simplest models suggest that the luminosity of a star goes as the 3.5 power (i.e., $L \sim M^{3.5}$), meaning that even a slightly larger star will require a much larger luminosity. More sophisticated models modify that idea somewhat, but the general theme holds true. We need to emphasize that this relationship between mass and luminosity works for main sequence stars only; other luminosity classes have different behaviors.

Figure 15.10 shows both mass-luminosity relation and zero-age main sequence graphs. The scales on the vertical and horizontal axes for both graphs are logarithmic (powers of ten) in order to better understand the results. Remember that temperature, expressed as color index, increases to the left on the ZAMS graph.

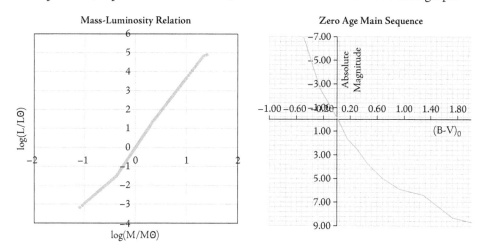

FIGURE 15.10. The relationship between mass and luminosity for main sequence stars (left); the zero-age main sequence (right).

These are important results. They show that the key property of a main sequence star is its mass; that is, the mass of the star determines where it lands on the HR diagram. Furthermore, all manner of star properties—not just temperature and luminosity, but radius, color, lifespan and even the relative numbers of stars—are primarily determined by mass. We will explore some of these issues next and delve into the role of mass more fully in the next chapter.

2. Spectroscopic Parallax

Currently astronomers can reliably determine distances to stars via trig parallax out to 1,000 parsecs or so, as the parallax angles become too small to measure with precision. How then can we discuss distances to stars further away than that? Or, equivalently, is there another dependable way to estimate star distances? One method is nicknamed *spectroscopic parallax*.

It will help to do an example. Taygeta is a main sequence star and one of the "7 Sisters" of the Pleiades cluster. Observations show Taygeta has a color index (B-V) of −0.11 and an apparent magnitude of +4.3. Looking at the zero-age main sequence graph (Figure 15.10), we see that a star with a color index of −0.11 should have an absolute magnitude of −1.2. Then the distance to Taygeta is

$$d(\mathrm{pc}) = 10^{\frac{1}{5}(m-M+5)} = 10^{\frac{1}{5}(4.3-(-1.2)+5)} = 10^{2.1} = 130 \, \mathrm{pc}$$

A recent measurement via geometric means suggests the distance to the Pleiades cluster is 132 pc.

How exactly was this done? Recall the discussion regarding the zero-age main sequence graph. By measuring the color index (or surface temperature, or spectral type) of a main sequence star, we can use the ZAMS graph to estimate the star's absolute magnitude. We can then combine the absolute magnitude of the star with its apparent magnitude to calculate its distance. Note that the term "spectroscopic parallax" is a bit misleading; while the spectrum of a star is used, parallax is not. Similar considerations (though not "zero age," of course) can be used for other luminosity classes.

3. Stellar Clusters

The ZAMS graph can also be used to estimate distances to stars if they belong to a cluster. Let's try this for two separate clusters, the Pleiades and M3.

The Pleiades are an "open" or "galactic" cluster. With approximately 3,000 members, the Pleiades do not possess enough mass to keep all their stars together permanently, therefore the "open" label. They also live in the disk of the galaxy (along with us) and are on the order of a few hundred million years old. The color-magnitude diagram (a version of the HR diagram) for the Pleiades is shown in Figure 15.11.

By contrast, M3 is a "globular" cluster, much larger (about 500,000 stars) and much older (several billions of years) than the Pleiades. The "globular" title comes from the appearance of M3 and similar clusters. Because of its age and distance, the color-magnitude diagram for M3 is much different (Figure 15.12).

A quick glance suggests that the color-magnitude diagram for the Pleiades is very similar (though not identical) to the ZAMS graph, whereas the color-magnitude diagram for M3 is almost unrecognizable. This is due not to the distances to the clusters, nor the numbers of stars in each cluster, but rather to their ages.

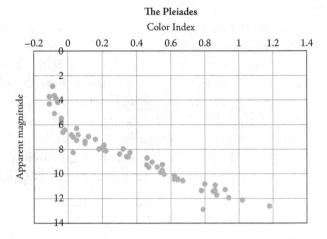

FIGURE 15.11. A color-magnitude diagram for the Pleiades.

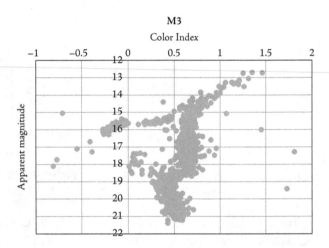

FIGURE 15.12. A color-magnitude diagram for M3.

Stars must resist the pull of their own gravity, or they collapse. A star on the main sequence makes use of hydrogen fusion to supply the energy needed for this resistance (we will cover this topic in more detail in future chapters). Therefore the lifespan (not age) of an individual star is determined by two competing ideas: how fast it burns[7] its hydrogen fuel, and how much hydrogen fuel it has in the first place. Perhaps counterintuitively, the larger a star is, the shorter its lifespan, since the increase in the rate of its fuel consumption is so much more than the increase in its available fuel supply. This means that more massive stars run out of fuel faster, and therefore have shorter lives on the main sequence, than less massive stars.

Determining the age of a star is tricky. But if we have a cluster of stars, the task is much easier. Since stars in a cluster tend to form at the same time—not entirely true, but a good starting point—they all should be the same age. Theoretical calculations not only suggest where a star should sit on the main sequence, but also its potential lifespan.

If a cluster is brand new, then it should have a complete main sequence identical to the ZAMS. As the cluster ages, bright (massive) stars will run out of fuel first and peel away from the main sequence. The age of the cluster can be estimated by looking for the "turn-off" point on its HR diagram: If a star has already run out of fuel, it will have already moved away; if it has plenty of fuel remaining, than it will still be on the main sequence (see Figure 15.13).

---

[7] By "burn" we do not mean chemical reactions. "Burn" is used here as shorthand for nuclear fusion.

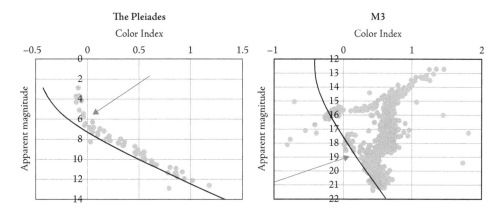

FIGURE 15.13. Turn-off points for the Pleiades (left) and M3 (right). The curved diagonal is a simplified ZAMS.

To find the age of a cluster, determine the color index of the turn-off point on its color-magnitude diagram. For example, this occurs near –0.01 for the Pleiades. This suggests (Figure 15.14) the Pleiades cluster has an age of 160 million years, though more careful considerations yield 115 million years.

What about distance? The turn-off point helps us again. Let's again refer to the Pleiades as an example. Find the apparent magnitude of the turn-off point on the color-magnitude diagram for the Pleiades (it is about +6.5). Then find the equivalent

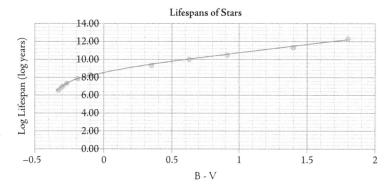

FIGURE 15.14. A graph showing theoretical lifespans of stars (as the base-10 log, in years) as a function of color index.

absolute magnitude on the ZAMS (it is about 0). This yields a distance of about 200 pc. More careful ZAMS fitting of the Pleiades using data from the Hubble Space Telescope suggests a distance of 135 pc.

Section 15.6: Binary Systems

When we introduced binary systems (chapter 13), we limited the discussion to the history of binaries, their importance in determining masses of stars, and the methods we use to find them. We haven't yet talked about how they behave.

We can classify binaries by how they interact (or don't interact) with each other:

+ Detached binaries
+ Semi-detached binaries
+ Contact binaries

Before we get into the distinctions, it will be helpful to introduce *Roche lobes*. Roche lobes—named after the French astronomer Edouard Roche (1820–1883)—are similar to tides (chapter 4) in that they result from gravitational forces; but whereas tides are specifically the difference (subtraction) of gravity at different locations, Roche lobes represent the region surrounding an object where its gravity dominates, compared to its companion(s).[8]

---

[8] The point at which a small object, like an icy moon, gets so close to its planet that the planet's tides rip it apart is called the *Roche limit*. We encountered this idea in chapters 4 and 8.

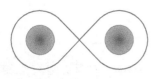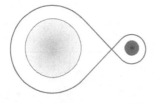

FIGURE 15.15. Left: Roche lobes for a pair of identical stars. Right: Roche lobes for relatively large and small-mass stars.

Since that's vague, let's set up some examples. Suppose a small rock is floating through space between the Earth and Moon, slowly enough that it is guaranteed to be pulled toward one or the other object. Roche lobes around the Earth and Moon define the boundaries within which that rock will be pulled toward either the Earth or the Moon.

A Roche lobe surrounding a star tends to be spherical in shape, except it tapers off like a raindrop in the direction of its companion star. As you might expect, the relatively larger the mass of the star (not the larger across the object) the larger its Roche lobe. The point between the stars where the lobes meet is where the gravitational pull from the two stars exactly cancels.

Now we are ready to describe the three types of mutual behaviors of binary stars. A *detached binary* is a system where the two stars are nestled so deep within their Roche lobes that there is no chance they will directly affect each other's development, hence, "detached". The majority of binary systems are of this type; despite their sizes, stars are actually very small compared to the spaces they inhabit. A *semi-detached binary* is a system where one star is large enough to overflow its Roche lobe, and the gravity of its companion is pulling material from the larger to the smaller star. Several of these are suspected, but few are actively observed; the Algol system is an example. Finally, the contact binary is a system where the two stars are so close that they actively share their outer atmospheres. Next to none of these are currently known, but their existence is a practical certainty; for example, gravitational waves have been discovered from a pair of colliding neutron stars and several pairs of colliding black holes. The binary system PN G054.2-03.4 is a possible contact binary—interactions between the stars are throwing off a brightly colored planetary nebula—but a contact binary between two "normal" stars is not expected.

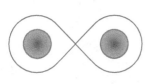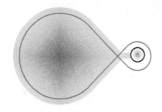

FIGURE 15.16. Left: Roche lobes for a detached binary system. Right: Roche lobes for a semi-detached binary system. The larger star is overflowing its own Roche lobe and gases from it are flowing to its smaller companion.

How might living in a binary system affect a star's life? If the stars are detached, then by definition there are no noticeable effects; the stars develop independently. But if two stars live in a semi-detached binary, then the effects can be very important. The life of a star can be lengthened or shortened, or a star can even be destroyed—ideas we will return to in chapter 18.

Summary

In this chapter, we reviewed the following:

► How astronomers use trig parallax to estimate distances to nearby stars

► How astronomers use spectroscopic parallax to estimate distances to further stars

► How astronomers use clusters of stars to estimate both distances to and ages of stars

► The HR diagram, which plots luminosities of stars vs. their temperatures

► Correlations between stellar properties such as mass, luminosity, temperature, and radius

► Spectral types of stars

► Luminosity classes of stars

Questions

1. How much is a light year in terms of miles? Hint: The speed of light is 186,000 miles per second; there are about 365 ¼ days per year, 24 hours per day, 60 minutes per hour, and 60 seconds per minute.

2. How much is a light year in terms of meters and kilometers? Hint: The speed of light is 300 million meters per second.

3. How much is a parsec in terms of miles, meters, and kilometers?

4. How much is a parsec in terms of astronomical units?

5. Hadar, the second-brightest star in the constellation of Centaurus, has an apparent magnitude of +0.6 and an absolute magnitude of −5.4. Find the distance to Hadar.

6. Deneb, the brightest star in the constellation of Cygnus, has an apparent magnitude of +1.24 and is approximately 990 pc away. Find its absolute magnitude.

Activities

▸ *Astrophysics activity 15.1*: Describe how and why astronomers use colored filters and compare the results to that of the human eye.

▸ *Astrophysics activity 15.2*: Provide a quick summary of how the stellar magnitude system works, with examples.

▸ *Astrophysics activity 15.3*: Give a set of simulations comparing different spectral types of stars.

▸ *Astrophysics activity 15.4*: Students are assigned one star from each of the following three lists: The 50 nearest stars; the 50 brightest stars; 50 stars from the Pleiades cluster. Then students construct HR diagrams as a class for each list.

Works Referenced

A summary of measurements of the Earth-Moon distance by lasers can be found at "Apollo 11 Experiment Still Going Strong After 35 Years": www.jpl.nasa.gov

An announcement to the end of the Lunar ranging program at McDonald Observatory (in Texas) was made in https://www.theguardian.com/technology/2009/jun/21/mcdonald-observatory-space-laser-funding (note that other observatories still do this work).

The length of the astronomical unit was set by the International Astronomical Union in 2012: International Astronomical Union. (2012, August 31). RESOLUTION B2 on the redefinition of the astronomical unit of length. https://www.iau.org/static/resolutions/IAU2012_English.pdf Retrieved 2019-04-20.

Finding distances to nearby stars with trig parallax is found in the following sources:

The cat-with-the-missing-eye story is true; related to the author by Sirola, C. (2017, March). Depth perception. *Physics Teacher*, 55, 78–79.

Data on distances and magnitudes of various stars comes from several sources:
    www.atlasoftheuniverse.com/stars.html
    www.atlasoftheuniverse.com/nearstar.html
    https://www.cosmos.esa.int/web/hipparcos/brightest

Hoffleit, D., & Warren W., Jr. (1991). *Harvard revised bright star catalogue* (5th ed.). Retrieved 2019-04-20. http://tdc-www.harvard.edu/catalogs/bsc5.readme

Data for the Pleiades comes from the Australia National Telescope Facility:

www.atnf.csiro.au/outreach/education/senior/astrophysics/stellarevolution_pleiadesdata.html

A biography of Henry Draper can be found at www.saburchill.com/HOS/astronomy/033.html

Information about the Henry Draper medal is found at www.nasoline.org/programs/awards/henry-draper-medal.html?-referrer=https://en.wikipedia.org/

The graph depicting relative abundances of spectral lines: www.handprint.com/ASTRO/specclass.html

Pickering's invention of his multiple-spectra technique is covered in Bunch, B. H. & Hellemans, A. (2004). *The history of science and technology: A browser's guide to the great discoveries, inventions, and the people who made them, from the dawn of time to today.* Boston, MA: Houghton Mifflin.

The development of spectral types is discussed in "Annie Jump Cannon": www.projectcontinua.org/annie-jump-cannon. Retrieved 2019-04-20.

A listing of Nobel Prize winners in physics can be found at https://en.wikipedia.org/wiki/List_of_Nobel_laureates_in_Physics

Sources about the life and work of Annie Jump Cannon include the following:

Bok, P. F. "Annie Jump Cannon, 1863–1941". *Publications of the Astronomical Society of the Pacific*, 53, No. 313 p. 168. Retrieved 2019-0420. http://adsabs.harvard.edu/full/1941PASP...53..168B

Cannon, A. J. (1916). Spectra having bright lines. *Annals of Harvard College Observatory*, 76(3), 19–32. Retrieved from https://iiif.lib.harvard.edu/manifests/view/drs:12044514$1i

DeVorkin, D. H. (2000). *Henry Norris Russell: Dean of American astronomers.* Princeton, NJ: Princeton University Press.

Luminosity classes are described in the following sources:

Morgan, W. W., & Keenan, P. C. (1973). Spectral classification. *Annual Review of Astronomy and Astrophysics.* 11, 29–50. doi:10.1146/annurev.aa.11.090173.000333

Morgan, W. W., Keenan, P. C., & Kellman, E. (1943). *An atlas of stellar spectra, with an outline of spectral classification.* Chicago, IL: University of Chicago Press.

Sources about the life and work of Cecilia Payne include the following:

Payne, C. H. (1925). *Stellar atmospheres: A contribution to the observational study of high temperature in the reversing layers of stars* (Doctoral dissertation). Radcliff College, Cambridge, MA.

Payne-Gaposchkin, C. (1979). *The dyer's hand: An autobiography.* Privately printed. This was reprinted in 1984 in *Cecilia Payne-Gaposchkin: An autobiography and other recollections.* Cambridge, UK: Cambridge University Press.

Turner, J. (2001, March 16). Cecilia Helena Payne-Gaposchkin. *Contributions of 20th Century Women to Physics.* UCLA. Retrieved 2019-04-20. http://cwp.library.ucla.edu/Phase2/Payne-Gaposchkin,_Cecilia_Helena@861234567.html

Russell's admission of Payne's correct assessment of stellar elemental abundances is in Padman, R. (2004). Ceceila Payne-Gaposchkin (1900–1979). *Newnham College Biographies.*

The zero-age main sequence figure was generated by the author based on models of how stars generate energy via hydrogen fusion as a function of their masses. Sources for those models comes from the following:

Kuiper, G. P. (1938). The empirical mass-luminosity relationship. *Astrophysical Journal, 88,* 472–506. doi:10.1086/143999

Salaris, M., & Santi C. (2005). *Evolution of stars and stellar populations.* Hoboken, NJ: Wiley.

"Mass-Luminosity relationship": hyperphysics.phy-astr.gsu.edu/hbase/Astro/herrus.html#c3

Duric, Nebojsa (2004). *Advanced astrophysics.* Cambridge University Press. p. 19. ISBN 978-0-521-52571-8.

Research concerning the Pleiades cluster and M3 can be found in the following sources:

The distance to Atlas (a giant star in the Pleiades), and therefore the distance to the Pleiades, was discussed in Zwahlen, N., North, P., Debernardi, Y., Eyer, L., Galland, F., Groenewegen, M. A. T., & Hummel, C. A. (2004). A purely geometric distance to the binary star Atlas, a member of the Pleiades. *Astronomy and Astrophysics Letters*, 425(3): L45–L48. doi:10.1051/0004-6361:200400062

A ZAMS fit using infrared data from the Hubble Space Telescope is described in Majaess, D., Turner, D. G., Lane, D. J., & Krajci, T. (n.d.). *Deep infrared ZAMS fits to benchmark open clusters hosting δ Scuti stars*. Retrieved from https://arxiv.org/pdf/1102.1705.pdf

Basri, G., Marcy, G. W., & Graham, J. R. (1996). Lithium in brown dwarf candidates: The mass and age of the faintest Pleiades stars. *Astrophysical Journal*, 458, 600. doi:10.1086/176842

Sandage, A. R. (1953). The color-magnitude diagram for the globular cluster M3. *Astronomical Journal*, 58(3), 61–75.

Ushomirsky, G., Matzner, C. D., Brown, E. F., Bildsten, L., Hilliard, V. G., & Schroeder, P. C. (1998). Light-element depletion in contracting brown dwarfs and pre-main-sequence stars. *Astrophysical Journal*, 497, 253–266. doi:10.1086.305457

Possible shapes of Roche lobes are described in Eggleton, P. P. (1983, May 1). Approximations to the radii of Roche lobes. *Astrophysical Journal*, 268, 368–369. doi:10.1086/160960

Credits

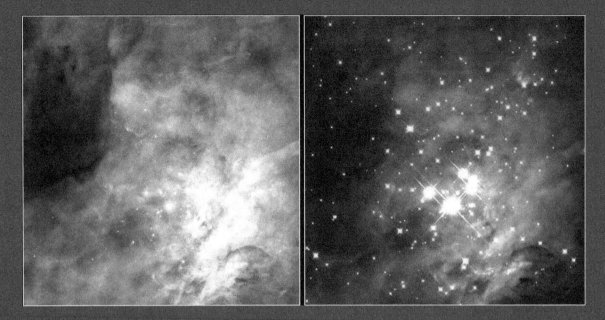

Two views of the "Trapezium," four new stars at the center of the Orion Nebula, both by the Hubble Space Telescope. At left: A visible light image taken by the WFPC2 camera; at right: A near-infrared image taken by the NICMOS camera. Credit: NASA.

CHAPTER 16

THE BEGINNINGS OF STARS

To discuss the origins of stars

OBJECTIVES

▸ To describe the interstellar medium

▸ To review different stages of star formation

▸ To review different types and populations of stars

INTRODUCTION

Now that we have spent some time discussing basic properties of stars, we can move on to talking about how they behave—specifically, how they are formed, age, and end. The chapter focuses on star formation.

The story of how stars form is less well known than other stages, primarily for one reason: Most of the activities associated with star formation occur at wavelengths other than visible light, whereas most of the rest of star lives are broadcast in visible light. Although astronomers have speculated for decades (centuries, even) about how stars come to be, we didn't really have much in the way of data until the advent of equipment—telescopes and satellites—able to see the universe in infrared light. While a picture is coming into focus, star formation is one of the topics in astronomy for which we still want a complete understanding.

KEY TERMS

Absorption nebula (aka **dark nebula**): A nebula that absorbs most of the light that tries to get through it

Accretion disk: A donut-shaped region surrounding a protostar where, due to conservation of angular momentum, infalling material has garnered a fast rotational speed

Angular momentum: The tendency of objects to continue spinning. If an object (or nebula) shrinks, the speed of the spinning increases, and vice versa

Bok globule: A relatively small absorption nebula within which anywhere from a few to a few dozen stars are beginning to form

Brown dwarf: A failed star, due to not being massive enough to sustain hydrogen fusion in its core

Chondrite: A type of asteroid made of rock that has not undergone extensive melting or shocks. In interstellar space, chondritic dust is often covered by carbon compounds such as frozen carbon monoxide. Chondrites make up the most common types of dust particles in interstellar space

Cross section: The "size" of an object (like a dust particle or hydrogen atom) as seen by a potential colliding object (like a photon)

Density, mass: The amount of mass concentrated in a specific volume

Density, number: The number of particles concentrated in a specific volume

Emission nebula: A nebula that emits spectral radiation (mostly from hydrogen)

Evaporating gaseous globules (aka EGGs): Gas and dust being slowly peeled away from a protostar by ultraviolet light from outside sources

Extinction (or stellar extinction): Starlight that is removed from our line of sight by either absorption or reflection

Gas pressure: The force (per unit area) of a large number of collisions between and amongst gas particles; has the net effect of pushing the overall mass of particles outward

Gravity: The force of nature that pulls objects together; the larger the masses, the stronger the gravity; the further apart the masses, the weaker the gravity

Henyey track: Named after their discoverer, they show the last expected movement of protostars greater than half a solar mass on the HR diagram until they join the main sequence

Herbig-Haro object: A stage where a protostar is surrounded by an accretion disk and exhibits jets of highly charged matter escaping at either pole

HI region: An emission nebula with temperatures cool enough for neutral hydrogen atoms to dominate

HII region: An emission nebula with temperatures hot enough for ionized hydrogen atoms to dominate. Often associated with star formation and/or nearby bright blue stars

Hyashi tracks: Named after their discoverer, they show the one of the last stages of expected movement of protostars less than three solar masses on the HR diagram

Interstellar medium (a.k.a. ISM): Literally, the material ("medium") between the stars

Magnetism: A force created by moving electric charges. Magnetic fields, in their turn, can affect the motions of other moving electric charges

Metal: For astronomers, any element besides hydrogen and helium. Currently the galaxy is (by number) about 90% hydrogen, 9% helium, and 1% metals

Molecular cloud: A nebula with a high-enough density and low-enough temperature for molecules to form

Nebula: A "cloud" of gas and dust in space

Opacity: The overall effect of a large mass of particles (like a nebula) in damping the intensity (flux) of light trying to get through

Population (a.k.a. Pop): Astronomers recognize three major epochs of star formation. The current epoch is called Population I, older stars (as currently reside in globular clusters) are Population II, and the very first stars are Population III

Protostar: An object that is almost, but not quite, a stable star

Radiation pressure: The force (per unit area) of photons pushing on other small particles

Reddening: The making of a star's color more red (percentage wise) due to stellar extinction

Reflection nebula: A nebula with enough dust to reflect light (mostly blue)

Star: An object that naturally sustains nuclear fusion in its core

T-Tauri object: An unstable protostar with extreme flares

21-cm line: A spectral line emitted when an electron of a hydrogen atom "flips." This reaction requires very cold temperatures and very low densities

KEY INDIVIDUALS

Ambartsumian, Victor: An Armenian astrophysicist living in Soviet Russia of the mid-20th century who emphasized the importance of nebulae (clouds) in interstellar space, including the study of T-Tauri stars and Herbig-Haro objects

Bok, Bartholemeus Jan "Bart": A Dutch-born American astronomer of the mid-20th century who was known for his work on the Milky Way and who discovered the small, concentrated nebulae ("Bok globules") that bear his name

Haro, Guillermo: A Mexican astronomer of the mid-20th century who, independently of *George Herbig*, discovered a class of protostars

Hartmann, Johannes: A German astronomer of the late 19th/early 20th century who discovered the interstellar medium

Henyey, Louis George: An American astronomer of the mid-20th century who discovered that protostars greater than 0.5 $M_{\odot}$ experience a final stage of heating and shrinking before joining the main sequence

Herbig, George: An American astronomer who, independently of *Guillermo Haro*, discovered a class of protostars

Herschel, William: A German-British astronomer of the late 18th/early 19th century who, among other things, discovered planetary nebulae

Hyashi, Chushiro: A Japanese astronomer of the mid-20th century who plotted behaviors for protostars of various masses on the HR diagram

Messier, Charles: A French astronomer of the 18th century who, in the process of searching for comets, constructed a list (the "Messier Catalog") which includes a variety of nebulae

Slipher, Vesto: An American astronomer of the early 20th century who, among other discoveries, noted that light from bright blue stars can reflect off dust in certain nebulae

Section 16.1: Nebulae

How do stars form? Before we address that question, we need to know what stars are made from, and where that material comes from.

About 90% of the "normal" matter of the Milky Way (our home galaxy) is bound up in stars, leaving the other 10% to be free-floating material between the stars.[1] While this sounds like there is little left from which to construct stars, the Milky Way is a fairly active galaxy as far as star formation is concerned, with a rate estimated anywhere from 1.5 to 20 new stars per year. If we simply wait thousands or millions of years, we generate a large number of new stars. Star formation is also a relatively inefficient process; only between 1% and 10% of a typical star-forming regions mass actually become stars. Finally, the most massive stars live short lives, astronomically speaking ("only" a few tens of millions of years), and return themselves back to the galaxy via explosions.

> **Check Your Neighbor**
>
> The galaxy started off as a giant cloud of hydrogen and helium gas many billions of years ago. Was the rate of star formation higher or lower than it is today? Briefly defend your answer.

The material between the stars—whether gathered together in nebulae or free-floating atoms—is called the *interstellar medium*. The possibility of material between the stars was raised at least as far back as the 17th century, but our modern understanding of it began in the early 20th century. William Hershel was the first person to identify individual clouds in space long before that, but the first detection of matter not associated with a specific object was done by Johannes Hartmann (1865–1936) in 1904. The interstellar medium (*ISM* for short) mostly consists of "clouds" in space—an idea first proposed by the Soviet Armenian astrophysicist Victor Ambartsumian (1908–1996) around 1932, except that astronomers call them *nebulae* (singular *nebula*) instead. Some nebulae are associated with stars ("planetary nebulae" and "supernovae remnants" are common); we will discuss those in future chapters. For now, we are concerned with nebulae that are not associated with mature stars; instead, the nebulae we are talking about now are either not related to stars in any way or are bound up with forming stars.

> **Check Your Neighbor**
>
> Nebulae in space are primarily made of hydrogen and helium gas, whereas clouds on Earth are made of tiny water droplets. What other differences can you think of between nebulae in space and clouds on Earth? And are there any similarities?

Nebulae have a wide range of sizes (masses and radii), but it is not uncommon for a typical nebula (one capable of star formation, if not actively producing stars) to have

---

[1] The Milky Way does have a supermassive black hole of about 4 million solar masses at its center. But even so, our galaxy is so large that the central black hole still counts for less than 1% of the Milky Way.

from several hundred to several tens of thousands of solar masses of material, and be from a few to a few hundred parsecs across. Most nebulae are found in the disk of the galaxy (see chapter 21 for more about the disk), and especially along its spiral arms.

Somewhat similar to how light is manipulated, astronomers categorize nebulae according to how they treat light—or, sometimes, from which perspective we view them. In fact, it's possible (although not guaranteed) that a single nebula could look like three different types of nebulae, depending on the relative angles we observe it from (Figure 16.1):

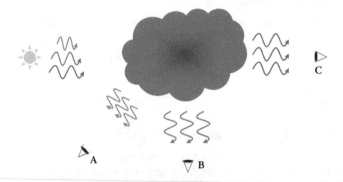

FIGURE 16.1. The same nebula may look different from different perspectives. Light of various wavelengths leaves a hot star (far left) and encounters the nebula. Ultraviolet and blue light is reflected off the nebula to be seen by observer A. Pinkish-purple light from hot hydrogen gas is emitted by the nebula to be seen by observer B. Visible light is mostly absorbed, but infrared light passes through the nebula to be seen by observer C.

1. Absorption Nebula

Also known as a dark nebula, an absorption nebula describes what it does as much as what it is: A "dark" nebula is thick enough to blot out stars or other sources of light behind it; the "absorption" term describes how this is usually accomplished. An important subset of absorption nebulae are *molecular clouds*, so called because they are cold and dense enough to possess simple molecules and not just atoms.

The main culprit responsible for absorption or dark nebulae is interstellar dust. About 90 of every 100 atoms is hydrogen and 9 out of 100 helium, leaving only 1% of atoms for the rest of the periodic table. However, interstellar space is so vast, and individual nebulae so large, that this apparent restriction really isn't much of one. Dust particles, usually smaller than a millimeter in length, do well at either reflecting visible light or absorbing it. The process isn't even across all colors; by and large, the shorter the wavelength, the more likely it will be affected by dust.

Interstellar dust particles tend to be similar, in many respects, to rock dust here, excepting the popularity of biological dust on Earth. Rocks are made of combinations of silicon and oxygen atoms; the most common combination is one silicon to every four oxygen atoms, although other combinations are often seen. Other atoms—iron and magnesium, for

FIGURE 16.2. The "dark" absorption nebula LDN 1768 in the constellation of Ophiuchus. The darkness is not a hole in space, but instead due to relatively thick dust blocking starlight from behind it. Credit: ESO.

example—can fill in-between spaces. Most interplanetary and interstellar dust is chondritic; that is, from asteroids that coalesced from electrostatic and gravitational forces but did not experience large-scale melting. In interstellar space, far from stars and their heat, dust particles are often coated with frozen carbon monoxide (chemical formula CO). Aside from dust, atomic hydrogen, and helium, astronomers also find molecular hydrogen (H_2), carbon sulfide (CS), ammonia (NH_3), formaldehyde (H_2CO), and other simple molecules. In rare cases, more complicated organic molecules have been seen, though nothing remotely as complex as DNA.

Dust particles can form in a variety of environments. Perhaps surprisingly, dust particle formation is least efficient in interstellar space, even though we see dust there; the densities are too low to bring atoms and molecules together very often. Rather, dust formation is more associated with planetesimals (see chapter 7) and even in the outer atmospheres of old, giant stars where the temperatures are high enough to drive away volatiles (i.e., materials easily evaporated) but low enough for rock to remain solid. If dust is not swept up in the eventual formations of planets and stars, radiation pressures from stars and protostars tend to drive the dust particles away.

When astronomers began to account for the effects of dust particles on their observations, they first modeled dust particles as little spheres. That approach turned out to be very deficient, and in recent decades (especially with the return sample missions of probes such as *Stardust*), we now know that dust particles have a variety of shapes (Figure 16.3).

Temperatures in dark or absorption nebulae tend to be very cold, even by astronomical standards; it is not uncommon to find temperatures on the order of 10 K (about −440°F), though temperatures can be as "high" as 100 K (−280°F). Such temperatures simply relay the fact that such nebulae are often far from sources of heat (like bright stars) and, even if involved themselves in star formation, represent the earliest stages. Conversely, densities tend to be relatively high—compared to other nebulae—coming

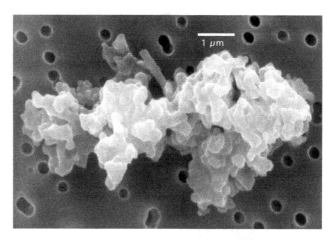

FIGURE 16.3. An extreme close-up of a "chondrite," a type of interplanetary dust grain, imaged with a scanning electron microscope. Credit: Donald E. Brownlee and Elmar Jessberger.

in from about a thousand to a million particles per cubic centimeter. We will note a general trend as we progress through this chapter: The hotter the nebula, the lower the density.

Molecular clouds are the most common type of absorption nebula, and in fact the most common type of nebula in the Milky Way. About half of the total mass of the interstellar medium appears locked up in molecular clouds, and currently astronomers estimate there are about 6,000 of them in the galaxy. A typical molecular cloud is about 30 parsecs (100 light years) across, has a temperature of 10 K and a density of 100 particles per cubic centimeter. An individual molecular cloud possesses about 100,000 solar masses of material, though some have been found as large as several million $M_\odot$. We will see later in this chapter that star formation tends to start in molecular clouds.

It is possible for dust particles to be free floating; that is, not associated with specific clouds or nebulae. Astronomers see the effects of dust most dramatically when looking toward the center of the Milky Way—it is completely blotted out in visible light, and astronomers must use different wavelengths, such as infrared or x-ray—to penetrate toward our galaxy's core (see chapter 21 for details). Astronomers also note an effect called *reddening*, because interstellar dust either reflects away or absorbs starlight along our line of sight. Because shorter wavelengths (like blue) are affected more than longer wavelengths (like

Check Your Neighbor

If a star is "reddened" by interstellar dust, does this mean the star was made to look <u>brighter</u> in red than it really does?

FIGURE 16.4. A close-up image of the Horsehead Nebula, an absorption nebula silhouetted against a brighter emission nebula. A protostar is emerging from the top of the Horsehead. Also note the reddening of stars peeking through the Horsehead. Credit: NASA, NOAO, ESA and the Hubble Heritage Team STScI/AURA.

FIGURE 16.5. The emission nebula LHA 120-N55 in the Large Magellanic Cloud. Neighboring young blue stars heat the gas of the nebula. Credit: ESO.

Check Your Neighbor

Why are the cavities or "holes" round in shape? Hint: Do stars shine their light in preferred directions or equally in all directions?

red), the dust effectively subtracts more blue light than red and makes stars appear more "red" than they otherwise should. Astronomers tend to bundle the combination of reflection and absorption of light with the term *stellar extinction* (think of "extinguishing" a fire).

Depending on specifics such as their temperatures/densities, sizes, and stages, whether participating in star formation or not, absorption nebulae split into a variety of individual types, from molecular clouds to Bok globules, of which we will later have more to say. For our purposes here, though, they all represent a like trend: relatively cold, thick nebulae laden with dust.

2. Emission Nebula

In contrast to absorption nebulae, which are almost by definition cold and dark, emission nebulae are hot and bright. Since nebulae don't normally become or remain hot on their own, emission nebulae require nearby sources of energy to make them hot.

Similar to an absorption nebula, the composition of an emission nebula has an enormous impact on how it appears. But in this case, the fact that nebulae are almost always 90% hydrogen is the important factor. Visible and ultraviolet light from nearby bright blue stars heats the gas which, since the gas is both hot and thin (i.e., low density), in its turn emits spectral lines. Because atomic hydrogen is the most prevalent material, its spectral lines tend to dominate. In visible light, hydrogen gas emits a red line (656 nm), a green-blue line (487 nm) and a violet line (434 nm), among others. To the human eye, these lines blend to form a pink-purplish color. Photos of the Milky Way and other nearby galaxies often show pinkish blobs, representing these emission nebulae.

Many nebulae (of all types) are star-forming regions. If the star-forming process is already underway, it is not uncommon for the light of its new stars—which will be bright and emit both visible and ultraviolet light—to push dust out of the nebula, carrying hydrogen and helium gas along with it. Some nebulae show spherical "holes" surrounding the new stars, carved out by the intense radiation (Figure 16.6).

Temperatures in emission nebulae are naturally much higher than in absorption nebulae. The coolest emission nebulae check in perhaps as low as 1,000 K

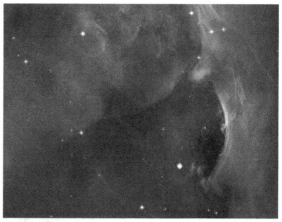

FIGURE 16.6. The Rosette Nebula (left) and a close-up of the Trapezium (right). The Rosette (credit Andreas Fink) has approximately 2,500 stars in its center, whose radiation has carved a spherical hole in the nebula. The image of the Trapezium (credit STScI) shows "arcs" where cavities overlap each other.

(2300°F), though 10,000 K (18,000°F) is typical. Densities are usually somewhat lower than that for absorption nebula, from 100 particles per cubic centimeter to 10,000 particles/cc.

Emission nebulae are sometimes distinguished by the status of their hydrogen atoms. Warm (~ 1,000 K) emission nebulae will be dominated by neutral hydrogen atoms, which in astronomer parlance is termed "HI" (pronounced "H–one"). "HII" (pronounced "H–two"), on the other hand, refers to ionized hydrogen, where the temperatures are so high as to rip electrons away from their protons. As electrons rejoin their protons, they emit various spectral lines, the visible photons having been described earlier. *HII regions*, as opposed to *HI regions*, are used by astronomers to mark the locations of star formation (since they need to be kept hot by young blue stars) and to mark individual spiral arms in the Milky Way (see chapter 21).

3. Reflection Nebula

Reflection nebulae are dominated, like absorption nebulae, by dust, though in this case we are observing how visible light reflects off of them. In many ways, the difference between a reflection nebula and an absorption nebula is a matter of perspective (again, see Figure 16.1). But since reflection occurs better for shorter wavelengths of visible light (blue) than longer wavelengths (red), reflection nebulae are often found near bright, blue stars, close enough that the light from the stars can visibly be seen reflecting off their dust particles but not so close that the dust particles are heated so much as to emit their own light.

FIGURE 16.7. The reflection nebula IC 2118, colloquially known as the Witches' Head nebula, in the constellation of Orion. It reflects blue light from the bright star Rigel, which lies just off the upper right of the picture. Credit: NASA.

For a while, astronomers weren't certain about the sources of light for reflection nebulae. Then in 1912, Vesto Slipher (1875–1969) compared the spectra of the stars Merope and Alcyone (of the Pleiades cluster) to the spectrum of the neighboring nebula and made the argument that the nebula was simply reflecting the light of those stars, rather than producing its own light. Enjar Hertzsprung performed calculations supporting this in the following year, and Edwin Hubble made the distinction between reflection and emission nebula in 1922.

FIGURE 16.8. M20, aka the Trifid Nebula. Credit: Hunter Wilson.

Check Your Neighbor

How many types of nebulae can you find in the image of the Trifid Nebula (Figure 16.8)?

Section 16.2: Other Parts of the Interstellar Medium

Many nebulae don't fit well in any of the categories previously discussed.

1. Planetary Nebula

Despite its name, a planetary nebula doesn't have anything to do with planets. Discovered by William Hershel, they were briefly thought to be planets, since the first examples appeared round and colorful through the telescope. However, planetary nebulae are really shells of expelled gas and dust from dying stars, the remnant of the star often visible at the very center of the nebula. We will discuss planetary nebulae in more detail in chapter 18.

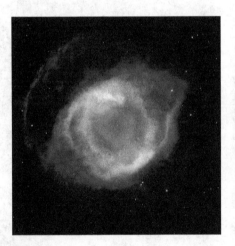
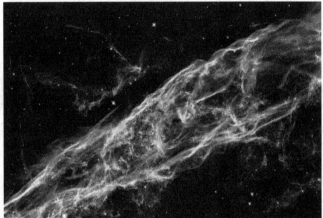

FIGURE 16.9. Examples of a planetary nebula and a supernova remnant: The Helix Nebula (left) and details of the Veil Nebula (right), both by the Hubble Space Telescope. Credit: NASA/STScI.

2. Supernovae Remnants

Rarely, stars may explode (don't worry; the Sun won't ever do this!), an event called a supernova. The remnants of supernovae tend to be far more chaotic than planetary nebulae, enough to be readily told apart. We will show how supernovae can facilitate star formation later in this chapter and discuss supernovae for their own sakes in chapters 18 and 19. The pieces or "remnants" of all types of dying stars fly back into the interstellar medium, eventually mixing with other gas and dust and possibly being swept up to form new stars.

3. Free-Floating Gas

Some gas in the interstellar medium is not associated with any particular nebula or object. The galaxy, like the solar system, is not a perfect vacuum, but contains free-floating gas and dust particles.

TABLE 16.1. Components of the Interstellar Medium

Component	Temperature (K)	Density (#/cc)	State of Gas
Molecular clouds	10–20	10^2–10^6	molecular
Cold neutral medium	50–100	20–50	neutral atomic
Warm neutral medium	6000–10,000	0.2–0.5	neutral atomic
Warm ionized medium	8000	0.2–0.5	ionized
HII regions	8000	10^2–10^4	ionized
Hot ionized medium (a.k.a. coronal gas)	10^6–10^7	10^{-4}–10^{-2}	highly ionized (includes metals)

Source: Ferriere, K. (2001), "The Interstellar Environment of our Galaxy", Reviews of Modern Physics, 73 (4): 1031–1066, arXiv:astro-ph/0106359, Bibcode:2001RvMP...73.1031F, doi:10.1103/RevModPhys.73.1031

Free-floating gas can be split into several categories, mostly dependent on their temperatures and/or the state of the gas. For example, astronomers recognize a "cold neutral medium," where the gas consists of neutral atoms and molecules, the temperatures are very low (10–20 K) and the densities relatively high (20–50 particles per cubic centimeter), compared to other regions of free-floating gases. In comparison, the "warm neutral medium" still is made of neutral particles, but the temperatures are higher (6,000–10,000 K) and the densities lower (0.2–0.5 particles per cc). Table 16.1 lists different components of the ISM. Note that "molecular clouds" refer to absorption nebulae and "HII regions" to emission nebulae (there is no equivalent for reflection nebulae), but all other components simply refer to the spaces between stars that are not bound in nebulae of various sorts.

One subcategory of free-floating gas is called "coronal" gas, using a similar description as was used for the Sun's corona (chapter 12). Gas particles can be highly energized from a variety of sources, such as shockwaves from supernovae or cosmic rays. But due to very low densities (10^{-3} particles/cc is common), particles have minimal chances of colliding with each other, and since other cooling mechanisms are inefficient, particles tend to retain their energies once heated.

Another subcategory of free-floating gas is atomic hydrogen that is both very cold and very thin (i.e., low density), which astronomers can detect using a special transition called the 21-centimeter line.

Both protons and electrons possess a quantum mechanical property labeled "spin," where they behave like little spheres that rotate. But the "quantum" of quantum mechanics puts restrictions on its properties. In this case, the proton and electron can be perfectly aligned with each other or aligned exactly opposite each other (Figure 16.10). The alignment of the proton and electron possesses just a little more energy than the opposite alignment of the proton and electron. Left to themselves, it is just possible for the electron to spontaneously "flip" its spin. The system emits a photon in order to drain away the excess energy.

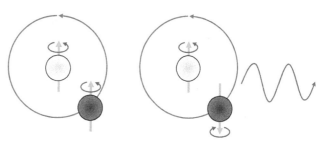

FIGURE 16.10. In a neutral hydrogen atom, the proton and the electron's spins are normally oriented in the same direction (left). If the electron "flips" its spin, the atom emits a photon with a wavelength of 21 centimeters (right).

However, a few of the specifics of this process make it difficult to detect. First, the difference in energy is very slight, 5.874 micro-electron-volts. To put this into perspective, the energy of the red photon we've discussed earlier for hydrogen gas is 1.89 electron-volts, about 320,000 times more energetic. The photon emitted by this spin-flip process has a wavelength of 21 centimeters, which places it in the microwave region (i.e., we need to use radio (microwave) telescopes to detect it). Interference from ground traffic in radio transmissions makes this difficult.

Second, the transition is very rare. The half-life (the amount of time for half of the atoms, on average, to make this happen) is about 10 million years. Fortunately, because space is so vast, there are easily more than enough hydrogen atoms available to make it possible for radio telescopes to detect this line. Unfortunately, collisions between hydrogen atoms disturb the atoms so as to "reset" the clock, so to speak, so the gas needs to be fabulously thin in order for atoms <u>not</u> to collide with each other very frequently. Thus the 21-cm line acts to track thin, cold hydrogen gas throughout the galaxy.

What have 21-cm line studies found? One of the first works showed that 21-cm gas can track the shapes of the spiral arms in the Milky Way. Other research suggests the galaxy spreads out much further than its visible sections admit. Cosmologists are also interested in the 21-cm line, as it may show information about the universe between the times that neutral atoms first formed (about 380,000 years into the life of the universe) and when stars first "turned on" (starting around 150 million years into the life of the universe). Since there were virtually no other objects emitting light during this span, cosmologists refer to it as the universe's "dark ages"; 21-cm radiation may help us see into that gap.

Section 16.3: Star Formation Part I: The Initial Collapse

The basics of star formation are in some ways very similar to those of planet formation. As we did for planets (chapter 7), we will briefly review the physics of star formation. One of the major differences will be the role played by dust; while dust (for the most part) promoted planetary formation, it will inhibit star formation.

- **Gravity:** Gravity is the force of nature that has all objects pulling each other together. Here, the gravity of a nebula can collapse a nebula, or portions of one.
- **Density:** Density is the measure of the concentration of mass, usually expressed per unit volume. The higher the density of an object, other things being equal, the stronger its surface gravity.
- **Angular momentum:** For an isolated system, the conservation of angular momentum tells us that as a nebula collapses, (a) it will spin faster and (b) it will tend to flatten into a disk.
- **Gas pressure:** The higher the temperature, the faster particles move inside a gas. The faster particles move, the more often and more violently they collide with each other. The net effect is that the gas exerts an outward pressure.
- **Magnetism:** Magnetic fields can exert forces on moving electric charges; magnetic fields themselves are made by moving electric charges.
- **Radiation pressure:** Like gas pressure, light (photons) can exert force, pressure, and momentum on objects. But only very small objects, items such as dust particles, have low enough masses to significantly "feel" pressure from light.
- **Cross-sections/opacity:** It's not just the small mass of dust particles (or hydrogen atoms etc.) that make it possible for them to respond to light pressure. The strength of the response also depends on how large the particle appears to the light, an idea astrophysicists call its *cross section*. The overall effect of a large mass of particles (such as a nebula or star's atmosphere) is called *opacity*.

And just as the formation of planets is known well enough to be broken down into a series of steps or events, so can the formation of stars. But also, like planets, star formation is a science in many ways still in its adolescence, and we have many things yet to learn about it.

1. To build a star, we first need some raw materials. Free-floating gas is simply too diffuse, and all observed star formation is associated with large nebulae.
2. Most nebulae are in a state of equilibrium; the force holding it together (its own self-gravity) balances the force(s) pushing it apart (primarily gas pressure at this stage). To promote star formation, we need to have an imbalance of forces, so gravity can pull the nebulae together.
3. Sometimes a nebula can begin shrinking according to gravity on its own. Mostly, though, it appears star formation benefits from a "kick-start," an event that gives gravity an edge.

4. The most common way to do this is via a supernova. The explosion of a star sends shockwaves into the nearby ISM. The shockwaves simply pass through free-floating gas without much effect. On the other hand, such shockwaves can compress gas and dust as they travel through a nebula, much like a snowplow creates a wedge of snow as it clears a road. There is a bit of a symbiotic process at work, here; the stars most likely to become supernovae are also those most likely to form first, hence once a nebula starts producing stars, the speed of production also tends to ramp up.

FIGURE 16.11. A snowplow enhances the density of snow (left); shockwaves from a supernova enhance the density of gas in a nebula (right). The shockwave (pink, in false color) is crashing into dust particles in a surrounding nebula. Credits: Simon P. (left); Chandra/Spitzer telescopes (right).

5. Once begun, gravity "sifts" the nebula. Gravity is stronger in these concentrated regions of relatively higher density, and thus tends to concentrate mass in smaller and smaller areas (Figure 16.12). At these beginning stages, the densities are still easily vacuum thin by Earth standards, and the temperatures tend to be frigid.

6. The cloud begins to fragment into smaller pieces as local densities increase. The densities of some regions rise so high as to render the region completely opaque to visible light. These regions are called *Bok globules*, after their discoverer, Bart Bok (1906–1983), and are among the coldest objects known. Bok suggested that these super-cold, super-dark nebulae were in fact hiding objects destined to become stars. Because they were both opaque and cold, little was known about them until

> **Check Your Neighbor**
>
> What type of nebula—HII region or molecular cloud—are we most likely discussing at this stage?

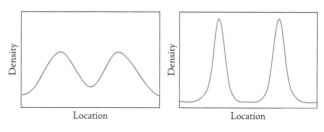

FIGURE 16.12. The sifting of a nebula via gravity. Regions of relatively higher density (the peaks in the figure at left) become more pronounced and concentrated (right) over time.

observations in infrared light in 1990 confirmed the presence of protostars within. Bok globules are relatively small, often only a parsec or less across and containing about 10 solar masses of material on average. Bok globules are also suspected of encouraging the formation of binary (two-star) systems.

7. The enhancement of densities can have other effects. If a thick nebula harboring potential stars is near sources of intense ultraviolet light (by this, we almost always mean O and B-type stars) the UV light can sculpt the nebula, their radiation pressure evaporating and/or pushing back dust around the denser globules. In fact (perhaps to show that astronomers are as susceptible to bad puns as anyone else), these dense knots of material left behind are often termed *evaporating gaseous globules*, or *EGGs* for short. EGGs are smaller than, and in fact are sometimes found within, Bok globules. A typical EGG may be just around

FIGURE 16.13. Bok globules embedded within the nebula NGC 281. Credit: NASA, ESA, and The Hubble Heritage Team (STScI/AURA).

100 astronomical units across and will contain just one or a few (gravitationally bound) protostars inside.

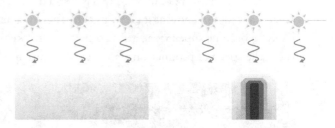

FIGURE 16.14. Intense ultraviolet light from several O and B-type stars heads toward a molecular cloud containing protostars (left). With time, the thinner gas and dust is pushed away, leaving behind a thick envelope surrounding an EGG, with streamers of gas and dust trailing behind the EGG (right).

As the UV light pushes away the thinner material, the EGG, being much denser and therefore harder to move, stays behind, and a streamer of material trails behind it, much like water flowing around a rock in a stream, or (to cite other astronomical examples) the tail of a comet or the distortion of a planet's magnetic field by the solar wind. The most famous of these events is the "Pillars of Creation," an image of the center of the M16 nebula made famous by the Hubble Space Telescope. The tips of the finger-like structures of M16 are thought to contain many of these EGGs. The sculpting of the pillars is an ongoing process and the pillars are expected to exist for about another 100,000 years before dissipating completely.

Section 16.4: Star Formation Part II: Protostars

We can now narrow our focus to individual stars. As with the collapsing nebulae, there are different stages; here, there are also individual quirks such as the mass of the forming star or the prevalence of dust. Processes such as radiation pressure, magnetic fields, and angular momentum now become important enough to include in our story. For our purposes, we will consider the individual objects destined to be stars, the central masses at the hearts of EGGs, as *protostars*.

8. As with most of our studies, the more massive a protostar, the quicker everything happens. Higher masses mean higher amounts of gravity, of course, and the stronger the gravity, the more mass the protostar tends to draw to itself. Given this, why doesn't a star continue to grow forever? After all, the more mass a protostar has, the more it is likely to gather, adding to its mass, seemingly indefinitely. That this doesn't happen is due to several factors:

FIGURE 16.15. Four cameras and 32 images were combined to make this composite image of the inner region of M16, the Eagle Nebula. The colors come from different elements: green for hydrogen, red for sulfur and blue for oxygen. Credit: NASA, Jeff Hester, and Paul Scowen (Arizona State University).

a. Much of the energy of gravity used to shrink the star goes into heating its gas. Initially this isn't of major importance, since the initial temperatures are so low, but eventually the protostar becomes hot enough to start emitting significant amounts of infrared light. The IR light heats dust particles better than it does hydrogen or helium atoms, and the dust in return emits its own, lower-energy infrared light. Combined with the shroud of matter still surrounding the protostar, most studies of protostars require infrared telescopes.

b. As the temperature increases, the emitted light reaches the visible band (and for very massive stars, ultraviolet). This light exerts small but significant amounts of radiation pressure on the dust particles. The protostar itself therefore sets a limit of sorts on its own growth.

c. Also, as the protostar shrinks, its rate of spin speeds up. Conservation of angular momentum states that, as a large object shrinks, its speed of rotation increases. This has the effect of creating a flat donut-shaped region of material (*accretion disk*) around the protostar. Some of this region is destined to become planetesimals (see chapter 7).

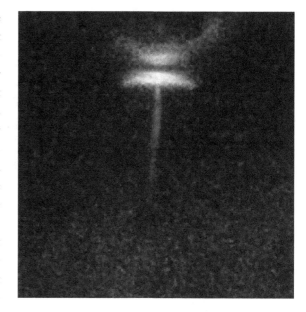

FIGURE 16.16. Herbig-Haro object #30 as seen by the Hubble Space Telescope. HH 30 shows a protoplanetary disk and reddish jets of material shooting away at both poles. The protostar itself is concealed behind dust. Credit: NASA.

Magnetic fields are induced by moving electric charges. When a protostar is hot enough, the gases in its accretion disk become ionized, and therefore the protostar grows a magnetic field. Magnetic fields in turn affect the paths of moving electric charges, and one of the consequences is that jets of infalling charged particles are diverted away along each of the poles (from top and bottom, so to speak) of the protostar. This is another way in which the protostar limits its own growth; it shoots material away from itself. This particular outgrowth of a protostar is known as a *Herbig-Haro object*, after its discoverers, George Herbig (1920–2013) and Guillermo Haro (1913–1988). The jets become visible as they collide with other material far from the protostar. This particular phase of a protostar's development can last for tens of thousands of years, though observers have noted changes over times scales of just a few years.

We should emphasize at this point that these factors competing with gravity slow down, but do not halt, the collapse of the protostar. That will wait until nuclear fusion becomes an ongoing concern in its core (see #9).

Check Your Neighbor

Besides the options provided, can you think of a really obvious (once we've said it) reason why a protostar stops growing?

9. Protostars go through hiccups, or outbursts and explosions, before finally settling down to become permanent stars. We can define a star as an object that naturally sustains nuclear fusion, and here is one reason why we do so. A protostar might briefly in its core fuse protons (through a few steps) to form helium-3, for example, or lithium, combining with protons to form beryllium, but these are relatively temporary and do not halt the general collapse of the star.

At this stage, a protostar is much brighter than it will be as a main sequence star, though this is obscured by the fact that the protostar's emissions are still primarily in infrared light. Curiously, star of spectral type F and

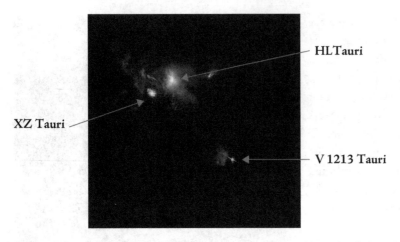

FIGURE 16.17. Embedded in a larger nebula are several T-Tauri objects, labeled here. Credit: ESA/Hubble & NASA, Acknowledgement: Judy Schmidt.

smaller are more prone to growing pains than their larger brethren, being highly convective, exhibiting large flares, and emitting copious amounts (up to a thousand times more than the Sun) of x-rays and radio waves. If anything, this seems to be worse for the smallest M-type stars, leading some astronomers to wonder if life is possible for planets orbiting such stars due to the violence of the stars during their early history.

Such a star is often termed a *T-Tauri object*, after the first one of its kind discovered. They spend several million years at this stage, taking longer for smaller-mass stars. T-Tauris do utilize nuclear fusion, but of lithium, which fuses with protons to form beryllium and helium at lower temperatures than that used by hydrogen. Since the T-Tauri is highly convective, it mixes its matter throughout the entire protostar, allowing all of the lithium to eventually be consumed. Astronomers can in fact use the abundance of lithium as a time marker of sorts, which gives us rough estimates as to the ages of different T-Tauris.

10. The advent of a protostar onto the main sequence—which for our purposes is where we will define the object as a true star—requires it maintain hydrogen fusion as its energy source in its core. This means a minimum core temperature of about 10 million K is needed, though the core temperature can be much higher (it is about 16 million K for the Sun) for more massive stars. While the protostar's core is settling down, its photosphere is finally clearing away all remaining gas and dust (except for those objects thick enough to become planets, etc.), removing its cover and exposing the star to the rest of space. At this point we can label the object a star. If the object is not massive enough to make this happen, it becomes what astronomers call a *brown dwarf*, essentially the boundary between giant planets like Jupiter and M-type stars like Proxima Centauri. Because brown dwarfs do not emit visible light and are small by star standards, astronomers have only discovered a few of them and are not sure how many of them are in our galaxy.

We haven't spent any time using the HR diagram on star formation, and we've only mentioned the main sequence as a goal to be attained. The reasons are straightforward: Nearly all the important steps of star formation occur at infrared wavelengths, meaning star formation is virtually impossible to observe via ground-based telescopes. It is only with the advent of infrared satellites that astronomers have been able to acquire good information regarding star formation.

Nevertheless, we can talk a little about how protostars "move" on the HR diagram. The Japanese astronomer Chushiro Hyashi (1920–2010) performed theoretical calculations in conjunction with observations to estimate how protostars less than 3 $M_\odot$ (virtually all stars) act as they settle onto the main sequence. In graph form, these are now referred to as *Hyashi tracks* (Figure 16.18).

The Hyashi tracks show the behavior of a protostar in its last T-Tauri stages. The protostar slowly shrinks while maintaining the same surface temperature; therefore, the luminosity of the protostar drops because the size (radius) of the protostar drops. For protostars of 0.5 $M_\odot$ or less, this process continues until the star stabilizes. For protostars larger than 0.5 $M_\odot$, there is a final stage where the protostar instead experiences a slow increase in temperature accompanied by a slow shrinking in size, keeping its luminosity approximately constant, before joining the main sequence. This leads to horizontal movements to the left on the HR diagram and are called *Henyey tracks* after their discoverer, Louis George Henyey (1910–1970).

If a protostar is emits more light (luminosity) than it will as a main sequence star, and its temperature is lower, than what can we say about the size of the protostar compared to its future main sequence self?

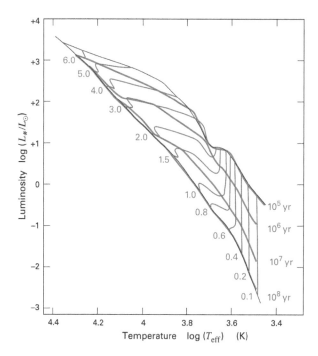

FIGURE 16.18. Hyashi-Henyey tracks on the HR diagram. The diagonal from upper left to lower right is the main sequence and is outlined with various masses of stars in terms of solar masses. The red lines indicate the ages of the protostars. The vertical sections of the blue lines are Hyashi tracks, whereas the horizontal sections are known as Henyey tracks. Credit: Steven W. Stahler and Francesco Palla.

Section 16.5: Star Formation Part III: The Very First Stars

So far, we have described star formation for the current epoch. Let's go back in time (for the galaxy, that is) to peek at how star formation has changed over the eons.

The current distribution of elements in the galaxy (by number) is about 90% hydrogen, 9% helium, and 1% everything else, or what astronomers call *metals*.[2] But the universe started with virtually no metals at all (see chapter 23 for details). The metals we have, as small a percentage as it seems, is crucial for understanding star formation in our current epoch. How would the absence of metals affect stars?

An important big difference between hydrogen and helium versus metals is that hydrogen and helium (alone, anyway) cannot produce dust. As we have seen, dust has a large cross-section for radiation pressure, meaning dust acts to limit the growth of stars when it is swept away by the newly bright light from protostars. But the cross-sections of hydrogen and helium are much smaller. This means that it is very difficult to sweep away hydrogen and helium via radiation pressure, which in turn means there are no effective limits on how much mass a protostar could gather.

Astronomers envision the very first stars having the ability to grow to hundreds of solar masses apiece or larger. These first stars would have been so massive as to be unstable from the beginning and end their lives rather quickly (i.e., within a few million years) via exploding as supernovae. We will examine supernovae in more detail in chapters 18 and 19, but for now we can say supernovae make metals during their explosions and thus also spread these metals throughout the galaxy.

These first stars (confusingly labeled "Population III") seeded the galaxy with metals, some of which became

FIGURE 16.19. A supernova remnant in both x-rays from the Chandra satellite (blue) and visible light from the Hubble Space Telescope (pinkish-red). The metals manufactured by this explosion are spreading throughout the galaxy. X-ray credit: NASA/CXC/Rutgers/J. Hughes; optical credit: NASA/STScI.

---

2 Perhaps needless to say, this is a <u>very</u> different usage of the term "metal" than how chemists talk about metals.

dust particles. These metals would have then affected the next round of star formation ("Population II"), and in turn their supernovae affected the next round ("Population I" or "Pop I" for short). The Sun is considered a Population I star. Most of the stars in the galactic disk are also Pop I stars, though we do see a few Pop II stars (such as Barnard's Star) passing through. Pop I stars are found mostly in the galactic halo, where globular clusters live. While Pop I stars tend to consist of 1% metals, Pop II stars can be around 0.01% metals or lower. Globulars were the first large-scale structures to form in the galaxy, and in fact are older than the galaxy itself. Nevertheless, globulars are Pop II and cannot be the original stars.

Astronomers have serious problems locating Pop III stars. The more massive Pop III stars exploded billions of years ago as supernovae and are therefore long gone. It is possible that, if some very small Pop III stars formed (0.8 solar masses or less), they may still be in existence. But (a) such stars are very dim and thus hard to find, and (b) they have been cruising through the galaxy for the past 10–12 billion years, and even though they began without metals, they are likely to have picked up some simply by passing through the ISM. Therefore, as of this writing, while there are a few candidates, no observations of any Pop III stars have been confirmed as such.

If it was possible to form truly gigantic stars at the beginning, the reverse is true: Stars forming now have larger percentages of metals and dust and are therefore are likely to be smaller. Stars in the tens of solar masses are not unheard of, but they are fantastically rare—85% of all stars in the galaxy today are M-type, roughly half a solar mass apiece or less. As the galaxy ages, this trend can be expected to continue.

Why is any of this worthy of our attention? Earth-like planets are made primarily of metals (Earth itself is 55% oxygen by mass) and we ourselves are made of them. Without previous generations of stars to manufacture metals, we could not be here.

Section 16.6: Star Formation Wrap Up

How quickly do stars form? We have a few ways to answer that question.

The Milky Way—our home galaxy—has about 400 billion stars, although some astronomers do estimate it as low as 100 billion. Assuming the Milky Way is 12 billion years old (the oldest globular clusters are about this age), this implies an average rate of 33 new stars each year in the Milky Way. The current rate appears to be anywhere from 7 to 20 new stars per year.

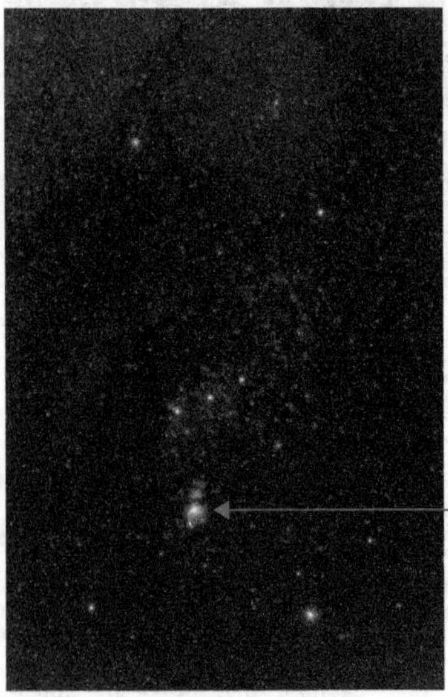

But stars do not all require the same amount of time to form, nor do they have the same lifespans. The more massive a star, the quicker its formation process and the shorter its lifespan; stars with masses about 10 $M_\odot$ or more tend to form in less than 100,000 years and have lifespans of about 10 million years. On the other hand, stars with masses about 0.1 $M_\odot$ tend to take over 100 million years to form and have lifespans over a trillion years long. The galaxy has an age of about 12 billion years, which implies it has had time to sustain many generations of massive stars, but any star with 0.8 $M_\odot$ or less, even if it formed at the very beginning of the Milky Way, is likely still here.

Star formation is also a fairly inefficient process, if we think of efficiency as being the percentage of gas and dust from the original nebula in question being swept up to become stars. Only about 1% of a nebula ever is turned into stars during a bout of star formation. Even though 90% of the visible Milky Way is in stars and less than 10% in the ISM, a more efficient process would have turned virtually all the gas and dust into stars. This is possible; other types of galaxies

FIGURE 16.20. A photo of the constellation of Orion the Hunter. The thick star-looking object at the tip of the hunter's scabbard is not a star; instead, it is the Orion Nebula, one of the largest star-forming regions in the Milky Way.

Orion Nebula

than the Milky Way[3] do in fact seem to be bereft of any free gas and dust. Still other types of galaxies have larger proportions of gas and dust (their own ISMs) compared to the Milky Way and correspondingly have faster rates of star formation now.

It takes free gas and dust (we include nebulae here) to manufacture stars, of course, which means locations with lots of gas and dust are more likely to have faster rates of star formation. In the Milky Way, the section with the most nebulae is its disk, the section to which we belong. The central section of the galaxy—called the "nucleus" or "bulge"—is more packed with stars and has little free gas or dust, and thus shows little current star formation. Similarly, another section of the galaxy that envelops it, the "halo," contains few nebulae but is strewn with hundreds of globular clusters, where star formation has by and large finished.

There are hints that our neighboring (if you consider 2.5 million light years a "neighbor") spiral galaxy, M31, is on a collision course with us in the Milky Way. Assuming that happens, 3 billion years from now is a common estimate, the stars will be very unlikely to collide, being so small compared to the volume of space they inhabit, but nebulae from both galaxies are likely to hit each other. When that day (epoch?) comes, we can expect a virtual explosion of new stars to result. That should be fun!

Summary

In this chapter, we did the following:

- Introduced the interstellar medium (ISM)
- Identified different ways in which we see nebulae
- Reviewed basic facts about the ISM
- Told the story of how stars form
- Identified different physical processes that affect star formation

Questions

1. Suppose the current rate of star formation in the Milky Way is 10 new stars per year. How many new stars have been formed in a million years?

2. The Milky Way currently has about 400 billion stars and has existed for about 12 billion years. The current rate of star formation is no larger than 20 new stars per year. What does this imply about the rate of star formation in the distant past?

3. Stars don't all live forever; very massive stars may live for "only" 10 million years or so. What does this imply about the total number of stars that have <u>ever</u> lived in the Milky Way; is it larger, the same, or smaller than the 400 billion that exist now?

Refer to Figure 16.19 to help with the following questions:

4. About how long does it take for a 6 $M_\odot$ star to form? For a 2.0 $M_\odot$ star to form? For a 0.1 $M_\odot$ star to form? What does all this say about the relationship between initial mass and the time required to form a star?

5. What do the units on the vertical scale, "log $(L_\star/L_\odot)$," mean? How bright is a star with a value of "0" on the vertical axis?

6. Does the vertical scale refer to the luminosity of a protostar in <u>visible</u> light, or its luminosity in <u>all</u> wavelengths? Hint: Recall the discussions regarding star formation in this chapter.

---

[3] The Milky Way is a "barred spiral," a type of galaxy that has a moderate current rate of star formation. "Ellipticals" by comparison have virtually no current star formation, which is another way of saying their star formation rates were much larger in the past.

7. How bright does this graph predict our Sun was at its birth: brighter than it is today, the same as it is today, or dimmer than it is today? Hint: What is the mass of the Sun, by definition? You may find it helpful to use a straightedge.

8. The Hyashi track (the final vertical portion of a protostar's motion on the HR diagram) of a 0.2 $M_\odot$ star shows its luminosity going from 0 to −2 as it completes its formation.
   * By what (multiplicative) factor does its brightness change as it completes forming?
   * Does the protostar get brighter, dimmer, or retain the same luminosity as it completes forming?
   * Does the protostar get hotter, cooler, or retain the same surface temperature as it completes forming?
   * Does the protostar expand, shrink, or maintain its same size (radius) as it completes forming?

9. What do the units on the horizontal scale, "log T_{eff}" mean? (Hint: "eff" stands for "effective.") What is the effective temperature of a protostar with a value of 4.0 on the horizontal axis?

10. The Henyey track (the final horizontal, more or less, portion of a protostar's motion on the HR diagram) of a 5.0 $M_\odot$ star shows its temperature going from 4.05 to 4.2 as it completes its formation.
    * What was its effective temperature at the beginning of its Henyey track? At the end of its Henyey track?
    * Does the protostar get brighter, dimmer, or retain the same luminosity as it completes forming? Assume the Henyey track is perfectly horizontal for simplicity.
    * Does the protostar get hotter, cooler, or retain the same surface temperature as it completes forming?
    * Does the protostar get larger, smaller, or remain the same size (radius) as it completes forming?
    * If we look carefully, the Henyey track is not perfectly horizontal, but has a slight upward slope as the protostar completes forming. Does its luminosity therefore slightly increase, slightly decrease, or remain the same as it completes forming?

11. More massive stars form more quickly and are brighter than less massive stars. What would you expect the overall color of new stars to be in a star-forming region: blue, yellow, or red?

12. In a star-forming region (such as an HII region), bright blue stars irradiate the rest of the nebula with UV light. What would you expect to be the overall color of the gas in the nebula, and why? Hint:
    * 90% of the gas is hydrogen.
    * The gas will be heated by the UV light.

13. We often see "holes" inside star-forming regions, with a bright blue star or stars at their centers. Briefly explain why this happens.

14. Which stars take the most amount of time to form, O-type or M-type? Which stars have the longer lifespans, O-type or M-type? Briefly explain why the answers to both questions are the same.

15. What happens to the overall metallicity (i.e., percentage of metals) in the ISM as the galaxy ages? Briefly defend your answer.

16. The first population of stars ("Pop III") in the Milky Way could have been as large as 100 $M_\odot$ or more. We do not think current stars are likely to get that large. Why not?

17. In which portion of the galaxy do we expect to find Population I or Population II stars dominating?
    * The bulge (aka nucleus)
    * The disk
    * The halo

18. Population III stars are the original stars, having formed before the rest of the galaxy itself formed. List some reasons why astronomers haven't confirmed finding any of them yet.

19. Galaxies that show extremely rapid rates of star formation are often termed "starburst" galaxies. Starburst galaxies often result from collisions between galaxies. Briefly relate these two statements.

Activities

▸ *Astrophysics activity 16.1:* Review questions concerning the interstellar medium and star formation.

Works Referenced

Observations regarding interstellar dust grains can be found in the following sources:

Di Francesco, J. Hogerheidje, M. R., Weelch, W. J., & Bergin, E. A. (2002). Abundances of molecular species in Barnard 68. *Astronomical Journal, 124*(5), 2749–2755.

Jessberger, E. K., Stephan, T., Rost, D., Arndt, P., Maetz, M., Stadermann, F. J., & Kurat, G. (2001). Properties of interplanetary dust: Information from collected samples. In E. Grün, B. A. S. Gustafson, S. F. Dermott, & F. Fechtig (Eds.), *Interplanetary dust* (pp. 253–294). Springer-Verlag.

More sources regarding distinguishing the interstellar medium are as follows:

Alves, J., Lada, C., & Lada, E. (2001). *Tracing H2 via infrared dust extinction*. Cambridge, UK: Cambridge University Press.

Asimov, I. (1982). *Asimov's biographical encyclopedia of science and technology: Updated and Illustrated*. Doubleday. New York, NY.

Chandrasekhar, C. (1989). To Victor Ambartsumian on his 80th birthday. *Journal of Astrophysics and Astronomy, 18*, p. 3.

Ewan, H. I., & Purcell, E. M. (1951, September). Observation of a line in the galactic radio spectrum. *Nature, 168*(4270), 356. doi:10.1038/168356a0

Ferriere, K. (2001), The interstellar environment of our galaxy. *Reviews of Modern Physics, 73*(4), 1031–1066. doi:10.1103/RevModPhys.73.1031

Hertzsprung, E. (1913). Über die Helligkeit der Plejadennebel. *Astronomische Nachrichten, 195*, 449–452. doi:10.1002/asna.19131952302

Hubble, E. P. (1922). The source of luminosity in galactic nebulae. *Astrophysical Journal, 56*, 400. doi:10.1086/142713

Muller, C. A., & Oort, J. H. (1951, September). The interstellar hydrogen line at 1,420 Mc./sec., and an estimate of galactic rotation. *Nature, 168*(4270), 357–358. doi:10.1038/168357a0

Sanders, D. B., Scoville, N. Z., & Solomon, P. M. (1985, February 1). Giant molecular clouds in the Galaxy. II—Characteristics of discrete features. *Astrophysical Journal, Part 1, 289*, 373–387. doi:10.1086/162897

Slipher, V. M. (1922). On the spectrum of the nebula in the Pleiades. *Lowell Observatory Bulletin, 2*, 26–27.

Williams, J. P., Blitz, L., & McKee, C. F. (2000). The structure and evolution of molecular clouds: From clumps to cores to the IMF. *Protostars and Planets IV*, pp. 97–120. Eds. Mannings, V., Boss, A., & Russell S. S.

Various stages of star formation are discussed in the following sources:

Clemens, D. P., Yun, J. L., & Meyer, M. H. (1991, March). BOK globules and small molecular clouds–Deep IRAS photometry and (C-12)O spectroscopy. *Astrophysical Journal Supplement, 75*(3), 877–904. doi:10.1086/191552

Hayashi, C. (1961). Stellar evolution in early phases of gravitational contraction. *Publication of the Astronomical Society of Japan, 13*, 450–452.

Henyey, L. G., Lelevier, R., & Levée, R. D. (1955). The early phases of stellar evolution. *Publications of the Astronomical Society of the Pacific, 67*(396), 154–160. doi:10.1086/126791

Herbig, G. H. (1974). Draft catalog of Herbig-Haro objects. *Lick Observatory Bulletin, 658*, 1–11.

Launhardt, R., Sargent, A. I., Henning, T., Zylka, R., & Zinnecker, H. (2000). Binary and multiple star formation in Bok globules. *Birth and Evolution of Binary Stars, Poster Proceedings of IAU Symposium No. 200 on the Formation of Binary Stars*. Potsdam, Germany: Bo Reipurth and Hans Zinnecker.

Reipurth, B., & Bertout, C. (Eds.). (1997). 50 years of Herbig–Haro research. From discovery to HST. *Herbig–Haro Flows and the Birth of Stars, IAU Symposium, 182*, 3–18.

Weisstein, E. W. (c. 1996–2007). Evaporating gas globule. In *Eric Weisstein's World of Astronomy*. Wolfram Research. http://scienceworld.wolfram.com/astronomy/EvaporatingGasGlobule.html

Yun, J. L., & Clemens, D. P. (1990, December 20). Star formation in small globules–Bart Bok was correct. *Astrophysical Journal Letters*, 365(2), L73–L76. doi:10.1086/185891

Yun, J. L., & Clemens, D. P. (1992, January). Discovery of outflows from young stellar objects in BOK globules. *Astrophysical Journal Letters*, 385, L21–L25.

Speculations and observations concerning the very first stars can be found in the following sources:

Heger, A., Fryer, C. L., Woosley, S. E., Langer, N., & Hartmann, D. H. (2003). How massive single stars end their life. *Astrophysical Journal*, 591, 288–300. doi:10.1086/375341

Overbye, D. (2015, June 17). "Traces of Earliest Stars That Enriched Cosmos are Spied." *New York Times*. https://www.nytimes.com/2015/06/18/science/space/astronomers-report-finding-earliest-stars-that-enriched-cosmos.html Retrieved 2019-04-20.

Rydberg, C. E., Zackrisson, E., Lundqvist, P., & Scott, P. (2013, March). Detection of isolated Population III stars with the James Webb Space Telescope. *Monthly Notices of the Royal Astronomical Society*, 429(4), 3658–3664. doi:10.1093/mnras/sts653

Salaris, S. Degl'Innocenti, S. & Weiss, A. (1997). The age of the oldest globular clusters. *Astrophysical Journal*, 479(2), 665–672. Retrieved from http://iopscience.iop.org/article/10.1086/303909

Tominga, N., Hideyuki, U., & Ken'ichi, N. (2007). Supernova nucleosynthesis in population III 13-50 Msolar stars and abundance patterns of extremely metal-poor stars. *Astrophysical Journal*, 660(5), 516–540. doi:10.1086/513063

Trager, S. C., Faber, S. M., & Dressler, A. (2008). The stellar population histories of early-type galaxies–III. The Coma cluster. *Monthly Notices of the Royal Astronomical Society*, 386, 715–747. doi:10.1111/j.1365-2966.2008.13132.

Credits

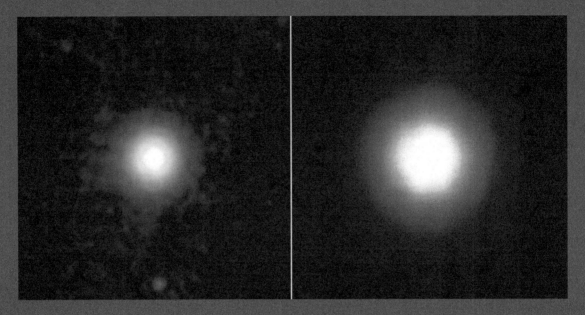

The main sequence star Vega, seen in infrared light by the Spitzer Space Telescope at 24 micrometers (left) and 70 micrometers (right). The "fuzzy" features in each image are due to dust in front of the star. Credit: NASA/JPL-Caltech/University of Arizona.

CHAPTER 17

GRAVITY AND MAIN SEQUENCE STARS

PURPOSE

To discuss the importance of mass for stars

OBJECTIVES

- To describe hydrostatic equilibrium
- To explore the ideal gas law
- To show the details of hydrogen fusion
- To describe the changes undergone by stars during their main sequence lives
- To estimate the lifespan of a star
- To compare semi-detached and contact binary stars to single stars

INTRODUCTION

Mass, as mentioned in previous chapters, is the most important property of a star. Knowing the initial mass of a star helps us estimate its luminosity, radius, temperature (both on its surface and in its core), lifespan, and more. As Einstein showed, mass determines gravity, and since astronomy is the discipline that deals with extremely large masses, gravity is the force of nature that matters most when studying stars and groups of stars. As such, stars are characterized by the forces that resist their own weight. In this chapter, we focus on how gravity matters for normal (main sequence) stars.

KEY TERMS

Antimatter: Particles that have all the same properties as their corresponding matter particles, except that one property will be exactly opposite (for example, an antielectron will have a positive instead of a negative charge). Matter and antimatter particles will annihilate each other and send out a pair of gamma rays if they meet

Center of mass: A position for a system of objects where we can mathematically treat the system as if all the system's mass were at that point. Commonly discussed as a point that each star in a binary system orbits

CNO cycle: A six-step reaction cycle by which hydrogen is converted into helium and energy, using the elements carbon, nitrogen, and oxygen as catalysts. The process most preferred by stars with more than twice the mass of the Sun

Contact binary: A binary system where both stars share their outer atmospheres

Detached binary: A binary system where the stars are far enough away from each other that their outer atmospheres do not touch

Deuterium: A hydrogen nucleus consisting of a proton and a neutron

Electromagnetism: One of the fundamental forces of nature. Much stronger than gravity and also unlimited in range. Possesses both positive and negative charges, meaning that it can be either repulsive or attractive

Electron: A fundamental particle, the defining property of which is a set amount of negative charge

Gravity: One of the fundamental forces of nature. Although the weakest of the fundamental forces of nature, it is important in astronomy because (a) it is solely attractive, whereas a force such as electromagnetism can both attract and repel, and (b) it has unlimited range, whereas a force such as the strong nuclear force is restricted to the atomic nucleus

Hydrostatic equilibrium: When gas pressure from the interior of a star, pushing outward, is equal to the inward pressure due to the star's own weight (gravity)

Lifespan: Simply, the amount of time astronomers expect a star to exist

Main sequence star: A star that specifically uses hydrogen as nuclear fuel inside its core

Mass transfer: The movement of gas from one star to another

Neutrino: A particle with no electric charge and extremely low mass/energy. It is often the product of weak force radioactive decay and is part of hydrogen fusion

Neutron: A particle with no electric charge and almost the same mass as a proton. It does not feel electric forces but does exert strong nuclear forces and therefore helps hold atomic nuclei together

Proton: A particle some 1,800 times more massive than and possessing the same amount of charge as an electron, except that its charge is positive. The number of protons at the center (nucleus) of an atom defines which element it is

Proton-proton chain: A series (chain) of nuclear reactions by which hydrogen is converted into helium and energy. The process most preferred by stars with less than twice the mass of the Sun

Roche lobe: A region surrounding a star where its gravity's influence tends to pull objects into it. A concept that arises in discussions of binary systems

Semidetached binary: A binary system where the gravity of one object pulls material toward itself from its companion

Star: An object that naturally sustains nuclear fusion

Strong nuclear force: One of the fundamental forces of nature, responsible for holding protons and neutrons together inside atomic nuclei. The strongest of the forces, but extremely short range

Weak nuclear force: One of the fundamental forces of nature, responsible for certain types of radioactive decay. Extremely short range

Zero-age main sequence (also ZAMS): A theoretical main sequence for brand new stars

Bethe, Hans: A German physicist who outlined how hydrogen fusion can work inside stars

Eddington, Arthur: A British astronomer from the early 20th century who described in detail the physics of how stars behave in their interiors

Section 17.1: Hydrostatic Equilibrium

Stars are large balls of gas that hold themselves together via their own gravity, or weight. How does that work? Or, conversely, why don't stars collapse completely in on themselves?

Recall Newton's law of gravity:

Equation 17.1

$$F_g = -G\frac{Mm}{r^2}$$

which reminds us that the force of gravity is (a) only attractive, (b) depends on mass, and (c) depends on distance. Or, (a) gravity only tries to pull things to a common center, (b) the more massive the star, the higher its self-gravity, and (c) the larger across the star, the less its self-gravity at its surface.

Gravity does not require a fuel supply, nor does it have an off switch. Unless there is another force (or forces, plural) acting simultaneously to oppose gravity, then a star will collapse into itself. Since stars live for millions or even billions of years, such opposing forces not only must exist, but also be powerful in their own right.

One possible way to fight against the pull of gravity is via rapid rotation. As an object shrinks in size, it spins faster, due to conservation of angular momentum (see chapter 4 for further details). While most stars do not tend to rotate rapidly enough to make a noticeable difference, it is seen for a few stars (Figure 17.1).

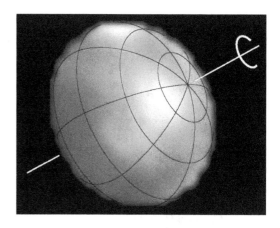

FIGURE 17.1. An image of Altair, from the MIRC imager on the CHARA array at Mt. Wilson. Whereas the Sun takes about a month to rotate once on its axis, Altair, which has roughly twice the diameter of the Sun, has a rotational period of only 9 hours.

However, while rotation can distort the shape, and therefore other items such as surface temperature and luminosity, it alone is insufficient to support a star against its own weight. More importantly, since the majority of stars rotate rather sedately—the Sun's average rotational period is about 1 month—spin cannot be the explanation for their stability. Nor will other methods, with one exception.

Stars are so hot, even at their surfaces, that they are completely gaseous. This implies that stars, even as large as they are, obey the ideal gas law. The ideal gas law states

Equation 17.2

$$PV = nRT$$

which states that the pressure P exerted by a gas is directly related to its temperature T, the number of particles (or "mols") of gas n, and is inversely related to its volume V. Which is to say, the pressure of the gas inside a star increases if (a) the temperature increases, (b) the number of particles increases, or (c) the volume of the star decreases.

If a gas is forced to shrink (by gravity, for example), its temperature and pressure will increase. If a gas is forced

Check Your Neighbor

Suppose the density of the core of a star increases. What will happen to the pressure inside the core? Hint: Density equals mass per unit volume.

to expand, conversely, its temperature and pressure will decrease. Finally, it is worth knowing that the temperature of a star at its core (16 million K inside the Sun, for example) is much higher than at its surface (6,000 K for the Sun). Other quantities such as pressure and density will behave likewise.

Until the early 20th century, the leading explanation for the energy output of the Sun was due to gravitational shrinking. Astronomers and physicists (the most famous being Lord Kelvin) estimated that the Sun could have an age of about 20 million years, given its luminosity and diameter. They discounted gas pressure as being able to keep a star's size stable, since there was no known source of energy to keep the gas hot enough. A star's brightness isn't free; if a star did not have a way to replenish the energy it was emitting into space, it would slowly collapse.

It was a British astronomer named Arthur Eddington (1882–1944) who first suggested convincingly that nuclear fusion was responsible for replenishing a star's energy. Einstein's famous equation, $E = mc^2$, implied that a small amount of mass could possibly be converted into a large amount of energy. Then-recent studies of radioactivity and mass differences between hydrogen and helium made it plausible as the source. Eddington did not know the details of

FIGURE 17.2. Arthur Eddington (left); Hans Bethe (right).

hydrogen fusion, nor the true percentages of hydrogen in stars (Cecilia Payne's work would not be published until years later), but his basic thesis was correct.

When the gas pressure pushing outward is equal to the pressure (force) due to gravity pulling inward, we term this *hydrostatic equilibrium* (Figure 17.3).

Eddington also suggested that other fusion processes might be present in stars. This turns out to be correct; other stars, in different stages or of different masses, can fuse helium, carbon, oxygen, silicon, and other elements and release energy thereby.

Finally, suppose we could somehow disturb the core of a star by slightly shrinking it. What would happen?

By shrinking, the temperature and pressure would increase accordingly. But the increase in pressure would act to expand the core. In other words, the core will have a tendency to restore itself should changes occur. This is negative reinforcement; or, if you will, a star has the equivalent of a thermostat inside it. Conditions inside the core of a star thus tend to change slowly, only as the percentage of hydrogen fuel notably changes, or for the special cases of supergiants near the ends of their lives.

FIGURE 17.3. Hydrostatic equilibrium: Gravity pulling in (red arrows) versus gas pressure pushing out (green arrows) inside a star.

Section 17.2: Nuclear Reactions Inside Stars

1. Nuclear Reactions

Before we begin this section, it will help to review some chemistry.

Chemical reactions depict the reaction substances on the left and the results on the right, using an arrow (rather than an equal sign) to show the direction of the reaction. Chemical reactions follow several basic rules, some of which are listed:

+ Individual atoms are identified by their chemical symbols, the same ones used in the periodic table. "H" stands for hydrogen, "He" for helium, "C" for carbon, and so on.
+ The total number of atoms on the left must be the same as the total number of atoms on the right.
+ The total number of elements on the left must be the same as the total number of elements on the right. For example, if the reaction requires two hydrogens on the left, there must be two hydrogens on the right.
+ The total amount of electric charge on the left must be the same as the total amount of electric charge on the right. For example, if the reaction has an extra electron on the left, it must have an extra electron (or, equivalently, a singly charged ion) on the right.
+ The total mass of the substances on the left must be the same as the total mass of the substances on the right.
+ The number of atoms in a single substance is denoted with a subscript. The famous formula for water is H_2O, meaning two hydrogen atoms and one oxygen atom.
+ If a substance is used more than once, it can be denoted with a number in front. If we used two water molecules in a reaction, for example, it would be $2H_2O$.

As an example, let's look at the combustion of propane. Propane has the chemical formula C_3H_8. When propane combines with oxygen, it forms carbon dioxide and water:

$$C_3H_8 + 5O_2 \rightarrow 3CO_2 + 4H_2O$$

Counting carefully, you will note both at left and right 3 carbon atoms, 8 hydrogen atoms, and 10 oxygen atoms. The chemical reaction has the effect of rearranging the atoms but does not change the atoms themselves. Other considerations (the requirement of a spark to start the reaction, the energy released by the reaction, etc.) are not usually included in the writing of the reaction, though of course chemists are aware of them.

When scientists discovered radioactivity in the late 1800s and realized the possibility of nuclear fusion a few decades later, they borrowed the basic format from chemistry—indeed, many of the scientists involved were chemists and physicists both—but realized they needed to change some of the underlying assumptions.

For nuclear reactions, it _is_ possible to change an element, or elementary particles. The restriction on mass conservation is also removed, to be replaced with a more comprehensive conservation of mass/energy, as suggested by Einstein's famous formula $E = mc^2$.

Therefore, the modified rules for nuclear reactions are as follows:

- Individual particles are identified by symbols, much like elements are. "p," for example, stands for the proton. But this is different than a hydrogen atom ("H"), in that a neutral hydrogen atom includes an electron orbiting the proton, whereas the "p" refers to just the proton alone.
- The total number of particles does _not_ have to be the same on the left as on the right.
- However, the total number of baryons[1] (particles like protons and neutrons) _does_ need to be the same on both sides.
- The total number of leptons[2] (particles like electrons and neutrinos) also needs to be the same on both sides.
- The total amount of electric charge must be the same on both sides (this rule did not change).
- The total amount of mass + energy must be the same on both sides. This implies that the total amount of mass alone or the total amount of energy alone _can_ change; again, this is facilitated by Einstein's $E = mc^2$.
- The numbering system for particles tends to be similar to that used for atoms in chemistry.

For example, a famous radioactive decay process has an isotope of uranium breaking apart to form thorium and helium:

$$^{238}_{92}\text{U} \rightarrow \,^{234}_{90}\text{Th} + \,^{4}_{2}\text{He}$$

The total mass of the particles is the same on the left (238) as on the right (234 + 4), and the total number of protons is the same on the left (92) as on the right (90 + 2). On the other hand, the elements are not the same on either side. As with chemistry, the energy involved is not explicitly stated.

Another important difference is that common nuclear reactions are hundreds of thousands to millions of times more energetic than chemical reactions. Whereas chemical energies refer to the binding and unbinding of electrons in various substances, nuclear energies come from the conversion of mass into energy.

2. The Proton-Proton Chain

Eddington proposed nuclear fusion as the energy source keeping stars hot inside but did not possess the details of the reaction, nor did he (or anyone else) originally know

Check Your Neighbor

The fusion of hydrogen into helium only converts 7/10 of a percent of the mass of the four hydrogens involved. Why then is it so energetic? Hint: What does the "c" in Einstein's famous formula $E = mc^2$ represent, and how large is it in standard units?

---

[1] A "baryon" is a particle that feels the strong nuclear force, which binds atomic nuclear particles together. Typical baryons are protons and neutrons. You may also have heard of quarks.

[2] Similarly to baryons, leptons are particles that feel nuclear forces; but in this case, the weak nuclear force. Weak forces are responsible for certain types (not all) of radioactive decay. Electrons and neutrinos are examples of leptons.

that stars primarily consist of hydrogen. By the 1930s, though, this knowledge became available (via Cecilia Payne, see chapter 15) and physicists were beginning to address the issue.

George Gamow and Carl Friedrich von Weizsäcker suggested the Sun is powered by the nuclear reaction

$$p + p \rightarrow {}_1^2D + e^+ + \nu$$

where two protons ("p") combine to form one deuterium ("D"), a positron (e^+) and a neutrino ("ν"). What are these particles?

- A deuterium is a form of a hydrogen nucleus, but instead of a bare proton, it has a neutron attached. Because deuterium is about twice as massive as a proton, deuterium is sometimes called "heavy" hydrogen.

- A positron is an example of an antimatter particle (you have probably heard about antimatter in science fiction). Antimatter was predicted by the British physicist P. A. M. Dirac in 1928 and has two interesting notions: First, an antimatter particle has the same properties as a "normal" particle, but usually with one difference; second, when an antimatter particle collides with its corresponding matter particle, they react and become a pair of gamma rays. Thus, the "positron," or "positive electron," has the same mass and behaviors as an electron, except that it has a positive charge.

- The neutrino, as its name suggests, is electrically neutral. The particle was proposed by Wolfgang Pauli in 1930 in order to conserve energy, momentum, and angular momentum (elementary particles by then had been shown to possess their own intrinsic angular momentum, or spin) in certain nuclear reactions. Neutrinos rarely interact with matter and individually carry little energy. Neutrinos are leptons, like electrons, and help conserve the number of leptons in nuclear reactions. We encountered neutrinos in our chapter on the Sun and will see them again in our chapter on supernovae; for now, they are necessary components of nuclear fusion but will not contribute to the energy supporting stars.

However, this reaction alone does not release enough energy to account for the stability of stars. Hans Bethe and Charles Critchfield, working during a conference on theoretical physics in 1938, completed the set of reactions needed, the most important of which are (including the first step) as follows:

$$p + p \rightarrow {}_1^2D + e^+ + \nu$$

$$e^+ + e^- \rightarrow \gamma + \gamma$$

$$ {}_1^2D + p \rightarrow {}_2^3He + \gamma$$

$$ {}_2^3He + {}_2^3He \rightarrow {}_2^4He + p + p$$

The positron collides with an electron (e^-) and turns into a pair of gamma rays. Other reactions include the deuterium colliding with another proton to produce a helium-3 (that is, 2 protons and 1 neutron) and a gamma ray, and two helium-3 nuclei producing a helium-4 and two protons.

Helium-4, the end product, consists of two neutrons and two protons and is the most stable of all such combinations. As a consequence, the most popular elements in the universe (after hydrogen and helium itself) are multiples of helium-4; examples include carbon-12 and oxygen-16.

Check Your Neighbor

In order for the final step to run, we need two helium-3 nuclei. What does this say about how often the other reactions need to run?

The net reaction, the combination of all the reactions, essentially boils down to this:

$$4p \rightarrow {}^4_2\text{He} + \text{energy}$$

Here, we have eliminated particles that show up on either side of the reaction and combined all releases of energy (mostly by gamma rays) into one term.

Let's examine some statistics regarding how the proton-proton chain is used inside the Sun:

+ The temperature at the core of the Sun is approximately 16 million K. Protons carry positive charges; they try to repel each other via electrical forces. In order to overcome this repulsive force, the protons must be moving at extremely high speeds, therefore the high temperatures.

+ Even so, the chances for a successful first step in the chain are very low. A pair of protons may wait on average a billion years before undergoing a reaction.[3]

+ If proton-proton reactions are so scarce, how can they keep the Sun upright against its own weight? The Sun is so large that, even with such a difficult reaction, about 600 million tons of hydrogen are converted into helium every second.

+ Only 7/10 of a percent of the mass of the four protons are converted into energy; the other 99.3% is turned into a helium-4 nucleus.

+ Nevertheless, this is an enormous amount of energy. The proton-proton chain releases approximately a million times more energetic (pound for pound) than burning gasoline.[4] Hydrogen fusion is also the most efficient type of fusion available for stars; while we will see that other elements may also serve as nuclear fuel, hydrogen is the "best."

+ Finally, why focus so much attention on the proton-proton chain instead of other reaction processes? Because about 93% of the Sun's energy is generated in this fashion.

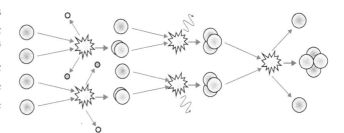

FIGURE 17.4. An illustration of the major steps in the proton-proton chain. At the far left, four protons go in; at the far right, one helium comes out. Not all reactants are shown.

3. The CNO Cycle

Hans Bethe (1906–2005) had a long and productive career, spanning over 7 decades, but it nearly didn't happen. Because he had Jewish ancestry in Hitler's Germany (his mother was Jewish), Bethe was fired from his position at Tübingen University. He bounced around several countries and had temporary positions before landing at Cornell University in the United States in 1935.

Upon returning to Cornell after a 1938 research conference, Bethe continued working on the question of nuclear fusion inside stars and realized there is another path to turning hydrogen into helium. He wrote up his results for both sets of reactions and submitted it to the journal *Physical Review* for publication. But his mother was still in Germany, and now fearing for her safety, Bethe needed a way to get her out of that country. Being a citizen of Strasbourg, which had once been French, he arranged for her to immigrate to the United States on the

---

[3] Also, when protons collide with other protons, they tend to form a combination called "protonium," two protons combined together to make an isotope of helium. This almost always decays back into separate protons. Only on very rare occasions does it decay into a deuterium, a positron, and a neutrino.

[4] For example, the complete proton-proton chain liberates 12.86 million electron-volts (MeV) of energy per reaction. In comparison, the burning of propane liberates 23 electron volts per reaction.

French quota, the German quota for immigrants having run out. To finance her move, he pulled his paper from *Physical Review* and instead entered it into a contest being run by the New York Academy of Sciences for the best unpublished paper on stellar energy, which Bethe won. This delayed paper (it would be published a few months later) became the basis for his 1967 Nobel Prize.

Besides the proton-proton chain, what did Bethe discover? Carbon, nitrogen, and oxygen nuclei can act as catalysts for hydrogen fusion via what is called the *CNO cycle*:

$$^{12}_{6}C + p \rightarrow ^{13}_{7}N + \gamma$$

$$^{13}_{7}N \rightarrow ^{13}_{6}C + e^{+} + \nu$$

$$^{13}_{6}C + p \rightarrow ^{14}_{7}N + \gamma$$

$$^{14}_{7}N + p \rightarrow ^{15}_{8}O + \gamma$$

$$^{15}_{8}O \rightarrow ^{15}_{7}N + e^{+} + \nu$$

$$^{15}_{7}N + p \rightarrow ^{12}_{6}C + ^{4}_{2}He$$

The CNO cycle contains more steps and requires the presence of carbon nuclei in order to operate, but releases the same amount of energy as does the proton-proton chain. Why then does a star like the Sun generate 93% of its energy via the proton-proton chain? The CNO cycle works better at higher temperatures, pressures and densities than the proton-proton chain, which do better at relatively less intense conditions.[5]

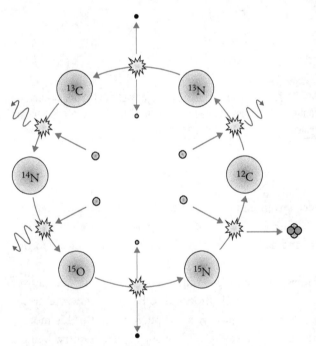

FIGURE 17.5. An illustration of the CNO cycle. It begins with the ^{12}C nucleus at the far right, then continues counterclockwise. As with the proton-proton chain, a total of four protons are transformed into one helium nucleus.

> **Check Your Neighbor**
>
> Why do we call the proton-proton set of reactions a "chain" while the carbon-nitrogen-oxygen facilitated reactions are a "cycle"?

The dividing line between proton-proton chain and the CNO cycle is at 1.4 $M_\odot$. This means that the vast majority of stars rely primarily or exclusively on the proton-proton chain, as stars with 1.4 $M_\odot$ or more are actually very rare. It doesn't seem so, given the stars we tend to see with the naked eye, but remember that the more massive stars are also the brighter stars.

What do stars do when they run out of hydrogen? We will address this question more fully in a future chapter, but we can note for now that, depending on the

---

[5] Specifically, the proton-proton chain goes as the fourth power of the temperature, whereas the CNO cycle goes as the 17th power of the temperature. The proton-proton chain is dominant for stars below 1.4 $M_\odot$, the CNO cycle dominant for stars above 1.4 $M_\odot$.

mass, it is possible for a star to use the helium produced by hydrogen fusion as fuel for the next stage in its life. Further, very massive stars can use other forms of fusion as they progress through their lives—topics for future chapters.

This leads us to a quick definition of a star. A *star* is an object large enough to naturally sustain itself against its own weight via nuclear fusion.

Section 17.3: The Main Sequence Life of a Star

While a star is fairly stable during its main sequence life, it does undergo important changes. After all, if it's fusing hydrogen into helium in its core, this means that the amount of hydrogen is decreasing and that of helium is increasing. Compared to the total mass of a star, the mass converted from hydrogen into helium each second, or even each year, is trivial, but differences will become apparent over millions of years.

Again, to analyze this situation, let's follow the progress of a 1 solar mass star as it consumes its hydrogen fuel. More massive stars will go through their fuel more quickly and lower mass stars more slowly, but the basic story will be the same for almost all stars.

In chapter 15, we introduced the zero-age main sequence (ZAMS), the diagonal (more or less) on the HR diagram that displays the luminosities and temperatures of brand-new stars. Let's take a look at it again, in conjunction with the Pleiades cluster (Figure 17.6):

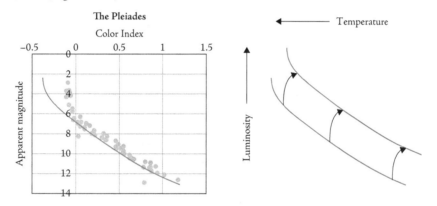

FIGURE 17.6. Left: An HR diagram (i.e., color-magnitude diagram) for the Pleiades. The red diagonal shows the ZAMS for the Pleiades. Right: An exaggerated picture, showing the thickening of the HR diagram of a cluster over time.

If the Pleiades were literally a brand-new cluster, all of its member stars would lie on the red ZAMS curve. But the Pleiades, while young, are not new; they have been around now for several hundred million years, and its stars are slowly aging. The Pleiades main sequence is somewhat thick, not thin, and some of its members have even run out of hydrogen fuel and begun their movement away from the main sequence.

Check Your Neighbor

Why are we looking at the HR diagram of a cluster of stars? Why not just look at an individual star instead?

The reasons for this behavior require some explaining. The interstellar medium consists of 90% hydrogen, 9% helium, and 1% everything else ("metals"); therefore, any new stars made from the ISM also contain the same percentages. The core of a new star thus begins with a rich mix of hydrogen fuel.

As time goes by (again, these are amazingly long-time scales for people), the star necessarily uses hydrogen to sustain itself, in the process turning it into helium. Thus, the relative amount of hydrogen decreases and that of helium increases (Figure 17.7):

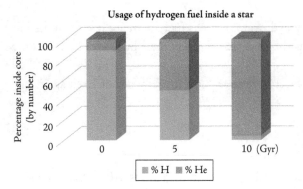

Usage of hydrogen fuel inside a star

FIGURE 17.7. The percentage (by number) of hydrogen and helium atoms in the core of a main sequence star over time (other atoms are ignored). Note that "Gyr" is short for "Gigayears," or billions of years.

It is important to keep in mind that the star's core is only capable of converting hydrogen into helium. Helium can in theory be used as a nuclear fuel, but only under more extreme conditions (i.e., higher densities and temperatures).

Furthermore, while hydrogen is a very efficient nuclear fuel, the "mix" (percentages) of hydrogen matters. A more rich mix of fuel, 90% hydrogen in the core, for example, makes it easier for hydrogen to be fused than a less rich mix of fuel. At this time in the Sun's life, for example, the mix is thought to be roughly 50–50 between hydrogen and helium. This means it is not as easy for hydrogen to react as it was when the Sun was younger.

We can therefore trace the following chain of logic:

- As a star gets older, its richness of hydrogen fuel decreases.
- The nuclear reactions inside the star become more difficult.
- To compensate for the slower rate of reactions, the core of the star shrinks.
- Shrinking the core heats up the gas, bringing the hydrogen nuclei closer together, making it easier for them to react.
- In response, the rest of the star expands due to the higher temperatures from the core.
- The temperature of the outside of the star drops.
- The overall (black body) color of the star moves toward longer wavelengths.
- The surface area of the star has expanded more than the flux of the star has dropped, and so the luminosity of the star increases.

A few caveats: First, it appears the star is thinking about how it needs to react to its internal changes. It isn't, of course; stars aren't truly living beings, even if we talk about their "lives" and "lifespans." It's more a limitation of our language at work.

Second, listing the various changes as separate steps makes it seem as if those steps are indeed separate. They are not; all the changes happen gradually and slowly.

Third, the amount of change is small, even over the complete life of a star. The Sun's luminosity may have doubled in its first 5 billion years; when the Sun becomes a giant, its luminosity will increase by several hundred times or more, and in a much shorter span of time.

FIGURE 17.8. Changes in the appearance of the Sun over time. Left: At its birth. Center: Today. Right: In 5 billion years, when it runs out of hydrogen in its core. The colors and changes in size are exaggerated for clarity.

In chapter 7, we introduced the notion of a "habitable zone," a region around a star where the heat of the star makes it possible for water to exist as a liquid. Now we see that a habitable zone isn't truly a permanent feature. In the early days of the solar system, Venus would have been inside the habitable zone of the Sun (whether it was inhabited or not is a different question!) and the Earth too far away; in fact, there is geological evidence that the Earth has passed through several worldwide ice ages during its history. Right now, the Earth is inside this region, while Venus is too close to the Sun. As the years go by, the Sun's luminosity will slowly increase, and the habitable zone will move outward. By some estimates, life on Earth (again, defined in this way) has about 250 million years or so left to it, after which the heat from the Sun will simply be too much, and "global warming" will take on a whole new meaning. Perhaps Mars will have become a habitable planet by then. But our species is only about a few hundred thousand years old, and these changes in the Sun's output are not an issue we will need to deal with anytime soon.

Section 17.4: Stellar Lifespans

How long can a star keep up hydrogen fusion?

A quick way to estimate the *lifespan* of a star, that is, the amount of time it sustains itself via nuclear fusion, is to compare its luminosity versus its mass. We've already looked at the zero-age main sequence and how it can be used to get ages from clusters of stars. Theoretical considerations also hint at how long stars can "live."

To understand how to estimate stellar lifespans, let's review how gravity and nuclear fusion operate inside the core of a star. The more massive a star, the more inward pressure is exerted by its own gravity (weight). The higher the inward pressure, the higher the temperature of the core. But the higher the temperature, the more rapid the nuclear reactions in the core, which leads to a higher outward pressure due to the faster speeds of the particles in the core. But the more rapid reaction rate implies the hydrogen fuel is expended more quickly. Long story short: The more massive a star, the harder it needs to work to support itself.

But a more massive star also has more fuel to "burn." Which factor counts more—the larger amount of fuel or the faster rate of consumption of fuel—when discussing the star's lifespan? We can't peer directly into the core of a star (yet!), but we can look at the proxies of both gravity and fuel consumption: the star's mass and the star's luminosity, respectively.

The time for a process to last (assuming it runs at an approximately constant rate) is the amount of the quantity in question divided by the rate at which it occurs. For example, if a car drives 30 miles at an average speed of 60 miles per hour, then the time to make the trip is

$$\text{time} = \frac{\text{distance}}{\text{speed}} = \frac{30 \text{ miles}}{60 \text{ miles/hour}} = 0.50 \text{ hours}$$

For a star's lifespan, we can estimate the time by dividing the amount of fuel (or its proxy, mass) by the rate at which the fuel is consumed (or its proxy, luminosity). To express this result in understandable terms, we use solar units for both mass and luminosity, then multiply this ratio by the lifespan of the Sun, 10 billion years:

Equation 17.3

$$\text{Lifespan} = \left(\frac{\text{mass}}{\text{luminosity}} \right) \times 10 \text{ billion years}$$

Sample Calculation

Which star, Beta Pictoris or van Biesbroeck's star, has a longer lifespan? Beta Pictoris has a mass of 2 $M_\odot$ and a luminosity of 20 $L_\odot$; van Biesbroeck's star has a mass of 0.1 $M_\odot$ and a luminosity of 0.001 $L_\odot$.

First, Beta Pictoris:

$$\text{Lifespan (Beta Pic)} = \left(\frac{2 \text{ M}_\odot}{20 \text{ L}_\odot} \right) (10 \text{ billion years}) = 1 \text{ billion years}$$

Next, van Biesbroeck's star:

$$\text{Lifespan (v. B.)} = \left(\frac{0.1 \text{ M}_\odot}{0.001 \text{ L}_\odot} \right) (10 \text{ billion years}) = 1000 \text{ billion years}$$

So, even though Beta Pictoris is more massive than van Biesbroeck's star, its lifespan is shorter because it burns its fuel so much faster. This expresses a general result: The more massive a star, the shorter its lifespan.

One final quick comment: These results are specifically considering main sequence stars only. In previous chapters, we merely noted that 90% of all stars are on the main sequence. Now we can more carefully define a *main sequence star*: one that uses hydrogen fuel in its core. Other luminosity classes (such as giants) also have nuclear fusion but use different fuels and/or have nuclear fusion happening in other locations besides their cores.

Section 17.5: Binary Stars

Up until now we have considered single stars in isolation. But a third or more stars live in multiple star systems. What can they tell us about themselves? Can they affect each other?

1. Determining Masses of Stars Using Binaries

Suppose two stars are in a mutual orbit. Both stars will move, of course, but there will be a specific point that always remains at rest between the two stars. This is the *center of mass* of the system and can be thought of as a point around which the stars balance each other. If the distance for each star from the center of mass is labeled with an *r*, then

Equation 17.4

$$\frac{r_1}{r_2} = \frac{m_2}{m_1}$$

with *m* representing the mass of a star and the numbers *1* and *2* identifying the individual stars.

We know that Kepler's third law (see chapter 3) applies for stars orbiting each other, just as it applies for planets orbiting the Sun. The difference is that the law now incorporates the total mass of the binary star system:

Equation 17.5

$$\frac{a^3}{P^2} = M$$

where *P* represents the period of the orbit in Earth years, *a* the semi-major axis of the mutual orbit of the stars (or, half of the sum of r_1 and r_2) in astronomical units, and *M* the total mass of the system in units of solar masses. These two equations, put together, help astronomers determine the individual masses of stars.

How might we do this? Let's consider a real example: the Sirius system.

Sample Calculation

Estimate the individual masses of Sirius A and Sirius B, given that the period of their mutual orbit is 50.13 years, the distance from Sirius B to the center of mass is about 14.0 au, and the distance from Sirius A to the center of mass is about 5.8 au. Find the masses of each star.

First, find the total mass of the system:

$$M = \frac{a^3}{P^2} = \frac{(19.78)^3}{(50.13)^2} = 3.08\ M_\odot$$

With $M = m_A + m_B$, some algebra shows that

$$m_A = \frac{M}{(1 + r_A / r_B)} = \frac{3.08\ M_\odot}{\left(1 + \left[\dfrac{5.8\text{au}}{14.0\text{au}}\right]\right)} = 2.07\ M_\odot$$

and $m_B = 1.01\ M_\odot$

More careful research shows that Sirius A has a mass of 2.063 $M_\odot$ and Sirius B a mass of 1.018 $M_\odot$. One issue we ignored is that the plane of the orbit of the two stars may be tilted compared to our line of sight; in this case, the angle was not extreme enough to make a large difference.

Check Your Neighbor

The orbital period of Sirius B around the center of mass of the Sirius system is about 50 years. What is the orbital period of Sirius A around the center of mass of the system?

2. Interacting Binary Stars

Mass, as we have seen, is the defining characteristic of a star. But what happens if a star's mass changes? One way that this can happen is by having stars interact with each other.

Suppose a small object moves at a moderate speed through space. If it is far enough away from a star, it will pass by the star or fall into orbit. But if the object is close enough, it will fall into the star due to the star's gravity. This notion, whether the object will "hit" the star or not, is called the collisional cross-section of the star (or, if you will, the size of the "target"). As indicated, the cross-section of the star depends on the speed of the object and the mass of the star. Astronomers have observed comets plunging into the Sun, so we know this can happen.

Instead, suppose we have two stars in a binary system. Then the question is not so much if the stars will collide with each other (while possible, such an event is exceedingly rare). The question is, if an object is near both stars, toward which star will it be pulled? The region surrounding a star for which this can happen is called a *Roche lobe*.

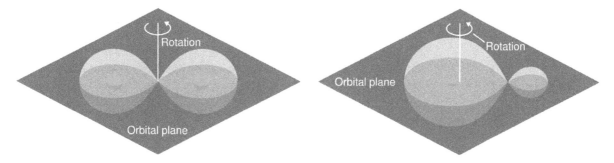

FIGURE 17.9. Roche lobes for two stars with identical masses (left); when one star has 10 times the mass of its companion (right). For each image, we are 60 degrees above the mutual orbital plane. Credit: Philip D. Hall.

If stars are far enough apart, the stars will both be well inside their respective Roche lobes, and no gas will be pulled from one star to the other. If the stars are close enough, it is possible their Roche lobes intersect each other; further, if one star is larger than its Roche lobe, the gas at its outer edges will flow toward the other star. If both stars overflow their Roche lobes, then matter will flow freely between the outer atmospheres of the two stars. These types of binaries are called *detached*, *semidetached*, and *contact*, respectively.

In practice, anything but a detached binary is rare. Despite their sizes, which are enormous in human terms (the Sun is close to a million miles across), they are actually fairly compact objects compared to the spaces they inhabit. Usually, a dramatic event or change needs to occur for one star to overflow its Roche lobe and spill onto its companion.

An example of a semidetached binary is the Algol system, visible to the naked eye in the constellation of Perseus. Algol is also by chance an eclipsing binary,[6] so we know to fair precision the respective masses of each of its stars. Interferometric images of the Algol system show a distortion of Algol B as the stars approach each other in their mutual orbits (Figure 17.10):

---

[6] The Algol system is suspected to possess a third companion star, extremely far from the other two stars and in orbit about them.

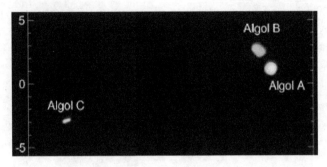

FIGURE 17.10. The Algol system imaged by CHARA in infrared light on August 12, 2007. The distortion of Algol B is real; the distortion of Algol C is not. Credit: Fabien Baron.

Interestingly, Algol A is a more massive main sequence star and Algol B is a less massive subgiant. This is opposite of what we expect; before, we made a point to emphasize that the more massive a star, the quicker it burns through its fuel. If the stars were detached, this would indeed be a mystery. However, the stars are so close to each other (they are about 0.060 astronomical units from each other and only need 2.87 days to complete a mutual orbit) that when Algol B became a subgiant, it quickly (by astronomy terms) outgrew its Roche lobe and began spilling gas onto Algol A, a process called *mass transfer*. This implies that Algol B was originally more massive than Algol A, but the two stars have traded places, mass wise.

What are the consequences of these interactions? Because Algol A is more massive than it was originally, it will need to burn its hydrogen fuel more quickly than before and its lifespan will be shortened somewhat. Conversely, Algol B finished its tour on the main sequence first, but now that its mass is less, it won't have to work as hard to support itself against its own weight, and its life will thus be somewhat extended. If (when?) Algol A itself moves off the main sequence, it too may possibly fill its Roche lobe and then either the transfer of mass will reverse itself, or the two stars may become a true contact binary, sharing each other's outer atmospheres.

How does this affect our understanding of the life cycles of stars? If stars live in binary (or other multiple) systems, and the stars are close enough to each other, they can significantly alter each other's destinies.

> **Check Your Neighbor**

Will the Sun ever change its mass due to mass transfer? (Hint: Do we live in a binary system?)

Summary

In this chapter, we discussed the following:

- How astronomers define stars

- Hydrostatic equilibrium: the balance of gas pressure versus gravity pressure for stars

- The specific reactions inside stars that convert hydrogen into helium and energy

- The major influences on the potential lifespan of a star, including the following:
  + Mass
  + Luminosity
  + The presence of a companion (as part of a multiple-star system)

- How orbits of binary stars can be used to estimate the masses of the individual stars in the system

Questions

1. A gas of set volume and number of particles has its temperature doubled. What happens to the pressure? What happens to the pressure if the temperature doubles and the volume is shrunk by half?

2. A star is sometimes described as having a "thermostat," a device found in most homes that controls the temperature. Let's explore how the thermostat might work:
   + Suppose the core of a star shrinks a little bit:

- What happens to the temperature of the core?
- What happens to the outward pressure of the core?
- What happens to the size of the core as a consequence?

- Suppose the core of a star expands a little bit:
  - What happens to the temperature of the core?
  - What happens to the outward pressure of the core?
  - What happens to the size of the core as a consequence?

3. Recall (from chapter 10) how gas properties like temperature and pressure are related to the speed of a gas. What happens to the average speed of protons in the core of a star if the temperature increases? If the pressure increases?

4. Sirius A is a little over twice as massive as the Sun. Compare their following properties:
   - Which star (Sirius A or the Sun) has a higher surface temperature?
   - Which star has a higher temperature in its core?
   - Which star favors using the proton-proton chain of reactions more in its core?
   - Which star has a larger radius?
   - Which star has a longer lifespan?
   - Which star has a brighter luminosity?

5. The Algol system has two interacting stars in a mutual eclipsing orbit (there is a third star, much farther away). The mutual period of the two stars is 2.87 days. The heavier star (Algol A) is about 0.010 au from the center of mass and the lighter star (Algol B) is about 0.050 au from the center of mass. Determine the mass of each star.

Activities

▸ *Astrophysics activity 17.1*: Use simulations to address how gases behave inside stars.

Works Referenced

The photos of Vega are from the Spitzer Space Telescope: http://photojournal.jpl.nasa.gov/catalog/PIA07218

The montage of rapidly rotating stars is from the CHARA (Center for High Angular Resolution Astronomy) array, out of Georgia State University (courtesy of John Monnier): www.chara.gsu.edu/astronomers/science-highlights/54-rapid-rotators. Specific findings for each star are listed as follows:

Regulus and Beta Cas: Che, X., Monnier, J. D., Zhao, M., Pedretti, E., Thureau, N., Mérand, A., ... & Sturmann, L. (2011). Colder and hotter: Interferometric imaging of β Cassiopeiae and α Leonis. *Astrophysical Journal*, 732(2), 68–80. Retrieved from http://adsabs.harvard.edu/abs/2011ApJ...732...68C

Rasalhague and Alderamin: Zhao, M., Monnier, J. D., Pedretti, E., Thureau, N., Mérand, A., ten Brummelaar, T., ... & Farrington, C. (2009). Imaging and modeling rapidly rotating stars: α Cephei and α Ophiuchi. *Astrophysical Journal*, 701(1), 209–224. Retrieved from http://adsabs.harvard.edu/abs/2009ApJ...701..209Z

Altair: Monnier, J. D., Zhao, M., Pedretti, E., Thureau, N., Ireland, M., Muirhead, P., ... & Berger, D. (2007). Imaging the surface of Altair. *Science*, 317(5836), 342. Retrieved from http://adsabs.harvard.edu/abs/2007Sci...317..342M

Arthur Eddington's life and relevant work for this chapter can be found in Plummer, H. C. (1945). Arthur Stanley Eddington, 1882–1944. *Obituary Notices of Fellows of the Royal Society*, 5(14), 113–126. doi:10.1098/rsbm.1945.0007

Eddington, A. S. (1916). On the radiative equilibrium of the stars. *Monthly Notices of the Royal Astronomical Society*, 77, 16–35.

Eddington, A. S. (1920, October). The internal constitution of the stars. *The Scientific Monthly*, 11(4), 297–303.

Hans Bethe's life and relevant work can be found in the following sources:

Bernstein, J. (1980). *Hans Bethe, prophet of energy*. New York, NY: Basic Books.

Schweber, S. S. (2012). *Nuclear forces: The making of the physicist Hans Bethe*. Cambridge, MA: Harvard University Press.

The discovery of antimatter was announced in Dirac, P. A. M. (1928). The quantum theory of the electron. *Proceedings of the Royal Society A*, 117(778), 610–624. doi:10.1098/rspa.1928.0023

The history of the discovery and naming of the neutrino are in Brown, L. M. (1978). The idea of the neutrino. *Physics Today*, 31(9), 23–28.

Statistics on binary stars come from Duchêne, G., & Kraus, A. (2013, August). Stellar multiplicity. *Annual Review of Astronomy and Astrophysics*, 51(1), 269–310. doi:10.1146/annurev-astro-081710-102602

Harvard-Smithsonian Center for Astrophysics. (2006). *Most Milky Way stars are single*. Retrieved from https://www.cfa.harvard.edu/news/2006-11

Data for the Sirius system comes from Bond, H., Schaefer, G. H., Gilliland, R. L., Holberg, J. B., Mason, B. D., Lindenblad, I. W., … & Spada, F. (2017). The Sirius System and its astrophysical puzzles: Hubble Space Telescope and ground-based astrometry. *Astrophysical Journal*, 840(2), 70. doi:10.3847/1538-4357/aa6af8

Images and movies of Algol and other semidetached binaries are from CHARA out of Georgia State University: www.chara.gsu.edu/astronomers/science-highlights/55-eclipsing-binaries

Credits

Polaris, the current North Star, is actually a three-star system. The brightest component, Polaris Aa, is a yellow Cepheid variable with a period of only 4 days. Polaris B is an F3 main sequence star and Polaris Ab an F6 main sequence star. Polaris B is 2,400 au from Polaris Aa, and was discovered in 1779 by William Hershel; Polaris Ab is so close to its supergiant companion (18.8 au) that it wasn't discovered until 1929. Credit: NASA/HST.

CHAPTER 18

THE ENDS OF STARS I

To discuss how low-mass stars end their lives

OBJECTIVES

- ▸ To review the importance of hydrostatic equilibrium
- ▸ To discuss nuclear fusion of helium in stars
- ▸ To show the origins of subgiant and giant stars
- ▸ To show the origins of planetary nebulae and white dwarfs
- ▸ To compare the ends of single versus binary stars

INTRODUCTION

A normal, or main sequence star, is the stage at which stars spend the majority of their lives, being determined by the fusion of hydrogen into helium in their cores. But what happens when the hydrogen fuel runs out?

We will follow the progress of a star like the Sun as it nears the end of its life. Such stars do not simply fade away, nor do they necessarily explode. Rather, there is a detailed process that such stars follow, and which gives rise to many of the objects in stellar astronomy familiar to us: giant stars, planetary nebulae, white dwarfs, and at least one version of supernova. We will also compare the progress of a single star like the Sun versus the case of binary systems where the stars are close enough to significantly affect each other.

We will leave the story of stars much more massive than the Sun (typically 8 $M_\odot$ or more) for chapter 19. Finally, we will wrap up our discussion of the ends of stars with neutron stars and black holes in chapter 20.

KEY TERMS

Algol paradox: A situation possible for stars in a semi-detached binary, where the less-massive star is the further along in its life than its more-massive companion

Cepheids (also **Cepheid variables**): A type of variable that both is very bright and has a distinct periodic behavior

Chandrasekhar limit (also **mass limit**): Electron degeneracy pressure cannot support a white dwarf larger than 1.44 $M_\odot$; named after its discoverer

Contact binary: A binary system where the two stars are close enough to freely share their outer atmospheres

Degeneracy pressure (also **electron degeneracy pressure**): Outward pressure exerted by overcrowded electrons because of the exclusion principle

Degenerate matter: Matter so crowded together that the exclusion principle is at work supplying outward pressure to sustain its weight

Electron degeneracy pressure: Outward pressure exerted by overcrowded electrons because of the exclusion principle

Exclusion principle (also **Pauli Exclusion principle**): A quantum-mechanical property that only allows one subatomic particle in one location at one time

Giant: A star whose outer atmosphere has been expanded about 100 times its original size

Giant branch: The region of the HR diagram where giants are located

Helium flash: An explosive fusion of much of the helium of a low-mass star, changing its core from degenerate to "normal" matter

High mass star: a star whose initial mass is more than about 8 solar masses

Low mass star: a star whose initial mass is less than about 8 solar masses

Nova (also **classical nova**): A flare from hydrogen gas fusing explosively on the surface of a white dwarf

Planetary nebula: The outer atmosphere of a giant that has been expelled back into the interstellar medium

Roche lobe: The "boundary" around a star defined by its gravity; important for semi-detached binaries

RR Lyrae: The type of variable that the Sun will become near the end of its life

Semi-detached binary: A binary system where one object's gravity is ripping material off of its companion

Shell burning: Fusion occurring not at the core, but in a spherical shell(s) concentric around the core of a star

Stellar remnant: The remains of a dead star; can include both a planetary nebula and a white dwarf

Subgiant: A star in the process of transforming from the main sequence to the giant branch

Triple-alpha process: A three-step reaction process that converts helium into carbon and energy

Type Ia supernova: An explosion that occurs when a white dwarf is pushed over its mass limit

Variable: A stage in the life of a star where it changes its brightness dramatically. *Periodic* (or quasi-periodic or recurrent) variables repeat their behaviors; *cataclysmic* variables represent explosions. The categories are not necessarily exclusive

White dwarf: The remnant of a low-mass star held up via the *exclusion principle*

Blazkho, Sergey: A Russian astronomer of the early 20th century who determined that RR Lyrae variables have a secondary period of variability

Chandrasehkar, Subhartha: An Indian physicist of the mid-20th century who determined that white dwarfs have a mass limit determined by the exclusion principle

Fleming, Williamina: A Scottish-American astronomer of the late 19th/early 20th century who discovered the nature of RR Lyrae variables. One of the female astronomers who worked under Edward Pickering at Harvard Observatory

Fowler, William A.: An American physicist of the mid-20th century who helped determine how nuclear fusion operates in stars

Hershel, William: A German/British astronomer of the late 18th/early 19th centuries, who (among many other findings), discovered and named *planetary nebulae*

Messier, Charles: A French astronomer of the mid-18th century who compiled a catalog of deep-sky objects in order to facilitate his searches for comets

Section 18.1: Review of Luminosity Classes

Before we begin our story regarding the ends of stars, it would be good to review which classes of stars are which.

The Yerkes luminosity classes are also a way of detailing the various life stages of stars, with some modifications. Some behaviors (such as planetary nebulae) are not stars as such but are still important stages. As discussed in the previous chapter, protostars don't really show up on the HR diagram, but other life stages are there. In rough chronological order, they are as follows:

+ Main sequence: Mature stars; that is, stars that are fully formed and using hydrogen fusion in their cores

- Subgiants: Stars that have used up hydrogen in their cores and have begun hydrogen shell burning
- Giants: Stars that are using helium fusion in their cores
- Variables: Stars that have become unstable in their cores and/or shells
- Planetary nebulae: Outer layers of stars that have been ejected back into the interstellar medium
- White dwarfs: The dead remnants of stars

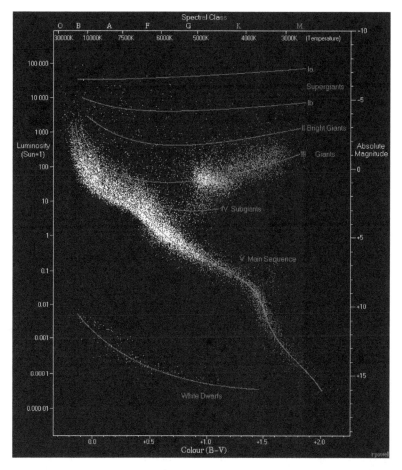

FIGURE 18.1. The HR diagram, using 22,000 stars observed by the Hipparcos satellite. Credit: Richard Powell.

You might note we have skipped several items. Some are due to interactions between stars (such as Type Ia supernovae) and will be discussed later in this chapter. Others (such as super-giants) are for very massive stars (8 $M_\odot$ is a rough cutoff) and will be dealt with in their own chapter. Further exotic remnants of stars (neutron stars and black holes) also receive their own treatments in a separate chapter. Finally, other factors such as unusual metallicities or rapid rotation can affect the development of a star. As usual, life is not simple, and we always have complicated situations to consider.

To start, here we will be reviewing the fates of stars much like the Sun, focusing our attention on single solar-mass stars. The galaxy is not so old (granted, it sounds odd to say an object 10 billion-plus years old is too young) as to follow the fates of stars less than 0.8 $M_\odot$ or so, since none of them will have run out of fuel yet, even if they formed at the beginning of the galaxy's history. But stars greater than 8 $M_\odot$ follow a different path, and 85% of all stars are 1 $M_\odot$ or smaller, so it makes sense to restrict our discussions to stars near the Sun's mass, at least for the time being.

Section 18.2: Subgiants: Transitional Stages

As has been the case for forming stars, so it is for aging stars: Gravity always tries to compress the star, and the star's class is characterized by how the star resists the compression.

When a star is on the main sequence, it resists the inward compression of gravity via gas pressure, which is sustained by energy generated via hydrogen fusion (see chapter 17 for details). Stars like the Sun (i.e., one solar mass or so)[1] have cores that don't mix well with their surroundings, and so the inner 10% of the star (by mass) is virtually separate from the rest of the star, at least in terms of how it acts. Hydrogen is slowly converted into helium inside the core, but the hydrogen outside the core—the other 90% of the star—is pretty much left alone.

---

[1] Stars with masses much less than the Sun, 0.4 $M_\odot$ or less, are fully convective; that is, the core mixes freely with the rest of the star. This means far more hydrogen fuel is available for such a star, which extends its lifespan enormously.

At some point, the core has run out of hydrogen to use as fuel. This means there is no longer a source of energy to replenish energy lost to space. The star therefore starts doing the following:

- The outward gas pressure in the core drops
- The core begins to shrink as the inward pull of gravity is stronger than the outward push of gas pressure
- This forces the core gas to shrink, increasing its temperature
- Gas surrounding the core also feels a temperature increase
- Gas surrounding the core begins to fuse hydrogen into helium, a process called *shell burning*
- The higher temperatures of the shell produce more energy (especially as far as the rest of the star is concerned) than the core
- The increase in energy production increases the gas pressure from within, and the exterior of the star expands
- This forces the outer gas to expand, decreasing its temperature
- The outside of the star becomes larger and its color shifts to longer wavelengths

This process continues until the star becomes a giant, which is when helium fusion takes over in the core. As with previous similar discussions, the list is not a series of discreet steps, but a chain of logic showing what happens and why. All the actions are happening simultaneously.

Check Your Neighbor

How is energy lost to space by a star?

How long do these events take to play out? The Sun's main sequence lifespan is a little less than 10 billion years; it may spend a few more as a subgiant and/or giant. Obviously we can't wait that long to confirm our estimates, but astronomers can and do compare their models to the general population of stars. An example of some model calculations is depicted in Table 18.1.

TABLE 18.1. Transitions of Main Sequence Stars to Giants

Star Mass ($M_\odot$)	Example	M.S. (Gyrs)	"Hook" (Gyrs)	Sub (Gyrs)
.6	61 Cygni B	58.8	N/A	5.1
1.0	The Sun	9.3	N/A	2.6
2.0	Sirius	1.2	0.010	0.022
5.0	Alkaid	0.1	0.0004	0.015

"M.S." represents time spent on the Main Sequence, "Hook" represents the time between the end of H core burning and the onset of H shell burning, and "Sub" represents time spent as a subgiant. Credit: Pols et al. (1998). "Stellar Evolution Models for Z = 0.0001 to 0.03". Monthly Notices of the Royal Astronomical Society. **298** (2) 525.

The same model suggests what we can expect for a star's properties as it enters and leaves the subgiant stage (Table 18.2).

TABLE 18.2. Changing Conditions of Subgiant Stars

Star Mass	Beginning			End		
($M_\odot$)	T(K)	R ($R_\odot$)	L ($L_\odot$)	T(K)	R ($R_\odot$)	L ($L_\odot$)
0.6	4760	0.9	0.9	4630	1.2	0.6
1.0	5770	1.2	1.5	5030	2.0	2.2
2.0	7490	3.6	37	5220	5.4	20
5.0	14,540	6.3	1570	4740	44	870

T(K) is the effective surface temperature of the star; R($R_\odot$) is the radius of the star in solar units; L($L_\odot$) is the luminosity of the star in solar units. Credit: Pols et al. (1998). "Stellar Evolution Models for Z = 0.0001 to 0.03". Monthly Notices of the Royal Astronomical Society. **298** (2) 525.

The model agrees with our basic understanding of stars. First, the more massive a star, the quicker everything happens. Second, this isn't a small difference. A star like 61 Cygni B, with 0.6 M$_\odot$, might spend 60 billion years on the main sequence;—again, remember the galaxy itself is only 10–12 billion years old—and another 5 billion as a subgiant. But a star like Alkaid, with 5 M$_\odot$, "only" has a main sequence life of 100 million years and spends much less time (15 million years) as a subgiant. Note that in all cases, though, a star easily spends the majority of its life as a main sequence star, telling us that hydrogen core fusion is the most stable source of energy a star can have.

Third, the outer appearance of a star—properties like its surface temperature, its radius, and its luminosity—agree with our depictions earlier. In all cases, the surface temperature of the star drops and its radius increases, affecting its luminosity accordingly. Finally, the changes are more dramatic as the mass of the star increases. Much like the questions regarding lifetimes, the larger masses require larger changes in other properties. The temperature of a star such as Alkaid drops far more (by about a factor of 3), both in absolute and percentage terms, than a 61 Cygni B. In fact, a star with as low a mass as 61 Cygni B barely notices any changes at all. It is worth mentioning that these are <u>not</u> the same statements to be made as will be for stars that have joined the giant branch—that is a different situation altogether.

Check Your Neighbor

<u>Why</u> do events happen more quickly for more massive stars compared to less massive stars?

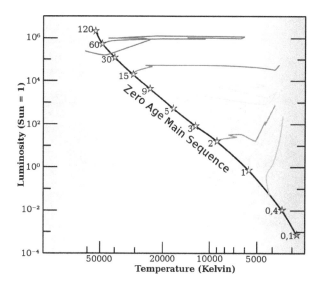

FIGURE 18.2. Transitions of stars from the main sequence to the giant branch. The numbers along the main sequence refer to the masses of the stars in solar units.

Finally, there is a column in Table 18.1 labeled "hook." What is that all about?

The changeover from hydrogen fusion in the core of a star to hydrogen fusion in a concentric shell surrounding the core is not necessarily smooth. The lower the mass of the star, the easier the transition, and stars like the Sun or smaller, simply move from one version of energy generation to the next. But this isn't the case for larger stars. Stars like Sirius (around 2 M$_\odot$, for example) have a larger region surrounding the core, susceptible to convection. Therefore, the core becomes larger as it pulls hydrogen into itself from its surroundings. The net effect is to make a core much larger than it would otherwise be and to deplete the shell surrounding the core of hydrogen. Eventually, the core does completely run out of hydrogen, but with a lack of hydrogen in the shell around it, shell burning is delayed until the core shrinks much more and hydrogen in the rest of the star falls in after it. On the HR diagram, this process is represented as a sharp turn or "hook" in the post-main sequence track of the star.

One last issue is to consider how the metallicity of a star affects its progress. A Population II star, with far less metals than a Population I star like the Sun, tends to have higher temperatures and luminosities by the end of their subgiant lives. This tendency is more pronounced for lower mass stars than high mass stars; by the time we consider stars 8 M$_\odot$ or larger, the differences in metal content no longer appear to matter.

Section 18.3: Life on the Giant Branch

Stars with less than 0.4 M$_\odot$ will never become giants, as they do not have the ability to generate the core temperatures and pressures necessary to go beyond hydrogen fusion in their cores. Instead, they will end their lives as helium dwarfs, remnants of stars made almost entirely of helium. We do not expect them to shrink due to

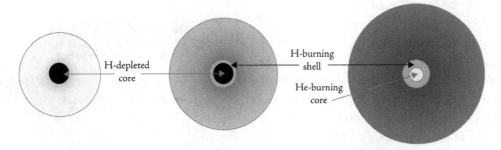

FIGURE 18.3. Changes in a star's surface (outer circles) and its core and concentric shells (inner circles) as it transitions from hydrogen to helium fusion. Left: A star at the end of its main sequence lifetime. Center: A star during its subgiant phase. Right: A star at the beginning of its giant phase. Sizes are indicative and not to scale.

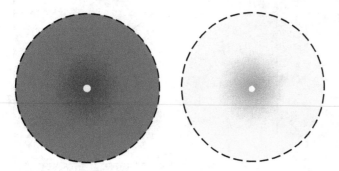

FIGURE 18.4. The enormous changes in size for a giant star, compared to its original main sequence self. Left: The surface of the giant (large dashed red circle) compared to the original main sequence star (small yellow circle at center). Right: The surface of the original main sequence star (large dashed yellow circle) compared to the core of the giant (small white circle at center). The size differences in both cases are still about three times too small; if drawn to scale, the inner circles could not be seen clearly.

gravity indefinitely, however, for reasons that will be discussed later in this chapter.

Stars larger than 0.4 $M_\odot$ will have the ability to go beyond hydrogen fusion, whether in their cores or the surrounding concentric shells. Our task in this section is to follow what changes occur to such stars (like the Sun) when this happens.

As we saw in the previous section, main sequence stars tend to lower their effective surface temperatures as they transition into subgiants. This trend continues when the stars become giants, as do the increases in the radii of their surfaces. But a big difference is how much the radii change compared to the temperatures; while the temperatures drop enough for a star to move over one or two spectral types (from G to M-type, for example), the stars may grow by a factor of 100 or more! For example, the Sun, which is just shy of 1/100 of an astronomical unit across, may swell to become larger than an astronomical unit in radius when it stabilizes on the giant branch. The incredible growth in size also may add to the luminosity of the star, though (as seen earlier for subgiants) the effect is greater the lower the initial mass of the star.

Why the incredible shift in size? The story of a star entering into its giant phase is similar to the one we've already told for subgiants, but many of the changes are much exaggerated in comparison. Let's tell the story in bullet form first:

+ A concentric shell of hydrogen gas surrounding the core continues to fuse into helium
+ The core continues to shrink as the inward pull of gravity is stronger than the outward push of gas pressure
+ This forces the core gas to shrink, increasing its temperature
+ Eventually the core temperature (and density) becomes high enough to start helium fusion
+ Gas surrounding the core also feels a jolt of temperature increase
+ The increase in energy production from both core and shell increases the gas pressure from within, and the exterior of the star expands
+ This forces the outer gas to expand, decreasing its temperature
+ The outside of the star becomes larger and its color shifts to longer wavelengths

Again, this is more of a chain of logic than a series of discreet steps (with some exceptions). The larger change here is the addition of a new source of energy: helium fusion. Helium, the leftovers (ash, if you will) of the previous round of fusion become the new fuel for the next round. When the Sun becomes a giant, it will turn helium into carbon in its core. This has major consequences.

We might expect a helium nucleus (element #2) to combine with another helium nucleus to form a beryllium nucleus (element #4). This reaction requires energy instead of liberating it; furthermore, beryllium-8 is unstable. Instead, the combining of helium into beryllium is a way-stop to carbon (element #6). The reactions look like this:

Check Your Neighbor

If the Sun's radius indeed grows larger than an astronomical unit in size when it completes its transformation into a giant, what does that mean for the Earth?

$$ {}^{4}_{2}\text{He} + {}^{4}_{2}\text{He} \rightarrow {}^{8}_{4}\text{Be} $$

$$ {}^{4}_{2}\text{He} + {}^{8}_{4}\text{Be} \rightarrow {}^{12}_{6}\text{C} $$

The reaction of helium with beryllium does produce a large amount of energy and therefore is suitable for contributing energy to the core of the star. By the way, this pair of reactions together is called the *triple-alpha process*, because (a) helium nuclei were originally called "alpha" particles when they were first discovered, and (b) three alpha particles are used to produce a single carbon nucleus.

A secondary reaction can also occur between helium and carbon:

$$ {}^{4}_{2}\text{He} + {}^{12}_{6}\text{C} \rightarrow {}^{16}_{8}\text{O} $$

By interesting coincidence, the amount of energy released during the making of oxygen from helium and carbon is nearly the same as that released by making carbon from helium and beryllium.[2] Of course, the star's core needs to make the carbon first before the reaction to make oxygen can happen.

We have several things to say about all this. First, the production of carbon and oxygen in the cores of giants helps explain why they are the next most popular elements in the universe (oxygen is #3 and carbon #4). Second, the energy

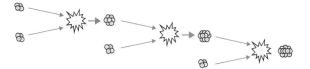

FIGURE 18.5. An illustration of the major steps in the triple-alpha process, plus an extra step. Two helium nuclei (alpha particles) make one beryllium; one beryllium and another alpha make carbon. The extra step shows one carbon and one helium making oxygen.

liberated by these reactions goes into heating the core and replenishing the energy lost by the star as it shines, thus halting the collapse of the star. The star once again is a stable object and remains so as long as the helium lasts.

But helium isn't as good a fuel as hydrogen, for these reasons:

+ The triple-alpha process requires much higher temperatures and densities than either the proton-proton chain or the CNO cycle for hydrogen fusion. The very center of the Sun is at about 16 million K (it drops to 7 million K at the edge of its core); the center of a comparable giant will be in the neighborhood of 100 million K, about six times hotter.

+ We get more energy out of hydrogen fusion than helium fusion. A complete set of reactions turning four protons into one helium nucleus liberates 12.86 MeV per reaction. The energy liberated by the triple-alpha process is 7.28 MeV per reaction. Hydrogen fusion therefore gives us more "bang for the buck."

+ Helium fusion won't last as long. The Sun's main sequence lifetime is (more or less) about 10 billion years long; it will be able to use helium fusion for about 1 billion years. Imagine going to the gas station to fill

---

[2] The step reacting helium and beryllium into carbon liberates 7.367 million electron-volts (MeV) of energy; the step reacting helium with carbon into oxygen liberates 7.162 MeV.

up your car. You have two choices of fuel, brand A or brand B. Brand B costs more than brand A, it is harder on your engine, and it gives you a significantly lower gas mileage. Which brand would you prefer, if you had a choice?

The end results are stunning. In order to shrink to the incredibly high temperatures needed for the triple-alpha process to operate, the core has shrunk to several times its original radius, and the density has correspondingly increased dramatically (remember that density goes as the inverse of volume, or the cube of the radius). In fact, for a star originally the mass of the Sun, the core may be no larger across than the Earth! By contrast, the outside of the star (its "surface") may have grown by a similar factor. In return, since the surface of the star has expanded, its temperature has dropped. A star like the Sun, whose effective surface temperature may

Check Your Neighbor

The Sun has an appreciable supply of helium in its core. Why then doesn't the Sun already use helium fusion to generate energy?

Check Your Neighbor

Refer to the HR diagram in this chapter (Figure 18.1). Suppose the Sun transitions from a main sequence star to a giant. In which vertical direction will it go on the diagram: up or down? In which horizontal direction will it go: left or right?

have been close to 6,000 K, can drop in half to 3,000 K by the time its growth stabilizes. Such stars are often called "red" giants, since their colors are more in the red region of the visible light spectrum. Finally, the luminosity has jumped up by several magnitudes, the increase in size (radius) more than offsetting the decrease in temperature.

One last wild detail needs to be mentioned. The cores of stars with total masses less than 2.25 $M_\odot$ don't fuse helium willingly, so to speak. As the core shrinks, a quantum-mechanical property known as *degeneracy pressure* comes into play and takes over the task of gas pressure in opposing the inward pull of gravity. Degeneracy pressure isn't affected by temperature, and so the core continues to get hotter and hotter without appreciably changing size. Finally, when the temperature reaches 100 million K, the helium fuses in a rush, an event nicknamed the *helium flash*. For just a few seconds, the energy output of the core is 100 billion times stronger than the star's normal rate of energy production. In another setting, this would tear apart the star and the explosion would be seen to light up its surrounding portion of the galaxy,[3] but degenerate matter is a different phase of matter. Instead of heating up the gas of the star or blowing it apart, the energy released goes into transforming the degenerate matter back into "normal" matter, and the change barely even registers on the rest of the star. Once the helium flash is over, the star's core settles down to fuse its remaining helium at a calmer rate, and the star's radius and luminosity also decreases rather quickly—by astronomy standards, that is, being on the order of 10,000 years—and the star takes its place on the giant branch. Stars over 2.25 $M_\odot$ don't go through this internal stage, but instead transition far more gradually to helium fusion in their cores.

Any star of mass greater than 0.4 $M_\odot$, and recall the universe isn't old enough for all such stars to have run out of hydrogen fuel anyway, will eventually become a giant. The statistics are telling: About 90% of all stars are on the main sequence, and stars spend about 90% of their lives using hydrogen as nuclear fuel. About 10% of all stars are on the *giant branch*[4] (a "branch" off the main sequence that tends to go up and to the right somewhat on the HR diagram), and stars spend about 10% of their lives using helium as fuel. Any remaining stages happen much more rapidly.

---

[3] Models estimate a 1-$M_\odot$ star undergoing a helium flash releases 0.3% of the power emitted by a Type Ia supernova, which can be seen across the known universe by modern telescopes.

[4] Note that we are not including white dwarfs in these statistics, largely because white dwarfs are not officially stars, but instead are dead remnants of stars.

Section 18.4: Life After the Giant Branch

At some point, the helium also runs out in the core of the star. The process repeats itself, meaning the core shrinks and heats, the shell surrounding the core also shrinks and heats, and as a consequence we now have two shells of fusion, the inner shell turning helium into carbon and oxygen, the outer shell turning hydrogen into helium.

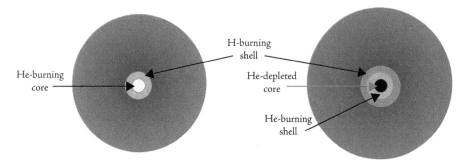

FIGURE 18.6. Changes in a star's surface (outer circles) and its core and concentric shells (inner circles) as it runs out of helium in its core. Left: A star burning helium in its core with a hydrogen-burning concentric shell. Right: A star that has run out of helium in its core; instead, now there are two shells, one burning helium and one burning hydrogen.

Three events or stages happen upon the onset of helium shell burning.

1. Variable Stars

The energy production in the shells of the star add an even larger boost of energy to the rest of the star. Given this, and the higher temperatures and densities in the shells, the energy production becomes unstable and the star becomes a *variable*.[5]

What do we mean by the term "variable"? After all, doesn't the Sun vary, too? We saw before (in chapter 12) that the Sun exhibits a "solar cycle" averaging 11 years, where the number of sunspots, the tangling of its magnetic field and even its irradiance, alter. But calling the Sun a "variable" is like calling you a "variable person." Think about it: Properties belonging to you—your weight and height, for example—change a little bit throughout the course of each day. But we don't think of ourselves as varying to any great degree. Similarly, the changes the Sun experiences are very small scale; its irradiance goes up and down by a tenth of a percent over the solar cycle. When we use the term "variable" in astronomy, we mean <u>really</u> obvious changes.

We've mentioned the role of dust in obscuring light when discussing planetary and star formation (chapters 7 and 16, respectively). In this case, the largest amount of opacity arises from doubly ionized helium gas. Let's follow the generalized steps of the star's variable behavior:

+ The opacity of the gas near the core and shells traps the high-intensity radiation
+ The radiation pressure pushes the gas outward
+ The rest of the outside of the star follows suit
+ Eventually the star has expanded so much that the density drops enough (equivalently, the opacity drops enough) to allow radiation to pass through
+ The outward pressure decreases
+ Gravity (the weight of the star) is now larger than the outward radiation pressure, and the star contracts
+ The star eventually contracts enough that the opacity is large enough to prevent radiation from escaping, and the process repeats

---

[5] As we have done before, we are simplifying the story somewhat. The actual onset of variability depends on factors such as the mass and the metallicity of the star.

FIGURE 18.7. RR Lyrae stars are mixed in with others near the center of the Milky Way in this infrared image taken by the VISTA telescope. As RR Lyrae stars are very ancient, this suggests this region was made in part from mergers of globular clusters. Credit: ESO/VVV Survey/D. Minniti.

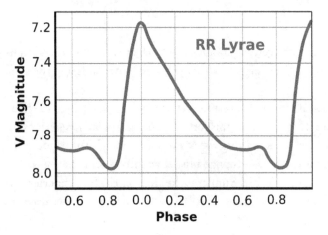

FIGURE 18.8. A sample light curve for RR Lyrae. The curve does not exactly repeat itself due to a secondary oscillation. Credit: RJ Hall.

How much do the properties of the star change during this cycle? One class of variables is called an *RR Lyrae*, after its most famous member star. Its luminosity can increase and decrease by about half a magnitude from its average brightness (recall that a magnitude translates to a factor in brightness of 2.5 times). Imagine your height is 6 feet in the afternoon. Tonight your height expands to 9 feet 6 inches, but in the morning you wake up with a height of 3 feet 10 inches. No person does this, of course, but stars can do the equivalent. <u>This</u> is what we mean by the term "variable."

Variables come in a variety of classes, depending primarily on their initial mass and metallicity. The RR Lyraes are worth looking at for a moment, if only because this is considered the most likely fate of the Sun. The nature of RR Lyraes was discovered by Williamina Fleming (1857–1911), one of the group of women astronomers at Harvard Observatory (see chapters 13 and 15 for others) in 1901. RR Lyrae itself changes its apparent magnitude from +7.06 to +8.12 over a period of 13 hours and 36 minutes and its pulsations cause it to grow and shrink between 5.1 and 5.6 solar radii. The period itself is not permanent and shifts over a larger period (discovered by the Russian astronomer Sergei Blazhko [1870–1956]) of 39 days.

RR Lyrae-class variables result when stars of initial masses similar to the Sun become unstable as giants. But a star like the Sun has a lifespan close to 10 billion years. This means that only very ancient stars have lived long enough to become RR Lyraes, the types of stars that tend to belong to globular clusters. Because the period and luminosity of an RR Lyrae behaves according to discernable patterns, by observing the period of an RR Lyrae, astronomers can estimate its absolute magnitude (luminosity) and therefore calculate its distance. RR Lyraes are bright enough that this trick works well for globulars within the Milky Way, but not too much farther out. In other words, such variables are not only interesting for their own sakes, but also are useful for understanding scales.

The most famous of all variables are called *Cepheids*. Cepheids come in a variety of subclasses, some of which arise from low-mass stars. However, the most useful (for astronomers) of the Cepheids arise from higher-mass stars, and will be dealt with in the following chapter.

2. Planetary Nebulae

As a star becomes more and more unstable, it begins to shed layers of itself back into space. Ionizing radiation from deeper inside the star hits the escaping gas and heats it, which then (because it is now hot and thin) emits spectral radiation from various elements. From a distance, the escaping gas can look like a colorful bubble. The first astronomer to note planetary nebulae was Charles Messier in the 1760s, who crafted his famous catalog in order to avoid objects that were not comets. The astronomer to get the first true sense of their nature was probably William Herschel in the 1780s,[6] who had recently discovered the planet Uranus. Tradition ascribes to him the term *planetary nebula*, because they appeared round and colorful like a planet. Hershel realized fairly quickly that these objects were not planets (if nothing else, they don't orbit the Sun) and we now know they have nothing to do with planets, but astronomers have kept the name nonetheless.

The first few planetary nebulae discovered were round, suggesting them to be spherically symmetric. This turns out not to be the case, as only about 1/5 of planetary nebulae are shaped this way. Planetary nebulae instead show a wide variety of shapes, sizes, and colors, which depend on many factors, including their masses and metallicities, but also the rotation of the star, whether it has a companion star or not, its local environment in the interstellar medium, and the presences of magnetic fields among other items. Nevertheless, planetary nebulae are usually distinct from other nebulae in that they tend to have a wide variety of colors and (especially) are associated with white dwarfs that lie at their centers.

Also, the expulsion of gas from the outer layers of the star is not necessarily smooth. Suppose one shell of gas is "gently" let go and drifts off into space at a relatively slow speed. Later, another shell of gas is violently ejected, racing away from the star at a relatively high speed. Eventually, the inner fast-moving shell collides with the outer slow-moving shell, the collisions heating the outermost gas so that it gives off light and shows evidence of the collisions (see Figure 18.10, for example).

A typical planetary nebula, like many other nebulae, is hot and thin, though the planetary nebulae are always linked with their dying stars. The density of the gas starts out relatively thick—a million particles per cubic centimeter is possible—but drops as the gas dissipates through expansion down to 100 particles per cc before the nebula becomes too thin to see. Coronal gas near the star can be as hot as 1,000,000 K, but the visible parts of the planetary nebula range from 25,000 K at the inner edges of the nebula to 10,000 K at the outer edges. Planetary nebulae can reach diameters up to a light year (3/10 of a parsec)

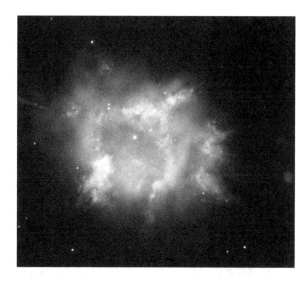

FIGURE 18.9. Planetary nebula NGC 6326 and its associated white dwarf, as seen by the Hubble Space Telescope. The HST's WFPC2 camera used filters to highlight hydrogen (red), oxygen (blue), and various stars (green/white). Credit: ESA/Hubble and NASA.

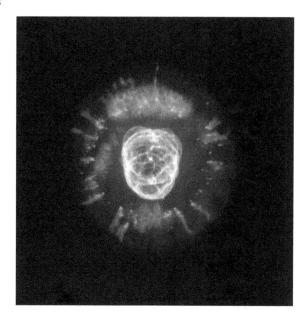

FIGURE 18.10. The Eskimo Nebula, as seen by the Hubble Space Telescope. Its WFPC2 camera used filters to highlight nitrogen (red), hydrogen (green), oxygen (blue), and helium (violet). Credit: NASA, ESA, Andrew Fruchter (STScI), and the ERO team (STScI + ST-ECF).

across before spreading too thin to be seen. The amount of gas shed by a star in this fashion is not trivial; it is expected that anywhere from 40% to 60% of the Sun will be ejected back into interstellar space during its planetary nebula phase.

---

[6] It is possible that a French astronomer named Antoine Darquier de Pellepoix compared the Ring Nebula, a true planetary nebula, to the planet Jupiter in 1779, prior to Herschel's discovery.

FIGURE 18.11. The Lemon Slice Nebula, as seen by Hubble. Credit Howard Bond, Robin Ciardullo and NASA.

FIGURE 18.12. The Necklace Nebula, recently discovered by the HST. A binary system is responsible for the nebula's jewels. A small companion object actually moves inside the outer atmosphere of the larger star, spraying its gas outward. The stars are only a few million kilometers apart (i.e., only a few tenths of an au) and their mutual orbit lasts only a single day. Credit: NASA, ESA and the Hubble Heritage Team (STScI/AURA).

Astronomers know of about 3,000 planetary nebulae in the Milky Way, which sounds like a lot until we remember there are several hundred billion stars in our galaxy. The reason is that planetary nebulae are, by astronomy standards, rather transient phenomena, existing on average for about 10,000 years until completely dissipating into the interstellar medium. They are most often seen near the plane of the galaxy, close to the center (bulge) of the galaxy, and occasionally in globular clusters. Planetary nebulae can exist for stars much more massive than the Sun, but also disperse much more quickly, and are rarely seen for that reason. On the other hand, the more massive the star, the more likely its core is to mix with the outer regions of the star, and so planetary nebulae made from massive stars are better able to seed the ISM with metals.

3. White Dwarfs

What happens to a star that has exhausted all possible sources of fuel and can no longer sustain itself via nuclear fusion? To address this question, we need to both explore some of the world of quantum mechanics and the life of an astrophysicist who began his life in India.

Subrahmanyan Chandrasekhar (1910–1995) was born in Lahore in the Punjab province of British India (now part of Pakistan) but spent his childhood in Madras after age 8. His parents were intellectuals and his paternal uncle was the Nobel Prize (in physics) Laureate C. V. Raman, and he was inspired to pursue physics by them and Arnold Sommerfeld, another Nobel Laureate. After earning his B.S. in physics in 1930, he won a scholarship for graduate studies in Cambridge, England. On the several weeks-long trip from India to England by boat, he worked out an improved representation of how electrons behave in white dwarf stars, which ultimately became the basis for his own Nobel Prize in 1983, which he shared with William A. Fowler (1911–1995), who made important contributions to our understanding of stellar nuclear fusion.

FIGURE 18.13. Subrahmanyan Chandrasekhar.

What did Chandrasekhar (pronounced "Shan – dra – sayk – har") find? The question we posed was an active pursuit amongst astrophysicists of the time, and new discoveries in quantum mechanics posed the possibility of an answer.

The word "quantum" in quantum mechanics means that, at the tiniest of levels, quantities like energy, mass, and angular momentum come in tiny chunks, amounts or "quanta."[7] Quantum mechanics specifically limits certain quantities to set numbers; for example, while one could spin a basketball along any direction one wants at any speed, an electron can only spin with its axis pointed "up" or "down" and with the same amount of spin. We've seen this before, when we encountered the 21-cm line emitted when an electron "flips" its spin (chapter 16) for thin hydrogen gas in the interstellar medium.

Several quantum properties behave this way, not just spin. This property—called the *exclusion principle* in physics—means that a particle can only possess one unique set of quantum "numbers" (spin being just one of them) at the same place and at the same time.

FIGURE 18.14. Left: A macroscopic object like a basketball can be spun in any direction. Right: A microscopic particle like an electron can only spin in one of two directions.

What does this mean for our collapsing stars? Let's explore this idea with an analogy. Suppose we wish to spend a night at the Electron Motel. The Electron Motel is cheap (in fact, no cost at all), but has some peculiar rules. First, only one guest may inhabit a room at any time. This rule is absolute; no two guests in any individual room, for any reason whatsoever. Second, a guest may change rooms at any moment, as long as (in accord with rule #1) the room is unoccupied.

FIGURE 18.15. Left: A motel with just a few guests. Right: A motel at capacity.

If the Electron Motel only has a few guests, then guests can pretty much move freely from room to room. But if the Electron Motel is at capacity, no vacancy, then all the guests are stuck in their rooms. Furthermore, no more guests are allowed. It's not that the motel manager doesn't want to double up guests in order to earn a little more money; it's that the rules forbid adding any new guests at all.

Let's return to our shrinking star, or more specifically, the core of the star. The last we left off, it had run out of helium for fusion and was again shrinking due to its own weight overcoming the outward gas pressure. For a 1 $M_\odot$ star (although, to be honest, there's probably only 0.5 $M_\odot$ left of it after having lost gas to its planetary nebula), it's not possible for its core to achieve the densities and pressures necessary to use carbon and/or oxygen as nuclear fuel. So, the core continues to shrink until its electrons (we'll discuss how protons and neutrons behave in a future chapter) start bumping into each other's quantum numbers. Eventually, each electron has its own "room" with its own unique set of quantum numbers, and no other electrons can invade that room. But if electrons can't get any

---

[7] To "quantify" simply means to count. The science of quantum mechanics, in a sense, is simply the counting up of tiny bits in physics.

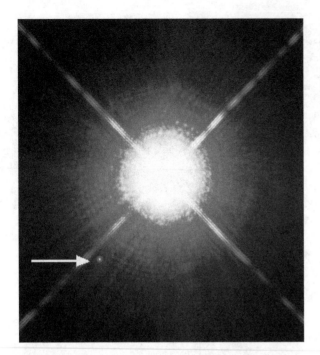

FIGURE 18.16. Sirius A and Sirius B (identified by an arrow) as seen by the Hubble Telescope. The spikes and rings around Sirius A are artifacts of the image and are not real. Can you tell which object is the white dwarf? Credit: NASA.

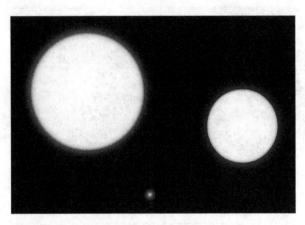

FIGURE 18.17. An artist's rendition of the IK Pegasi binary system, to scale, and including the Sun for reference.

closer together, that acts as an outward pressure—or, if you prefer, a resistance to the inward pressure from gravity—and the core stops shrinking.

Check Your Neighbor

Can you think of any other analogies that might help you understand the exclusion principle?

When the core stops shrinking because the exclusion principle supplies the outward push to balance the inward pull of its own weight, it once again achieves balance ("hydrostatic equilibrium"). Since the exclusion principle doesn't depend on temperature, the core no longer needs a source of energy, and the situation is permanent. Such an object—the leftover core of a star—is called a *white dwarf.*

Check Your Neighbor

What properties do you expect a white dwarf to possess, compared to the star it was originally? Will it be

- hot or cool?
- small or large?
- thick (high density) or thin (low density)?

A white dwarf possesses some amazing properties. The density of a white dwarf is about a ton per teaspoon, or, if you like, similar to crushing an SUV into the volume of a common playing die. Its temperature is incredibly hot, having been the core of a star, but the temperature drops with time, as there is no source of energy to replenish the heat. Despite the high temperature (and the appellation "white" dwarf), its luminosity is very small, since the white dwarf has shrunk to an incredibly tiny size.

Two figures show off these facts. Figure 18.16 is a photo from the Hubble Space Telescope of Sirius, which is a binary system. One object is the star we see in the night sky, Sirius A, and is an A-type main sequence star. The other object can only be seen with a sizeable telescope (at least a 12-inch aperture is recommended) and is a white dwarf. Figure 18.17 is an artist's representation of the IK Pegasi binary system, showing its main sequence star (large white disk), its white dwarf (tiny white dot), and the Sun (yellow disk) for reference, all to scale. In fact, if (when) the Sun turns into a white dwarf, it will likely end up about the same size across as the Earth, a shrinking of a factor of 100 or so in radius, and over a million in terms of volume.

Check Your Neighbor

Which star was <u>originally</u> more massive (i.e., when the stars were first formed): Sirius A or Sirius B? Briefly defend your answer.

White dwarfs don't have to be in binary systems, of course, but often they're easier to find in binaries. They have very low luminosities—none are visible to the naked eye—but their gravity still influences any partners they might have, and we can discern their presence that way (see chapters 13 and 15). Since white dwarfs are essentially permanent (with an interesting exception to be discussed later), their numbers simply pile up as the galaxy ages; there are eight known white dwarfs among the 100 closest star systems to ours. Also, as the vast majority (97% or more) of all stars are 8 $M_\odot$ or smaller, which is the largest initial masses stars can have in order to end up as white dwarfs, we can expect the galaxy to continue accumulating white dwarfs. White dwarfs are expected to be as popular, if not more so, than giants.

Check Your Neighbor

We don't consider white dwarfs to be stars any longer. Why not?

What are white dwarfs made of? Stars less than 0.4 $M_\odot$ are not capable of fusing helium into carbon, and so their cores would supposedly be made of helium—but as noted earlier, no stars of this small a mass will have run out of fuel yet, so helium-based white dwarfs are theoretical so far. The majority of white dwarfs are mostly carbon (with some oxygen), which leads to jokes that the skies are populated by a large number of lumps of burned-out charcoal. A few white dwarfs came from stars large enough to have gone further in their nuclear fusion, and so may contain elements such as silicon, sulfur, and/or magnesium.

Having said this, white dwarfs are no longer made of the same "matter" as you or I. Instead, physicists describe such matter as *degenerate*. This doesn't imply any moral failing by the white dwarf; rather, it incorporates this notion that the electrons are overcrowded and can't move due to the exclusion principle. We saw this idea pop up earlier in our discussion regarding the helium flash (at the end of section 18.3); now we can see why the term "degenerate" was used at the time.

Besides what we've already mentioned, degenerate matter has other odd behaviors. For normal matter, all else begin equal, the more massive an object, the larger across this is, an idea generally applicable to people and stars both. But the more massive a white dwarf—the more degenerate matter it possesses—the <u>smaller</u> the white dwarf gets. Furthermore, to properly calculate how this effect works, we have to account for relativistic effects, something that Chandrasekhar took into account when on his ocean voyage.

One more item: The shrinking of a white dwarf cannot continue forever; or, the doors of the Electron Motel can only withstand so much pounding from insistent extra guests. The exclusion principle for electrons only holds up to 1.44 $M_\odot$, a notion called the *Chandrasekhar limit*, after which the white dwarf collapses catastrophically. We will explore the consequences of this possibility in the last section of this chapter.

Section 18.5: The Ends of Stars in Interacting Binary Systems

So far we have only considered single stars. What if stars live in binary systems?

Stars in binary systems are not guaranteed to impact each other's development. It is possible, most likely, even, that the two stars are far enough apart that they will remain separated (a situation called a *detached binary*), regardless of how large they grow upon becoming giants. What we want to explore here are situations

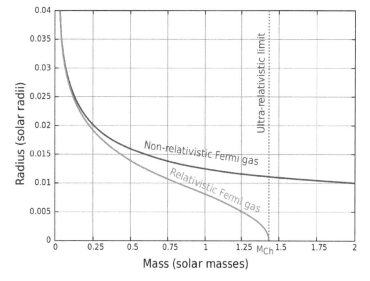

FIGURE 18.18. The mass-radius relation for a white dwarf, labeled as "Relativistic Fermi Gas." The "non-relativistic" curve does not account for relativistic effects. Note: The radius shrinks until we reach 1.44 solar masses.

where the stars do interact, which we called *semidetached* and *contact binaries* (chapter 15). This brings back another idea we've played with in the past, that of the *Roche Lobe*, or the region around a star dominated by its gravity.

Three different outcomes can occur, which are not exclusive; indeed, one often leads to another. The first involves changing the rates at which stars run through their lives, the second involves explosions of hydrogen on the surfaces of white dwarfs, and the third the utter destruction of white dwarfs.

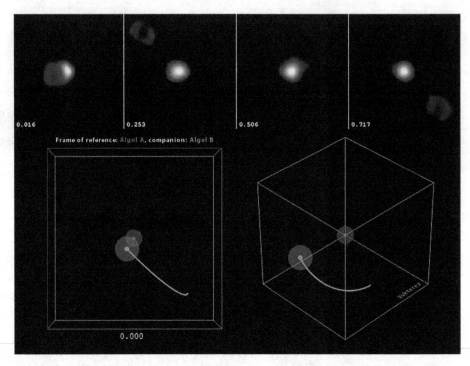

FIGURE 18.19. Top: Still images from CHARA's infrared interferometer of the Algol system. Bottom: 2D and 3D interpolations of the orbit of Algol B about A. Credit: Simon Tyran.

1. Mass Exchange Between Stars

One of the most famous (for astronomers) multiple star systems is Algol, in the constellation of Perseus. We've encountered it before as an example of an eclipsing binary system, but here we want to explore in detail how its stars affect each other. Algol appears to be a trinary (three-star) system, but the third member is far enough away from the other two (2.69 au) that it is unaffected except for its orbit about the others. The other two stars, Algol A and B, are close enough to each other (only 0.062 astronomical units apart) that mass is being transferred between them.

Strangely at first glance, of the close pair, the more massive star (A has a mass of 3.17 $M_\odot$) is on the main sequence, but the less massive star (B has a mass of 0.70 $M_\odot$) is a subgiant. But we earlier stated the more massive a star is, the faster it goes through its life processes, and therefore the more massive star should be the subgiant and the less massive star the main sequence star. This observation is sometimes called the *Algol paradox*, and begs the question: How did this happen?

The answer is that Algol is a semidetached system. Algol B was originally more massive than Algol A, and therefore went through its hydrogen fuel more quickly. As B entered its subgiant phase, its outer atmosphere (surface) expanded until it became larger than its Roche lobe (see chapter 15) and began to spill material onto A. A continues to pull gas from B and eventually became more massive as a result.

> ### Check Your Neighbor
>
> The changes in mass will affect the lifespans of Algol A and B. Given these statements, which star will have its life shortened by this exchange? Which will have its life extended?

The exchange of matter between the two stars cannot reverse time; Algol B has still run out of hydrogen fuel and will remain in its subgiant phase, as there is no mechanism to replenish its hydrogen-depleted core. Algol A is still a main sequence star but has added a significant amount of mass, meaning it has to work harder to maintain itself than it did originally. If Algol A joins the subgiant phase soon, the two stars may become a contact binary, where gas is freely exchanged between the two stars.

2. Classical Novae

Back in 1572, Tycho Brahe noted the appearance of a "nova" in the skies. "Nova" is Latin for "new," and Brahe thought he was possibly witnessing the birth of a star. We now know he had it backward; what he saw was what astronomers now term a "supernova," an exploding star. Astronomers have also learned in the meantime that some explosions don't completely destroy the star, but instead create enormous flares, a type of event that astronomers now term a *nova*. As usual, there are variations of this theme, and we will describe the simplest version, a "classical" nova.

We know of many systems with a main sequence star and a white dwarf—Sirius is an example—but most such systems don't exhibit mass exchanges. Rather, imagine the following scenario: Instead of two "normal" stars in a semidetached binary, one

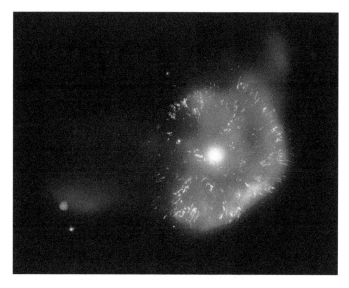

FIGURE 18.20. Remnants from the classical nova GK Persei, as seen in x-rays by the Chandra spacecraft (blue), in visible light by Hubble (yellow), and in radio by the Very Large Array (pink).

of the objects is a giant (in order to overflow its Roche lobe) and the other a white dwarf. While the core of the giant has long been depleted of hydrogen, this isn't true of the rest of the star, which is still 90% hydrogen. As this gas is pulled toward the white dwarf, it can pile up at on one particular spot on the surface of the white dwarf until it reaches a critical mass, and then explode as the built-up hydrogen violently undergoes nuclear fusion. Or, long story short, the white dwarf lights up a gigantic nuclear bomb on its surface.

The GK Persei system is an example. First discovered in 1901, it faded after reaching a peak apparent magnitude of +12 but then started exhibiting quasi-periodic outbursts starting in 1980. The Chandra x-ray telescope took observations in February 2000 and again in November 2013, allowing it to compare differences in the debris. The explosion fragments are moving at speeds over 300 kilometers per second (700,000 miles per hour), or nearly 1,000 astronomical units in a little under 14 years. The high speeds are mainly due to the violence of the flares; other reasons include the apparent lack of gas in the local interstellar medium to produce friction with the explosion fragments.

Binary systems, giants and white dwarfs are all relatively popular in the galaxy, so it shouldn't be too surprising that these events are common. A recent estimate places the rate of novae at 50 per year in the Milky Way, though only an average of 10 per year are observed here (the others are likely obscured by dust, mostly from the galactic plane). The increase in brightness (it is possible for a nova to become over 10 magnitudes brighter (i.e., 10,000 times brighter or more) than the white dwarf on its own) is offset somewhat by the dimness of the white dwarf, which rarely reaches naked-eye visibility. Nevertheless, occasionally novae do become bright enough for all of us to see; the brightest nova in recent times was Nova Cygni 1975, which reached an apparent magnitude of +2, comparable to the North Star. Also, since an explosion by definition is a violent expulsion of material from a central location, only 5% of the hydrogen typically detonates—the rest of the hydrogen is simply blown away—so a nova could potentially be many times brighter. Despite this, the amount of material expelled by the white dwarf is small; perhaps 0.000 01 (i.e., one ten-thousandth) of a solar mass of matter is sent into the interstellar medium, much less than either that of planetary nebulae or supernovae. As such, novae do not contribute significantly to the seeding of the ISM.

A star that changes its brightness many times over is a *recurrent variable*. Many of these (not all) do this on a regular basis and are also termed *periodic variables* for that reason. A stellar object that changes its brightness through explosions is a *cataclysmic variable*. The RR Lyraes (see section 18.4) are examples of recurrent or periodic variables, and supernovae are examples of cataclysmic variables. Classical novae can be both; after all, there is no reason why, after a flare, that hydrogen gas from a giant companion can't pile up again on the surface of the white dwarf and repeat the process. RS Ophiuchi is a well-studied example; it has been known to flare up to 8 separate times since 1898, the last one occurring in 2006. Given the statistics, it is likely to flare again within the next decade. It is also a candidate for a Type-Ia supernova event, which is our last stop in our discussions regarding low-mass stars.

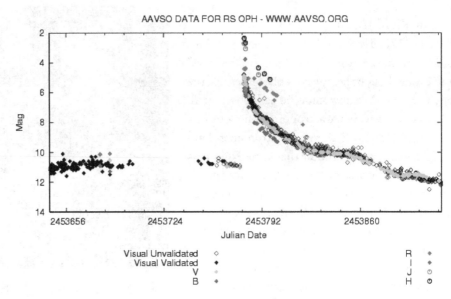

FIGURE 18.21. The 2005 light curve of recurrent nova RS Ophiuchi, using data from the American Association of Variable Star Observers (AAVSO). The different colors refer to different filters, for example, the green dots are labeled "V" for the visible band. Credit: Aaron Price/AAVSO.

Check Your Neighbor

Can you think of any analogies to a white dwarf-giant semidetached binary system? Hint: Think of a certain genre of horror shows involving the dead trying to eat the living.

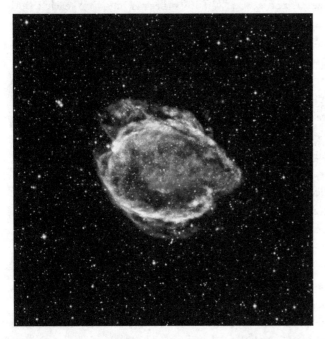

FIGURE 18.22. The remnants of a Type Ia supernova labled G299 are depicted in false color from the Chandra x-ray telescope. Credit: NASA/CXC/University of Texas.

3. Type Ia Supernovae

For a white dwarf/giant semidetached binary, not all of the gas pulled from the giant is blown off the surface of the white dwarf during a nova, and some of the matter never flares in any case. This means that the white dwarf gets more massive with time. At some point, the mass of the white dwarf can reach 1.44 $M_\odot$, the Chandrasekhar limit (also called its *mass limit* for short), which means the exclusion principle for electrons is no longer strong enough to resist the weight of the white dwarf. The result is a titanic explosion called a *Type Ia supernova*.

For decades, astronomers thought the white dwarf would simply collapse in on itself after exceeding its mass limit, and then somehow "rebound," with the resultant shockwaves destroying the white dwarf. This no longer seems to be the case. When a white dwarf reaches 99% of the mass limit, its internal temperatures and pressures turns the interior of the white dwarf fully convective, a stage that lasts for about 1,000 years. At some yet-undetermined stage and location, carbon fusion begins (some oxygen also undergoes fusion). In a "normal" stellar core, the addition of such a large source of energy would act to expand the core, but degenerate matter is virtually impervious to changes of temperature. The result is that, rather than a slow, controlled burn, the carbon is fused in a runaway reaction.

The fusion occurs extremely fast; a (former) star that may have lived for hundreds of millions to billions of years exhausts its carbon/oxygen fuel in a matter of a few seconds.

The white dwarf is completely disintegrated by the violence of the explosion. Fragments go off in all directions at speeds of 18,000 km/s or faster (6% the speed of light), and the peak brightness of the explosion reaches an absolute magnitude of −19.3, about 5 billion times the luminosity of the Sun. The reason astronomers call it a "Type Ia" supernova are historical but are rooted in the idea of the strength of hydrogen spectral lines. Because Type Ia supernovae originate from binary systems, and because binaries can exist in many environments, astronomers see them from all regions of the galaxy, and in all types of galaxies (which is not true of other types of supernovae).

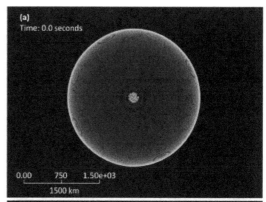

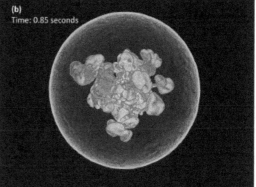

Check Your Neighbor

Do we expect to see relatively strong or relatively weak hydrogen spectral lines from a Type Ia supernova? Hint: What is the white dwarf made of right before the explosion?

Type Ia supernovae were originally thought to arise solely from the accretion of matter from a larger companion onto a white dwarf, as described. Recent studies suggest this specific mechanism only accounts for 20% of Type Ia supernovae. The key in making a Type Ia supernovae is to push a white dwarf right up to its mass limit, and there are several other ways to make that happen. Another possibility is that friction between the white dwarf and its companion make the two objects spiral inward until they collide. A third version of this idea is that two white dwarfs collide with each other (though in that case the mass limit is no longer a constraint), a subtype labeled a "double degenerate progenitor" as opposed to the "single degenerate progenitor" supernovae where only one of the objects was a white dwarf.

Radioactive isotopes close to iron on the periodic table are manufactured during the explosion, and their effects become visible after a few months have passed (so that the gas becomes thin enough to see through). Specifically, radioactive nickel-56 decays to radioactive cobalt-56, which in its turn decays to iron-56. The energy released by these decays is not small; the remnants of the supernovae remain bright for far longer (months to years) after the original explosion should have faded.

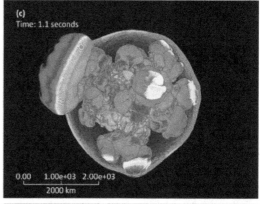

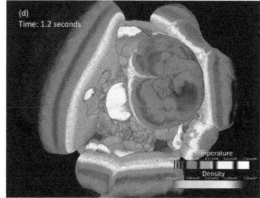

FIGURE 18.23. Four frames in succession of a supercomputer simulation of the interior of a white dwarf during a Type Ia supernova. The green circle represents the surface of the white dwarf. Credit: Argonne National Laboratory/U.S. Department of Energy.

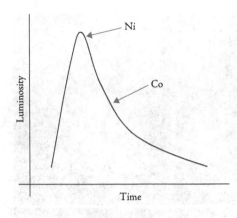

FIGURE 18.24. A generic light curve for a Type Ia supernova. Arrows point out the stages where the radioactive decay of nickel (Ni) and cobalt (Co) supplies energy to keep the remnants bright.

The light curve of a Type Ia supernova (Figure 18.24) illustrates two important conclusions. First, because the white dwarf is supposedly always the same composition, the explosion follows the same steps and its light curve is subsequently always the same shape. Second, because the white dwarf (for a single progenitor supernova) is always the same mass, the "bomb" is always the same size (i.e., the same luminosity). This means we can use Type Ia as a kind of "standard candle" to calculate distances. Supernovae are rare events inside the Milky Way—one is visible every few centuries—but the universe has many galaxies, and supernovae are so bright as to be seen from essentially anywhere. The use of Type Ia supernovae as distance indicators has had profound consequences for our understanding of cosmology, a topic we will cover in detail in chapter 23.

Summary

In this chapter, we have covered the following:

- The aging process of single, low mass stars, covering these stages:
    + Main sequence
    + Subgiant
    + Giant
    + Planetary nebula
    + White dwarf

- The effects stars can have on each other in close binary systems, including the following:
    + Changes to stellar lifespans
    + Classical novae
    + Type Ia supernovae

Questions

For the following questions, also consult Table 15.2 in chapter 15:

1. A star like 61 Cygni B would have a temperature of 4,760 K at the beginning of its subgiant phase and a temperature of 4,630 K at the end of its subgiant phase. Does it change its spectral type during this phase, and if so, from which to which type?

2. A star like Alkaid would have a temperature of 14,540 K at the beginning of its subgiant phase and a temperature of 4,740 K at the end of its subgiant phase. Does it change its spectral type during this phase, and if so, from which to which type?

3. For a star like 61 Cygni B, would it change its surface color significantly while in its subgiant phase? How about for a star like Alkaid?

4. In which case does a subgiant show more changes, when the star has a lower or a higher mass?

5. Why isn't the fusion of two helium nuclei into one of beryllium suitable for the core of a star?

6. Suppose a 1 $M_\odot$ star on the main sequence has a surface temperature of 6,000 K and a radius of 1 $R_\odot$. When it becomes a giant, it will have a surface temperature of 3,000 K and a radius of 100 $R_\odot$. Has its luminosity increased or decreased by becoming a giant, and by how much (as a ratio)?

7. Spectroscopy reveals the outermost edges of a planetary nebula to be moving away from its star at 30 km/s (30,000 m/s). The nebula subtends an angle of 10 arcseconds and is estimated to be 10,000 years old. Assume the speed of the ejected gas is constant.

   ✦ How large across is the nebula? Express your answers in units of (a) meters, (b) light years, and (c) parsecs. Recall that 1 ly = 9.46×10^{12} m and 1 pc = 3.26 ly

   ✦ How far away is the nebula? Hint: 1 degree = 3600 arcseconds

8. A white dwarf, the Sun, and a yellow giant each have effective surface temperatures of 6,000 K. The white dwarf has an absolute magnitude of +15, the Sun an absolute magnitude of +5, and the yellow giant an absolute magnitude of 0.

   ✦ How much brighter (in terms of ratios) is the yellow giant compared to the Sun?
   ✦ How much brighter (in terms of ratios) is the Sun compared to the white dwarf?
   ✦ How large (in terms of solar radii) is the yellow giant?
   ✦ How large (in terms of solar radii) is the white dwarf?

9. We observe a Type Ia supernova in a distant galaxy. Its apparent magnitude is +11. Assuming the absolute magnitude of a Type Ia supernova is –19, determine the following:

   ✦ The difference in magnitudes
   ✦ The ratio of brightness between the supernova's absolute and apparent magnitudes
   ✦ The square root of the ratio of the brightnesses
   ✦ The distance to the supernova (and therefore its host galaxy) in units of parsecs
   ✦ The distance to the supernova (and its host galaxy) in units of megaparsecs. Note: The prefix "mega" means "million"

Activities

▸ *Astrophysics activity 18.1:* Use spectroscopic parallax to determine distances to stars.

▸ *Astrophysics activity 18.2:* Use HR diagrams of stellar clusters to determine distances to and ages of clusters.

▸ *Astrophysics activity 18.3:* Review the video "The Lives of the Stars" from the original *Cosmos* series (Episode #9).

Works Referenced

The Polaris system is described in the following sources:

Evans, N. R., Sasselov, D. D., & Short, C. I. (2002). Polaris: Amplitude, period change, and companions. *Astrophysical Journal*, 567(2), 1121. doi:10.1086/338583

There's More to the North Star Than Meets the Eye. (2006, January 9). Retrieved 2019-04-20. http://hubblesite.org/news_release/news/2006-02

The behaviors of stars leaving the Main Sequence, transitioning through subgiants and becoming giants is shown in the following:

Pols, Onno R., Schröder, K. P., Hurley, J. R., Tout, C. A., & Eggleton, P. P. (1998). Stellar evolution models for Z = 0.0001 to 0.03. *Monthly Notices of the Royal Astronomical Society*, 298(2), 525–536. doi:10.1046/j.1365-8711.1998.01658.x

Russell, H. N. (1914). Relations between the spectra and other characteristics of the stars. *Popular Astronomy*, 22, 275–294.

The triple-alpha process, including the history of its discovery and the helium flash, is recounted in the following sources:

Deupree, R. G., & R. K. Wallace. (1987). The core helium flash and surface abundance anomalies. *Astrophysical Journal, 317*, 724–732. doi:10.1086/165319

Edwards, A. C. (1969). The hydrodynamics of the helium flash. *Monthly Notices of the Royal Astronomical Society, 146*(4), 445–472. doi:10.1093/mnras/146.4.445

Hansen, C. J., Kawaler, S. D., & Trimble, V. (2004). *Stellar interiors: Physical principles, structure, and evolution* (2nd ed.). Springer.

Kragh, H. (2010). *When is a prediction anthropic? Fred Hoyle and the 7.65 MeV carbon resonance.* Retrieved from http://philsci-archive.pitt.edu/5332/

Laughlin, G., Bodenheimer, P., & Adams, F. C. (1997, June 10). The end of the main sequence. *Astrophysical Journal, 482*, 420–432. doi:10.1086/304125

Mocák, M. (2009). *Multidimensional hydrodynamic simulations of the core helium flash in low-mass stars* (Unpublished doctoral dissertation). Technische Universität München, Munchen, Germany.

Salpeter, E. E. (1952). Nuclear reactions in stars without hydrogen. *Astrophysical Journal, 115*, 326–328. doi:10.1086/145546

Salpeter, E. E. (2002). A generalist looks back. *Annual Review of Astronomy & Astrophysics, 40*, 1–25. doi:10.1146/annurev.astro.40.060401.093901

Wilson, R. (1997). Chapter 8: The Stars: Their Birth, Life and Death in *Astronomy through the ages: The story of the human attempt to understand the universe.* CRC Press.

Variable stars are discussed in the following sources:

Burnham, R., Jr. (1978). *Burnham's celestial handbook.* New York, NY: Dover.

Clement, C. M., Muzzin, A., Dufton, Q., Ponnampalam, T., Wang, J., Burford, J., … & Sawyer, H. (2001). Variable stars in galactic globular clusters. *Astronomical Journal, 122*(5), 2587. doi:10.1086/323719

Eddington, A. S. (1917). The pulsation theory of Cepheid variables. *The Observatory, 40*, 290.

Freedman, W. L., Madore, B. F., Gibson, B. K., Ferrarese, L., Kelson, D. D., Sakai, S., … & Stetson, P. B. (2001). Final results from the Hubble Space Telescope key project to measure the Hubble Constant. *Astrophysical Journal, 553*, 47–72. doi:10.1086/320638

Kolenberg, K., Fossatti, L., Shulak, D., Pikall, H., Barnes, T. G., Kochukhov, O., & Tysmbal, V. (2010, September). An in-depth spectroscopic analysis of the Blazhko star RR Lyrae. I. Characterisation of the star: Abundance analysis and fundamental parameters. *Astronomy and Astrophysics, 519*, A64. doi:10.1051/0004-6361/201014471

Majaess, D. J., Turner, D. G., & Lane, D. J. (2009). Characteristics of the galaxy according to Cepheids. *Monthly Notices of the Royal Astronomical Society, 398*, 263–270. doi:10.1111/j.1365-2966.2009.15096.

Planetary nebulae are discussed in the following sources:

SEDS Messier Database: "Antoine Darquier de Pellepoix (November 23, 1718 – January 18, 1802)." Retrieved 2019-04-20. http://www.messier.seds.org/xtra/Bios/darquier.html

Gurzadyan, G. A. (1997). *The physics and dynamics of planetary nebulae.* Springer.

Majaess, D. J., Turner, D., & Lane, D. (2007, December). In search of possible associations between planetary nebulae and open clusters. *Publications of the Astronomical Society of the Pacific, 119*(862), 1349–60. doi:10.1086/524414

Olson, D., & Caglieris, G. M. (June 2017). Who discovered the ring nebula? *Sky & Telescope*, 32–37.

Parker, Q. A., Acker, A., Frew, D. J., Hartley, M., Peyaud, A. E. J., Ochsenbein, F., … & Vaughan, A. E. (2006, November). The Macquarie/AAO/Strasbourg Hα Planetary Nebula Catalogue: MASH. *Monthly Notices of the Royal Astronomical Society, 373*(1), 79–94, doi:10.1111/j.1365-2966.2006.10950.x

Wood, P. R., Olivier, E. A., & Kawaler, S. D. (2004). Long secondary periods in pulsating asymptotic giant branch stars: An investigation of their origin. *Astrophysical Journal, 604*(2), 800. doi:10.1086/382123

White dwarfs are discussed in the following sources:

Chandrasekhar, S. (1931). The maximum mass of ideal white dwarfs. *Astrophysical Journal, 74,* 81. doi:10.1086/143324

Chandrasekhar, S. (1935). The highly collapsed configurations of a stellar mass (Second paper). *Monthly Notices of the Royal Astronomical Society, 95*(3), 207–225. doi:10.1093/mnras/95.3.207

Henry, T. J. (2009, January). The one hundred nearest star systems. *Research Consortium on Nearby Stars.* http://www.recons.org/TOP100.posted.htm Retrieved 2019-04-20.

More about the Algol system can be found in the following sources:

Meltzer, A. S., (1957). A spectroscopic investigation of Algol. *Astrophysical Journal, 125,* 359.

Pustylnik, I. (1995). On accretion component of the flare activity in Algol. *Baltic Astronomy, 4*(1–2), 64–78.

Classical novae are discussed in the following sources:

http://www.nasa.gov/mission_pages/chandra/mini-supernova-explosion-could-have-big-impact.html

Chesneau (2007). AMBER/VLTI interferometric observations of the recurrent Nova RS Ophiuchii 5.5 days after outburst. *Astronomy & Astrophysics, 464*(1), 119–126. doi:10.1051/0004-6361:20066609

Davis, K. (2010). GK Persei. Retrieved from https://www.aavso.org/vsots_gkper

Downes, R.,Webbink, R. F., & Shara, M. M. (1997, April). A catalog and atlas of cataclysmic variables, second edition. *Publications of the Astronomical Society of the Pacific, 109,* 345–440, doi:10.1086/133900

Prialnik, D. (2001). "Novae." In P. Murdin (Ed.), *Encyclopedia of astronomy and astrophysics* (pp. 1846–1856). Institute of Physics Publishing/Nature Publishing Group, Boca Raton, LA.

Shafter, A.W. (2017, January). The galactic nova rate revisited. *Astrophysical Journal, 834*(2), 192–203. doi:10.3847/1538-4357/834/2/196

Type Ia supernovae are discussed in the following sources:

Plewa, T., Calder, A. C., & Lamb, D. Q. (2004) "Type Ia Supernova Explosion: Gravitationally Confined Detonation". *The Astrophysical Journal Letters, 612,* L37-L40.

Gamezo, V. N., Khokhlov, A. M., Oran, E. S., Chtchelkanova, A. Y., & Rosenberg, R. O. (2003, January 3). Thermonuclear supernovae: Simulations of the deflagration stage and their implications. *Science, 299*(5603), 77–81. doi:10.1126/science.1078129

González Hernández, J. I., Ruiz-Lapuente, P., Tabernero, H. M., Montes, D., Canal, R., Méndez, J., & Bedin, L. R. (2012). No surviving evolved companions of the progenitor of SN 1006. *Nature, 489*(7417), 533–536. doi:10.1038/nature11447

Hamuy, M., et al. (1993). The 1990 Calan/Tololo supernova search. *Astronomical Journal, 106*(6), 2392.

Hillebrandt, W., & Niemeyer, J. C. (2000). Type Ia Supernova Explosion Models. *Annual Review of Astronomy and Astrophysics, 38*(1), 191–230. doi:10.1146/annurev.astro.38.1.191

Langer, N., Yoon, S. C., Wellstein, S., & Scheithauer, S. (2002). On the evolution of interacting binaries which contain a white dwarf. In B. T. Gänsicke, K. Beuermann, & K. Rein (Eds.), *The physics of cataclysmic variables and related objects, ASP Conference Proceedings* (pp. 252–260). San Francisco, CA: Astronomical Society of the Pacific.

Lieb, E. H., & Yau, H. T. (1987). A rigorous examination of the Chandrasekhar theory of stellar collapse. *Astrophysical Journal, 323*(1), 140–144. doi:10.1086/165813

Mazzali, P. A., Röpke, F. K., Benetti, S., & Hillebrandt, W. (2007). A common explosion mechanism for Type Ia supernovae. *Science, 315*(5813), 825–828. doi:10.1126/science.1136259

Phillips, M. M. (1993). The absolute magnitudes of Type Ia supernovae. *Astrophysical Journal Letters, 413*(2), L105. doi:10.1086/186970

Röpke, F. K., & Hillebrandt, W. (2004). The case against the progenitor's carbon-to-oxygen ratio as a source of peak luminosity variations in Type Ia supernovae. *Astronomy and Astrophysics, 420*(1), L1–L4. doi:10.1051/0004-6361:20040135

Wheeler, J. C. (2000, January 15). *Cosmic catastrophes: Supernovae, gamma-ray bursts, and adventures in hyperspace*. Cambridge, UK: Cambridge University Press.

Credits

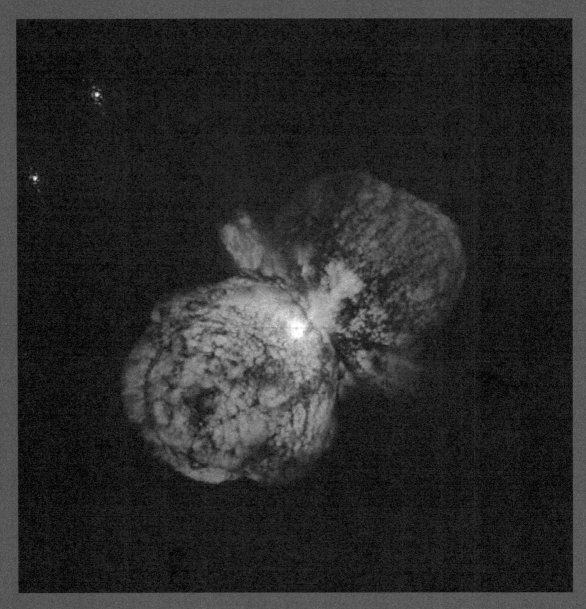

The supergiant star Eta Carinae. An enormous explosion over 170 years ago produced as much light as a supernova but somehow did not destroy the star. Two lobes of high-energy gas are flying outward at over 1.5 million miles per hour. Credit: Jon Morse/NASA.

THE ENDS OF STARS II

PURPOSE

To discuss how high-mass stars end their lives

OBJECTIVES

- To list the various types of nuclear fusion in a high-mass star
- To study in detail the Eta Carinae system
- To recap the role of neutrinos in nuclear processes
- To describe how Type II supernovae are initiated
- To follow the formation of elements during a supernova
- To study in detail Supernovae 1987A

INTRODUCTION

In the last chapter, we looked at how low-mass stars (typically 8 $M_\odot$ or less) end their lives. This led us to cover different types of nuclear fusion (the triple-alpha process, for example), degenerate matter, planetary nebulae and white dwarfs, and ended with a look at how a binary system can initiate a supernova.

This chapter describes the end-of-life behaviors of high-mass stars (typically 8 $M_\odot$ or more), broadly called supergiants. We consider how supergiants continue past helium fusion until they form iron, which is as far up the periodic table as fusion can go and still yield energy. We will then describe how such stars can explode as supernovae on their own via core collapse, and the consequences of these types of supernovae.

Will anything be left after a supergiant explodes? We will explore this possibility, neutron stars and black holes, in the following chapter.

KEY TERMS

Binding energy (also **nuclear binding energy**): The amount of energy stored in an atomic nucleus that is used to hold the individual *nucleons* together

Baryons: A class of subatomic particles (including protons and neutrons) that feels the *strong nuclear force*

Eta Carinae: A binary system where both stars are 30 $M_\odot$ or more, and the larger component may originally have been as much as 250 $M_\odot$

Hypernova: A greater version of a supernova, both in terms of brightness and duration

Leptons: A class of subatomic particles (including electrons and neutrinos) that feels the *weak nuclear force*

Neutrino: A subatomic particle with no electric charge and an extremely small mass that barely interacts with matter

Nucleon: A particle that exists in the nucleus of an atom; simply, a proton or a neutron

Nucleosynthesis: The making of different elements via nuclear fusion and/or other nuclear reactions

Onion structure: A nickname given to the concentric layers (shells) at the core of a supergiant during its last few days

Photodisintegration: Literally, the disintegration of matter by shining light on it; occurs during the last few seconds of the life of a supergiant

Progenitor: The original star, which exploded as a supernova

Strong nuclear force (also just **strong force**): A fundamental force of nature that is attractive and only works over distances as short as that of atomic nuclei. Also stronger than any other force. Works on *bosons*, which include protons and neutrons

Supernova 1987A (abbreviated **SN 1987A**): A famous Type II supernova first detected in February of 1987

Supergiant: A star roughly 8 $M_\odot$ or greater

Type II supernova: The explosion of a single supergiant via the collapse of its core when it completely runs out of nuclear fuel

Weak nuclear force (also just **weak force**): A fundamental force of nature that is responsible for certain types of radioactive decay and only works over distances shorter than atomic nuclei. Stronger than gravity, but weaker than the strong force or electromagnetism. Works on *fermions*, which include electrons and neutrinos

Wolf-Rayet stars: A class of quasi-periodic variable associated with supergiants and large expulsions of gas

KEY INDIVIDUALS

Hershel, John: A British astronomer of the early 19th century who, among many other discoveries, was instrumental in determining the variable nature of Eta Carinae

Leavitt, Henrietta Swan: An American astronomer of the late 19th/early 20th century who discovered a relationship between the period of a Cepheid variable and its average luminosity

Maury, Antonia: An American astronomer of the late 19th/early 20th century who categorized stars according to their spectra as part of the Draper catalog out of Harvard Observatory

Shelton, Ian: A Canadian astronomer of the late 20th/early 21st century who discovered Supernova 1987A

FIGURE 19.1. The Jewel Box cluster. The four brightest blue stars are supergiants, as is the red star at the center of the cluster. This image was produced by the Very Large Telescope at the ESO's Paranal Observatory in Chile. Credit: ESO/Y. Beletsky.

Section 19.1: Introduction to Super-Giants

Of all the different classes of stars discussed in the previous chapter, we left one alone in order to focus on it here: *supergiants*. There is not a specific definition universally agreed on by astronomers, but for our purposes we will assume this means stars with initial masses of 8 $M_\odot$ or greater. We also know of stars less than 8 $M_\odot$ that exhibit supergiant features (certain variables such as *Wolf-Rayet stars* are examples), but our interest here is in stars with larger initial masses. Technically, there are several subcategories of supergiants, but for simplicity's sake we will treat them as a coherent group and point out distinctions when needed.

With these caveats, the term "supergiant" is straightforward: These are stars that are far larger, in all respects, than any other class. Compared to main sequence stars, or even giants, supergiants are not just more massive, but also generally larger in diameter and are much more luminous than their counterparts.

Although not yet called supergiants, they were first noted by Antonia Maury of Harvard Observatory in 1897. She distinguished stars by their spectra, and a few stars exhibited very thin spectral lines. We now know that, paradoxically, the largest stars have the thinnest spectral lines, because spectral line widths are determined primarily by the density of the gas. Supergiants are spread out, so to speak, and thus the densities of their outer atmospheres are far thinner than those of any other class of star. The first use of the term "supergiant" appears to be by Harlow Shapley in 1925, and other astronomers like Cecilia Payne were also soon using the new name. They were given their own luminosity class in 1943 as part of the Yerkes classification scheme.

In today's nomenclature, there is an extreme version of super-giants called "hypergiants" (class 0) and two other subclasses (Ia and Ib). This reflects the intrinsic brightnesses of supergiants, whose absolute magnitudes range

from −3 to −8 or higher. Perhaps the two most familiar super-giants to the average person are Rigel and Betelgeuse, both in the constellation of Orion the Hunter. Rigel is a blue super-giant (B8 Ia) with an absolute magnitude of −7.84, and Betelgeuse is a red supergiant (M2 Ia) with an absolute magnitude of −5.85. Their spectral types also illustrate something about supergiants: There are few restrictions on their effective surface temperatures. Rigel's temperature is 12,100 K and Betelgeuse is at 3,590 K, yet they are both supergiants. Recall that giants tend to be restricted in color from yellow to red (i.e., G to M-type) and while main sequence stars also span the entire visible spectrum for their colors, these depend on the masses of the main sequence stars. The temperatures of supergiants tend to go back and forth horizontally across the HR diagram and depend on several factors.

FIGURE 19.2. Orion the Hunter. The bright reddish star at upper left is Betelgeuse; the bright blue star at lower right is Rigel.

As with many other objects in astronomy (or everyday life), the more massive a star, the rarer it is. It is estimated that perhaps 75,000 supergiants inhabit the Milky Way, which appears to be a large number until compared to the Milky Way's total of up to 400 billion stars. Luminosities of supergiants range from about a thousand to a million or more times as bright as the Sun, so even if a supergiant is very far away, its apparent magnitude can be very bright; Rigel and Betelgeuse are both in the top 10 for brightest nighttime stars, but the distances to Rigel and Betelgeuse are 260 pc and 200 pc, respectively. Deneb, the bright star in the constellation of Cygnus the Swan, has an apparent magnitude of +1.25 but may be as far away as 1,000 pc.

The range of sizes (radii) of supergiants is also wide, anywhere from a few tens of solar radii to over a thousand. At such sizes (especially at the larger end), the surface gravity of the supergiant is weak; not only is the density of the outer atmosphere very low, but it is barely held onto by the supergiant. Any small shock that would be contained for another star leads to large mass loss. We might expect that, the larger the mass, the stronger the gravity and therefore the more stable the star; in practice, the largest of supergiants are also the most unstable. Supergiants are also partly convective and tend to churn up some of the material from near the core to the surface, meaning the metallicities of supergiants are usually enhanced relative to other nearby classes.

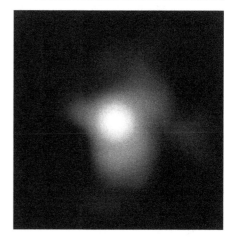

FIGURE 19.3. An infrared close-up image of Betelgeuse by the Very Large Telescope. Adaptive optics were used for the best close-up of a supergiant ever achieved. Credit: ESO/P. Kervella.

Supergiants cover the entire range of spectral types (O through M), but B-type supergiants outnumber the rest of them combined. This hints at high rates of nuclear fusion, as we would expect given the large masses supergiants need to support. This also tells us to expect their lifespans to be short; supergiants can expect to work hydrogen fusion from about 30 million years to as short as a few hundred thousand years, compared to the 10-billion-year lifespan of the Sun. Yet another consequence is that, because the lifespans of supergiants are so short (astronomically speaking), they will be found near where they originally formed. The Sun has orbited the center

Check Your Neighbor

Cite another reason, besides their short lives, why supergiants are good markers for spiral arms.

of the Milky Way about 20 times since its formation; a supergiant like Deneb will have barely started its orbit before it comes to an end. Astronomers use supergiants to map the positions of spiral arms in the Milky Way; since supergiants form there, and they don't live long enough to escape, they serve as markers for the spiral arms.

For a star with the mass of the Sun, fusion halts in its core because its mass is not large enough to generate the temperatures and densities needed to go beyond helium fusion. But supergiants don't have this problem (if we can call this a "problem"). Supergiants also skip the helium flash stage; the core of a supergiant is always so hot that it doesn't reach a degenerate state. Instead, a supergiant smoothly (relatively speaking) eases into using carbon and oxygen as fuel for further nuclear fusion, and so on.

In other words, the story is pretty much the same, but extended. The core of the supergiant runs out of nuclear fuel. Lacking a source of energy, the core shrinks. Nuclear fusion starts in a concentric shell and the outer atmosphere expands. The core eventually reaches high enough temperatures and densities that the ash of the previous round of fusion becomes the fuel for the next round. With the advent of a new source of energy, the core halts its shrinking and the supergiant stabilizes. This process continues until the core fills with iron, which we will discuss in the next section. Table 19.1 shows some estimates of core temperatures and times a particular core fuel will last for a generic supergiant of mass $25 \, M_\odot$.

TABLE 19.1. Conditions for Nuclear Fusion at the Core of a $25 \, M_\odot$ Supergiant

Fuel Burned	Temperature (K)	Lifetime	Density (g/cc)	Products
Hydrogen	7×10^6	10^7 years	10	He
Helium	200×10^6	10^6 years	2000	C, O
Carbon	800×10^6	1000 years	10^6	Ne, Na, Mg, Al
Neon	1600×10^6	3 years	10^7	O, Mg
Oxygen	1800×10^6	100 days	10^7	Si, S, Ar, Ca
Silicon	2500×10^6	5 days	10^8	Ni, Fe

The build-up of several concentric shells of nuclear fusion has acquired the nickname *onion structure*. It's worth noting, though, that the full-blown "onion" doesn't appear until just a few days before the end of the supergiant's life. Silicon is turned into iron but only lasts on the order of a few days—an amazing statistic for a star that likely lived for several million years.

Section 19.2: Case Study: Eta Carinae

Each addition of a new shell of concentric fusion pushes (relatively speaking) the outermost shell of hydrogen burning that much more outward, and supergiants tend to

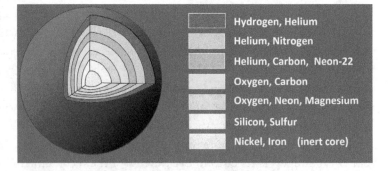

FIGURE 19.4. A cutout of a super-giant's core, showing its "onion" structure of concentric shell fusion.

become more and more unstable (including shedding large amounts of their outer atmospheres) as they near their end. We are far from being able to predict the exact moment when a supergiant runs out of fuel in its core for good, and time scales tend to be long (carbon burning can last for many centuries) compared to people. Still, there are a few supergiants that appear to be jumping up and down, so to speak, and announcing loudly that they are about to explode. One supergiant astronomers currently track is Eta Carinae.

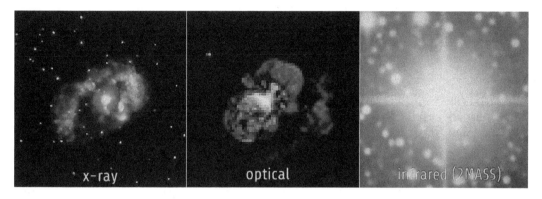

FIGURE 19.5. Eta Carinae and its surroundings. X-rays (observed by the Chandra satellite) show heating from shock waves from the star; visible light (HST) show bubbles of gas expanding in opposite directions; and infrared (2MASS telescope) looks inside obscuring dust to reveal one of the most luminous stars in the galaxy.

Eta Carinae has a declination of −59° 40', which makes it so far to the south as to be unobservable for observers living at latitudes greater than 30° in the northern hemisphere. As a consequence, it appears not to have been reliably cataloged by European astronomers until Edmund Halley in 1679. Backtracking from Halley's notes, modern astronomers give it an apparent magnitude of +3.3 for that year, and it appears to not have made an impression of being anything other than a normal, stable star for many decades thereafter, despite some occasional hints as to its nature. It wasn't until 1827 that William Burchell (1781–1863), an English naturalist, recorded it at as bright as +1, suggesting to him variability. In the 1830s, John Hershel (1792–1871) took on an organized set of observations of Eta Carinae, finding it to be around +1.4 magnitude until December 16, 1837, when it suddenly burst past Rigel (magnitude +0.13) for over 18 years, an event nicknamed the "Great Eruption."

Eta Carinae faded away afterward for several decades, though with occasional jumps in brightness. Eta Carinae may have settled down, or it may be the dust it had shed from the Great Eruption actually masked subsequent large outbursts. By the 1990s Eta Carinae was again showing evidence of periodic ups and downs, verified after a predicted increase in brightness toward the end of 1997 was confirmed. Eta Carinae is a binary system, and the larger star's outbursts are timed to the orbit of its companion. The orbit is modeled to be very eccentric, so the two stars spend most of their time far apart but get very close during

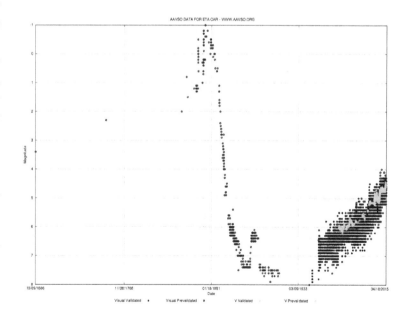

FIGURE 19.6. A visual light curve for Eta Carinae from the 17th century to the present. Credit: AAVSO.

periastron,[1] which is only 1.6 au (apastron is about 30 au). The orbit is currently 5.54 years, but due to friction in the clouds of material, the orbit seems to be decaying every time the smaller star passes through it. The enormous clouds of ejected gas and dust make it difficult to get precise estimates of the masses of the individual stars.

The total mass of the system is at least 90 $M_\odot$, given the brightness of the two stars, and probably much larger. Eta Carinae A may be anywhere from 100 to 120 $M_\odot$ and Eta Carinae B (an extremely large star in its own right) as much as 30 $M_\odot$. The enormous blasts of gas loss hint that Eta Carinae A may have been between 150 and 250 $M_\odot$ before the Great Eruption.

The Eta Carinae system is so far unique in the galaxy; how two such large stars formed in the present-day Milky Way, when the trend is to form smaller and smaller stars, remains to be understood. Eta Carinae A is the largest known example of a type of variable called *Wolf-Rayets*; Eta Carinae B may also be variable, but this can't be known thanks to the nebula created by Eta Carinae A's outbursts. In fact, the system's overall brightness is counterintuitive; while the stars are each likely millions of times brighter than the Sun, this fact is literally obscured by the gas and dust blown off of Eta Carinae A. Basic facts such as luminosity, radius, and temperature are still educated guesses because of this.

Eta Carinae's fate (A and/or B) is not yet known. It may appear that, if any star should explode soon, it would be Eta Carinae, and there are some observations of supernovae from other galaxies that support this. It is possible even that Eta Carinae A would become an exaggerated version of a supernova called a *hypernova*, being both much brighter and longer lasting than a comparable supernova. On the other hand, there is the interesting possibility that, since Eta Carinae A is so massive, rather than the core's collapse instigating an explosion, it will continue to collapse into a black hole. The attempt at being a supernova would be snuffed out, in a real sense.

Are we in any danger from Eta Carinae? Most likely not. The Eta Carinae system is 2,300 parsecs away (7,500 light years). A star with the estimated mass of Eta Carinae A would produce a supernova that, at that distance, would be about as bright as the planet Venus (apparent magnitude −4). Any intense beams of radiation produced are unlikely to head our direction (the rotational poles of the Eta Carinae system are not pointing toward us) and our atmosphere is thick enough to absorb any gamma rays that might reach here. Eta Carinae A has a total lifespan of 3 million years or so, but we have no real idea of when it formed and therefore how old it is; thus, it might explode tomorrow, but given typical astronomical time scales, it is unlikely any of us or our near descendants will see it. Nevertheless, Eta Carinae is a system to which astronomers will pay attention for a long time.

FIGURE 19.7. An artist's rendition of a possible fate for Eta Carinae A. Credit: Nicolle Rager Fuller of the National Science Foundation (NSF).

Section 19.3: Type II Supernovae, Part I: Core Collapse

What happens to a super-giant when its fuel supply is completely exhausted? The most common response is for the star to blow itself apart as a *Type II supernova*.

A quick digression regarding lingo: A Type II supernova is the result of a single star blowing itself up. A Type I (specifically, Type Ia) supernova results from the interactions of two stars, typically a giant

---

[1] "Periastron" is a term like perihelion, which is the closest a planet gets to the Sun during its orbit. Periastron is when the two stars in a binary system are closest to each other. "Apastron" is when the stars are farthest apart.

dumping gas onto a white dwarf. This sounds backward; Type I → two stars, whereas Type II → one star. The (unnecessary) confusion arises from history. Before astronomers knew the causes of supernovae, they categorized them according to the strengths of their hydrogen spectral lines. A supernova with extremely weak hydrogen lines was Type I; a supernova with strong hydrogen lines was Type II.

When last we left our supergiant's core, it was fusing silicon into iron. This is actually shorthand for a chain of reactions starting with silicon and helium that runs through sulfur, argon, calcium, titanium, chromium, iron, nickel, and zinc, though the reactions making zinc actually steal energy from the core rather than releasing it. This series of steps lasts at most a few days before running out of silicon, after which no fuel remains to sustain the core.

Iron and nickel[2] can't serve as nuclear fuel, because iron and nickel have the highest amounts of *binding energy per nucleon*. What does this mean? First, a "nucleon" is simply a particle that lives in the nucleus of an atom (i.e., a proton or neutron). Second, "binding energy" refers to the energy needed to hold the nucleons together. In order to get at this idea, we need to divert for a moment into nuclear physics.

Check Your Neighbor

A Type Ia supernova has relatively weak hydrogen spectral lines because the object that explodes is a white dwarf made mostly of carbon and oxygen. Why would a Type II supernova have strong hydrogen lines?

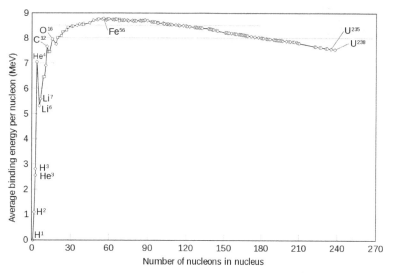

FIGURE 19.8. The binding energy per nucleon of atomic nuclei as a function of atomic number.

Neutrons are electrically neutral (the name was chosen on purpose) but protons are not. Protons each have positive electric charge, and one of the mainstays of electricity is that like charges (i.e., like signs) repel each other. We saw the consequences of this before when discussing the proton-proton chain (chapter 17), where we found that a nuclear reaction between two protons has a 50/50 chance only once every billion years or so. The reason is that when we bring two protons near each other, they exert very powerful forces to push themselves apart.

To hold protons together (or protons to neutrons, or neutrons to neutrons, etc.) requires a different force of nature. Physicists call this the *strong nuclear force*, or "strong force" for short. The strong force is (as its name states) very strong, about 100 times stronger than electric repulsion, and is attractive, meaning that it can hold an atomic nucleus together against the collective outward push of its protons. Another major feature of the strong force is that it is short range; unlike gravity and electromagnetism, the strong force really only acts over the scales of an atomic nucleus. A third feature is that it only works on certain types of particles (nicknamed *baryons*), the most common of which are protons and neutrons; electrons and neutrinos belong to a different class of particles that don't feel the strong force. A useful analogy is the miniature plastic hooks of products like Velcro; the hooks yield a strong binding force, but only when they are brought together. Similarly, protons and neutrons can be held together by the strong nuclear force, but only when they are brought together.

In short, the strong force supplies the energy needed to bind nucleons together to make atomic nuclei. The amount of energy required goes up with increasing atomic number until we reach iron and nickel (elements #26

---

[2] Iron-56 is often cited as the nucleus with the largest binding energy per nucleon, but this is not strictly true. Both iron-58 and nickel-62 have slightly more energy than iron-56, for example.

FIGURE 19.9. An analogy for the strong nuclear force: A magnified image of a strip of plastic hooks.

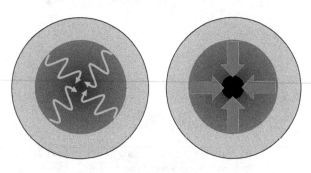

FIGURE 19.10. Iron and nickel require energy to fuse, rather than emitting energy when they fuse. This leads to the collapse of the core (dark gray). The core is still surrounded by its onion layers of concentric-fusing shells (the nearest to the core in light gray).

and #28, respectively), then decreases again. An important consequence is that we can get energy out of fusing together elements lighter than iron and nickel (like the triple-alpha process fuses three helium nuclei to form carbon), and we can split apart larger nuclei via radioactivity (such as the decay of uranium into thorium and helium), but we can't get energy out of iron and nickel this way. This doesn't prevent iron and nickel from participating in nuclear reactions, but it keeps a supergiant from getting energy out of these reactions.

We return once again to the dominant problem facing stars: the battle against gravity trying to pull itself toward its center. For a supergiant, all its previous stages had involved nuclear fusion producing energy, which supplied the outward pressure to resist the star's own weight. But when the core consists of solely iron (or an iron/nickel mix), it no longer produces energy, and the core crashes.

The laws of physics don't stop operating just because nuclear fusion has stopped. As the core shrinks, it will yet again become more dense and hot, but now there is no source of energy to halt this. Nor is it possible for electron degeneracy pressure to stop the collapse: The super-giant already has much more than the Chandrasekhar limit of 1.44 $M_\odot$. If anything, it becomes a runaway process related to the fourth fundamental force of nature—the *weak nuclear force*, or *weak force* for short.

We've seen the weak force briefly before, again during the proton-proton chain (chapter 17). The very first step smashes two protons together and produces a deuterium (proton + neutron) nucleus, a positron (antielectron) and a neutrino. Neutrinos result from weak force reactions, which we know in everyday life as radioactive decay. Neutrinos, like electrons, belong to a class of subatomic particles called *leptons*, which are sensitive to the weak force but not the strong force or, because neutrinos are electrically neutral, electromagnetism. In fact, neutrinos barely react with anything and see the universe as virtually transparent.

In the core of our supergiant, the temperatures and pressures are such that iron begins to undergo a process called *photodisintegration*. Photodisintegration means what it says; photons are so energetic at these temperatures that they are powerful enough to split apart atomic nuclei like iron. When an iron nucleus is hit by one of these photons, it splits apart into 13 alpha particles (helium nuclei) and four neutrons. Photodisintegration isn't limited to iron; it also affects helium nuclei, each reaction producing two protons and two neutrons. But neutrons themselves are not stable particles outside of an atomic nucleus; they decay into protons, electrons, and neutrinos. The reactions look like this:

$$\mathrm{Fe}_{26}^{56} + \gamma \rightarrow 13\mathrm{He}_2^4 + 4\mathrm{n}$$

$$\mathrm{He}_2^4 + \gamma \rightarrow 2\mathrm{p} + 2\mathrm{n}$$

$$\mathrm{n} \rightarrow \mathrm{p} + \mathrm{e} + \nu$$

where, as you may recall, the ν ("nu") symbol stands for the neutrino. Each iron nucleus that photodisintegrates therefore births 30 neutrinos.

Neutrinos are tiny particles, but they aren't nothing, and each neutrino counts for a tiny amount of energy. As a penny doesn't represent much cash, but a million pennies do, the neutrinos add up. The neutrinos barely interact with the core and quickly race out of the core—and the rest of the supergiant—carrying away energy. But subtracting energy from the core means it has <u>less</u> energy available to support itself, and the shrinking therefore speeds up in a runaway process. The core col-

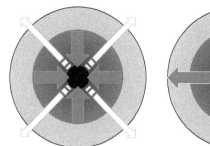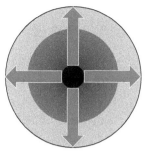

FIGURE 19.11. As the core collapses, photodisintegration produces a flood of neutrinos (green arrows), which leave the core. The collapse halts when the very center becomes degenerate neutron matter and the rebounding shockwaves travel outward.

lapses quickly—so quickly, it takes much less time to collapse than it does to read about it. Speeds of particles at the outer edges of the core reach nearly ¼ the speed of light, though very briefly. Within a second, the core is no more.

As with many of our stories, we've simplified some of the details. One interesting detail we can't pass over is the condition of the core, which has shrunk so much that neutron degeneracy pressure has come into play. Neutrons dominate in the core, either made as part of the photodisintegration process, or when protons and electrons are smashed together at high speeds, and so the core now resembles nothing so much as a gigantic atomic nucleus. The incredibly high temperatures so generated, 100 billion K or so, form "thermal neutrinos," which, along with those generated earlier, account for nearly all the energy released. The infalling matter "rebounds" off the super-hard core, and the shockwaves, along with some neutrinos captured by the outer atmosphere of the super-giant, rip it apart.

Section 19.4: Type II Supernovae, Part II: Remnants

The complete disintegration of a star is a colossal event, one that takes months or even years to play out. We still see the remnants of supernovae centuries after their original explosions. We now turn to understanding how the pieces of the explosion spread, and what, if anything, is left behind.

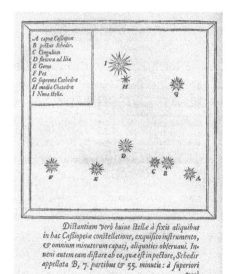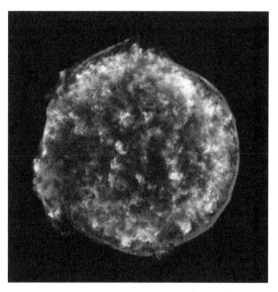

FIGURE 19.12. Left: Tycho Brahe's original star chart showing the position of SN 1572 in the constellation of Cassiopeia. Right: An x-ray image from the Chandra satellite over 4 centuries after the explosion. Credit: NASA/CXC/Rutgers/J.Warren & J.Hughes et al.

First, is there anything at all left behind? Perhaps surprisingly, the answer is yes. Current models argue that for a supergiant up to 20 $M_\odot$, the core will stabilize due to neutron pressure and become a neutron star. Above 20 $M_\odot$, the core will be unable to hold against its own weight and becomes a black hole. We'll talk more about these exotic objects in our next chapter.

Here, we are interested in the debris sent outward by the explosion. Supernovae are the most powerful explosions in the universe, and as such are not only very bright and destructive (of course), but also take a long time to play out. Let's review some of these ideas:

+ The light we see from a supernova peaks on the order of tens of billions of Sun's worth of luminosity; that is, at its peak, a supernova is as bright as tens of billions of Suns. This rivals the total brightness of a small galaxy's worth of stars, all at once, and all concentrated (as seen from a distance) in a single point.

+ Having said that, the light we see is only about 1% of the total energy released during the explosion. 90% of the energy actually escapes from the supernova in the form of neutrinos. The other 9% is used to physically blow apart the star. Or, the total energy released by a supernova is on the order of trillions of Suns.

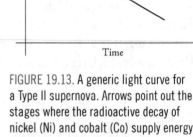

+ You might think the explosion would be at its peak brightness right away. We're fooled a bit because of our familiarity with explosions on Earth, which seem instantaneous. They aren't—high-speed cameras show this—but they are quick. But a firecracker can blow apart a few grams of material much more quickly than a supernova can blow apart several solar masses. It's common for a supernova to reach its peak brightness after only a few <u>months</u>.

FIGURE 19.13. A generic light curve for a Type II supernova. Arrows point out the stages where the radioactive decay of nickel (Ni) and cobalt (Co) supply energy to keep the remnants bright. Compare this curve to that of a Type Ia supernova (Figure 18.24).

+ Also, explosions we see in everyday life are one and done; that is, the pieces fly off into the distance and that's it. A supernova is so powerful that nuclear reactions occur in the debris. Alpha particles, protons, and neutrons in particular are captured by other nuclei as they travel near the speed of light, building elements beyond iron and nickel. Core-collapse supernovae do not appear to account for <u>all</u> of the elements (we'll talk about neutron star collisions in the next chapter) but many of them are. These elements—and the others made by various shells near the core—are scattered into the interstellar medium. The cliché that we are made of "stardust" happens to be true.

+ Some of the nuclei made during a supernova are radioactive. Notable amongst them are nickel-56 and cobalt-56. Nickel-56 is only one among dozens of potential isotopes (nickel-58 is actually the most popular isotope on Earth), but it is most easily made during a supernova. Ni-56 has a half-life of 6.075 days, decaying into Co-56 and releasing energy as it does. Cobalt-56 is also radioactive, with a half-life of 77.27 days, and also releases energy as it decays into iron-56. These two nuclei keep the explosion fragments hotter than they otherwise would be, and the amount of light from the supernova is kept brighter for longer as a result. The details are different than those of a Type Ia supernova (chapter 18), but the general idea is the same.

+ Supernova remnants affect their surroundings. We have already seen (chapter 16) how the shockwave of a supernova can compress gas and dust in an interstellar nebula, sparking star formation. Elements from the supernova remnant mix into the interstellar medium, especially creating conditions for dust and therefore the effects on stars and planets dust has. A typical supernova remnant expands into space at incredible speeds—ejecta can be traveling at tens of thousands of meters per second (10–20% of the speed of light) even months after the initial explosion—and can remain visible for thousands of years before spreading so thin as to become undetectable. Often the debris runs into gas and dust ejected from the star prior to the explosion (Eta Carinae is a candidate for just this behavior), and the shockwaves light up the older material.

- We've been using the term, but just what is a *supernova remnant*? It's pretty much what the term suggests: whatever is left over after a supernova event. An individual supernova can leave behind two separate remnants: one, a neutron star or black hole, the remains of the former core, and two, the debris of the rest of the star spreading out into space.

- Finally, have you ever wondered what a star looks like

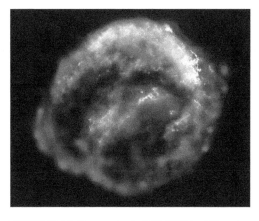

FIGURE 19.14. The remnant of SN 1604 in different wavelengths: X-rays (blue and green from Chandra), visible (yellow, Hubble), and infrared (red, Spitzer). Credit: NASA/ESA/JHU/R.Sankrit & W.Blair. Right: A model of a supernova remnant (photo by the author).

from the inside? A supernova is, in a sense, what happens when you turn a star inside out. In case you're wondering if there are any inside-out objects in everyday life, check out Figure 19.14.

Section 19.5: Case Study: SN 1987A

Ian Shelton (b. 1957) was a graduate student from Canada working at Las Campanas Observatory in Chile in 1987. On the night of February 24, he took a photograph of a satellite galaxy of the Milky Way, the Large Magellanic Cloud (LMC for short), using an old telescope he himself had refurbished. Later that night, he decided to develop the photographic plate and noticed something odd, a bright dot had appeared in the LMC:

> "It was incredibly bright" he recounted in an interview celebrating the 20th anniversary of the discovery. "I was looking at something pretty extreme."

Stepping outside, he looked at the LMC and was able to see the dot with the naked eye. In fact, it was easy to see, later being determined to have an apparent magnitude of +2, which placed it among the brighter stars in the sky. After confirming his find, he spread the word; a colleague at Las Campanas, Oscar Duhalde, saw it, and an amateur astronomer named Albert Jones from New Zealand also spotted it later that day.

It was quickly determined that this was a supernova. At the time, astronomers thought that only red giants (or red supergiants) could detonate as supernovae, so it was a surprise when the *progenitor* (original star), Sk-69 202, turned out to have been a blue supergiant. This wasn't the only important fact about the supernova; it was the first visible to

FIGURE 19.15. The Tarantula Nebula of the Large Magellanic Cloud, a satellite galaxy of the Milky Way. Supernova 1987A is the bright dot near the center of the image, which was taken by the Schmidt Telescope at the European Southern Observatory in 1987. At that time, the supernova was visible to the naked eye. Credit: ESO.

the naked eye since Kepler and his contemporaries witnessed a supernova in 1604. While SN 1987A[3] wasn't part

---

[3] "SN 1987A" simply means the first supernova ("A") discovered in the year 1987. This method of labeling supernovae is standard for astronomy.

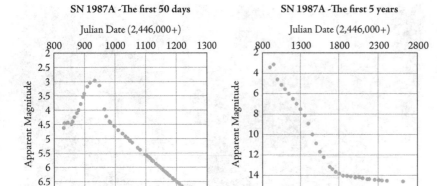

SN 1987A -The first 50 days

Julian Date (2,446,000+)

SN 1987A -The first 5 years

Julian Date (2,446,000+)

FIGURE 19.16. Light curves for SN 1987A. Left: Its first 50 days. Right: Its first 5 years. Compare the shape of the left-hand light curve to the generic curve shown in Figure 19.13.

FIGURE 19.17. SN 1987A 24 years later. A pair of faint rings surround a bright ring (bubble?) as shockwaves from the supernova encounter its local interstellar medium. Credit: ESA/ Hubble & NASA.

of the Milky Way, it did explode in a neighboring galaxy, close enough that people could see it with the naked eye for months.

If we are strict about the time of observation, then Ian Shelton wasn't the first to see it. It's just that people didn't realize it had been seen until afterward. Kamioka Observatory is an underground laboratory devoted to the study of neutrinos and gravitational waves. One of its experiments, Kamiokande-II, detected 11 thermally produced neutrinos from SN 1987A that officially reached Earth before the visible light did. This, by the way, tells us two things about neutrinos: First, that they are very hard to detect (only 11 found!) and second, that models concerning the core collapse hypothesis were on the correct track.

Much of what we have learned about supernovae has come from studying SN 1987A since it was discovered. We have had several items working in our favor: First, the supernova was relatively close by, so it has been easy to observe; second, it happened during our modern age of astronomical instruments, so data collection has been outstanding; third, astronomers had already observed the progenitor beforehand, so we knew what type and class of star had exploded.

It's also had a few other side benefits. For example, it allowed astronomers to determine a much more precise determination of the distance to the Large Magellanic Cloud. Let's consider the following chain of logic (and also refer to Figure 19.17):

+   A bubble (seen as a ring) of material was blasted from the star's original position.
+   Spectroscopy is able to determine the speed of the expanding ring via the Doppler effect.
+   We know when the supernova exploded, so we know how much time has passed.
+   Multiplying speed and time lets us calculate the physical diameter of the ring.
+   The ring is also visible in telescopes, so we can measure its angular diameter.
+   Comparing the angular to the physical diameter tells us how far away it must be.
+   Finally, since the supernova belongs to the LMC, we also know how far away the LMC must be.

By these measurements and calculations, the LMC is 51.4 kiloparsecs (or 168,000 light years) away.

> ## Check Your Neighbor
>
> Supernova 1987A was first seen in 1987. It happened in the LMC, which is 168,000 light years away. When did the supernova <u>really</u> explode?

SN 1987A solved many conundrums but has posed a few new ones. Figure 19.17 shows a bright ring; this is expected, as the shockwave of the original explosion travels through space. But there are also a pair of fainter, larger rings on opposite sides of the supernova's original location. These rings didn't exist prior to the supernova, but what specifically is causing them? Another mystery is that, whereas the progenitor star was of such a mass as to produce a neutron star, no neutron star has been found. It may be the neutron star is hidden behind thick dust, or that the neutron star was shot off sideways at high speeds (i.e., the explosion was not symmetrical), or no neutron star was formed in the first place. Or it may simply be we still have a lot left to learn about the brightest events nature has to offer.

Summary

In this chapter, we covered the following:

▸ How supergiants go through several types of nuclear fusion

▸ The case of Eta Carinae, a system containing one of the most massive stars known

▸ How the cores of supergiants collapse upon running out of nuclear fuel

▸ How the explosion fragments travel through and interact with interstellar space

▸ The case of Supernova 1987A, the first naked-eye supernova in nearly 4 centuries

Questions

1. Suppose a supergiant is at the same distance from the center of the galaxy as our Sun, so that its orbital speed is the same. Assume the orbits are circular. The Sun takes 240 million years to complete an orbit. If the super-giant has a lifespan of 10 million years, how far (in terms of degrees) along its "orbit" can it get before it dies?

2. Deneb, a blue supergiant in the constellation of Cygnus the Swan, is 800 pc away and has an apparent magnitude of +1.25. What is its absolute magnitude?

   The following questions relate to SN 1987A, given the following data:
   ◆ The speed of the expanding gas of the inner ring (bubble) was 27,000 km/s.
   ◆ This was measured for the ring 3.5 years after the initial explosion.
   ◆ The inner ring was 0.808 arcseconds across 3.5 years after the initial explosion.
     · Convert 3.5 years into its equivalent number of seconds.
     · Find the physical diameter of the inner ring, in units of kilometers. Assume the speed is constant. Hint: Remember that a diameter is twice the length of a radius.
     · Convert the diameter to units of parsecs. Recall 1 pc = 3.09 × 1013 km.
     · Convert the angular diameter of the inner ring to units of radians. There are 206,265 arcseconds in each radian.
     · If the angle is in radians and is small (is that true?), then the distance to the ring is its diameter divided by the angle. Find the distance to SN 1987A in units of parsecs.
     · Finally, convert the distance to SN 1987A in units of light years. One parsec equals 3.26 light years.

3. Eta Carina is among the most active and massive binary systems known. The current mutual orbital period of its two stars is 5.54 years, its periastron (the point of closest approach of the two stars) is 1.6 au, and its apastron (the point of furthest separation of the two stars) is 30 au.
   ◆ Find its semi-major axis.
   ◆ Estimate the total mass of the system, in units of solar masses (note this is actually a lower limit, since we don't currently know the inclination of the orbit).

4. If Eta Carina A blows itself up as a supernova, given its estimated mass, it should shine with a maximum (i.e., brightest) apparent magnitude of −4. The Eta Carina system is approximately 2300 parsecs distant. What would be its maximum absolute magnitude?

5. Suggest an analogy for the runaway behavior of neutrinos during the core collapse of a Type II supernova.

6. Which subatomic particle, a neutron or a proton, is more massive? Briefly defend your reasoning.

Activities

▶ *Astrophysics activity 19.1:* Conduct an experiment simulating weak and strong nuclear forces and explain how they help us understand stars.

Works Referenced

Supergiants are described in the following sources:

Harper, G. M., Brown, A., & Guinan, E. F. (2008). A new VLA-Hipparcos distance to Betelgeuse and its implications. *Astronomical Journal, 135*(4), 1430–1440. doi:10.1088/0004-6256/135/4/1430

Keenan, P. C., & McNeil, R. C. (1989). The Perkins catalog of revised MK types for the cooler stars. *Astrophysical Journal Supplement Series, 71*, 245. doi:10.1086/191373

Morgan, W. W., Keenan, P. C., & Kellman, E. (1943). *An atlas of stellar spectra, with an outline of spectral classification.* The University of Chicago Press, Chicago, IL.

Pannekoek, A. (1963). *A history of astronomy.* Dover Publications Inc., New York.

Payne, C. H., & Chase, C. T. (1927). The spectrum of supergiant stars of class F8. *Harvard College Observatory Circular, 300*, 1.

Przybilla, N., Butler, K., Becker, S. R., & Kudritzki, R. P. (2006, January). Quantitative spectroscopy of BA-type super-giants. *Astronomy and Astrophysics, 445*(3), 1099–1126. doi:10.1051/0004-6361:20053832

Schiller, F., & Przybilla, N. (2008). Quantitative spectroscopy of Deneb. *Astronomy & Astrophysics, 479*(3), 849–858. doi:10.1051/0004-6361:20078590

Shapley, H. (1925). S Doradus, a supergiant variable star. *Harvard College Observatory Bulletin, 814*, 1.

Sowell, J. R., Trippe, M., Caballero-Nieves, S. M., & Houk, N. (2007). H-R diagrams based on the HD Stars in the Michigan Spectral Catalogue and the Hipparcos Catalog. *Astronomical Journal, 134*(3), 1089. doi:10.1086/520060

Nucleosynthesis in supergiants is described in the following sources:

Burbidge, E. M., Burbidge, G. R., Fowler, W.A., & Hoyle, F. (1957). Synthesis of the elements in stars. *Reviews of Modern Physics, 29*(4), 547–650. doi:10.1103/RevModPhys.29.547

Hoyle, F. (1946). The synthesis of the elements from hydrogen. *Monthly Notices of the Royal Astronomical Society, 106*(5), 343–383. doi:10.1093/mnras/106.5.343

Hoyle, F. (1954). On nuclear reactions occurring in very hot STARS. I. The synthesis of elements from carbon to nickel. *Astrophysical Journal Supplement Series, 1*, 121. doi:10.1086/190005

"Supergiant Stars": http://cronodon.com/SpaceTech/Super-giant.html

Woosley, S., & Janka, H. T. (2005, December). The physics of core-collapse supernovae. *Nature Physics, 1*(3), 147–154. doi:10.1038/nphys172

Eta Carinae is discussed in the following sources:

Damineli, A. (1996). The 5.52 year cycle of Eta Carinae. *Astrophysical Journal Letters, 460*, L49. doi:10.1086/309961

Damineli, A., Kaufer, A., Wolf, B., Stahl, O., Lopes, D. F., & de Araújo, F. X. (2000). H Carinae: Binarity confirmed. *Astrophysical Journal*, 528(2), L101. doi:10.1086/312441

Frew, D. J. (2004). The historical record of η Carinae. I. The visual light curve, 1595–2000. *Journal of Astronomical Data*, 10(6), 1–76.

Groh, J. H., Meynet, G., Georgy, C., & Ekström, S. (2013). Fundamental properties of core-collapse supernova and GRB progenitors: Predicting the look of massive stars before death. *Astronomy & Astrophysics*, 558, A131. doi:10.1051/0004-6361/201321906

Halley, Edmund (1679). *Catalogus stellarum australium (Catalog of the Southern Stars)*.

Heger, A., Fryer, C. L., Woosley, S. E., Langer, N., & Hartmann, D. H. (2003). How massive single stars end their life. *Astrophysical Journal*, 591, 288. doi:10.1086/375341

Herschel, J. F. W. (1847). *Results of astronomical observations made during the years 1834, 5, 6, 7, 8, at the Cape of Good Hope: Being the completion of a telescopic survey of the whole surface of the visible heavens, commenced in 1825.* London, UK: Smith, Elder and Co.

Kashi, A., & Soker, N. (2010). Periastron passage triggering of the 19th century eruptions of Eta Carinae. *Astrophysical Journal*, 723, 602. doi:10.1088/0004-637X/723/1/602

Khan, R., Kochanek, C. S., Stanek, K. Z., & Gerke, J. (2015). Finding η car analogs in nearby galaxies using Spitzer. II. Identification of an emerging class of extragalactic self-obscured stars. *Astrophysical Journal*, 799(2), 187. doi:10.1088/0004-637X/799/2/18

Madura, T. I., Gull, T. R., Owocki, S. P., Groh, J. H., Okazaki, A. T., & Russell, C. M. P. (2012). Constraining the absolute orientation of η Carinae's binary orbit: A 3D dynamical model for the broad [Fe III] emission. *Monthly Notices of the Royal Astronomical Society*, 420(3), 2064. doi:10.1111/j.1365-2966.2011.20165.x

McKinnon, D., Gull, T. R., & Madura, T. (2014). Eta Carinae: An astrophysical laboratory to study conditions during the transition between a pseudo-supernova and a supernova. *American Astronomical Society*, 223, #405.03.

Smith, N., Mauerhan, J. C., Prieto, J. L. (2014). SN 2009ip and SN 2010mc: Core-collapse Type IIn supernovae arising from blue super-giants. *Monthly Notices of the Royal Astronomical Society*, 438(2), 1191. doi:10.1093/mnras/stt2269

Type II supernovae are described in the following sources:

Barwick, S., & Beacom, J., Working Group Leaders. (2004, October 29). APS Neutrino Study: Report of the Neutrino Astrophysics and Cosmology Working Group. *American Physical Society*. Retrieved 2019-04-21. https://www.aps.org/policy/reports/multidivisional/neutrino/upload/Neutrino_Astrophysics_and_Cosmology_Working_Group.pdf

Cardall, C. (2008). Degeneracy, the virial theorem, and stellar collapse. *American Journal of Physics*. Retrieved from https://arxiv.org/pdf/0812.0114.pdf

Clayton, D. D. (1983). *Principles of stellar evolution and nucleosynthesis*. Chicago, IL: University of Chicago Press.

Gilmore, G. (2004). The short spectacular life of a superstar. *Science*, 304(5697): 1915–1916. doi:10.1126/science.1100370

Gribbin, J. R., & Gribbin, M. (2000). *Stardust: Supernovae and life: The cosmic connection*. New Haven, CT: Yale University Press.

Fewell, M. P. (1995). The atomic nuclide with the highest mean binding energy. *American Journal of Physics*, 63(7), 653–658. doi:10.1119/1.17828

Fryer, C. L. (2003). Black hole formation from stellar collapse. *Classical and Quantum Gravity*, 20(10), S73–S80. doi:10.1088/0264-9381/20/10/309

Fryer, C. L., & New, K. C. B. (2006, January 24). "Gravitational waves from gravitational collapse." Max Planck Institute for Gravitational Physics. Retrieved 2019-04-21. https://link.springer.com/article/10.12942/lrr-2003-2

Lieb, E. H., & Yau, H. T. (1987). A rigorous examination of the Chandrasekhar theory of stellar collapse. *Astrophysical Journal*, 323(1), 140–144. doi:10.1086/165813

Rauscher, T., Heger, A., Hoffman, R. D., & Woosley, S. E. (2002). Nucleosynthesis in massive stars with improved nuclear and stellar physics. *Astrophysical Journal, 576*(1), 323–348. doi:10.1086/34172

Young, T. R. (2004). A parameter study of Type II supernova light curves using 6 M He cores. *Astrophysical Journal, 617*(2), 1233–1250. doi:10.1086/425675

The story of Supernova 1987A is told in the following sources:

Arnett, W. D., Bahcall, J. N., Kirshner, R. P., & Woosley, S. E. (1989). Supernova 1987A. *Annual Review of Astronomy and Astrophysics 27*, 629–700. doi:10.1146/annurev.aa.27.090189.003213

Howell, D. (2007, February 25). Whole new science exploded with supernova discovery 20 years ago. *Edmonton Journal.* Retrieved from https://web.archive.org/web/20100228163329/http://www2.canada.com/edmontonjournal/news/story.html?id=54ec9199-a661-4b8c-9f90-12a229b75446&k=33778

Kasen, D., & Woosley, S. (2009). Type II supernovae: Model light curves and standard candle relationships. *Astrophysical Journal, 703*(2), 2205–2216. doi:10.1088/0004-637X/703/2/2205

Kunkel, W., Lawrence, S., Crotts, A., Bouchet, P., Heathcote, S., & Probst, R. (1987, February 24). Supernova 1987A in the Large Magellanic Cloud. *IAU Circular, 4316*, 1.

Nomoto, K., & Shigeyama, T. Supernova 1987A: Constraints on the theoretical model. In M. Kafatos & A. Michalitsianos (Eds.), *Supernova 1987a in the Large Magellanic Cloud* (pp. 273–288). Cambridge, UK: Cambridge University Press.

Panagia, N. (1998). New distance determination to the LMC. *Memorie della Societa Astronomia Italiana, 69*, 225.

Sonneborn, G. (1987). The progenitor of SN1987A. In M. Kafatos, & A. Michalitsianos (Eds.), *A.supernova 1987a in the Large Magellanic Cloud* (pp. 5–12). Cambridge, UK: Cambridge University Press.

"IAUC 4316: 1987A; N Cen 1986": www.cbat.eps.harvard.edu

The light curve of SN 1987A for its first few years is detailed in the following sources:

Menzies et al. (1987). "Spectroscopic and photometric observations of SN 1987A: The First 50 days." *Monthly Notices of the Royal Astronomical Society (MNRAS), 227*, pp. 39–49.

Catchpole et al. (1987). "Spectroscopic and photometric observations of SN 1987A: Days 51 to 134", *MNRAS, 229*, pp. 15–25.

Catchpole et al. (1987). "Spectroscopic and photometric observations of SN 1987A: Days 135 to 260", *MNRAS, 231*, pp. 75–89.

Whitelock et al. (1988). "Spectroscopic and photometric observations of SN 1987A: Days 260 to 385", *MNRAS, 234*, pp. 5–18.

Catchpole et al. (1989). "Spectroscopic and photometric observations of SN 1987A: Days 386 to 616", *MNRAS, 237*, pp. 55–68.

Whitelock et al. (1989). "Spectroscopic and photometric observations of SN 1987A: Days 617 to 792", *MNRAS, 240*, pp. 7–24.

Caldwell et al. (1993). "Spectroscopic and photometric observations of SN 1987A: Days 793 to 1770", *MNRAS, 262*, pp. 313–324.

Credits

Fig. 19.5: Source: https://commons.wikimedia.org/wiki/File:EtaCarinaeStarSystem-3Views-XRayOpticalIR-20140826.jpg.

Fig. 19.6: Copyright © by AAVSO (CC BY 2.5) at https://commons.wikimedia.org/wiki/File:Historical_visual_lightcurve_for_Eta_Carinae_(1686_-_2014).png.

Fig. 19.7: Source: https://commons.wikimedia.org/wiki/File:Gamma_ray_burst.jpg.

Fig. 19.8: Source: https://commons.wikimedia.org/wiki/File:Binding_energy_curve_-_common_isotopes.svg.

Fig. 19.9: Copyright © by Natural Philo (CC BY-SA 3.0) at https://commons.wikimedia.org/wiki/File:Micrograph_of_hook_and_loop_fastener,(Velcro_like).jpg.

Fig. 19.12a: Source: https://commons.wikimedia.org/wiki/File:Tycho_Cas_SN1572.jpg.

Fig. 19.12b: Source: https://commons.wikimedia.org/wiki/File:Tycho-supernova-xray.jpg.

Fig. 19.14a: Source: https://commons.wikimedia.org/wiki/File:Keplers_supernova.jpg.

Fig. 19.15: Copyright © by ESO (CC BY-SA 4.0) at https://commons.wikimedia.org/wiki/File:Eso0708a.jpg.

Fig. 19.17: Copyright © by ESA/Hubble (CC BY 3.0) at https://commons.wikimedia.org/wiki/File:SN_1987A_HST.jpg.

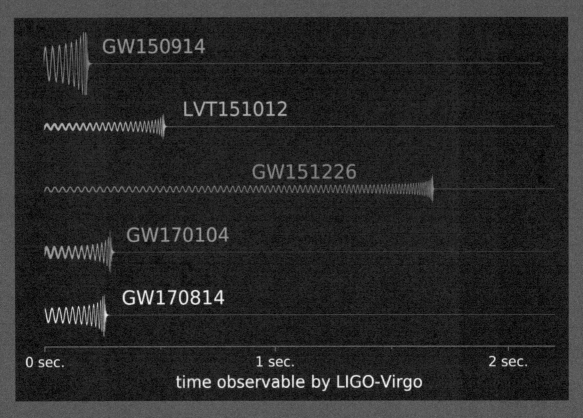

Five different gravitational waves were detected from space by LIGO by the end of 2017. Four are thought to originate from the mergers of pairs of black holes, the fifth from the merger of a pair of neutron stars. Credit: LIGO/Caltech/MIT/LSC.

CHAPTER 20

THE ENDS OF STARS III

To describe neutron stars and black holes

OBJECTIVES

- To distinguish between neutron stars and black holes
- To describe a neutron star
- To describe a black hole
- To survey the evidence for neutron stars and black holes
- To review the effects of neutron stars and black holes on their surroundings
- To describe the direct discovery of gravitational waves
- To relate black holes of different sizes, from stellar black holes to quasars

INTRODUCTION

Maybe the most iconic object in all of astronomy is a black hole. Black holes are the ultimate mystery; we cannot know what goes on inside them. Their effects on their environments is exotic, to say the least. They destroy the laws of physics at their centers. Yet there is overwhelming evidence for their existence. And our galaxy itself might never have formed without one.

Hardly second to black holes in oddness are neutron stars. That a former star, once millions of miles across, now is barely the size of a large city is extreme, to say the least. Neutron stars have their own history, separate from black holes, but are also amongst the strangest objects in the universe.

This chapter is devoted to understanding the ultimate ends of stars, neutron stars and black holes.

KEY TERMS

Accretion disk: A disk or torus of gas and dust swirling in circles as its matter spirals toward a compact object like a neutron star or black hole

Angular momentum (and **conservation thereof**): The amount of "spin" possessed by an object, dependent on its speed of rotation and the distribution of its mass. It is conserved (remains the same) for an object unless an external torque acts upon it

Black hole: Most simply, an object from which nothing can escape

Central engine: A black hole with an accretion disk emitting radiation

Crab Nebula: A remnant from a supernova seen in the year 1054 by people as far apart as the American Southwest and Eastern Asia

Ergosphere: A region surrounding a rotating black hole where trapped objects <u>cannot</u> remain at rest

Event horizon: The "boundary" of a black hole, defined from outside by the mass, electric charge and angular momentum of the hole

Gamma ray burst: A "burst" of gamma rays lasting perhaps only a few seconds; during the burst, the brightest objects in the universe. Suspected to result from collisions between neutron stars and/or black holes

Gravitational lensing: The gravity of a large amount of mass, especially if in a small volume, can act like a conventional lens in "bending" the paths of light rays from stars behind it

Gravitational redshift: The gravity of a neutron star or black hole is strong enough to significantly steal energy from any photons generated nearby, thus causing the wavelengths to become longer

Hawking radiation: Hypothesized virtual particles escaping from just outside the event horizon

Kilonova: An enormous stellar explosion, between the intensity of a nova and a supernova, possibly linked to the mergers of neutron stars and the production of certain heavy elements

Microquasar: Similar in structure to a quasar, but usually referring to a stellar-sized *black hole* rather than a *supermassive black hole*

Millisecond pulsar: A pulsar with a period of order 1/1000th of a second

Neutron degeneracy pressure (also just degeneracy pressure): A property of particles such as neutrons that prevent them from being in the same place at the same time

Neutron star: The remains of the core of a supergiant, which are now held up against its own weight by neutron degeneracy pressure

Occultation: When a relatively large (in terms of angular diameter) object moves in front of a smaller object

Polar jets: Jets of charged particles streaming in opposite directions at the poles of an accretion disk's magnetic field, emitting jets of radiation in their turn

Pulsar: A neutron star rotating such that a beam of radiation emitted from the neutron star rotates across our line of sight, thereby looking like a pulse of radiation

Quasar (quasi-stellar radio source): A *supermassive black hole* at the center of a young galaxy whose accretion disk is incredibly bright

QSO (quasi-stellar object): Similar to a quasar, except that bright radio emissions are not seen

Schwarzschild radius: The "size" of a black hole as seen from outside; an object going inside this boundary ensures that object cannot escape the black hole

Singularity: A theoretical object with mass but no size (radius) at all; thought to reside at the center of a black hole

Spaghettification: The stretching of an object into a long strand (like spaghetti) by the intense gravity tides of an object like a black hole

Supermassive black hole: A black hole with millions to billions of solar masses. Usually found at the cores of galaxies

Synchrotron radiation: A type of radiation emitted by charged particles spiraling close to the speed of light

Tolman-Oppenheimer-Volkoff (TOV) limit: Analogous to the Chandrasekhar limit for white dwarfs, it uses neutron degeneracy pressure and repulsion from the strong force to set a limit for how massive a neutron star can be. Currently thought to be 2.17 $M_\odot$

Uncertainty principle: From quantum mechanics, the idea that the uncertainty in the amount of energy possessed by a particle multiplied by the uncertainty in the duration of the particle's existence must be greater than a set number

Virtual particles: A consequence of the uncertainty principle, which implies that subatomic particles can "pop" into existence if they pop back out quickly enough

Wormhole: A theoretical connection between two different locations in space/time

KEY INDIVIDUALS

Bell, Jocelyn (later Jocelyn Bell Burnell): A Northern Irish astronomer of the late 20th/early 21st century who collaborated in the discovery of the first pulsar

Dicke, Robert: An American physicist of the mid-20th century who seems to be the first scientist to use the term *black hole*

Hazard, Cyril: An Australian astronomer of the late 20th century who helped uncover the nature of quasars

Hawking, Stephen: A British physicist of the late 20th/early 21st century who made important contributions to our understanding of black holes and who did a great deal to popularize black holes

Hewish, Antony: A British astronomer of the late 20th century who collaborated in the discovery of the first pulsar

Michell, John: A British natural philosopher (scientist) of the 18th century who was the first to discuss the concept of a black hole

Oppenheimer, Robert: An American physicist of the mid-20th century who made significant advances concerning our understanding of neutrons stars and black holes.

Most famous as the director of Los Alamos (i.e., the Manhattan Project) during World War II

Penrose, Roger: A British physicist of the late 20th/early 21st century who made important contributions in general relativity and to the understanding of black holes

Schmidt, Maarten: A Dutch astronomer of the late 20th century who helped uncover the nature of quasars

Schwarzschild, Karl: A German physicist of the late 19th/early 20th century, who first solved Einstein's field equations (for general relativity) for the case of a point mass, and thus discovered how the size (radius) of a black hole depends on its mass

Wheeler, John: An American physicist of the mid-20th century who is credited most with popularizing the term *black hole*, though he did not invent it

Section 20.1: The Discovery of Pulsars

Here are two might-have-been stories, in this case regarding one the universe's strangest classes of objects, pulsars.

In 1967, Charles Schisler was a staff Air Force sergeant at Clear Air Force Station in Alaska, tasked to monitor the Ballistic Missile Early Warning System, which was used to watch for potential nuclear missiles from Soviet Russia (the quickest path to the continental United States from Russia would take the missiles over the North Pole, hence the Alaska assignment). He detected a weak signal or "blip" on his radar that kept recurring. He then noticed that the blip would return each following day with a delay of 4 minutes—the difference between the sidereal day and the solar day (see chapter 3). In other words, the blip belonged to space, not the Earth.

After making the 125-kilometer drive to Fairbanks, he met with an astronomer who helped Schisler find the source of his blip: the Crab Nebula in the constellation of Taurus the Bull. Schisler went on to identify another dozen or so such objects but had no notion of what he was looking at until astronomers announced their discovery in 1968. Schisler kept quiet until 2007, when the early warning system he'd used was finally decommissioned: "I wish I'd had a way to communicate with the scientific community."

But Schisler wasn't the first to see these objects. In the late 1950s, a woman[1] visiting the University of Chicago looked through their telescope at the Crab Nebula (it was open to the public back then) and stated she was seeing flickering light from it. One of the astronomers assured her it was simply flickering or "scintillation," the twinkling of starlight we often experience due to turbulence in the atmosphere, despite the woman's statement that, as a pilot, she was familiar with scintillation and this wasn't it.

In case you're not aware of this, your lights at home flicker all the time. We don't mean the flickering when a light is bad and about to burn out; rather, this flickering happens because virtually all homes run on ac ("alternating current") electricity at a frequency of

FIGURE 20.1. The Crab Nebula, in x-rays (blue) and visible light (red). Credits: Optical: NASA/HST/ASU/J. Hester et al. X-Ray: NASA/CXC/ASU/J. Hester et al.

---

[1] Unfortunately, the woman's name is not recorded in any of the stories I was able to trace.

FIGURE 20.2. Jocelyn Bell in 1967.

60 hertz, meaning the lights turn on and off 60 times per second. The human eye can't follow changes that happen that quickly, and so the light bulb appears to be giving off a steady light. The object at the center of the Crab Nebula flickers at 30 hertz, which is at the outer range of what most people can perceive. This particular pilot, with experience and training, could detect this flickering, though the astronomer (!) could not.

Both anecdotes refer to the *Crab Nebula*, one of the most famous of supernova remnants. In the year 1054 CE, people across the world recorded the appearance of a bright star in their skies, from the American Southwest (by a people called the Anasazi) in the western hemisphere to the Chinese and Japanese in the eastern hemisphere. For a few months after the initial appearance of the star, it was bright enough to see during daylight, and to cast shadows and read by at night. By the early 1940s, astronomers Walter Baade and Rudolf Minkowski had narrowed the location of the original supernova (as astronomers by then understood it to be) to lie within the Crab Nebula.[2]

The official discovery of pulsars was made not in the Crab Nebula, though, but from a different source. Jocelyn Bell (later Jocelyn Bell Burnell, b. 1943) was a graduate student working with radio equipment under the British astronomer Antony Hewish (b. 1924) when she noted a particular source in the sky was pulsing with a period of 1.34 seconds. After eliminating the possibility of noise, they jokingly dubbed it "LGM-1" (for "Little Green Men 1") in case the source turned out to be intelligent in origin. Bell soon ruled out that possibility. Hewish (and others) eventually won the Nobel Prize in physics in 1974, but Bell was left out. To her credit, she has never showed any resentment, and when given the "Special Breakthrough Prize in Fundamental Physics" in 2018 (from the Fundamental Physics Prize Foundation, created by the Russian physicist Yuri Milner in 2012), she donated her winnings, worth several million dollars, to aid women, minorities and refugees in pursuing careers in physics.

Very soon after the announcement of the discovery in 1967, several other like objects were quickly discovered and confirmed, begging the question, exactly what did they find? They are now called *pulsars*, after the pulses of radiation (not only radio waves) they emit.

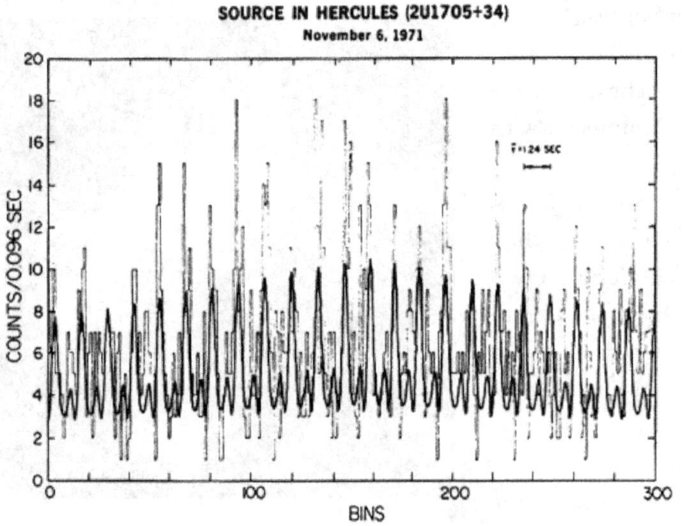

What causes the "pulses"? To determine potential sources, we must consider the most important piece of evidence: the period of the pulsations. First, the pulses were very short by astronomical standards; the pulsar discovered by Bell and Hewish (labeled PSR B1919+21) has a period just over 1 second. A pulsar was soon after found in the Crab Nebula, and its period is (as mentioned) 1/30th of a second. Several pulsars have been found with periods close to 1/1000th of a second and are labeled *millisecond pulsars* for that reason.

The second fact about the pulses is that they are remarkably regular. The period of PSR B1919+21 is officially 1.337 302 088 311 seconds, which states that the period remains

FIGURE 20.3. Radio signals from Hercules X-1 from the Uhuru satellite. Her X-1 has a period of 1.2 seconds and is a rotating neutron star. Credit: NASA.

---

[2] The "Crab" was named so its appearance through a telescope reminded an astronomer of that kind of creature.

constant within a billionth of a second. Pulsars could make very good clocks, if we were so inclined to use them that way.

Few objects (of any kind, not just astronomical) can produce both quickness and regularity on this level. Even the fastest variable stars (chapters 13 and 18) have periods no shorter than a day. Vibrations from other objects—white dwarfs and neutron stars—were ruled out when calculations showed such periods weren't possible. The rotation of white dwarfs was also eliminated from consideration when it became apparent that a white dwarf would have to rotate faster than the speed of light to make this work. The origin of pulsars lies in the rapid rotations of neutron stars, combined with beams of radiation emitted by their magnetic fields.

Section 20.2: Properties of Pulsars

The discovery of pulsars was not only important in its own right, but also confirmed the existence of *neutron stars*, objects long hypothesized but until then unobserved.

Let's recap how neutron stars form, to give us a better appreciation for these exotic objects. When a supergiant of mass approximately 8 $M_\odot$ to 20 $M_\odot$ finally runs out of fuel in its core, the core collapses. The core, which itself is about 1.44 $M_\odot$, (the rest of the star being outside the core), falls in on itself at close to a quarter of the speed of light, which takes less than a second. In this case, the collapse runs up against *neutron degeneracy pressure*, which is very similar to electron degeneracy pressure (it's the same type of quantum mechanics at work), but the individual "rooms" allotted for neutrons are much smaller than those for electrons. The rest of the collapsing gas runs up against this hard barrier and rebounds off the core, its shockwave destroying the rest of the star. This part of the story was already told in the previous chapter; now we concern ourselves with the core.

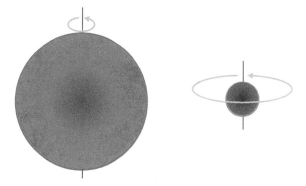

FIGURE 20.4. Most stars rotate slowly. When the core of a supergiant collapses to form a neutron star, conservation of angular momentum requires its rate of spin to increase dramatically.

One of the important laws of physics we've encountered in the past (with accretion disks, for example, in chapter 19) is the *conservation of angular momentum*. We see this with figure skaters; if a rotating figure skater brings in her or his arms, the skater rotates faster. This law works for stars as well as figure skaters. Most stars rotate relatively sedately (the Sun rotates about once per month), but now the original star—or more specifically, its core—has shrunk to the size of a large city. The core, having collapsed by a factor of a million times or more, now spins about a million times faster than before.

Along with the faster rotation comes an incredibly strong magnetic field. Magnetic fields are made from moving charges, which includes spinning, as we've seen in several other situations. Since the strength of a magnetic field goes as the speed of the moving charges, and the speed goes as the inverse of the radius, this means the strongest magnetic fields in the universe are found with neutron stars.

If the neutron star is surrounded by gas and dust, perhaps an accretion disk pulled off a companion star, some of that charged gas and dust gets swept up by the intense magnetic

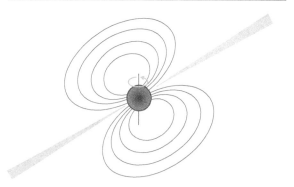

FIGURE 20.5. The origin of a pulsar. A neutron star has a powerful magnetic field (red ovals) that takes matter from an accretion disk (not shown) and sends it off in jets (blue) in opposite directions along its magnetic poles. It spins about its rotational axis (short vertical line through the neutron star), which is not lined up with the jets. As it rotates, the jets sweep out large circles. If one of the jets points toward us, we see it blink or pulse.

Isolated Neutron Star RX J185635-3754　　HST · WFPC2
PRC97-32 · ST ScI OPO · September 25, 1997
F. Walter (State University of New York at Stony Brook) and NASA

FIGURE 20.6. A visible light image of a neutron star taken by the WFPC2 camera of the Hubble Telescope. Credit: NASA/Fred Walter.

field and thrown away from the neutron star close to the speed of light. Charged particles accelerated in such as manner emit something called *synchrotron radiation*. This radiation then goes off into space and can light up any material surrounding the neutron star or, if oriented the right way, can be seen by us. As the neutron star rotates, this jet can be seen to blink or "pulse," much like a lighthouse signal.

If the neutron star doesn't emit a jet, or the jet goes away from us and doesn't light up any nebula or interstellar medium material, it will be very difficult to see. In everyday life, an object about 10 kilometers across—the size of a city—would be pretty easy to spot, but in astronomical terms this is tiny. Neutron stars are very hot, 600,000 K or more, but the small size (surface area) more than compensates for the high surface flux. The Milky Way, by some estimates, may have as many as a hundred million neutron stars, but we only know of about two thousand. The closest known neutron star is about 130 parsecs (400 light years) from us.

> ### Check Your Neighbor
>
> How do you think astronomers came up with the estimate of 100 million neutron stars in the Milky Way, when they only know of 2,000?

Neutron star properties are intense, to say the least. Essentially, with a star having been compressed into the size of a city, everything about a neutron star is extreme. The density of a neutron star is on the order of 10^{17} kg/m^3, similar to the density of an individual neutron. The temperature of a brand-new neutron star is about 100 billion K, though it quickly drops to a few hundred thousand kelvin as the neutron star emits neutrinos and rapidly cools. The magnetic field of a typical neutron star is at least 100 million times as strong as that on the surface of the Earth, and often several orders of magnitude higher. And the surface gravity of a neutron star is hundreds of billions of times that on the surface of the Earth—a "mountain" on a neutron star might reach as tall as a single centimeter (on an object 1,000,000 centimeters across)—making neutron stars the closest thing to a perfect sphere that natural objects can be.

While neutron degeneracy pressure helps hold up the weight of a neutron star, it does not on its own provide enough push to keep any neutron star above 0.7 M$_\odot$ from collapsing; repulsive nuclear (strong) forces take up the slack, so to speak. The "equation of state" that describes a neutron star is even more complicated than that of a white dwarf, and so it is only in recent times that researchers have been able to say with certainty how massive a neutron star can be. The *Tolman-Oppenheimer-Volkoff* (*TOV*) limit, the equivalent of the Chandrasekhar limit for white dwarfs, was originally calculated as long ago as 1939 to be anywhere from 1.5 to 3.0 M$_\odot$ for a cold, non-rotating neutron star; the discovery of gravitational waves from a pair of colliding neutron stars suggests this number is 2.17 M$_\odot$. Another observation, this of a neutron star in a binary system, indicates a mass of 2.27 M$_\odot$; if a neutron star is rotating (which is virtually a certainty), then the outward "force" of the rotation can also act to hold up the neutron star, and so its mass can be a little larger.

Section 20.3: Neutron Stars in Binary Systems

Astronomy is an ancient science, thousands of years old, perhaps the oldest science. Yet astronomy is also a growing science, with new discoveries every year. One of the newer discoveries is that of the *gamma ray burst*.

Gamma ray bursts have been noticed for a few decades, since the first gamma ray telescopes were launched into orbit. But gamma ray bursts presented several puzzles. First, they were very short in duration: 10 seconds at most, and often a second or less. This makes it very difficult for astronomers to tell others to look at the source before it fades away, to say the least (this problem is being addressed by linking together networks of telescopes that automatically turn to the source upon detection). Second, none of them have ever been observed to happen inside the Milky Way, implying they occur in other galaxies. This alone means they must be very energetic, in order for us to see them. When astronomers

FIGURE 20.7. A gamma ray burst (left) as seen by the Swift satellite, compared to visible and infrared observations (right). The source of the gamma rays is thought to be the formation of a black hole, at a distance of 12.8 billion light years. Credit: NASA/ Swift/Stefan Immler et al.

were able to determine reliable distances to them, most of them turned out to be billions of light years away. These two observations—their short durations and their far distances—make them the brightest, if for a brief moment, objects in the entire universe. Or, another way to say it, is that a gamma ray burst releases more energy in a few seconds than the Sun will during its entire 10 billion-year lifetime.

The solution to this mystery involves an observatory looking, not for gamma rays, but for gravitational waves. LIGO (Laser Interferometer Gravitational-Wave Observatory) announced its first extraterrestrial detection of gravity waves in 2015, which turned out to be the result of two black holes merging (more on this later in this chapter). Most of the discoveries by LIGO are of this kind, but one of them, in 2017, appears to be due to the merger of two neutron stars. LIGO (in collaboration with Virgo, a similar experiment based in Europe) observed GW 170817 on August 17, 2017. The source was located in NGC 4993, an elliptical galaxy in the constellation of Hydra, lasted for 100 seconds, and showed the intensity and frequency expected by theorists for a neutron star merger. It soon developed that the LIGO/Virgo detection was accompanied by a 2-second gamma ray burst, labeled GRB 170817A, that started 1.7 seconds after the gamma ray burst. Finally, a variety of other telescopes (from x-ray to radio) observed a separate brightening 11 hours later, initially labeled SSS17a, which showed evidence of being laden with neutrons.

The event—of a type sometimes labeled a *kilonova*—is important for another reason. Astronomers have long suspected that supernovae (of any type) are incapable of producing certain heavy elements such as gold, silver, and platinum in anything like the quantities observed in the interstellar medium. The spray of neutrons released during the merger of two neutron stars is a potential source of these elements.

How did the neutron stars merge? To start, they must have originally been in the same system (i.e., a binary system), since even more than stars, it would be incredibly difficult to get two free-floating neutron stars to ever come near each other. Even in a binary system, it is tough. A method we have encountered before is the friction generated when a large, compact object plows through a disk of gas and dust; for example, this is the preferred explanation for the migration of Jupiter and Saturn from the outermost regions of our solar system to their current locations (chapter 7). But it is possible for neutron stars to collide without the presence of gas and dust.

The warping of space/time close to a pair of neutron stars is so severe that, as they orbit each other, gravity waves are generated and spiral away from the system. Much like how an accelerating electric charge emits electromagnetic

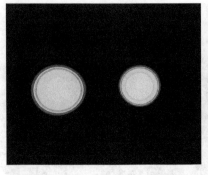 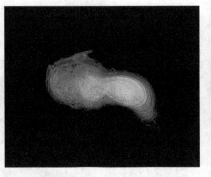 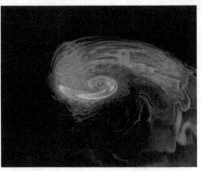

FIGURE 20.8. A supercomputer simulation of the merger of two neutron stars. Left: An 1.7 solar mass and a 1.4 solar mass neutron star are separated only by 7 kilometers (11 miles). Middle: Tidal forces have ripped apart the smaller star and shattered the crust of the larger star. Right: A torus of debris surrounds a newly formed black hole (the tiny grey sphere at the center). Credit: NASA/AEI/ZIB/M. Koppitz and L. Rezzolla.

FIGURE 20.9. An artist's depiction of the gravitational waves generated by two neutron stars spiraling toward each other. Credit: European Space Agency.

waves, and thereby loses energy, the pair of mutually orbiting neutron stars would lose energy by emitting gravity waves, and the energy lost would be taken from the orbit itself; that is, the orbit shrinks. The two neutron stars would sooner or later spiral into each other. Figure 20.8 shows a supercomputer simulation (commissioned by NASA) that covers a grand total of 20 milliseconds of time from the beginning to the end of such a merger, concluding with neutrons splattered into a torus and a brand-new black hole at its center.

Section 20.4: The History of Black Holes

Perhaps surprisingly, the concept of black holes goes back much further in time than neutron stars. Neutron stars weren't recognized as a possibility until scientists understood something about neutron degeneracy pressure and the strong nuclear force. But to conceive of a black hole only requires we recognize the possibility of an object trapping light.

The first person we know of to suggest the possibility of a black hole, though not the name, which would come much later, was John Michell (1724–1793) in a letter to the Royal Society[3] in 1784. Michell made contributions to many fields of science, though the depth and importance of them weren't recognized until long after his death. In physics, he constructed an apparatus later used by Henry Cavendish to determine the value of the universal gravitational constant and showed the strength of magnetic forces decreases as the square of the distance; in geology, he was the first to suggest that earthquakes travel through the Earth as waves and originate from what we now call faults in the Earth's crust; in astronomy, he proposed that many double stars are not merely line-of-sight issues but rather imply that many stars exist as partners in binary systems. Unfortunately, no portrait of him survives.

Regarding black holes, Michell suggested imagining a star 500 times larger across than the Sun (but keeping the same density); its surface escape speed would exceed the speed of light. Such a gigantic star would thus be invisible, though its effects could be detected by observing its effects on nearby objects. Michell pictured light behaving like a

---

[3] The Royal Society was Great Britain's first and foremost scientific institution, created in the 17th century, and is separate from the Royal Astronomical Society, which came later.

particle ("corpuscle" in his day), which one could imagine throwing up from the surface of the star, only to have it come back down due to gravity, much like any of us could do with any object now. Modern physics has a more complicated view of both light and gravity today, but the basic idea of gravity trapping light is correct.[4]

With the advent of the wave theory of light in the 19th century, the idea of a black hole (Michell has called it a "black star") faded, since it wasn't clear how gravity would affect such waves. The notion was revitalized with Einstein's publication of his theory of general relativity in 1915. Karl Schwarzschild (1873–1916), a German physicist, solved Einstein's equations for the case of a point mass; a year later, Johannes Droste, a physicist in the Netherlands, solved the problem independently and went into further details regarding the characteristics of the solution. Some of the terms in Einstein's equations go to infinity (i.e., become so large as to become meaningless) at a distance now called the *Schwarzschild radius*. At the time physicists didn't know how to physically interpret the solution; we now understand it to be the distance (as seen from outside the black hole) from the center of the black hole at which the escape speed equals the speed of light, and is understood to represent a type of boundary for the black hole.

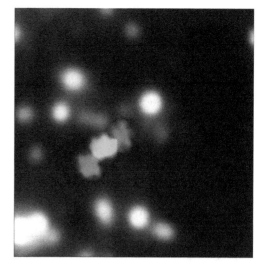

FIGURE 20.10. A gas cloud falls into Sagittarius A-star (Sgr A*), a supermassive black hole at the center of our galaxy as seen by the Very Large Telescope (VLT). Different colors represent different years: Blue is 2006, green is 2010, and red is 2013. Credit: ESO/S. Gillessen.

We have seen how Subramayan Chandrasekhar determined that electron degeneracy pressure can halt the collapse of a star's core, but also that it cannot sustain the core's weight if the mass exceeds 1.44 $M_\odot$. Several astronomers were skeptical of the idea, thinking that some other force must be able to prevent the complete collapse of a star regardless of its mass, but in 1939 Robert Oppenheimer (1904–1967) and colleagues showed that neutron stars (the next in line to resist a stellar collapse) also have a limit to the mass they

FIGURE 20.11. Left: Karl Schwarzschild (uncredited); Right: Robert Oppenheimer with General Leslie Groves at ground zero for the first atomic bomb test (Credit: U.S. Army Corp of Engineers).

can support and concluded it unlikely that any force of nature could resist a complete collapse. A few alternatives have been proposed—perhaps quarks[5] could resist the pull of gravity at even higher masses—but no neutron star has been found greater than 2.27 $M_\odot$, and even if "quark stars" were real, they also have a mass limit.

Michell's original term for this idea was a "black star" and various scientists described them as "gravitational collapsed objects," which doesn't roll off the tongue. It's not entirely clear who first came up with the term "black hole," but it seems to have been the American physicist Robert Dicke (1916–1997), who in the early 1960s compared the idea to the infamous "Black Hole of Calcutta," where supposedly captives would enter but never leave alive.

---

[4] The French scientist Pierre-Simon Laplace also suggested the concept of a black hole around the same time, though he did not develop it as fully as Michell.

[5] Quarks are elementary particles. Protons and neutrons, which are talked about a great deal in this book, are actually made of quarks.

The term was in use by 1963 (in *Life* magazine) and 1964 (in a report on a conference of the American Association for the Advancement of Science). In 1967, a student brought up the term during a lecture by the American theoretical physicist John Wheeler (1911–2008), who ran with the idea—Wheeler's work was in general relativity—and who thought the term neatly encapsulated the whole notion. Combined with the idea of a wormhole, a theoretical way to travel through space, black holes became popular cultural phenomena, making appearances (for examples) in movies since the late 1970s.

Section 20.5: Properties of Black Holes

What properties belong to a black hole? Or, more succinctly, what do black holes <u>do</u>?

One potential misconception is that black holes roam around the universe, sucking in everything in their path like cosmic vacuum cleaners. Ignoring the fact that this is a misleading description of vacuum cleaners, it doesn't apply generally to black holes. Black holes are the most compact astronomical objects possible, and the wild gravity effects associated with them are only evident up close; for example, if we could magically replace the Sun with a black hole of the same mass, the Earth's orbit would not be disrupted in any way.[6] Black holes also have a great amount of inertia, which is the resistance of an object to a change in its motion. Therefore, black holes don't tend to move around much, and are definitely not actively performing search-and-destroy missions. Our galaxy has a supermassive black hole (literally millions of times the mass of the Sun) at its core, but we are not in any danger whatsoever from it. If a black hole is a vacuum cleaner, then it is one that sits in one location on the floor. The floor underneath the vacuum will get very clean, but the dirt in the rest of the room won't be affected.

Perhaps the best way to illustrate this is with the Schwarzschild radius, which gives us a way to calculate how "large" a black hole is from the outside (we will see later why we need to make this "outside" distinction):

Equation 20.1

$$R_S = \frac{2GM}{c^2}$$

where G is the universal gravitational constant, M is the mass of the black hole, and c is the speed of light. This is equivalent to setting the escape speed of the hole equal to the speed of light. Let's explore this a bit with an example.

Check Your Neighbor

We might expect the Earth to have a smaller Schwarzschild radius than the Sun, but how much smaller? Hint: The Sun's mass is about 330,000 times more than the Earth's mass.

Sample Calculation

Suppose the Sun were to become a black hole but kept the same mass. What would be its Schwarzschild radius? Our constants are $G = 6.67 \times 10^{-11}$ N·m²/kg² and $c = 2.997 \times 10^8$ m/s. The mass of the Sun is 1.99×10^{30} kg. Then,

$$R_S = \frac{2GM}{c^2} = \frac{(2)\left(6.67 \times 10^{-11} \, \frac{N \cdot m^2}{kg^2}\right)(1.99 \times 10^{30} \, kg)}{\left(2.997 \times 10^8 \, \frac{m}{s}\right)^2} = 2950 \text{ m} \approx 3 \text{ km}$$

Another way to say this is that the Sun, as a black hole, would be 6 kilometers (about 4 miles) across—the size of a small city or township.

---

[6] Of course, other bad things would happen, since our source of light and heat would be gone.

Why do we keep emphasizing the Schwarzschild radius is as seen from "outside"? Remember Einstein's version of gravity, general relativity, which depicts gravity as a warping of space/time due to the presence of mass. A black hole doesn't simply warp space/time in this analogy; it rips a hole in it (Figure 20.12).

The most common analogy of a black hole is a "bottomless pit," where an object that falls in would fall forever. It's a bit misleading—perhaps a better word is "incomplete"—since in Einstein's view the warping of space/time is into a fourth physical dimension, which we can't perceive. Nor are there "walls" or sides of the black hole. Regardless, any object that falls closer to the black hole than its Schwarzschild radius cannot come back out. Further, Figure 20.12 tells us why we keep talking about the Schwarzschild radius being seen from the "outside"; distances lose their meaning inside the hole.

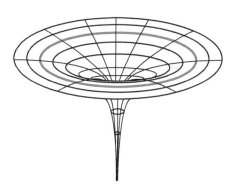

FIGURE 20.12. A set of grid lines showing the "bottomless pit" nature of a black hole. The red circle represents its Schwarzschild radius.

What it at the "bottom" of the hole? First, there is no bottom as such in this interpretation. But we can extrapolate. The hole becomes smaller and smaller, until it essentially has no size at all. In astrophysics, an object with zero size is called a *singularity*. Singularities pose mathematical (if not philosophical) problems for scientists: How can an object have some properties (mass and electric charge are possible) but not others (radius) and still others be infinite (density, for example)? You might remember from mathematics that dividing by zero is not allowed, because doing so yields nonsense results. Singularities represent a class of objects that we, by definition, will always find mysterious.

Despite all the weird behaviors and properties of a black hole, in the end black holes can be described fully with only three parameters: mass, electric charge, and angular momentum (spin). Black holes are not expected to have net electric charges, since (a) static electricity is very strong as a force and (b) electric charges come with positive and negative signs, and the charges are expected to cancel each other out. Black holes also cannot themselves possess magnetic fields, though accretion disks outside the holes can. On the other hand, black holes are expected to possess angular momentum; indeed, the rate of spin (angular speed) can be very fast, for the same reasons neutron stars are able to spin very fast. A black hole may spin of its own accord, or be influenced by an accretion disk,

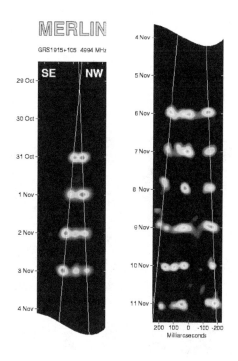

FIGURE 20.13. Radio observations in 1997 of bipolar jets ejected from the x-ray binary GRS 1915+105 at 90% of the speed of light. Credit: R. P. Fender et al.

or even in its turn affect the accretion disk. Much like a neutron star with an accretion disk, ions swept up by the magnetic field of the accretion disk (recall the black hole can't have its own magnetic field) are sprayed along the opposing north and south magnetic poles.

Other odd effects and properties of black holes, in no particular order, include the following.

1. Rotating Black Holes

If a black hole is rotating, it possesses one of the stranger regions in all of space, where objects <u>cannot</u> remain still. Remember that general relativity pictures mass as warping space/time; therefore it is fair to say that a warping of space/time represents mass, even for the "bottomless pit" analogy of a black hole. But the hole also affects space/time near it (refer to Figure 20.12); if the hole rotates, the distortion of space/time also rotates. An object caught

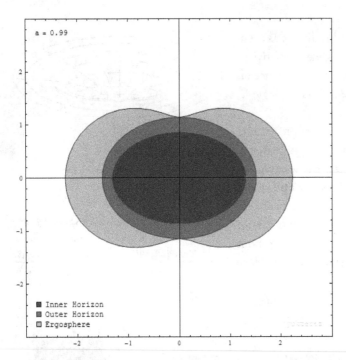

FIGURE 20.14. The ergosphere is a region surrounding a black hole within which the distortions of space/time ensure that objects <u>cannot</u> remain at rest. Credit: Simon Tyran.

FIGURE 20.15. Left: Roger Penrose at a science conference in Kansas City, 2011 (Credit: Biswarup Ganguly). Right: Stephen Hawking at NASA's Starchild Learning Center in 1999 (Credit: NASA).

up in this region, called the *ergosphere*, will be pulled along with the rotation of the black hole, a phenomena sometimes called "frame dragging."

Because such a black hole is rotating, the ergosphere (which does not exist for a non-rotating black hole) is outside of the *event horizon*, the boundary of the black hole. The physicist Roger Penrose (b. 1931) has speculated that, at least in theory, energy could be extracted from the black hole via the ergosphere.[7] It is possible to send an object into the ergosphere and have it come back out with more energy than it had when it went in, a process similar to the gravitational "slingshot" used by NASA for speeding up spacecraft in the solar system. The energy, like the energy gained by a spacecraft whipping around a planet, would be taken from the rotational energy of the black hole.

2. Hawking Radiation

Associated with the famous physicist Stephen Hawking (1942–2018), the radiation named after Hawking suggests the possibility that, despite their claim to fame (being objects that let nothing escape), black holes can evaporate. As with many of our recent discussions, this notion involves quantum mechanics.

Suppose we look, not inside the black hole or exactly at the event horizon, but just outside it. The severe warping of space/time by the black hole's mass implies that space/time itself near the hole (not just inside the hole) contains an enormous amount of energy. We also know that one of the most important tenets of quantum mechanics is the uncertainty principle, which states that the amount of energy contained in a particle and the duration of time the particle exists cannot both be perfectly known. This gives rise to the notion of *virtual particles*—particles that can, in essence, appear and disappear if they do so before much time has passed. While odd sounding, virtual particles have been observed in laboratory experiments, explain much about the behaviors of "normal" subatomic particles such as electrons, and even contribute to the proton-proton chain of nuclear reactions inside the Sun. Virtual particles still follow the other laws of physics; for example, they must appear in pairs, one a normal "matter" particle and one an "antimatter" particle, in order to conserve electric charge, and they will move in opposite directions, in order to conserve linear momentum.

Energy from the near-surroundings of a black hole can be "stolen" to temporarily create virtual particles. Usually, both particles either disappear quickly or fall inside the black hole's event horizon. On rare occasions, as one particle

---

[7] An "erg" is a unit of energy often used in astronomy, therefore the name "ergosphere."

is shot toward the black hole, its partner is shot away from the black hole with enough kinetic energy to escape. If so, the escaping particle takes its energy with it. But the energy originally came from the warping of space/time around the black hole, which represents its mass. Therefore, the black hole has lost mass or has "evaporated" by a tiny amount.

Hawking found that the evaporation process gets stronger as the mass gets smaller (the warping of space/time is more extreme around the event horizon of a smaller black hole). He was even able to assign the equivalent of a black body temperature to the black hole due to this evaporation process. It can be shown that the temperature of a Sun-massed black hole is incredibly cold—on the order of 6×10^{-8} K—but increases for smaller holes. This is much colder than interstellar space, which is on the order of 2.7 K, and so a Sun-massed black hole would still (slowly) gain mass even if otherwise isolated. A black hole of the mass of a small asteroid (10^{11} kg) would require a few billion years to evaporate completely, which is within the lifetime of the universe. On the other hand, if a black hole had the mass of a large person (100 kg), it would evaporate within about 1 100-billionth of a second. It seems unlikely, but astronomers are interested in finding any "primordial" tiny black holes, as that would tell us much about the conditions of the early universe.

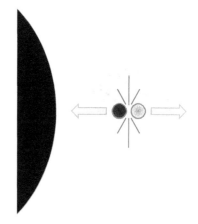

FIGURE 20.16. Hawking radiation: A pair of virtual particles is created out of the intense gravitational energy just outside a black hole. One particle falls into the hole, but the other escapes.

Check Your Neighbor

Recall Einstein's famous equation: $E = mc^2$. If an object has enough concentrated mass to form a black hole, does it also possess a lot of energy?

3. Tidal Forces

As we've seen many times before, tides are differences in gravity forces. The acceleration due to the Earth's gravity on your feet is just a little stronger than that on your head, since your feet are closer to the center of the Earth than your head. Normally this isn't noticeable, or even measurable in principle, being such a small difference, but we have talked about a few instances—planetary rings or semidetached binaries—where this effect is important. Getting too close to a compact object such as a white dwarf, neutron star, or black hole would really show off its importance in an effect jokingly nicknamed *spaghettification*.

Imagine an unfortunate astronaut floating in space toward a black hole, with the astronaut's feet pointing toward it. The gravity on the feet of the astronaut will be substantially stronger than the gravity on the head of the astronaut, and this difference would only increase as the astronaut falls toward the black hole. At some points, the tides would be so strong as to shred the poor astronaut to bits. But because the black hole has no limit—no "bottom" to reach—the tidal forces would continue to increase indefinitely. The tides would eventually tear individual molecules apart, then individual atoms, then individual subatomic particles and so on. By the "time" (this fall would last forever), from the perspective of the rest of us outside the hole, the fall came to an end, there would literally be nothing left but the contribution of the astronaut's mass to the overall size of the black hole itself.

FIGURE 20.17. The "spaghettification" of an astronaut unlucky enough to be too close to a black hole.

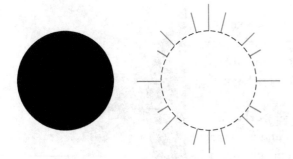

FIGURE 20.18. Suppose an astronaut were near a black hole. Looking toward the black hole (left), the astronaut would see black. Looking away from the black hole (right), all stars in the sky would look brighter and brighter, and be emitting more and more powerful photons, as the astronaut falls toward the hole.

4. Light and Black Holes

Suppose you (an astronaut) could somehow avoid being torn apart by intense gravitational tides. Then you would likely be disintegrated by intense radiation.

If the black hole has an accretion disk, then we're already familiar with what would happen. As matter spirals closer to the black hole, it moves faster and faster until it is traveling close to the speed of light. Collisions between particles would increase and generate intense heat; astronomers observe these effects via x-ray telescopes. The high temperatures—potentially millions of degrees—would vaporize anyone long before they fell into the hole.

But even if the black hole were isolated, the situation would quickly deteriorate. Suppose our astronaut looks toward the black hole. The intense gravity of the hole robs photons of their energy (an effect called a *gravitational redshift*), so the photon's wavelengths become indefinitely long and thereby invisible (or nonexistent, if you prefer), and so the hole appears "black." But the opposite would happen if the astronaut turned around. Now all the photons are gaining energy as they "fall" into the black hole. As the astronaut approaches the black hole, the stars both become brighter and their radiation trends toward shorter and shorter wavelengths. By the time our astronaut crossed the event horizon, the light from individual stars would have been blinding and possibly intense enough to disintegrate our space traveler. The gravitational "blueshift" experienced by the astronaut would not be comfortable, to say the least!

The gravitational effects of a black hole on light can be, in theory, detected from a distance. A light ray passing by a large mass has its path deflected by the curvature of space/time created by the mass; this effect was how the British astronomer Arthur Eddington provided strong evidence for Einstein's general relativity (we will see more of this in chapter 23), an effect called *gravitational lensing*. Astronomers have just begun to see gravitational lensing for individual black holes—remember, black holes are (a) black on a black background and (b) extremely small and therefore very hard to find when isolated—but computer simulations show us what to expect.

FIGURE 20.19. A computer simulation of gravitational lensing by a black hole in front of the Large Magellanic Cloud, a satellite galaxy of the Milky Way. The observer is nine times farther from the hole than its Schwarzschild radius.

Figure 20.19 shows what this might look like. The observer is placed nine times farther from the black hole than its Schwarzschild radius. The hole is in front of the Large Magellanic Cloud (LMC), a satellite galaxy orbiting us in the Milky Way, and has a few tens of billions of stars. The shape of the galaxy is severely distorted by the presence of the black hole, and several "Einstein rings," the spreading of the light of a compact source like a bright star, appear around the hole. Einstein himself suggested gravitational lensing as a possible effect of large, concentrated masses but did not expect astronomers would ever see them. While we have just started seeing them for individual black holes, astronomers have detected such distortions for distant quasars and clusters of galaxies for several decades.

5. Colliding Black Holes

We've already talked a bit about gravitational waves and colliding neutron stars. But the first detection of gravitational waves came from colliding black holes.

LIGO is one of the most sensitive experiments ever conceived. It has two sections, one outside Livingston, Louisiana, and the other outside Hanford, Washington. They are separated and oriented in such a way as to eliminate false positives (i.e., false detections). Each has two "arms" 4 kilometers (2.5 miles) long, each in an "L" shape, and each arm is a self-contained ultra-high vacuum system through which lasers travel. By using the interference property of light waves (chapter 5) of lasers traveling back and forth along each arm, differences in displacements of 1/1000th of the width of a proton (!) can be measured. This incredibly precise ability is needed to detect gravitational waves. The Livingston and Hanford facilities also allow researchers to identify the direction from which a signal might arise. Gravity waves travel at the speed of light; at 3,000 kilometers apart, a signal from space can arrive at one detector before the other, and even a few milliseconds of time delay is easily within the capabilities of LIGO to measure. Finally, the governmental agency behind its funding is not NASA; instead, the National Science Foundation (NSF), which tends to handle more physics- and less astronomy-related research, is responsible. When funded at $395 million in 1994, LIGO stood as the most expensive research project ever approved by the NSF.

The first direct observation of astronomical gravitational waves happened on September 14 of 2015 and, after much checking, was reported on February 11 of 2016. Both LIGO installations, including collaborative work from the European Virgo project, confirmed that a pulse of gravity waves had shaken the universe—this is not an exaggerated statement—from the collision of two black holes. The event was titled "GW 150914," as in "**G**ravitational **W**ave detected in the year 20**15**, month **09**, day **14**." Gravitational waves were predicted by Einstein as early as 1915 (a century prior), and their presence inferred from other observations (such as two neutron stars in a mutual binary orbit), but this was the first true direct detection. In a way, LIGO marks yet another milestone in science: We are now able to see gravity directly.

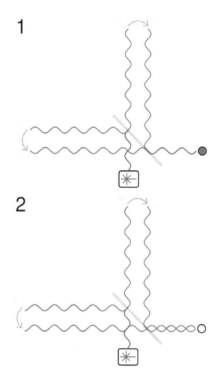

FIGURE 20.20. A laser interferometer used by LIGO. Top: A laser beam traveling forward (up in the figure) is split in two, one part of the beam continuing forward, the other going to the left. Both beams reflect off mirrors and return. They are then recombined and sent to the right. Above: The same system, but now a gravity wave approaches from the left, changing the wavelength of the light, and therefore changing how the beams recombine to the right.

The collision was immense by any description. Calculations show that the two black holes were previously 35 $M_\odot$ and 30 $M_\odot$, respectively, forming a combined black hole of 62 $M_\odot$ after the collision. About 3 $M_\odot$-worth of energy was released within a few milliseconds; or, if you prefer, on the order of 10^{49} watts, which is to say an amount of power greater than that of all the stars in the visible universe!

LIGO went on to detect five other black hole mergers and one neutron star merger (described earlier in section 20.3). As of this writing (early 2019), LIGO is undergoing upgrades and should be ready again in 2020; LIGO is expected to detect not just a few, but perhaps up to 1,000 black hole mergers in its next incarnation.

6. Wormholes

The most fanciful, and that's saying a lot, speculation regarding black holes is the *wormhole*. Analogous to a wormhole of an apple, a wormhole in space would be a connection between two otherwise widely separated locations in space (and possibly time). Most often depicted in science fiction, it would theoretically allow space travelers to fly from one place to another in far less than the usual time. The German mathematician and physicist Hermann Weyl first introduced the notion in 1928, and the nickname "wormhole" was first used by the American physicist John Wheeler in 1957. A wormhole is a solution of Einstein's general relativity (again remember that Einstein's gravity tells us that mass warps space/time), but while wormholes appear to be possible in theory, nothing remotely like a wormhole has actually been found or created, and many astronomers are cool to the idea.

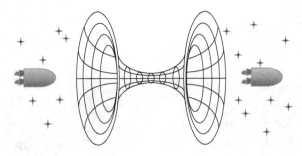

FIGURE 20.21. A wormhole is a theoretical tunnel that would allow a space traveler to reach a destination in less than the usual time.

What's wrong with it? First, we aren't near anywhere possessing the technology to travel through space in any sense approaching "fast"; our fastest spacecraft are moving at about 1/10,000th of the speed of light. So even if we could find a wormhole in our solar system—suppose there was one near the orbit of Saturn, for example—it would take years just to get to the wormhole. Then it would likely take many more years to get to the destination, assuming we knew where we were going. Second, a wormhole would need to incorporate a black hole, maybe two, or something like them. All the dangerous effects we discussed before (regarding tides and radiation) still apply. Also, it's likely the "connection" between the two holes would have to shrink to zero size, meaning any spaceship (and travelers) would be crushed along the way. Third, there are a fair number of physicists who doubt the entire idea, or at least a version that would operate in any meaningful way for space travelers. Finally, there's absolutely no evidence for any such thing.

Astronomers are people, too, and many of us would be extremely happy and excited should the wormhole suggestion turn out to have merit. But science doesn't work with wishes. Before we get too invested in ideas like this, we need evidence they may carry some weight.

Black holes are incredible objects, and we have just scratched the surface of their strangeness. But all this is moot if black holes don't exist. What evidence do we have that black holes are out there? We'll discuss the supermassive black hole at the center of the Milky Way in the next chapter. Here, let's consider two other cases: First, Cygnus X-1, a stellar-sized black hole in the Milky Way, and second, an entire class of black hole-related objects called quasars.

Section 20.6: Case Study: Cygnus X-1

X-rays do not penetrate the Earth's atmosphere. Thus, if we want to study potential astronomical sources of x-rays, we have to lift our instruments above the air. Such projects became possible with the advent of flight, especially space flight.

Usually when astronomers are presented with a new way of observing, such as access to a previously unavailable range of wavelengths of light, they first perform surveys of the sky. Such a project was undertaken from White Sands Missile Range in New Mexico in 1964, where suborbital rockets were equipped with Geiger counters. One of the sources discovered was Cygnus X-1, whose name simply means the brightest x-ray source in the constellation of Cygnus the Swan. No optical source was linked to Cygnus X-1 at the time.

In 1970, NASA launched their first x-ray satellite, Uhuru. Uhuru discovered 300 new x-ray sources and revisited previous discoveries, including Cygnus X-1. The most interesting observation uncovered was that the x-rays showed variations on the order of several times per second. Since the speed of light is the fastest

FIGURE 20.22. Cygnus X-1 in x-rays. Left: From the HERO balloon launch in 2001 (Credit: NASA/ Marshall Space Flight Center). Right: From the Chandra satellite in 2009 (Credit: NASA/CXC).

information can travel, this implies the object emitting the x-rays could not be larger across than about 100,000 km, or less than 10% of the diameter of the Sun.

Soon afterward, in 1971, astronomers from both Leiden Observatory (in the Netherlands) and the National Radio Astronomy Observatory, or NRAO, detected radio waves coming from the same location in the sky and identified its optical component as a star catalogued HDE 226868. While the apparent magnitude of this star renders it too faint for the naked eye (its apparent magnitude is +8.95), the actual star in question is a blue supergiant. This presented an immediate puzzle: blue supergiants do not emit copious amounts of either x-rays or radio waves, and there is no mechanism by which such a star could vary its output of x-rays several times per second if it did emit them.

Other teams of astronomers performed spectroscopy on the HDE 226868 system, and via Doppler measurements of its spectra showed the star has an unseen companion several times the mass of the Sun (current observations place the unseen companion's mass at 14.8 $M_\odot$). Since neutron stars were known to be limited to 3 $M_\odot$ or less (the modern estimate is 2.17 $M_\odot$; see section 20.2), astronomers concluded the object must be a black hole.

The system is not an eclipsing binary, so the angle of inclination of the Cygnux X-1 system is uncertain, with a current estimate being 48°. The orbital period is 5.60 days, the mutual orbits are nearly circular, and the distance between the two objects is thought to be only 0.20 astronomical units. The system is 1,860 parsecs (6,070 light years) away, and may be part of a nearby association of massive stars named Cygnus OB3—Cygnus X-1 is only 60 parsecs from the center of the association—that formed about 5 million years ago. This agrees in general with the fact that one star has already completed its life cycle and the other is a supergiant with a lifespan of only a few million years. The supergiant does not appear to have expanded beyond its Roche lobe but is experiencing a strong stellar wind, losing up to a solar mass of matter every 400,000 years, and the black hole appears to be drawing some of that matter into an accretion disk.

FIGURE 20.23. An artist's depiction of Cygnus X-1. Gas from a supergiant is drawn to an accretion disk; the point of contact is extremely hot. Gas in the accretion disk gets hotter as it spirals into a black hole. Jets of ionized gas are blown in opposite directions along the axis of the accretion disk. Credit: NASA/CXC/M.Weiss.

What happened to turn HDE 226868's companion into a black hole? The largest star in the nearby Cygnus OB3 association comes in at 40 $M_\odot$, which is another clue: If Cygnus X-1 was once part of the association, this shows that stars massive enough to become black holes are possible. As discussed before (chapter 19), stars with greater than 20 $M_\odot$ are likely to become black holes. The collapse of such a star's core dampens the strength of its explosion, so it's probable that the progenitor star never became a true supernova.

Cygnus X-1 is the most studied of all black hole candidates, with over 1,000 published papers in just a few decades. When pressed, astronomers hold off on declaring an object like Cygnus X-1 a "black hole" and instead officially label it a "black hole candidate," since the actual black hole has never been directly seen. Nevertheless, all we know about stars and stellar remnants leaves us with the conclusion that Cygnus X-1, and several others in the Milky Way, must be black holes. We even have good reasons to believe a black hole lies at the center of the Milky Way, a distant relative of a special class of objects called quasars, to which we now turn.

Section 20.7: Quasars

How large can a black hole be? Theoretically, there is no limit to the mass of a black hole; it depends on the mass of the original star, the odds of black holes (or neutron stars) colliding to form larger black holes, and the amount of matter available for a black hole to "eat." When there is a lot of matter, black holes can grow to astounding masses. What do such monstrous objects look like?

By the 1960s, astronomers were used to measuring cosmological redshifts for galaxies (we will discuss this in further detail in chapter 23), which meant, among other things, that many galaxies were tens to hundreds of millions of parsecs away. Stars, on the other hand, tend to be split among redshifts and blueshifts (meaning they are just as likely to approach us as recede from us), and their speeds were usually slow compared to those of galaxies. But a strange class of objects would occasionally combine both ideas; they looked like stars but had large redshifts. Many astronomers initially looked skeptically at these observations, contending that perhaps the redshift measurements were in error or misinterpreted.

FIGURE 20.24. The quasar 3C 273. Left: In visible light (Credit: ESA/Hubble & NASA); Right: In x-rays (Chandra). Note the jet of material in both images.

The object at the bottom of this is 3C 273.[8] 3C 273 presented a different mystery at first, since it was detected in radio waves before any other wavelength regime. Further, the poor resolution of radio telescopes of the time (this was in the 1950s) meant that astronomers couldn't tell if the radio waves came from a point source or an extended object.

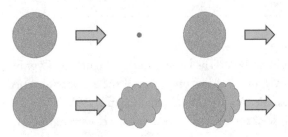

FIGURE 20.25. Cyril Hazard's occultation experiment for 3C 273. If the source of the radio waves is a compact object, then the radio waves should disappear quickly when the Moon passes over it (top). If the source of the radio waves is an extended object, then the radio waves should gradually diminish as the Moon passes over it (above).

In 1963, Australian astronomer Cyril Hazard (b. 1928), working with the Parkes Radio Telescope, noticed that 3C 273 lay in the path of the Moon across the sky. We've seen eclipses (when one object covers another of similar size) and transits (when a small object cuts in front of a larger object). The term for the instance of a large object cutting in front of a small object is an *occultation*. The Moon, at half a degree across, is easily much larger (in angular size) than any star or planet and can therefore serve to occult smaller objects if they happen to lie in the Moon's path. If 3C 273 is small (like a star), then the radio waves would be cut off quickly as the edge of the Moon passed it by; if 3C 273 is large (like a nebula or galaxy), then the

---

[8] "3C 273" is simply the 273rd object listed in the third catalog of radio sources compiled by Cambridge University.

radio waves would slowly diminish as the Moon moved across it. Hazard found the first option to be correct.

Soon after, a colleague of Hazard's named Maarten Schmidt (b. 1929) used the 200-inch reflector at Mount Palomar to identify the equivalent optical source of the radio waves. Further, he obtained a spectrum. At first the spectrum was very confusing, until he realized he was looking at hydrogen spectral lines severely Doppler shifted to the red (i.e., to longer wavelengths). Its distance is currently determined to be 750 megaparsecs (i.e., 750 million parsecs, or 2.4 billion light years) away.

3C 273 opened the door to a new class of objects. Because they were originally found via their radio emissions and look like stars in visible light through telescopes, they were eventually called *quasi-stellar radio sources*, which was quickly shortened to *quasars*. In later years, astronomers realized most of these objects do not emit much in the way of radio waves, and the more general name of *quasi-stellar object*, or *QSO* for short, was applied. Because the lack or presence of radio waves appears to be more a feature of how we see them, rather than what they are doing, the terms are almost interchangeable, and we'll refer to them as quasars, here.

First, let's list some of the basic observations of 3C 273 and other quasars:

- Quasars typically look like stars (point sources of light) through optical telescopes (see Figure 20.24), though we do have a few more detailed images now.
- No quasars are visible to the naked eye, though moderate-sized and larger telescopes can see them without difficulty.
- Quasars show very large redshifts of their spectral lines. No quasars are observed to have small redshifts or blueshifts at all.
- There is no set temperature for quasars. Unlike a black body, which shows a peak wavelength, quasars emit radiation over a large range, often all the way from x-rays through radio waves.
- Quasar spectral lines show hydrogen (to be expected, since 90% of all atoms are hydrogen), but also other elements such as carbon, nitrogen, helium, and oxygen.
- The spectral lines are usually emission lines of multiplied-ionized gases. For example, "N V" is a line sometimes seen in a quasar spectrum. In astronomy jargon, "N I" means neutral nitrogen, "N II" means one electron is missing from the nitrogen atom, and so on. Therefore "N V" means four electrons have been stripped from the nitrogen atoms.
- The spectral lines are also "broad"; that is, they are thicker than lines we typically see from stars.
- In about 10% of quasars, we also see broad absorption lines, always of the same elements, and always just to the shorter wavelength side of their corresponding emission lines.
- Quasars tend to vary their light output over short amounts of time. While variations in light output tend to take months or years, it is common to witness variations as quick as hours or even minutes.
- Bipolar jets are sometimes seen (see Figure 20.24) ejected from the center of the quasar.
- Radio waves are seen in about 10% of quasars (or QSOs).
- Tens of thousands of quasars are now known. Statistics hint that individual quasars therefore can have lifespans in the hundreds of millions of years.

FIGURE 20.26. An artist's impression of the quasar ULAS J1120+0641, highlighting its accretion disk and bipolar jets. This quasar is thought to possess a black hole of about 2 billion solar masses. Credit: ESO/M. Kornmesser.

What do all these observations tell us? Let's follow the logic:

+ High redshifts mean quasars are very far away, usually hundreds of millions to billions of parsecs. No quasars are seen relatively nearby (in this case, we mean within a few tens of millions of parsecs!).
+ Since quasars don't exist nearby, this implies there was a time when quasars were popular, but that they have since died out.
+ The combination of large distances and moderate apparent magnitudes (3C 273 has an apparent magnitude of +12.9) implies incredible luminosities. Absolute magnitudes of quasars are often between –25 and –30. For comparison, the Sun's apparent magnitude is –26. A typical quasar would thus be about as bright as the Sun from 10 parsecs (33 light years) away.
+ Another comparison: 3C 273 is estimated to be 4 trillion times as bright as the Sun; or, in other words, 3C 273 gives off 4 trillion Suns' worth of light, more than all but the largest galaxies.
+ The emission lines imply extremely high temperatures.
+ The thickness of the emission lines imply fast-moving clouds of gas.
+ The occasional presence of absorption lines implies clouds of gas further from the heat (so the gas is cool enough to absorb rather than emit light), but only in certain regions, and not completely surrounding the quasar.
+ The quickness of light variations implies very small objects, given the total amount of light emitted. An object brighter than a galaxy occupies a space smaller than a solar system.
+ The small number of quasars that emit relatively large amounts of radio waves (10%) indicates that we have to be aligned just right in order to see the radio emission.

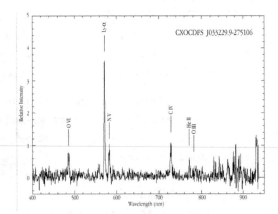

FIGURE 20.27. A spectrum in optical and near-infrared obtained by the Very Large Telescope of a quasar. Note the general background shape of the spectrum is flat. Several emission lines from ionized elements are labeled. Credit: ESO.

The modern model for a quasar is that it is powered by what astronomers term a *supermassive black hole*. This is one of our instances where the name means what it says; a supermassive black hole can be in the millions or even billions of times the mass of the Sun.

A quasar is a monstrous version of an arrangement we have talked about before. Matter falls in toward the supermassive black hole as part of an enormous accretion disk. The gas gets incredibly hot as it spirals in, emitting a copious amount of radiation as it does so, and the combination of supermassive black hole plus accretion disk is often nicknamed the *central engine* of the quasar. Intense radiation from the central engine heats clouds of gas and dust outside the accretion disk and radiation pressure pushes these clouds away at high speeds. A torus (donut-shaped) region containing clouds even further out is also pushed away, though these clouds are far enough that they can absorb the radiation rather than re-emit light due to their temperatures. A giant magnetic field is generated by the ionized in-spiraling accretion disk, and some of that material is shot away from the quasar in perpendicular (bipolar) jets. Sometimes the jets can be seen on their own; sometimes they run into the intergalactic medium (like the interstellar medium, but between galaxies instead), and these collisions induce radio emissions.

How does a quasar produce so much energy? First, the black holes are supermassive, so their gravity is intense and influences a relatively large region of space. It is thought to be typical for a quasar's black hole to "eat" an Earth's-worth of mass every day! Second, the efficiency of energy generation is very high. Recall that the proton-proton chain of hydrogen fusion, the most efficient of all the nuclear fuels, turns 0.7% of the ingoing mass into energy. Matter falling into a black hole can be turned into energy (radiation) at efficiencies of 10% or even 20%, many times more than hydrogen fusion. Third, quasars were active during the early days of the universe, when galaxies were closer to each other and far more likely to collide and mix together, thereby bringing matter to the black holes to be eaten.

We know of far many more quasars than stellar-sized black holes. Quasars are associated with young galaxies and are extremely bright, so they (now that we know what to look for) are relatively easy to spot; a stellar-sized black hole in the galaxy, especially if it formed from a single supermassive star, is hard to see. The ubiquity of quasars has in a sense turned around the terminology; if a stellar-sized black hole (like Cygnus X-1) is accompanied by an accretion disk, we now tend to call these *microquasars*.

Check Your Neighbor

Why aren't there any quasars around now? Hint: Did they have infinite amounts of gas and dust to consume?

As the preliminary version of this textbook was going to press, astronomers of the Event Horizon Telescope (EHT) Collaboration revealed the very first direct image of a black hole. This is a supermassive black hole—now estimated to be 6.5 million solar masses—at the heart of the elliptical galaxy M87. M87 itself resides in the nearby (for extragalactic astronomers!) Virgo cluster of galaxies, some 17 million parsecs (55 million light years) away.

Figure 20.28 doesn't actually show just one image of M87's black hole. Instead, this image was crafted from nearly a year and a half's worth of observations taken by 8 different radio telescopes across the globe. Some 13 different institutions contributed facilities and personnel to the project, and funding was provided by governments from North America, Europe, and Asia. The radio telescopes made use of interferometry (chapter 5) to get phenomenal resolution—as low as 20 micro-arcseconds, or, as EHT's web site states, the ability to read a newspaper in New York City from Paris.

If this black hole is so far away—tens of millions of parsecs—why did the project concentrate on it rather than other, closer targets? First, even though M87 is so far away, its black hole is still so much larger compared to a stellar black hole like Cygnus X-1 that it is easier to image. Second, though the Milky Way's supermassive black hole (nicknamed Sagittarius Astar) itself is supermassive—about 4 million solar masses—dust in the plane of the Milky Way obscures our view. Nevertheless, EHT is supposedly working next on an image of Sgr A*.

One last item to consider: Our galaxy, the Milky Way, has a supermassive black hole at its center, about 8,000 parsecs (28,000 light years) away. But it is not a quasar because it has eaten virtually all the free-floating gas and dust that once was available. Is it possible to reawaken the beast? If the Milky Way were to somehow gather large amounts of free gas and dust, its central engine could

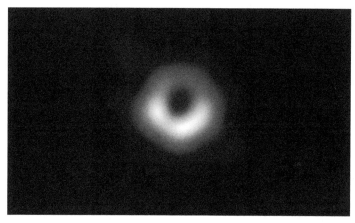

FIGURE 20.28. The very first reliable image of a black hole, released in the spring of 2019, was taken by the Event Horizon Telescope. The EHT is actually a consortium of eight separate radio telescopes situated at various locations on the Earth, and the image was painstakingly constructed over nearly a year and a half. Compare to Figure 20.19. Credit: Event Horizon Telescope Collaboration.

light up again. Astronomers hypothesize that the Milky Way is on a collision course with another similar galaxy called Andromeda, and the collision could bring on such a situation. Fortunately, this won't happen for another 3 billion years, giving us plenty of time to prepare!

Summary

In this chapter, we covered the following:

▶ The discovery of neutron stars

▶ Basic properties of neutron stars

- Examples of collisions between neutron stars and between black holes
- The discovery of black holes
- Cygnus X-1, the most famous of black holes in the Milky Way
- Supermassive black holes, which can generate quasars

Questions

1. Why can't rotating white dwarfs be pulsars? Suppose a white dwarf has a diameter of 10,000 km and rotates 25 times per second, a common rate for a pulsar. How fast is a point on the edge of the white dwarf moving? Recall that the speed of light is 300,000 km/s.

2. The first neutron star discovered, PSR B1919+21, has a diameter of 22 km and rotates with a period of 1.34 seconds. How fast is a point on the edge of the neutron star moving?

3. Neutron star PSR J1748-2446ad has a diameter of 10 km and rotates 716 times per second. How fast is a point on the edge of this neutron star moving?

4. The Sun's current radius is 696,000 km and its equator rotates once every 25 days. Suppose it were to turn into a neutron star (it won't, by the way) with a diameter of 10 km. What would be its rotational period as a neutron star?

5. The Sun's current radius is 696,000,000 meters and its mass is 1.99×10^{30} kg. What is its current density? Hint: The volume of a sphere is $(4\pi/3)r^3$.

6. Suppose the Sun turned into a neutron star with a radius of 5,000 meters and kept its current mass. What would be its density?

7. Suppose the Sun turned into a black hole, retaining its current mass. How does its Schwarzschild radius compare to the radius of a typical neutron star of the same mass: larger, smaller, or the same?

8. Suppose the Earth turned into a black hole, retaining its current mass. What would be its Schwarzschild radius? Compare your result to a commonplace object or location.

9. The black hole at the center of the Milky Way has a mass of 4 million solar masses. What is its Schwarzschild radius? Express your result in a variety of units:
   - In meters
   - In solar radii
   - In astronomical units
   - In parsecs
   - Which unit really illustrates how small a black hole is, especially for astronomy?

10. 3C 273 has an apparent magnitude of +13 and is 800 million parsecs away. What is its absolute magnitude?

11. A typical quasar "eats" an Earth's-worth of mass each day. Recall that the Earth has a mass of 6×10^{24} kg, a day lasts 86,400 seconds, and the Sun's luminosity is about 4×20^{26} watts. Assume the efficiency of turning mass into energy for a black hole is 10%. How bright is the quasar? Specifically,
   - how much energy is generated by eating an Earth each day? Hint: Use Einstein's famous formula $E = mc^2$ and then multiply by 10% to account for the efficiency of the black hole
   - divide by the number of seconds in a day to get the luminosity expressed in watts
   - compare the luminosity of the quasar to the luminosity of the Sun
   - suppose the quasar lasts for 100 million years. How much matter did it ultimately "eat"?

12. An interesting hypothesis suggests that supermassive black holes are essential partners in the formations of galaxies and that the mass of the supermassive black hole is about half of a percent of the total mass of the galaxy. Observations place the mass of the Milky Way's supermassive black hole at 4 million solar

masses. How much mass should the Milky Way have under this hypothesis? Note that other observations estimate the Milky Way's mass at a trillion solar masses.

13. The black hole of Cygnus X-1 has a mass of 14.8 Ms and is 1860 pc distant. The supermassive black hole of M87 has a mass of 6.5 million solar masses and is 17 million pc distant. Which one shows a larger angular size, and by how much (expressed as a ratio)? Hint: Recall that the "size" of a black hole (its Schwarzschild radius) scales linearly as its mass.

Activities

▸ *Astrophysics activity 20.1:* Submit your own questions regarding black holes to the instructor as part of a roundtable discussion.

Works Referenced

The discovery of pulsars and neutron stars is described in the following sources:

"Breakthrough Prize—Special Breakthrough Prize In Fundamental Physics Awarded To Jocelyn Bell Burnell For Discovery Of Pulsars". https://breakthroughprize.org/News/45 Retrieved 2019-04-21

Arzoumanian, Z., Nice, D. J., Taylor, J. H., & Thorsett, S. E. (1994). Timing behavior of 96 radio pulsars. *Astrophysical Journal*, 422(2), 671. doi:10.1086/173760

Brecher, K.; Fesen; Maran; Brandt. (1983). Ancient records and the Crab Nebula supernova. *The Observatory*, 103, 106. Bibcode:1983Obs...103..106B.

Baade, W. (1942), The Crab Nebula. *Astrophysical Journal*, 96, 188. doi:10.1086/144446

Brumfiel, G. (2007), Air force had early warning of pulsars", *Nature*, 448 (7157): 974–975. Retrieved 2019-04-21. https://www.nature.com/articles/448974a

Ghosh, P. (2018, September 16). Bell Burnell: Physics star gives away £2.3m prize. *BBC News*. Retrieved 2019-04-21. https://www.bbc.com/news/science-environment-45425872

Hargittai, I. (2003). *The road to Stockholm: Nobel Prizes, science, and scientists*. Oxford, UK: Oxford University Press.

Hewish, A., Bell, S. J., Pilkington, J. D. H., Scott, P. F., & Collins, R. A. (1968). Observation of a rapidly pulsating radio source. *Nature*, 217(5130), 709. doi:10.1038/217709a0

Minkowski, R. (1942). The Crab Nebula. *Astrophysical Journal*, 96, 199. doi:10.1086/14444

Sample, I. (2018, September 6). British astrophysicist overlooked by Nobel wins $3m award for pulsar work. *The Guardian*. Retrieved 2019-04-21. https://www.theguardian.com/science/2018/sep/06/jocelyn-bell-burnell-british-astrophysicist-overlooked-by-nobels-3m-award-pulsars

Properties of neutron stars are described in the following sources:

Camenzind, M. (2007, February 24). *Compact objects in astrophysics: White dwarfs, neutron stars and black holes*. Springer.

Cho, A. (2018, February 16). A weight limit emerges for neutron stars. *Science*, 359(6377), 724–725. doi:10.1126/science.359.6377.724

Kiziltan, B. (2011). *Reassessing the fundamentals: On the evolution, ages and masses of neutron stars*. Universal-Publishers/Dissertation.com.

Linaris, M., Shahbaz, T., & Casares, J. (2018). Peering into the dark side: Magnesium lines establish a massive neutron Star in PSR J2215+5135. *Astrophysics Journal*, 285(1). doi:10.3847/1538-4357/aabde6

Margalit, B., & Metzger, B. D. (2017, December 1). Constraining the maximum mass of neutron stars from multi-messenger observations of GW170817. *Astrophysical Journal*, 850(2), L19. doi:10.3847/2041-8213/aa991c

Oppenheimer, J. R., & Volkoff, G. M. (1939). On massive neutron cores. *Physical Review, 55*(4), 374–381. doi:10.1103/PhysRev.55.374

Posselt, B., Neuhäuser, R., & Haberl, F. (2009, March). Searching for substellar companions of young isolated neutron stars. *Astronomy and Astrophysics, 496*(2), 533–545. doi:10.1051/0004-6361/200810156

Tolman, R. C. (1939). Static solutions of Einstein's field equations for spheres of fluid. *Physical Review, 55*(4), 364–373. doi:10.1103/PhysRev.55.364

Neutron stars in binary systems are found in the following sources:

Abbott, B. P., et al. (LIGO Scientific Collaboration & Virgo Collaboration). (2017, October 16). GW170817: Observation of gravitational waves from a binary neutron star inspiral. *Physical Review Letters, 119*(16). doi:10.1103/PhysRevLett.119.161101

Abbott, B. P., et al. (LIGO, Virgo and other collaborations), (2017, October). Multi-messenger observations of a binary neutron star merger. *Astrophysical Journal, 848*(2), L12. doi:10.3847/2041-8213/aa91c9

Barish, B. C., & Weiss, R. (1999, October). LIGO and the detection of gravitational waves. *Physics Today, 52*(10), 44. doi:10.1063/1.882861

NASA. (2012). *Gamma rays.* https://science.nasa.gov/ems/12_gammarays Retrieved 2019-04-21.

PhysOrg. (2017, July 26). *Massive star's dying blast caught by rapid-response telescopes.* Retrieved 2019-04-21. https://phys.org/news/2017-07-massive-star-dying-blast-caught.html

Troja, E., Ryan, G., Piro, L., van Eerten, H., Cenko, S. B., Yoon, Y., ... & Veilleux, S. (2018, October 16). A luminous blue kilonova and an off-axis jet from a compact binary merger at z = 0.1341. *Nature Communications, 9*(4089). doi:10.1038/s41467-018-06558-7

The history of black holes is recounted in the following sources:

Abbott, Benjamin P., et al. (LIGO Scientific Collaboration and Virgo Collaboration) (2016). Observation of gravitational waves from a binary black hole merger. *Physical Review Letters, 116*(6), 061102. doi:10.1103/PhysRevLett.116.061102

APS Physics. (2009). This month in physics history: November 27, 1783: John Michell anticipates black holes. Retrieved 2019-04-21. https://www.aps.org/publications/apsnews/200911/physicshistory.cfm

Baker, J. G., Centrella, J., Choi, Dae-I., Koppitz, M., & van Meter, J. (2006). Gravitational-wave extraction from an inspiraling configuration of merging black holes. *Physical Review Letters, 96*(11), 111102. doi:10.1103/PhysRevLett.96.111102

Carroll, S. M. (2004). *Spacetime and geometry; An Introduction to General Relativity.* Addison Wesley. Boston, MA.

Droste, J. (1917). On the field of a single centre in Einstein's theory of gravitation, and the motion of a particle in that field. *Proceedings Royal Academy Amsterdam, 19*(1), 197–215.

Hawking, S. (1988). *A brief history of time.* New York, NY: Bantam Books.

Kapusta, J. (1999). The last eight minutes of a primordial black hole. Retrieved 2019-04-21. https://arxiv.org/pdf/astro-ph/9911309.pdf

Location of the Source. *Gravitational Wave Astrophysics.* University of Birmingham.

Michell, J. (1784). On the means of discovering the distance, magnitude, and c. of the fixed stars, in consequence of the diminution of the velocity of their light, in case such a diminution should be found to take place in any of tthem, and such other data should be procured from observations, as would be farther necessary for that purpose. By the Rev. John Michell, B. D. F. R. S. in a letter to Henry Cavendish, Esq. F. R. S. and A. S. *Philosophical Transactions of the Royal Society, 74*, 35–57. doi:10.1098/rstl.1784.0008

Montgomery, C., Orchiston, W., & Whittingham, I. (2009). Michell, Laplace and the origin of the black hole concept. *Journal of Astronomical History and Heritage, 12*(2), 90–96.

Siegfried, T. (2013, December 23). 50 years later, it's hard to say who named black holes. *Science News.* https://www.sciencenews.org/blog/context/50-years-later-its-hard-say-who-named-black-holes Retrieved 2019-04-21.

Properties of black holes are described in the following sources:

Anderson, W. G. (1996). The black hole information loss problem. *Usenet Physics FAQ*. Retrieved 2019-04-21. http://www.edu-observatory.org/physics-faq/Relativity/BlackHoles/info_loss.html

McClintock, J. E., Shafee, R., Narayan, R., Remillard, R. A., Davis, S. W., & Li, L. X. (2006). The spin of the near-extreme Kerr black hole GRS 1915+105. *Astrophysical Journal*, 652(1), 518–539. doi:10.1086/508457

Preskill, J. (1994, October 21). Black holes and information: A crisis in quantum physics. *Caltech Theory Seminar*. http://www.theory.caltech.edu/people/preskill/talks/blackholes.pdf Retrieved 2019-04-21.

Visser, M. (2007). The Kerr spacetime: A brief introduction. https://arxiv.org/pdf/0706.0622.pdf Retrieved 2019-04-21.

Cygnus X-1 is discussed in the following sources:

Brocksopp, C., Tarasov, A.E., Lyuty, V.M. & Roche, P. (1999). An improved orbital ephemeris for Cygnus X-1. *Astronomy & Astrophysics*, 343, 861–864.

Bolton, C. T. (1972). Identification of Cygnus X-1 with HDE 226868. *Nature*, 235(5336), 271–273. doi:10.1038/235271b0

Bolton, C. T. (1975). Optical observations and model for Cygnus X-1. *Astrophysical Journal*, 200, 269–277.

Bowyer, S., Byrum, E. T., Chubb, T. A., & Friedman, H. (1965). Cosmic x-ray sources. *Science*, 147(3656), 394–398. doi:10.1126/science.147.3656.394

Kristian, J., Brucato, R., Visvanathan, N., Lanning, H., & Sandage, A. (1971). On the optical identification of Cygnus X-1. *Astrophysical Journal*, 168, L91–L93. doi:10.1086/180790

Mirabel, I. F., & Rodrigues, I. (2003). Formation of a black hole in the dark. *Science*, 300(5622), 1119–1120, doi:10.1126/science.1083451, PMID 12714674

Oda, M., Gorenstein, P., Gursky, H., Kellogg, E., Schreier, E., Tanabaum. H., & Giacconi, R. (1999). X-ray pulsations from Cygnus X-1 observed from UHURU. *Astrophysical Journal*, 166, L1–L7. doi:10.1086/180726

Orosz, J. (2011, December 1). The mass of the black hole in Cygnux X-1. *Astrophysical Journal*, 742(2), 84. doi:10.1088/0004-637X/742/2/84

Reid, M. J., McClintock, J. E., Narayan. R., Gou, L., Remillard, R. A., & Orosz, J. A. (2011, December). The trigonometric parallax of Cygnus X-1. *Astrophysical Journal*, 742(2), 83. doi:10.1088/0004-637X/742/2/83

Rolston, B. (1997, November 10). The first black hole. *University of Toronto*. Retrieved 2019-04-21. https://web.archive.org/web/20080307181205/http://www.news.utoronto.ca/bin/bulletin/nov10_97/art4.htm

Shipman, H. L., Yu, Z., & Du, Y. W. (1975). The implausible history of triple star models for Cygnus X-1 Evidence for a black hole. *Astrophysical Letters*, 16(1), 9–12. doi:10.1016/S0304-8853(99)00384-

Staff. (2003, March 3). V* V1357 Cyg—High Mass X-ray Binary. *Centre de Données astronomiques de Strasbourg*. Retrieved 2019-04-21. http://simbad.u-strasbg.fr/simbad/sim-id?Ident=sco+x-1

Staff. (2003, June 26). NASA's HEASARC: The Uhuru Satellite. *NASA*. Retrieved 2019-04-21. https://heasarc.gsfc.nasa.gov/docs/uhuru/uhuru.html

Webster, B. L., & Murdin, P. (1972). Cygnus X-1—a Spectroscopic Binary with a Heavy Companion?. *Nature*, 235(5332), 37–38. doi:10.1038/235037a0

Quasars are discussed in the following sources:

Hazard, C., Mackey, M. B., & Shimmins, A. J. (1963). Investigation of the radio source 3C 273 by the method of lunar occultations. *Nature*, 197(4872), 1037. doi:10.1038/1971037a0

Oke, J. B. (1963). Absolute energy distribution in the optical spectrum of 3C 273. *Nature*, 197(4872), 1040. doi:10.1038/1971040b0

Schmidt, M. (1963). 3C 273: A star-like object with large red-shift. *Nature*, 197(4872), 1040. doi:10.1038/1971040a0

Sirola, C. J. (1995). The large-scale and small-scale geometries of broad absorption line regions of quasi-stellar objects (Ph.D. Dissertation). University of Pittsburgh, Pittsburgh, PA.

Credits

GALACTIC AND INTERGALACTIC ASTRONOMY

An infrared image taken by the Hubble Space Telescope of the central region of the Milky Way. Behind the brightest section is thought to lurk a supermassive black hole. Credit: NASA/HST.

CHAPTER 21

THE MILKY WAY

To review the formation, development, and structure of the Milky Way

OBJECTIVES

▸ To review historical concepts of the Milky Way

▸ To study the formation of the Milky Way

▸ To identify several different sections of the Milky Way

▸ To represent the scale of the Milky Way

▸ To describe the motions of stars and spiral arms of the Milky Way

▸ To discuss the concept of dark matter

INTRODUCTION

The Milky Way is our home galaxy. It is not merely where we live; it is where we will always live. At least in theory, we can think about flying away from Earth and cruising through the solar system, or landing on another planet. But the Milky Way is too large. The disk (the section in which we live) is several thousands of light years thick, and this is the smallest dimension to the galaxy. Describing the Milky Way is a little like describing the house or building you are currently in, without being able to move.

Nevertheless, astronomers have learned a great deal about our galaxy over the past century or so, and are still discovering new and wondrous things. In this chapter, we take a look in detail at our extended home.

KEY TERMS

Bulge (or **nucleus**): The central section of the Milky Way, housing the very center of our galaxy. One of the older sections of the Milky Way, relatively dust free and full of older stars

Corona: A section thought to extend about 10 times further across than the disk or halo. The corona is hypothesized to contain *dark matter*, whose purpose is to supply gravity that keeps the galaxy together

Dark matter: Theoretical material that does not interact with light, but does possess mass and therefore exerts gravity

Disk: A relatively flat, circular region concentric around the bulge. Most current star formation and other forms of stellar activity occur, here. The solar system belongs to the disk

Dust: Primarily rocky or carbon-rich dust grains are commonplace in the galaxy, but primarily are concentrated in the disk

Halo: A relatively spherical region concentric around the bulge. Contains globular clusters (and some field stars). The first section of the galaxy to form

Keplerian orbit: A shorthand term for describing how planets orbit the Sun. It was shown in the 1960s that stars do <u>not</u> follow this behavior as they orbit the center of the Milky Way

Nucleus: See *bulge*

Rotation curve: A plot of the rotational speed (or velocity) of stars and other objects as they orbit the center of the galaxy, compared to the distance of those objects from the center of the galaxy

Sagittarius A-star (also Sgr A*): A bright source of radio waves (and other EM waves) at the center of our galaxy, in the direction of the constellation of Sagittarius. A supermassive black hole of 4 million solar masses is at its heart

Section 21.1: The Naked-Eye View of the Milky Way

It is difficult for many modern people to see the Milky Way. Light pollution brightens the night sky and limits our ability to see faint objects and structures. But any foray into a location far from city lights brings out the Milky Way in its glory (Figure 21.1):

Even as a professional astronomer, one can be struck by the Milky Way. A quick personal story: I (and a few other professors) took some graduate students on a 10-day field trip to the American Southwest in the summer of 2005 for various projects in astronomy, biology, and geology. Our first major stop was at McDonald Observatory in west Texas. The Observatory runs an early-evening viewing session, where a representative gave us a tour of the sky as it darkened. Other observatory personnel manned telescopes pointed at interesting objects—a planet here or a globular cluster over there. I was quite pleased that my students (and the public) were able to get such a quality look at the heavens.

But what struck me most was the brilliance of the Milky Way. Living in cities of various sizes during my life, I rarely have a chance to even see the Milky Way; or, on trips to darker locations in my current home state of Mississippi, the Milky Way just appears to be a fuzzy band stretched across the sky. At McDonald Observatory, however, located in a dry climate and elevated well above sea level, the scattering of city lights and absorption by the air is limited, and the Milky Way dominated the sky. Even though I am a seasoned teacher of naked-eye astronomy, I had trouble identifying constellations because *too* many stars were available.

This is worth considering when we ask how other cultures, especially those of times before artificial lighting or in locations where

FIGURE 21.1. The Milky Way framed behind an ancient bunker in Albendin, Cordoba, Spain. Credit: Edmundo Sáez.

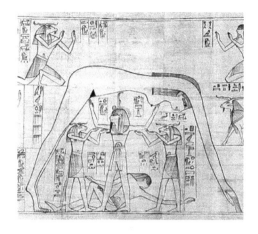

FIGURE 21.2. Compare the ancient Egyptian's view of the sky (from a papyrus c. 940 BCE, currently in the British Museum) with a modern picture of the Milky Way (Credit: European Space Observatory).

such lighting is not prevalent, view the Milky Way. Our modern understanding of the Milky Way really began with William Hershel's map in the late 18th century, but many people have had interesting versions ("takes") on what the Milky Way represents.

Legends from the American Southwest discuss how the trickster Coyote spilled stars across the sky to make the Milky Way. African cultures have depicted the Milky Way as the backbone of a great creature, which drapes itself across the sky. The ancient Egyptians had a similar notion, except the being making up the night sky was the goddess Nut. The term "Milky Way" comes from the ancient Greeks, whose goddess Hera spilled some of her breast milk as she was nursing one of her infants. The words "galaxy" and "lactose" (as in lactic acid, which is present in milk) share the same root.

It wasn't until Galileo (see chapter 3) turned his telescope to the Milky Way that its real nature, as a conglomeration of stars otherwise too faint to see, was understood. The first map of the Milky Way was made by William Herschel (chapter 13) and our relative location first shown by Harlow Shapley (also chapter 13) around 1920. In other words, our modern conception of the Milky Way as a galaxy, and that a "galaxy" is an independent object, is very recent indeed.

The Milky Way is a thick band of fuzzy white that extends across the

FIGURE 21.3. A 360-degree panorama of the plane of the Milky Way. Credit: European Space Observatory/S. Brunier.

entire sky. Depending on location (latitude) and time of year, it can reach from one end of the sky to the other; northern observers, for example, may find it easiest to see in the middle of summer or the middle of winter. Optical telescopes reveal much in the way of detail. The dominant color to the naked eye is blue, due to a preponderance of blue super-giants. A second color is a brown/black, representing copious amounts of interstellar dust. Finally, one occasionally sees patches of reddish-pink, representing nebulae (such as HII regions) at high temperatures.

While we can get a general sense that the visible Milky Way is centered roughly in the constellation of Sagittarius, we cannot see the center directly due to the large amounts of dust blocking our view. Otherwise, it is notable that the band is a band; rather than stars being scattered randomly across the sky, they instead show a pattern. That this band of light we call the Milky Way surrounds the entire sky is a hint that we are inside of it.

Table 21.1 shows a list of properties of the Milky Way. The values are rounded off, which indicates astronomers are still analyzing even basic facts about our galaxy.

TABLE 21.1. Basic Properties of the Milky Way

Type of galaxy	Barred Spiral
Diameter (visible)	100,000 light years (or 30 kiloparsecs)
Thickness	3,000 light years (or 1 kpc)
Distance from Sun to the center	26,000 light years (or 8 kpc)
Number of stars	400 billion
Total mass	1 trillion solar masses
Age	13 billion years

Even the "thinnest" portions of the Milky Way are thousands of parsecs across. This means, unlike the solar system,[1] we cannot view the Milky Way from a distance. Any image we have of the Milky Way is either a view from the inside—this is the "band" we see in the night sky—or a portrait created by astronomers and artists to portray what the Milky Way might look like from an appropriate distance (see Figure 21.5). This is the puzzle for modern astronomers who study the Milky Way: How do we know what it looks like, what parts it possesses, or how it behaves if we are trapped inside it?

An important approach used by astronomers is to look for objects that mark the location of the galaxy's spiral arms. For example, we know that very massive stars are both likely to emit ionizing radiation and to have relatively

Check Your Neighbor

Suppose we are sitting at a kitchen table inside a house and are asked to describe the layout of all its rooms and its appearance from the road but we are not allowed to leave the kitchen. What might we do?

Check Your Neighbor

Why does it matter that the very massive stars have relatively short lives when astronomers use them to map the spiral arms?

FIGURE 21.4. Studying the Milky Way is much like trying to study the structure and appearance of a house when one is only allowed to be in the kitchen. The Milky Way is so large that we will always be inside it and therefore never see it from a distance.

FIGURE 21.5. An artist's portrait of the Milky Way. The small disks represent HII regions, which can be used to trace the spiral arms. Credit: NASA/JPL-Caltech/ Federal University of Rio Grande do Sul.

---

[1] The Voyager II spacecraft, for example, is now over 100 astronomical units from the Sun, and therefore looks back at the solar system from a reasonably far vantage point.

short lives. The powerful radiation from such stars can heat up neighboring nebulae until the nebulae in turn emit light on their own as HII regions, which astronomers can detect.

Finally, astronomers view other galaxies for comparison. Other spiral galaxies have the same characteristics as the Milky Way—a central bulge, vigorous star formation, lanes of dust and gas, heated nebulae, clusters of stars, etc.—that help us understand how and where these objects are located.

Section 21.2: The Disk

Let's begin with the disk, since it's where we live.

The basic shape of the disk is like that of a Frisbee, or compact disk, or pizza, if we leave substantial space in the middle for the nucleus or "bulge" (we'll discuss that in the following section). It is roughly circular in shape, extending in visible light about 100,000 light years (30,000 kiloparsecs) in diameter and several thousand light years (2 to 3 kpc) thick.

The term "spiral" comes from arms of dust, gas, and bright stars that wheel around the disk in spiral patterns. The arms start at either end of the bar in the bulge and wind themselves outward. Astronomers still debate whether there are two or four separate arms, and each arm has several branches or "spurs." The arms move, though the Sun moves through space at a different rate. At this moment in astronomical history, the Sun and solar system are near the edge of a spiral arm.

FIGURE 21.6. M51, nicknamed the "Whirlpool Galaxy," may look much like the Milky Way. Credit: NASA/ European Space Agency.

FIGURE 21.7. Sections of the sky near the galactic equator (left) and galactic north pole (right). Charts courtesy of *Cartes du Ciel*.

Today, and for the past several billion years, the disk has been the section of the Milky Way conducting star formation. As we have learned (chapter 17), the more mass a star has, the quicker it forms, the brighter and bluer it is, and the quicker it runs through its life cycle. Dust and gas tend to pile up along the edges of the spiral arms, and since these are the raw materials for star formation, we also find bright blue stars tend to dominate the appearance of the arms. Other prominent colors tend to be brown (for dust) and pink (for hydrogen emission). Indeed, one method astronomers use to trace the shapes of the spiral arms is to search for dust and/or HII regions, where hydrogen emission dominates.

As stated before, the Sun also moves in the disk. We orbit the center of the galaxy in what appears to be close to a perfect circle, though some suspect we "bob" up and down vertically (i.e., compared to the plane of the galaxy) as we go (Figure 21.8). The Sun, dragging the rest of the solar system with it, moves at an estimated 250 kilometers per second, well over half a million miles per hour. Even so, we require about 240 million years to make a single orbit at our distance of 8 kiloparsecs from the center.

Virtually all the stars in the night sky belong to the disk. The Milky Way is so large (remember that even its "thinnest" part of the disk still extends for thousands of parsecs) that only on rare occasions is an object an appreciable distance from us in galactic terms. It is also possible that a star might be "visiting" from another section of the galaxy—Barnard's Star is a good example—but will still have to be very close by in order to be seen by us.

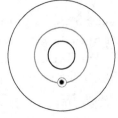

FIGURE 21.8. The Sun's orbital motion about the center of the Milky Way. The Sun "bobs" up and down inside the disk (left). The Sun's orbit is otherwise close to a perfect circle (right). In both, the Sun's motion is indicated in red.

Section 21.3: The Bulge

The central region of the Milky Way—alternatively called the nucleus or bulge—is distinct from the disk. It is more 3D; that is, it extends much farther above and below the plane of the galaxy than the disk. It has a yellowish color in visible light, in contrast to the blue that informs the disk. It is about 30,000 light years across (or 5 kiloparsecs in radius), compared to the 100,000 light year extent of the disk. It is virtually free of gas and dust. Finally, it is far more packed; the density of stars in the bulge is about 1,000 times that of our neighborhood in the disk.

Check Your Neighbor

The bulge lacks free gas and dust and its stars give off an overall color of yellow. What does this tell us about the relative age of the bulge compared to the disk?

It wasn't until relatively recently that astronomers confirmed we live in a barred spiral rather than a "normal" spiral. A barred spiral has a thick bar of material extending from one end of the bulge to the other, and the spiral arms begin at the ends of the bar, not the middle. Because gas and especially interstellar dust extinguish visible light, we cannot see to the center of the galaxy that way. Instead, telescopes using infrared, x-ray, and radio are used.

Of particular interest is the very center of the bulge. Karl Jansky, a researcher for Bell Laboratories, found several sources of "hiss" in 1931 when trying to identify sources of radio noise and linked one of them to the band of the Milky Way in the sky. Jansky was even able to show the brightest source of radio noise was coming from the constellation of Sagittarius. In 1974 Bruce Balick and Robert L. Brown were able to link the radio signal to the very center of the Milky Way (Brown labeled the source *Sagittarius A-star*, or *Sgr A**, in 1982). Subsequent observations in radio,

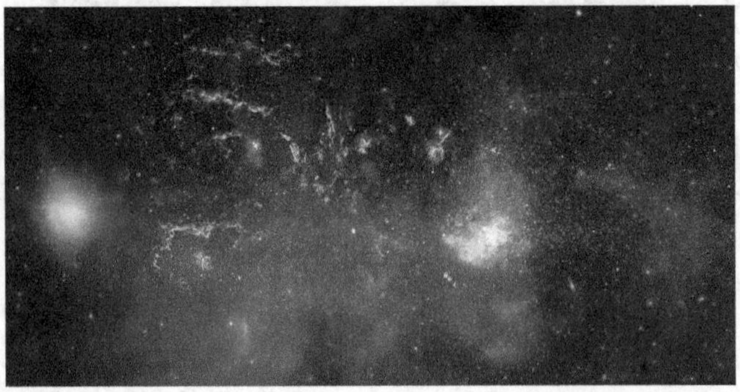

FIGURE 21.9. A composite of different wavelengths of the center of the Milky Way. Near-infrared from the HST is depicted in yellow; other infrared from Spitzer is in red; and x-rays are shown in blue and violet from Chandra. The very center, containing a supermassive black hole, is inside the bright region at lower right. Credit: NASA/JPL-Caltech/ESA/CXC/STScI.

FIGURE 21.10. Left: Karl Jansky's radio antenna, which was used to discover radio waves from the center of the Milky Way. It was approximately 100 feet long, 20 feet tall, and mounted on four tires that allowed it to move and rotate as needed. For that reason it was nicknamed "Jansky's Merry-Go-Round." Credit: NRAO.

infrared, and x-rays provide evidence that all the activity comes from a region surrounding a supermassive black hole. The emissions officially come not from the black hole itself, but most likely from gas and dust swirling at nearly the speed of light near the black hole.

More recently, astronomers have been able to get a solid estimate of the mass of the central black hole itself. Two groups of researchers—one German, one American—looked at the motions of stars very close to Sgr A* (see Figure 21.11) and used Kepler's third law to calculate the mass of the central object. The German group came up with a result of 4.31 million solar masses, whereas the American group determined it to be about 3.7 million solar masses. A third group instead used the proper motions of thousands of stars within 1 pc of Sgr A*, and their statistics suggest a mass of 3.6 million solar masses. In all three cases, the mass of the central object is about 4 million $M_\odot$.

Furthermore, astronomers can put a maximum size on Sgr A* using the orbits of those stars. The orbit of S14 takes it closer to Sgr A* than any of the other stars, passing within 45 astronomical units without colliding with Sgr A* or being obviously damaged. The central object therefore must be smaller than 45 au, and potentially must smaller, which suggests it is a black hole.

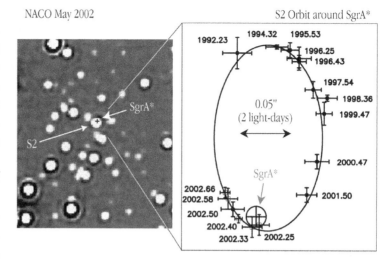

NACO May 2002 — S2 Orbit around SgrA*

FIGURE 21.11. The orbit of the star "S2" about the central supermassive black hole at the center of the Milky Way, designated with a crosshairs. The image at left was taken by the NACO instrument at the European Southern Observatory.

Check Your Neighbor

Astronomers say that the object at the center of Sgr A* is a black hole. Which of the previous facts helps us understand why?

Check Your Neighbor

Black holes are, by definition, objects that do not emit light. How did astronomers determine that the object at the center of Sgr A* is a black hole?

Section 21.4: The Halo

The most obvious (visible) parts of the Milky Way are the disk and the bulge, but the galaxy has other sections. The oldest of these is the halo.

The halo was discovered by Harlow Shapley, when he plotted the positions of globular clusters (chapter 13) and found them centered several thousand parsecs away. We now also know of many individual stars that inhabit the halo as well, Barnard's Star being the closest example. The current record-holder for age (as of 2018) is a star designated J0815+4729, which has about 70% the mass of the Sun and lives 7,000 pc away in the halo; it is estimated to have formed some 13.5 billion years ago, or when the universe itself was "only" 200–300 million years old.

Why is the halo the oldest section of the Milky Way, or, more carefully, why does the halo have the oldest objects, both field stars and clusters of stars? The speed at which a diffuse nebula collapses under gravity depends on its density and its temperature.[2] Theoretical calculations suggest that nebulae several tens of thousands to hundreds of thousands the mass of the Sun will collapse under gravity—and therefore form stars—faster than nebulae either much smaller or much larger. Many globular clusters have masses in those ranges. If these are the quickest structures to form, they also must be the oldest.

---

[2] The conditions under which a nebula can begin to collapse under gravity were first suggested by Sir James Jeans in 1902 and, although modified since then, are still discussed as the *Jeans instability*.

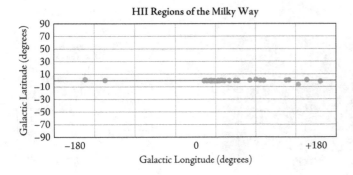

HII Regions of the Milky Way

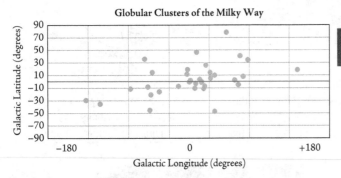

Globular Clusters of the Milky Way

FIGURE 21.12. Graphs of HII regions (top) and globular clusters (above) in the Milky Way. The line across the middle represents the equator of the galaxy.

The rest of the argument follows. The entire galaxy has a mass of approximately 1 trillion $M_\odot$. Individual globular clusters collapse first and "sift" out of the rest of the more-slowly collapsing galaxy. Globulars look the way they look—compact, yellow, little free gas or dust—because of their ages and masses. Field stars such as Barnard's Star might be lucky escapees from the edges of globulars and they too sifted out of the collapse that formed the rest of the Milky Way.

Check Your Neighbor

Figure 21.12 shows graphs both HII regions and globulars in the Milky Way. To which region do the HII regions belong? To which region do globulars belong? Why?

One method for estimating ages of stars is by main sequence fitting (chapter 17). Another method is by measuring their metallicities. We know that dying stars (primarily via supernovae) "seed" the galaxy with elements beyond hydrogen and helium. This means that as time goes by, the galaxy becomes enriched with metals. But by the same token, this implies that the galaxy possessed less metals in the past. The oldest of stars thus should have next to no metals at all. This is in fact what we see for globular clusters and individual stars such as J0815+4729.[3]

FIGURE 21.13. An aerial view of two-way traffic on California's I-405 highway. Credit: U.S. Geological Survey.

Another observation common for halo stars is that they tend to have large proper motions. Recall what we mean by "proper" motion; this term refers to the relative tangential velocity (i.e., the velocity across our line of sight) of a star compared to that of the Sun. Most stars in our neighborhood of the Milky Way have relatively slow proper motions (typically equivalent to a few tens of kilometers per second). But this is because these stars are part of the disk and tend to move along with us as we orbit the Milky Way (see Figure 21.13).

But stars from the halo don't move in the same sense as stars in the disk. While disk stars move in (more or less) circular orbits together, the orbits of

---

[3] Running the clock backward all the way to the beginning, we can expect that matter consists solely of hydrogen and helium. This is pretty much what astronomers do see and is consistent with theories concerning the early moments of the universe (see chapter 23).

halo stars are virtually random, except that they too orbit the center of the galaxy. Thus, while disk stars near the Sun tend to move in roughly the same direction at the same speed, halo stars are just as likely to be moving toward the Sun as away from it, and at a variety of angles.

Proper motion expresses the relative velocity of a star across our line of sight. But stars can also either be moving toward or away from us, which is called the star's radial velocity and can be determined via Doppler effect. The "total" or space velocity of a star is a combination of these two notions (again, see chapter 13).

Check Your Neighbor

Sirius A has a space velocity of 17 km/s and Kapteyn's Star a space velocity of 290 km/s. Which star belongs to the disk and which belongs to the halo?

Section 21.5: The Corona

Besides the shape and structure of the Milky Way, astronomers are interested in its dynamics, that is, the motions of its individual objects. Originally, astronomers expected stars and nebulae outside of the bulge to orbit the center of the galaxy much like planets orbit the Sun. Such an orbit, called "Keplerian" after the famous astronomer, assumes the central object is compact, meaning that the vast majority of its mass is contained within a definite border. The Sun, for instance, contains 99.9% of the mass of the solar system inside a radius less than half a percent of an astronomical unit. The Milky Way was expected to behave similarly.

A common mathematical tool is the *rotation curve* (sometimes also called a velocity curve). Astronomers plot the speed (or velocity) of objects in the disk of a spiral galaxy compared to the distances of the objects from the center of that galaxy. For Keplerian orbits, the speeds of objects should decrease as the square root of the distance (inside the object, the speed should rise linearly as the distance from the center of the object increases). Astronomers therefore expected to find results like the red curve depicted in Figure 21.14.

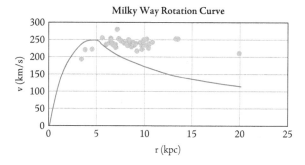

FIGURE 21.14. The velocity of stars as a function of distance from the center of the Milky Way. The red curve simulates the expected velocities of stars, assuming a bulge five kiloparsecs across. The blue dots represent actual measurements taken in 2013.

Since the details of the structure of the Milky Way were difficult to come by for many decades, astronomers first looked to other galaxies for comparison. When they did this for our neighboring spiral galaxies, M31 and M33, they found something else. Instead of a drop-off with the square root of the distance, the rotation curves of these galaxies tended to be flat; that is, they didn't change, all the way out to the edge of their disks.

The most influential work was performed by Vera Rubin (1928–2016) in the 1960s and 1970s. Using a (then-new) sensitive spectrograph, she was able to confirm this behavior for many other spiral galaxies. She and others also noted the implications: The mass of spiral galaxies (including the Milky Way) is <u>not</u> concentrated in the bulge, but is spread outward through the disk and likely beyond. This is the origin of the notion of *dark matter*; there is matter (mass) that we can't see but exerts powerful gravitational forces on the rest of the galaxy.

Check Your Neighbor

Sketch a best-fit line through the dots (representing velocity measurements) in Figure 21.14. Does the velocity seem to increase, decrease, or remain about the same as we go farther from the center of the galaxy?

The term "dark matter" isn't meant to be mysterious; it simply means matter that is dark. Otherwise, dark matter interacts with other matter via gravity. As of yet, astronomers have no idea what dark matter might be. Several candidates, both prosaic and exotic, have been considered: asteroids, planets, dim stars, black holes, neutrinos, as-yet-unknown subatomic particles, but none have adequately addressed the issue.

Furthermore, there are a few astronomers who believe that the dark matter issue isn't an issue at all. Rather, the "flat" behavior of rotation curves is due instead to innovative interpretations of gravity. The most common of these is nicknamed MOND ("Modified Newtonian Dynamics"), first proposed by Mordehai Milgrom in 1983. MOND is a "classical" theory—that is, it does not include Einstein's relativity—but more recent theories using general relativity are also attempting to solve the problem. At this time, no one idea has shown itself to be obviously superior to any other.

If in fact the dark matter notion is correct, then dark matter is a key component of our galaxy, indeed of the universe itself. In order to account for the flatness of the rotation curve of the Milky Way, the amount of dark matter may be as high as 10 times that of ordinary matter. Furthermore, this issue with gravity isn't restricted to rotation curves of spiral galaxies; it also shows up when astronomers try to understand how galaxies interact with each other inside galaxy clusters, for instance.

To account for this missing or "dark" matter, astronomers often postulate a 4th region for the Milky Way, nicknamed the galactic *corona*. The exact shape and extend of the corona is unknown, but it may extend up to 10 times further out from the galactic center than the edge of the disk. The corona contains

FIGURE 21.15. Vera Rubin with astronaut John Glenn, date unknown.

(would contain?) the mass, in the form of dark matter, needed to flatten the rotation curve observed in the Milky Way. Likewise, other spiral galaxies are expected to have similar coronae.

On the one hand, it is frustrating that we don't understand what appears to be a straightforward set of observations. On the other hand, questions like these are what drive many scientists; solving difficult problems is what they live for.

Section 21.6: A Quick Review

We live in an extremely large collection of stars, nebulae and other objects called the Milky Way. The Milky Way specifically is an example of a barred spiral galaxy. Its most visible section—the disk—is generally round and flat and contains its spiral arms. Because we live inside the Milky Way, and because it is so large, it is difficult to determine its structure and behaviors. Nevertheless, astronomers have identified three, perhaps four, distinct regions:

+ The bulge (the nucleus)
+ The disk (where we live)
+ The halo
+ The corona

Figure 21.16 depicts the first three regions. In this figure, we are looking at the Milky Way edge on. The bulge, colored orange, is a spheroid-shaped region at the center of the Milky Way and is about 10 kpc across. The blue line segment going

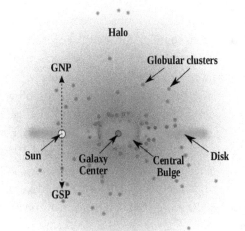

FIGURE 21.16. The three major components or sections of the Milky Way. The position of the Sun is labeled. "GNP" and "GSP" refer to galactic north and south, respectively. The entire image spans approximately 100,000 light years (30,000 parsecs). Credit: R. J. Hall.

across the figure is the disk, seen edge on, with the Sun's approximate position labeled. The larger spherical region surrounding the bulge and disk is the halo, and each small red dot represents a globular cluster. The entire figure is about 100,000 light years (or 30,000 parsecs) across.

FIGURE 21.17. A possible model of the galactic corona surrounding the rest of the galaxy. The specific shape and extent of the corona is as yet unknown.

The Sun is <u>not</u> shown to scale, here. Indeed, the Sun would be about as large across as an average bacterium in such a figure. Virtually everything we see in the night sky would be contained inside the small dot used to represent the Sun's position. In other words, the Milky Way is enormous.

Due to studies of the motions of stars and nebulae in the disk, there is a strong argument that the Milky Way includes material outside of these three regions. Because this material is made of objects too dim to see, or perhaps consists of exotic particles that don't interact with light, astronomers have (for the time being) labeled this "dark matter" (Figure 21.17).

What is the future of the Milky Way? It appears that while stars will continue to form for many billions of years to come, the most vigorous epoch of star formation has already passed. As stars age and die, they will seed the rest of the galaxy with heavy elements, making (perhaps) Earth-like planets, and perhaps life itself, more likely. Also, the Milky Way does not exist in isolation; we have a few dozen satellite galaxies (see the next chapter) currently orbiting us, and there are hints that the other major spiral galaxy in our galaxy cluster, M31, is heading for us. Should you and I be here in about 3 billion years, we will be treated to a spectacular view of the collision of two galaxies. Let the fun begin …

Summary

In this chapter, we have reviewed the basic properties and regions of the Milky Way, including the following:

- The nucleus (or bulge), including its supermassive black hole
- The disk, including spiral arms (and us!)
- The halo, including globular clusters
- The corona, including thoughts about dark matter

Questions

1. The distance to the Pleiades star cluster is about 440 light years. How far would it be on Figure 21.5? Hint: Refer to the scale given with the figure.

2. The diameter of the Pleiades star cluster is about 86 light years. How large across would it be on Figure 21.5? If you were asked to sketch a circle representing its size, could you do it?

3. It is about 8,000 parsecs to the center of the Milky Way. What would be the apparent magnitude of the Sun at such a distance, ignoring interstellar light extinction? The absolute magnitude of the Sun is +4.8.

4. Deneb is a super-giant and one of the brighter stars in our night sky. What would be the apparent magnitude of Deneb at the center of the Milky Way, if we were able to ignore interstellar light extinction? The absolute magnitude of Deneb is –8.4.

5. The Hipparcos satellite (operated by the European Space Agency from 1989 to 1993) measured the parallaxes of over 118,000 stars within about 1000 pc (3,000 ly). How large a circle would this make if we were asked to sketch this on Figure 21.5?

6. Star S2 has a period of 15.2 years and a semi-major axis of 983 au in its orbit about Sgr A*. What is the mass of Sgr A*? Hint: The mass of such an object, in units of solar masses, can be found using a version of Kepler's third law:

$$M(M_\odot) = \frac{a^3}{P^2}$$

7. How large across is Sgr A*? The "size" of a black hole, as seen from outside it, is the *Schwarzschild Radius*:

$$R_s = \sqrt{\frac{GM}{c^2}}$$

Use the result from the previous question for the mass of Sgr A*. Note that the speed of light is $c = 3.00 \times 10^8$ m/s and the universal gravitational constant $G = 6.67 \times 10^{-11}$ N · m²/kg².
   + Convert the mass of Sgr A* from units of solar masses to kilograms. Hint: $1\ M_\odot = 1.99 \times 10^{30}$ kg
   + Find the Schwarzschild radius of Sgr A* in units of meters
   + Convert the Schwarzschild radius to astronomical units. $1\ au = 1.50 \times 10^{11}$ m.

8. Vega has a metallicity 0.32 times that of the Sun and Groombridge 1830 has a metallicity 0.047 times that of the Sun. To which section of the galaxy, disk or halo, do these stars belong? Briefly defend your answer.

9. Barnard's Star is a distance of 1.83 pc away and has a space velocity of 143 km/s. To which section of the galaxy, disk, or halo, does Barnard's Star belong? Briefly defend your answer.

Activities

▸ *Astrophysics activity 21.1:* Do an exploration of the scale of the Milky Way.

Works Referenced

Galactic coordinate charts from free online software Cartes du Ciel: https://www.ap-i.net/skychart/en/start

Historical background on Karl Jansky is from "Karl Jansky: The Father of Radio Astronomy": www.armaghplanet.com/blog/karl-jansky-the-father-of-radio-astronomy.html

Balick and Brown's findings were recounted in W. M. Goss, Robert L. Brown, and K. Y. Lo (2003), "The Discovery of Sgr A*": https://arxiv.org/abs/astro-ph/0305074

The original discussion of the conditions under which a nebula might collapse under gravity is from Jeans, J. H. (1902). The stability of a spherical nebula. *Philosophical Transactions of the Royal Society A, 199*, 1–53. doi:10.1098/rsta.1902.0012

Data for HII region locations in the Milky Way comes from the following sources:

https://www.cv.nrao.edu/hrds/

Codella, C., Felli, M., & Natale, V. (1994). HII regions and IRAS PSC sources: The reliability of the association. *Astronomy & Astrophysics, 284*, 233.

Data for globular cluster locations in the Milky Way comes from Harris, W. E. (2003). Catalog of parameters for Milky Way globular clusters: The database. *Astrophysical Journal, 112*, 1487.

The discovery of the current record-holder for age amongst stars, J0815+4729, is described in Aguado, D. S., Gonzalez Hernandez, J. I., Allende Prieto, C., & Rebello, R. (2017). J0815+4729: *A chemically primitive dwarf star in the Galactic halo observed with Gran Telescopio Canarias.* Retrieved from https://arxiv.org/abs/1712.06487

Rubin and Ford's work on flat rotation curves for spiral galaxies was reported in the following sources:

Rubin, V. C., Thonnard, N., & Ford, W. K., Jr. (1978). Extended rotation curves of high-luminosity spiral galaxies. IV—Systematic dynamical properties, SA through SC. *Astrophysical Journal Letters, 225*, L107–L111. doi:10.1086/182804

Rubin, V. C., Thonnard, N., & Ford, W. K., Jr. (1980). Rotational properties of 21 Sc galaxies with a large range of luminosities and radii from NGC 4605 (R=4kpc) to UGC 2885 (R=122kpc). *Astrophysical Journal, 238*, 471. doi:10.1086/158003

A review of the rotation curve argument for dark matter can be found in Persic, M., Salucci, P., & Stel, F. (1996). The universal rotation curve of spiral galaxies – I. The dark matter connection. *Monthly Notices of the Royal Astronomical Society, 281*(1), 27–47. doi:10.1093/mnras/278.1.27

Data for the rotation curve of the Milky Way comes from Xin, X. S. & Zheng, X. W. (2013). A revised rotation curve for the Milky Way with maser astrometry. *Research in Astronomy & Astrophysics, 13*(7), 849–861. Retrieved from www.raa-journal.org/raa/index.php/raa/article/viewFile/1344/1160

An example of the application of MOND to the rotation curve problem can be found in McGaugh, S. S., & de Blok, W. J. G. (1998). Testing the hypothesis of modified dynamics with low surface brightness galaxies and other evidence. *Astrophysical Journal, 499*(1), 66–81. doi:10.1086/305629

Credits

The "Hubble Ultra Deep Field," a series of exposures from the Hubble Space Telescope taken intermittently between September 2003 and January 2004. The HST was pointed at an apparently blank space in the constellation of Fornax and the image covers approximately the area of the eye of President Roosevelt from a dime held at arm's length. Credit: NASA and the European Space Agency.

GALAXIES

To review the types, locations, and behaviors of galaxies

OBJECTIVES

- ▸ To compare and contrast the major types of galaxies
- ▸ To describe the results of collisions between galaxies
- ▸ To describe the Local Group
- ▸ To discuss clusters and superclusters of galaxies
- ▸ To show how galaxies are distributed in the universe

INTRODUCTION

The concept of a "galaxy" is a relatively new one; astronomers only realized galaxies are separate objects in the 1920s. Yet, in the intervening century, astronomers now estimate the accessible universe contains approximately 200 billion galaxies. Galaxies are the largest individual "objects" of which we know. Even the smallest galaxies themselves contain billions of stars, so the total number of stars is immense; one famous analogy recognizes that our universe contains more stars than the Earth has grains of sands on all its beaches.

In the previous chapter, we discussed our home galaxy, the Milky Way. What other types of galaxies are out there? How are they organized? What are they doing? This chapter's goal is to provide some answers to these questions.

KEY TERMS

Andromeda galaxy: See M31

Barred spiral: A version of a spiral galaxy, where the nucleus has a "bar" shape. Spiral arms begin at the ends, not the middle, of the bar.

Dwarf galaxy: A general term for a small galaxy, regardless of type, containing roughly a few to a few tens of billions of stars.

Elliptical: A type of galaxy that is ellipsoidal in shape, has little free gas or dust, and tends to possess only relatively older stars

Giant galaxy: A general term for a large galaxy, regardless of type, containing roughly a few trillion stars or more

"Great Wall": A nickname for one of the largest structures in the observable universe, an arc of galaxies extending up to a billion light years long

Hubble tuning fork: A diagram invented by Edwin Hubble, used to classify galaxies by their shapes

Irregular galaxy: A type of galaxy that has no specific shape, tends to have a lot of free gas and dust, and tends to show vigorous star formation

kpc: An abbreviation for "kiloparsec," or thousands of parsecs. Often used to describe distances within galaxies or diameters of galaxies

Large Magellanic Cloud (LMC): A satellite galaxy of the Milky Way, visible primarily from the southern hemisphere. It was likely a barred spiral galaxy until gravitational tides from the Milky Way distorted its shape

Lenticular galaxy: A type of galaxy that combines features of spiral and elliptical galaxies; their overall shapes are disks and possess lanes of dust, but they tend also to have older stars and are missing spiral arms

Local supercluster: A gathering of several clusters of galaxies, of which the Local Group is a member. The Virgo cluster is at its center

M31 (Andromeda galaxy): The largest galaxy in the Local Group, our cluster of galaxies. M31 is a spiral galaxy about twice the size of the Milky Way

Magellanic spiral: A class of galaxies; formerly spirals whose shapes have been severely distorted by the gravitational pull of much-larger neighboring galaxies. Named after the Large Magellanic Cloud

Mpc: An abbreviation for megaparsecs, or millions of parsecs. Often used to describe the diameters of clusters of galaxies and distances to far-away galaxies or clusters of galaxies

Polar ring galaxy: A special type of galaxy where a ring of stars and nebulae are concentric about the nucleus. Thought to be the result of a dead-on collision between galaxies, they are extremely rare

Redshift: In general, the stretching of light waves from an object moving away from an observer. In extragalactic astronomy, the distances to far-away galaxies can be estimated from their redshifts

Small Magellanic Cloud (SMC): A satellite galaxy of the Milky Way, visible primarily from the southern hemisphere. The SMC is a dwarf irregular galaxy

Spiral galaxy: A type of galaxy that has "arms" of stars, gas, and dust that spiral away from its nucleus. Spirals have moderate amounts of free gas and dust and star formation, and their most visible sections are flattened disks

Spiral nebula: A term sometimes used to describe what we now recognize as a spiral galaxy, before astronomers were convinced that they were in fact independent galaxies outside the Milky Way

Virgo cluster: The next nearest cluster of galaxies to ours, it contains well over 1,000 members

KEY INDIVIDUALS

Curtis, Heber: An American astronomer of the early 20th century who felt the Sun was near the center of the Milky Way but correctly advocated for the notion of "island universes" or galaxies separate from the Milky Way

Geller, Margaret: An American astronomer of the late 20th century who, with John Huchra, produced the first detailed maps of large-scale distributions of galaxies

Hubble, Edwin: An American astronomer of the early 20th century who discovered the nature of galaxies by using Cepheid variables to estimate distances to far-away galaxies. He also produced the first classification scheme for galaxies and named the local group of galaxies

Huchra, John: An American astronomer of the late 20th century who, with Margaret Geller, produced the first detailed maps of large-scale distributions of galaxies

Shapley, Harlow: An American astronomer of the early 20th century who helped determine the size and shape of the Milky Way. He argued that the Milky Way and the universe were synonymous

Section 22.1: The History of Galaxies

By the first decades of the 20th century, astronomers were beginning to get a sense of the true size and scope of the universe. Kepler and Galileo had long ago shown the Earth was not at the center, and various astronomers were beginning to use Cepheid variables to determine distances to globular clusters (see chapters 3 and 15).

On April 26, 1920, the "Great Debate" was held at the Smithsonian Museum of Natural History between astronomers Harlow Shapley and Heber Curtis. Shapley, who had used Cepheids to show that the Sun was far from the center of the Milky Way, took the position that the spiral-shaped nebulae were part of the Milky Way. Curtis, an expert on nebulae, took the position that the Sun was near the center of the Milky Way and that many of the spiral nebulae were actually "island universes" (a term invented by the famous philosopher Immanuel Kant in the 18th century) outside the Milky Way.

Shapley's argument was initially supported by observations showing one of these spiral nebulae (nicknamed the "Pinwheel") was visibly rotating, which could not be the case if it were far enough away to be outside the Milky Way. Shapley also stated that a nova in the spiral nebula M31 had been brighter than the rest of M31, which implied that a single star could outshine an entire galaxy if M31 were a separate galaxy. Curtis's response included noting that the spiral nebula M31 possessed more novae than the rest of the Milky Way, which would not make sense if M31 were just a nebula inside the Milky Way. Curtis also pointed out that many nebulae possess dust lanes similar to that of the Milky Way, another argument for them being independent of it.

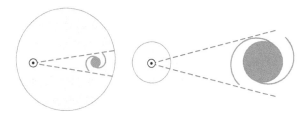

FIGURE 22.1. The differing ideas concerning spiral nebulae during the "Great Debate." At left, the Milky Way encompasses everything and spiral nebulae are relatively small. At right, the spiral nebulae are outside the Milky Way and thus relatively large.

During the following decade, Edwin Hubble ran a comprehensive program to observe hundreds of the spiral nebulae. As part of this work, he used Cepheids to estimate their distances, and determined that they are definitely independent galaxies outside the Milky Way. He also found that most of these "island universes" are moving away from each other, something we will examine in more detail later in this chapter.

Time has shown both participants in the debate to have correct and incorrect points. Shapley's estimate of the Sun's position in the Milky Way, and its overall extent, is much closer to our modern estimates than that of Curtis. But the observations concerning the pinwheel are now understood to be erroneous, and we do now know of objects (supernovae) that can outshine their host galaxies. Curtis's interpretations of properties such as dust lanes for spirals turned out to be right, and Hubble's distance measurements (themselves actually underestimates) made it clear that spiral nebulae must be far outside the Milky Way.

As a consequence, the term "island universe" fell out of use, "universe" now being used to represent all of existence, and "galaxy" began to represent extremely large conglomerations of stars. Astronomers also quickly realized that spirals are not the only types of galaxies.

Section 22.2: Basic Types of Galaxies

When Edwin Hubble and his collaborators (primarily Milton Humason) conducted their survey of "island universes," they soon realized that galaxies come in a variety of shapes, sizes, and even colors. To bring some order to their data, Hubble created a "sequence," colloquially known as the *Hubble tuning fork*:

Astronomers have long debated whether the figure represents a sequence of events or development of galaxies; in other words, do galaxies change from one

Check Your Neighbor

How was the Shapley-Curtis debate resolved: by weighing the arguments of the participants, or was it something else?

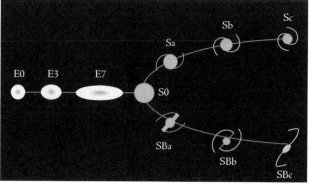

FIGURE 22.2. The Hubble "Tuning Fork" diagram, depicting major types of galaxies.

type to another, or change within each type as time goes by? The answer in general is probably not, although there are good arguments that collisions between galaxies can alter their types over the (very) long term. A century later, Hubble's scheme is still popular among astronomers, with some minor alterations.

The Milky Way is a barred spiral galaxy, probably a SBb in Hubble's nomenclature. But there are many versions of spirals, whether barred or not, and there are other types of galaxies. Let's examine them.

1. Spiral Galaxies (Including Barred Spirals)

Spiral galaxies are the prototypical objects one tends to picture when thinking about galaxies. While spirals are relatively common, they appear to do better when left to themselves; few are found in the centers of clusters of galaxies, where interactions between galaxies are relatively common. Roughly 2/3 of them have visible bars (a straight-line segment of dust lanes and stars) passing through the bulge, though there are some indications that all spirals have bars, some bars just being small enough to be contained within the bulge. There are also hints that bars evolve over time; only 10% of galaxies 8 billion years ago have them.

Hubble split spirals apart into "normal" spirals and barred spirals. Within both sub-types, he further divided them into further sub-categories. An "Sa" (or "SBa") spiral has a relatively large bulge and arms wound near the bulge. An "Sc" (or "SBc") spiral has a relatively small bulge and arms that trail far away from the bulge. "Sb" (and "SBb") spirals are intermediate.

FIGURE 22.3. To the left: NGC 1300, an example of a barred spiral galaxy. To the right: NGC 101, an example of a "normal" spiral galaxy. Credit: NASA, ESA, and the Hubble Heritage Team (STScT/AURA).

Spirals, whether barred or not, share these general characteristics:

+ A bulge (nucleus), ellipsoidal in shape, yellow in color, with a high density of stars but little free gas or dust. Star formation appears to have ceased here. At the center, we often find evidence for a supermassive black hole.

+ A flattened disk (the thickness of the disk usually being a few percent of the width of the disk), a lower density of stars, and much free gas and dust. Disks tend to possess three dominant colors: blue/violet (from bright young massive stars), brown (from absorption due to dust lanes), and pink (from emission by HII regions). All this implies continuous star formation.

+ Spirals are of course most famous for their arms. It is most common to see even numbers of arms (2 or 4), although odd numbers have been seen in rare cases. Arms tend to rotate around the bulge in one direction, "winding up", we might say, although again there are exceptions. Most of the activity—star formation, Type II supernovae, HII regions, etc.—is found in the arms. Individual stars tend to orbit the bulge at different speeds than the arms, so while massive stars don't live long enough to leave the arms, most other stars (spectral type A and cooler) do, filling out the rest of the disk. Open clusters also live long enough to leave the spiral arms where they were formed.

- A more-or-less spherical halo consisting of globular clusters, large enough to encompass the disk and bulge. Globulars are similar to the bulge in that they also are compact (i.e., have a high density of stars), yellow, and possess little gas or dust. Nearby spirals have been noted to possess a few hundred globulars. Presumably halos also include individual "field" stars, though they are often to dim to see individually.
- An unseen corona, extending far outward from the other visible sections. Observations of rotation curves of stars and other objects in the disks of many spirals hint at the presence of dark matter, forcing the stars to orbit faster than the visible masses alone can account.

If this description looks much like the details from the previous chapter, it should. The Milky Way is by all accounts a fairly typical representative of a spiral galaxy and shares all their major sections and behaviors.

What causes spiral arms? There are several options. The gravity of another, nearby galaxy can "draw" out spiral arms as it passes by. Otherwise, spiral arms can form on their own. The different rotational speeds of objects in the disk mean that gas and dust can pile up, forming the arm structures, whereas individual stars tend to move through them. Where gas and dust are condensed, star formation is more likely, and so all the behaviors associated with that process—more massive stars forming and dying more quickly, emission nebulae created by the powerful light from such massive stars, supernovae remnants further compressing gas and dust—are more likely in the arms. Once started, arms can be self-propagating structures, a notion often nicknamed the "density wave" theory (see Figure 22.4). Other attempts to explain spiral arms often invoke variations of Newtonian or Einsteinian gravity.

It is important to realize that spiral galaxies, indeed, all galaxies, are really exotic types of fluids, wherein each individual particle (stars here, instead of atoms or molecules) is more or less independent of its neighbors but is bound to the galaxy overall by the mutual gravitational attraction of all the stars and other objects in the galaxy.

Check Your Neighbor

Can you think of instances in daily life where objects are originally moving freely, then pile up for a while, then move freely again? (Hint: You may yourself have driven through a "jam" consisting of them!)

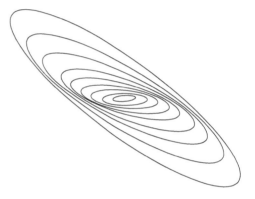

FIGURE 22.4. A series of ellipses tilted at slightly different angles, showing the "density wave" idea for the origin of arms in spiral galaxies.

2. Elliptical Galaxies

Elliptical galaxies are in many ways the opposites of spiral galaxies. Spirals have a variety of colors; ellipticals are a monochromatic yellow-white. Spirals have a definite structure; ellipticals are virtually structure less. Spirals show vigorous star formation; ellipticals have virtually no current star formation. Spirals have lots of free gas and dust; ellipticals are almost entirely gas and dust free. Spirals have a relatively narrow range of sizes (about 10 times smaller to 10 times larger across

FIGURE 22.5. To the left: M 87, a giant elliptical galaxy seen in visible light; to the right: M 110, a dwarf elliptical seen in infrared. The line coming from the center of M 87 is not an error; rather, it represents a jet of material emanating from the supermassive black hole at the heart of M87 (see Figure 20.28). For M 87, credit NASA, ESA and the Hubble Heritage Team (STScI/AURA); for M 110, credit the 2MASS team.

than the Milky Way); ellipticals range from dwarf to giant sizes (ellipticals have been observed as small across as 1 kpc and as large across as 200 kpc). Even their locations differ: Spirals tend to live in sparsely populated regions, whereas ellipticals are most common at the centers of compact clusters.

Because ellipticals have no individual parts, Hubble devised a different classification scheme for them compared to spirals. Hubble created a numbering system to express the elliptical nature of the galaxy:

Equation 22.1

$$10\left(1 - \frac{b}{a}\right)$$

where a is the semi-major axis and b the semi-minor axis of the ellipse. For example, if a galaxy appears to be a perfect circle, then the semi-major and semi-minor axes are the same, and we classify that as an E0 galaxy. The larger the number, the more stretched out the galaxy.

Sample Calculation

Suppose an elliptical galaxy's semi-minor axis appears to be 60% of the length of its semi-major axis. What is its classification?

Solution: The ratio of the semi-minor axis to the semi-major axis is 60%, or 0.6. So, the number we need is

$$10\left(1 - \frac{b}{a}\right) = 10(1 - .6) = 10(0.4) = 4$$

Therefore, the galaxy is classified as **E4**.

In a sense, the classification of an elliptical galaxy can be misleading. An elliptical galaxy may actually be quite stretched out but appear circular (spherical) from our vantage point because its end is pointing toward us. Therefore, all such classifications are relative. Furthermore, although galaxies have been classified as extreme as E7, astronomers have known for some time that galaxies from E4 to E7 are actually disk galaxies called *lenticulars*. Lenticulars are galaxies with properties somewhat between ellipticals and spirals; for example, they possess disks but no spiral arms. If a lenticular is seen from Earth as an obvious disk and not as an elliptical, then its Hubble designation is S0.

3. Irregular Galaxies

The name "irregular" gives it away: These are galaxies that have no regular structure or shape. Irregular galaxies tend to be small galaxies (10 to 100 times less massive than the Milky Way) and often are found in clusters of galaxies. This is a hint: Many irregulars show signs of having their shapes distorted by the gravitational influence of other, larger galaxies.

Thanks to having been "stirred up," irregulars often exhibit rapid star formation, more so than in spirals, and usually have large emission nebulae (though neither of these is a guarantee). Some irregulars show signs of having been spirals, for example, but their structures have been catastrophically disrupted by more massive neighbors; the Large Magellanic Cloud, a satellite of ours (i.e., the Milky Way) is a possible example. Astronomers therefore sometimes recognize subcategories of irregulars: those that used to have spiral arms and those that apparently never had any set structure. Perhaps a quarter of all galaxies are irregulars.

4. Interactions Between Galaxies

Stars are very tiny compared to the space they inhabit; for example, if the Sun were the size of a softball, the next nearest softball would be several thousands of miles away. This tends not to be true for galaxies. M31, the Milky Way's nearest spiral neighbor, is about 2.5 million light years (800 kpc)

FIGURE 22.6. Two irregular galaxies: To the left, NGC 1427A; to the right, NGC 4449. Credit: NASA, ESA and the Hubble Heritage Team (STScI/AURA).

distant, while the visible disk of the Milky Way is about 30 kpc across. If the Milky Way were a Frisbee about 9 inches across, M31 would be a similarly sized Frisbee about 60 feet away—the width of a moderately large lecture hall. Galaxies therefore inhabit a more crowded space, relatively speaking, than do stars, and interactions between galaxies are more common. A famous pair of galaxies, NGC 2207 and IC 2163, are two spiral galaxies in the beginning stages of a collision, which may last for several hundreds of millions of years.

The results of interactions between neighboring galaxies depends, as you might expect, on specifics. If the galaxies remain far apart as they pass by each other, then we might see a small distortion in the shape of one or both of the galaxies. If two galaxies collide or have a near collision, and one is much larger than the other, then the smaller galaxy's shape will likely be severely distorted. It is even possible one galaxy might "eat" the other galaxy, so that the smaller galaxy eventually becomes part of the larger one.[1] The Milky Way shows evidence of having built itself in part by consuming other dwarf galaxies and apparently is in the process of doing exactly that to a satellite galaxy called the Sagittarius Dwarf galaxy.

FIGURE 22.7. Spiral galaxies NGC 2207 and IC 2163 (together which look like a winking owl) are in the process of colliding. Credit: NASA, ESA and the Hubble Heritage Team (STScI/AURA).

Check Your Neighbor

Some astronomers think the Milky Way and M31 will collide in approximately 3 billion years. Is it likely individual stars will collide with each other when this happens? Briefly defend your answer.

What if two galaxies are truly comparable in size? Astronomers suspect that a collision between two large galaxies can ultimately result in an elliptical galaxy. This is thought to be likely even if the two galaxies in question were once both spirals. Hubble's tuning fork, or "sequence," is not a sequence of events (any more than the main sequence was for stars), but it does appear that galaxies can change their types, most dramatically via collisions.

Perhaps the most confusing (and most beautiful) irregular galaxy is a rare subtype called a *polar ring galaxy*. Polar ring galaxies are thought to be the results of either a near collision between a spiral galaxy and a smaller neighbor, or a direct, head-on collision of a small galaxy through the center of a spiral. The polar ring is often (not always) at right angles to the plane of the disk of the spiral galaxy and may be responsible for transforming the spiral into a lenticular. Polar rings are not thought to be permanent, but (like planetary rings, at least in this sense) inherently

---

[1] This is a process charmingly referred to as "galactic cannibalism."

FIGURE 22.8. The ring of material around the elliptical galaxy NGC 4650A may be the result of a direct collision between NGC 4650A and a smaller, compact galaxy. Credit: NASA, ESA and the Hubble Heritage Team (STScI/AURA).

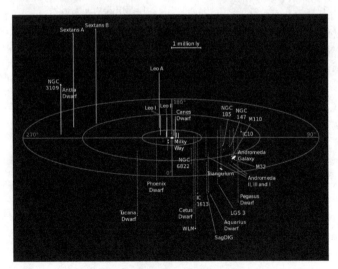

FIGURE 22.9. A three-dimensional map of the Local Group, with us (the Milky Way) at the center. Credit: Richard Powell.

unstable. About 100 such galaxies have been confirmed, but it has been suggested that up to 0.5% of current lenticulars and 5% of all lenticulars have had polar rings at some point in their lifetimes.

Section 22.3: The Local Group

Galaxies, even more so than stars, are prone to living in clusters. It is common for a cluster of galaxies to contain several hundred to a few thousand members, mostly either dwarf ellipticals or irregulars but with many spirals and a few giant ellipticals, within a space on the order of a few million parsecs across. Some clusters (the Virgo cluster is an example) have over a thousand member galaxies, all bound together by their mutual gravity. On the other hand, we live in a rather sparse cluster nicknamed the *Local Group*.[2] Since it is our home cluster of galaxies, it is worth a close look.

The Local Group contains about 50 galaxies (astronomers discover new members every few years) in a space about 3 million parsecs (10 million light years) across. Galaxies are not randomly distributed within the cluster. Most of the Local Group galaxies center about two large spirals, M31 and us, the Milky Way. With a smaller spiral, M33, the Local Group contains three spirals and miscellaneous dwarf ellipticals and irregulars, but no giant ellipticals. The shape of the Local Group can be thought of as a big—mind you, a very big—dumbbell, with one end at the Milky Way and the other at M31.

Despite belonging to our cluster, or even orbiting the Milky Way, few of the cluster member galaxies are visible to the naked eye. This sounds odd at first, since even a dwarf galaxy can contain about a billion stars, and these galaxies are relatively nearby. There are several reasons for this situation, but two stand out. First, many of the galaxies are on the other side of the Milky Way, and the dust of the disk blocks our view in visible light. Second, galaxies are not concentrated into points like stars, but rather spread out their light. M31 is about 10 times larger across as the full Moon on the sky, but only the very center of its bulge is bright enough to be visible (it looks like a fuzzy point to the naked eye under good seeing conditions). Third, there are a few members that are visible, besides M31, M33 can be seen (though as the faintest of dots) to a good observer under exceptionally dark skies, and both the Magellanic clouds are easily visible. Most people in the United States are unaware of the Magellanic clouds for the simple reason that they belong to the southern skies; our friends in locations such as Australia are perfectly familiar with them. Let's look at some of these more prominent galaxies.

---

[2] The other side of the Local Group is about a million parsecs distant, begging a new definition of "local."

1. M31 Andromeda

Of our sibling galaxies in the Local Group, the most famous is *M31*, also known as the *Andromeda galaxy* since it is located within (behind) the constellation of Andromeda. The first photographs of M31 were taken by the Welsh engineer and amateur astronomer Isaac Roberts in the late 19th century (see Figure 22.10). A triumph of the time for the nascent field of astrophotography, it clearly shows M31 to have a disk structure with spiral arms. Because the true scale of the Milky Way and the rest of the universe was not yet known, astronomers initially thought it to be a picture of a forming solar system. For comparison, a modern amateur photograph (digital instead of chemical) taken by Kees Scherer in 2015 is next to it. The updated photo also makes obvious M31 possesses satellite galaxies; for example, M32 is near the bulge of M31, and M110 is further away.

FIGURE 22.10. Our changing views of the Andromeda galaxy: M31 in 1899 (left); M31 in 2015 (right). Credits: Isaac Roberts and Kees Scherer, respectively.

M31 is a spiral (no bar is visible) galaxy approximately 2.5 million light years (780 kpc) distant, though this measurement is constantly being updated. Because its distance is not as well known as we might wish, we also are not quite sure of its mass and size. Most other observations, including the fact that M31 appears to have many more globular clusters than we do, support the notion that M31 is larger than the Milky Way. Assuming a distance of 780 kpc, M31 has a diameter of 67 kpc, a little more than twice that of the Milky Way. M31 also have over twice as many stars (approximately 1 trillion to our 400 billion) and a mass about twice that of the Milky Way (1.5 trillion $M_\odot$ to our 0.8 trillion $M_\odot$). By looking at the metal content of stars and clusters in M31, astronomers estimate it first formed approximately 10 billion years ago, similar to the Milky Way. It was detailed observations of Cepheid variables in M31 by Hubble in the 1920s supplied the evidence to settle the Shapley-Curtis debate.

Of long-term interest is the notion that M31 appears to be heading toward us. Its radial (straight-line) velocity is about 110 km/s, implying a collision (depending on how and when we define it happens) within 3 to 4 billion years. Given computer modeling and observations of other collisions between spirals, the net result will probably be a giant elliptical or lenticular galaxy. What will happen to the solar system is unknown; we may remain as part of the new, larger galaxy, or the solar system may be flung out of the new galaxy altogether. It is highly unlikely the planets will be ripped away from the Sun, though; remember how large the relative distances are between stars.

2. The Magellanic Clouds

When European sailors first ventured into the southern hemisphere in the 16th century, among the novel sights were two "clouds" that never dissipated, but instead followed the apparent rotation of the sky (of course, natives of that hemisphere were always aware of them). They have since been termed the *Magellanic Clouds*, after the famous explorer Ferdinand Magellan. Very simply, since one is obviously larger than the other, they are individually termed the Large and Small Magellanic Clouds. Astronomers have since determined they are actually satellite galaxies of the Milky Way.

The *Large Magellanic Cloud* (LMC) is 50 kiloparsecs (163,000 light years) away, a distance firmly measured using the remnant of supernova 1987A (see chapter 19). It is roughly 4.3 kpc (14,000 ly) across and has about

10 billion solar masses of material, or 1/100th of the Milky Way, making the LMC the fourth-most massive galaxy in the local group, after M31, the Milky Way, and M33. Under very dark skies, the LMC spans about 10° across (or 20 times the width of the full Moon); in other words, it is not a trivial addition to southern skies. It is so deep into the southern hemisphere that one needs to be south of 20° north latitude to even catch a glimpse of it; however, it is available to everyone living in the southern hemisphere.

Astronomers originally identified the LMC as an irregular galaxy, but subsequent research has revealed it is, or was, a barred spiral galaxy whose shape is being severely distorted by the gravity of the Milky Way. The LMC thus has generated a new subcategory called *Magellanic spirals*. Due perhaps from this distortion, the LMC exhibits

FIGURE 22.11. The Large Magellanic Cloud in visible light (left); the Small Magellanic Cloud in infrared (right). Credit: European Southern Observatory.

rapid star formation, most notably in the Tarantula Nebula, famous as the location of the supernova SN 1987A (chapter 19).

The *Small Magellanic Cloud* (SMC) is classified as a dwarf irregular, though it too may have been a barred spiral disrupted by gravity tides. It is further away than the LMC (about 60 kpc, or 200,000 ly), about 7,000 kpc across, and contains about 7 billion solar masses. Like the LMC, it has a low surface brightness, but extends 7° across under dark skies. It too is visible primarily in the southern hemisphere. It was in the SMC that Henrietta Leavitt first worked out the period-luminosity relation for Cepheid variables (see chapter 13) that is so valuable for finding distances in astronomy.

The LMC and SMC appear to be gravitationally bound, as there is a tenuous lane of gas and dust connecting the two galaxies, and they are surrounded by a common envelope of hydrogen. The two galaxies also have a relatively high space velocity; given the gravitational pull from the Milky Way, it may be they are passing by us rather than following a true orbit.

Section 22.4: Clusters and Superclusters

The Local Group is rather sparse as far as clusters of galaxies are concerned. A better representative is the *Virgo cluster*, the center of which is a little over 16.5 megaparsecs (54 million light years) away. Some of the more prominent members, such as M87, were observed by astronomers long before their true nature was realized. The cluster has a diameter of about 8° on the sky, which translates to about 4.4 Mpc across. The total mass of the cluster is estimated to be about 1.2×10^{15} $M_\odot$ (i.e., 1.2 quadrillion solar masses). Again, because galaxies (and now clusters of galaxies) spread out their light, the galaxies of the Virgo cluster all require telescopes in order to be seen.

Check Your Neighbor

Why do you think we call this the "Virgo" cluster?

The Virgo cluster is not notably much larger across than the Local Group (about three times the volume), but with estimates ranging as low as 1,300 and as high as 2,000 member galaxies (compared to the 50 or so of the local group), it is much more densely packed. The giant elliptical M87 is at its center, and ellipticals in general tend to spherically aggregate around its core, whereas spirals tend to live at its outskirts in an oblong pattern. The cluster also has many lenticular and spiral galaxies, though many spirals appear relatively gas-poor compared to the spirals of the local group, likely because tidal forces among members have stripped the gas away. The cluster has three separate sections (labeled Virgo A, B, and C); given that, and the high speeds of the members, it is possible the cluster is (a) still collapsing and (b) has a great deal of unseen mass.

The Virgo cluster is surrounded by "intercluster" gas hot enough (30 million K) to emit x-rays. Also, up to 10% of all the stars of the cluster live in the spaces between galaxies. The high temperatures are likely the result of shocks from supernovae into rarefied gas that has trouble releasing heat due to lack of collisions between gas particles; the stars are perhaps stragglers that were torn from their original galaxies due to strong tidal interactions between the member galaxies.

FIGURE 22.12. A close-up of the Virgo cluster of galaxies in ultraviolet light. Credit: NASA/JPL-Caltech/SSC.

The Virgo cluster is also the center of the local supercluster. In 2014, astronomers discovered that Virgo, the local group, and over 50 other clusters of galaxies are grouped together to form the *Laniakea*,[3] or local supercluster. Superclusters are so large that, while their gravity can affect member clusters somewhat, they are not bound by gravity, and they are so immense there are no orbits as such. Superclusters are the largest structures of any kind in the universe; Laniakea is estimated to be 150 Mpc (500 Mly) across. There are perhaps as many as 10 million superclusters in the observable universe.

This hints at how galaxies (or superclusters of galaxies) are arranged in the universe. Galaxies are not randomly distributed. Rather, they gather together more akin to the skins of soap bubbles. Galaxies lie along the edges of the bubbles (also called filaments) with the centers of the bubbles virtually free of galaxies.

The first astronomer to get a hint at this situation was George Abell in 1958. But the real confirmation of this was elucidated by astronomers Margaret Geller (b. 1947) and John Huchra (1948–2010) in the late 1980s. Knowing that the entire sky is too large to view all at once, given the equipment of the time, they decided to look at small slices of the sky, plotting positions of galaxies including their distances. They found what we mentioned: Galaxies are concentrated along edges of bubbles or filaments.

Subsequence observations over the succeeding decades have solidified this into a general result. One of the latest projects was run by the Sloan Digital Sky Survey, which has a much greater capacity (speed) to gather data, and therefore can

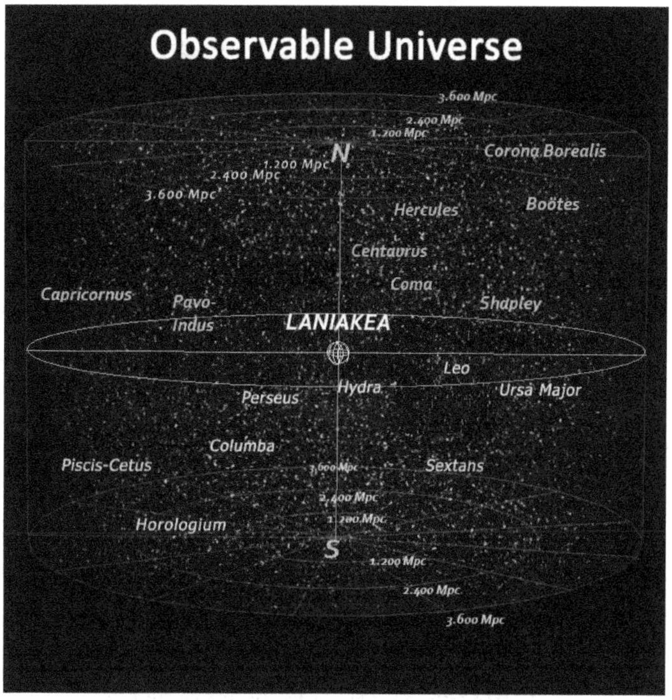

FIGURE 22.13. The Laniakea supercluster and its surroundings. Each white dot represents a galaxy in this computerized representation. Credit: J. A. Galán Baho.

[3] "Laniakea" stands for "immense heaven" in Hawaiian.

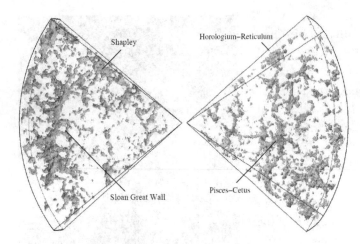

FIGURE 22.14. The "great wall," an arc of clusters of galaxies, is part of the Sloan Digital Sky Survey. We are at the center of the figure. Each wedge is about 2 degrees thick and extends a billion light years away from us. Credit: Willem Schaap.

make much more comprehensive observations. Figure 22.14 shows not just one, but many superclusters within 300 Mpc (1 billion light years), including a feature nicknamed the "great wall." Whether the great wall really represents a true structure is up for debate (it is not gravitationally, or in any other way, bound), it does illustrate just how large our universe is.

Section 22.5: The Deep Fields

It's common for people (students included) to ask an astronomer "how far" one can see into space. Astronomers don't tend to think in these terms. We know that our determinations of distances to objects depends on many factors, that the universe doesn't have a boundary or edge as we normally understand these terms (see chapter 23 for further discussions), and that the question assumes there is an answer. Rather, an astronomer would more likely than not address the idea of faintness: What is the faintest astronomical object we can see? On top of that, because the speed of light is finite, the further out we look into space, the further back in time we go. These notions are often bound together into the notion of "depth"; astronomers will usually talk about how "deep" an image goes instead of how far away an object is.

The Hubble Space Telescope (or HST) was launched in 1990, and astronomers quickly noticed its images did not exhibit the expected resolution (clarity). A special mission of the space shuttle *Endeavour* in 1993 installed corrective optics that not only restored its performance, but actually improved it compared to its originally-expected capabilities (see Figure 22.15):

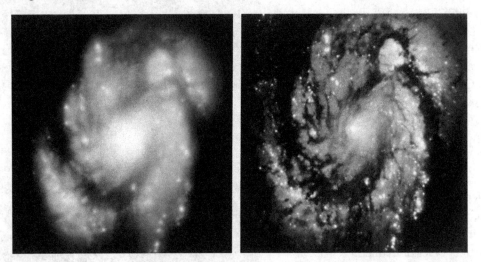

FIGURE 22.15. Images of the spiral galaxy M100 before and after corrective optics were installed by the crew of the space shuttle Endeavour in 1993. Credit: NASA.

After the mission of the Endeavour, the new camera (WFPC2, or the "Wide Field Planetary Camera 2")[4] was used to take images of distant galaxies in between other scheduled projects. Results from these short surveys,

---

[4] Despite its name, the Wide Field Planetary Camera is well suited to studying many other types of astronomical objects.

in conjunction with other ground-based projects, suggested that galaxies were substantially different in the far past compared to their appearances "today." With the discretion allowed to the Space Telescope Science Institute, the agency in charge of the operations of the HST, its then-director Robert Williams tasked the HST with a special project. Instead of taking shorter-duration images over a range of locations in the sky, the HST would spend a large amount of time accumulating light from a very narrow spot.

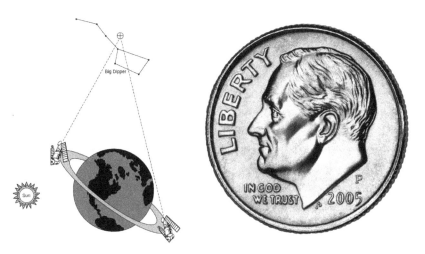

FIGURE 22.16. The target of the original Hubble Deep Field (left, credit: NASA); the eye of FDR on an American dime (right).

An apparently blank location near the bend of the handle of the Big Dipper was chosen for the first "deep field" image. The smallness of the target area is amazing; the diameter of the image was approximately 2.6 arcminutes, or about 1/12 of the diameter of the full Moon, and the area of the image is only about 1/24,000,000th of the entire sky. Another, more familiar way to express the diameter is to imagine oneself holding an American dime at arm's length; the area of the image is about the same as the size of FDR's eye.

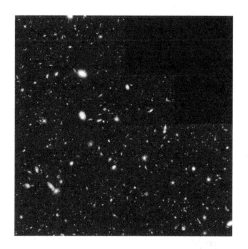 

FIGURE 22.17. The original Hubble deep field (left); details of the deep field (right). Credit: NASA.

To make the first Hubble deep field, 342 separate images were taken by the HST over the course of 10 days, from December 18 through December 28 of 1995. While we are looking through our galaxy in order to see objects beyond it, the "blank"-ness was chosen so well that only 20 of the approximately 3,000 objects in the image are foreground stars belonging to the Milky Way. To make a color image, exposures were made at different wavelengths, which were electronically combined, for example, 33.5 hours at 450 nanometers (violet) versus 30.3 hours at 606 nm (orange-red), among others.

What does the deep field show us? We can ignore the dots with spikes; these are foreground stars of the Milky Way, and the spikes are artifacts (i.e., not real) of the optics. Otherwise each object is a distant galaxy. Looking at close-ups of the deep field indicate that these galaxies are not as distinct as they are "today." This suggests that galaxies go through a long, drawn-out formation process and do not achieve their specific "looks" until after hundreds of millions, if not billions, of years. Having said that, galaxies appear to begin forming relatively quickly after the beginning of the universe. Galaxies also are more

Check Your Neighbor

What do the various colors of the galaxies suggest to you regarding the stars in these galaxies?

prone to collisions in the distant past and build themselves up by joining together via their mutual gravity. Whether galaxies change from one type to another is still a bit speculative, though early results suggest giant ellipticals can be make from the merging of other galaxies, even spirals. Finally, the number of quasars rises as we look into the past; it is easier to feed supermassive black holes when objects are much closer together than they are today (chapter 20).

Another item to consider is what the deep field implies about the sheer number of galaxies in the universe. Supposing this is fairly representative (granted, not a guarantee) of the sky about us, we can use these observations to estimate how populated a universe we live in:

Check Your Neighbor

Do you recognize any specific types of galaxies? If so, which types do you see?

Total galaxies = (Number of galaxies in the deep field) × (Number of deep fields in the sky)
Or the total number of galaxies = (3000) × (24,000,000) = **72 billion galaxies**

FIGURE 22.18. The Hubble Extreme Deep Field, in the direction of the constellation of Fornax, compiled in 2012. Credit: NASA.

This is the origin of the number reported in the news of the day that astronomers have estimated the total number of galaxies in the universe to be on the order of 100 billion. For limited surveys such as this, it doesn't make sense to ascribe much precision to the results. Nevertheless, this number (100 billion) has held up with subsequent "deep field" images.

The HST has since taken other "deep field" images, and all show the same general result: an otherwise blank-looking region of space in fact is peppered with distant galaxies, and the only reason we didn't previously realize this is because the galaxies are so distant and faint that they do not show up even with more commonly conducted astronomical imaging, much less via the naked eye.

As with improvements in observations of exoplanets over the past few decades (see chapter 7), astronomers' knowledge of the formation of galaxies is being revolutionized by the deep fields and other like work. The latest version of the deep fields is the "Hubble Ultra-Deep Field" (HUDF), compiled over a 3-year period by a team led by Alejandro S. Borlaff of the Instituto de Astrofísica de Canarias. The group combined hundreds of observations totaling 230 hours of observations with the Wide-Field Planetary Camera 3 (WFPC3), an update to the Hubble Space Telescope made in 2009.

The original HUDF was published in 2012; this new version was released to the public in 2019. By looking through archived data and improved image processing, the team was able to show (a) many galaxies are actually about twice as large as previous deep fields indicated, (b) many fainter galaxies lie between the brighter galaxies, and (c) there is lots of gas between galaxies. Like the other deep fields, it is a little misleading in that this

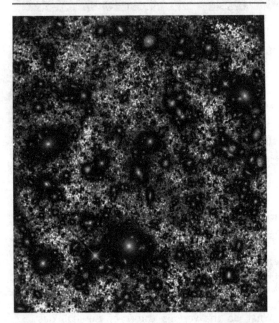

FIGURE 22.19. The Hubble Ultra Deep Field 2019, compiled over 3 years in order to bring out fainter objects between bright galaxies.

isn't something you could ever see with the naked eye—the galaxies are far too faint and distant for that—but it tells us that extragalactic space is much "busier" than we ever suspected.

The new HUDF is reminiscent of models of galaxy cluster formation that make the universe look like a conglomeration of bubbles or foam, where galaxies look like they exist at the boundaries of the bubbles and the centers of the bubbles were free of galaxies. This recent development may adjust that thinking; the new HUDF appears to show galaxies can be at the centers of the bubbles. Needless to say, we have a lot left to learn about how our universe is structured.

Summary

In this chapter, we described the following:

▹ Different types of galaxies

▹ Interactions between galaxies

▹ Clusters and superclusters of galaxies

▹ How "deep fields" have revolutionized our understanding of the numbers and evolution of galaxies over cosmological time

Questions

1. Shapley correctly stated that a nova should not be able to shine as brightly as an entire galaxy. Are there any objects that can do that, and if so, what are they?

2. A planetary nebula is approximately 1 pc across. If it is 1,000 pc away, what angle does it subtend?

3. A galaxy subtends an angle of 0.05° across. If the galaxy is 30,000 pc across, how far away is it?

4. An elliptical galaxy appears to have a semi-minor axis half as large across as its semi-major axis. What is its classification?

5. The average distance between stars near the Sun is about a parsec. How much relative space is there between stars? Hint: Find the number of kilometers in a parsec, then divide that number by the diameter of the Sun.

6. The distance between the Milky Way and the nearest large spiral like itself, M31, is about 800 kpc. How much relative space is there between these galaxies? Hint: Divide this distance by the diameter of the Milky Way. How does this compare to the relative average distances between stars near the Sun?

7. Assuming M31 is heading straight for the Milky Way, how long until they collide? Assume a distance of 780 kpc and an approach speed of 110 km/s. Hint: Convert units of kiloparsecs to kilometers.

8. Suppose the Local Group has a radius of about 1.5 Mpc and 50 member galaxies. How many galaxies are there per unit volume? Express the result in number of galaxies per Mpc. Assume for simplicity galaxy clusters have spherical shapes and the volume of a sphere is $(4\pi/3)R^3$.

9. Suppose the Virgo cluster of galaxies has a radius of about 2.2 Mpc and 1,300 galaxies. How many galaxies are there per unit volume? Again, express the result in number of galaxies per Mpc. How does this compare to the number density of the local group?

Activities

▹ *Astrophysics activity 22.1:* View and answer questions about "the edge of forever" from the original Cosmos series (episode #10), on galaxies and cosmology.

- *Astrophysics activity 22.2:* Join the *Galaxy Zoo* project, classify 10 galaxies as directed, and record the results.

- Discuss the role of debates in science, and what ultimately determines a "winner." Use the Shapley-Curtis "great debate" to illustrate your arguments.

Works Referenced

The Curtis-Shapley debate is discussed in "Why the 'Great Debate' was important": https://apod.nasa.gov/diamond_jubilee/1920/cs_why.html

Shu, F. (1982). *The physical universe: An introduction to astronomy.* Mill Valley, CA: University Science Books.

The Hubble sequence (or "tuning fork") was introduced by Hubble in the following sources:

Hubble, E. P. (1926). Extra-galactic nebulae. *Contributions from the Mount Wilson Observatory/Carnegie Institution of Washington, 324,* 1–49.

Hubble, E. P. (1926). Extra-galactic nebulae. *Astrophysical Journal, 64,* 321–369. doi:10.1086/143018

Hubble, E. P. (1927). The classification of spiral nebulae. *The Observatory, 50,* 276.

Spiral galaxies are discussed in the following sources:

Dressler, A. (1980, March). Galaxy morphology in rich clusters – Implications for the formation and evolution of galaxies. *Astrophysical Journal, 236,* 351–365. doi:10.1086/157753

Lin. C. C., & Shu, F. H. (1964, August). On the spiral structure of disk galaxies. *The Astrophysical Journal, 140,* 646–655. doi:10.1086/147955

Ringermacher, H. I., & Mead, Lawrence R. (2009). A new formula describing the scaffold structure of spiral galaxies. *Monthly Notices of the Royal Astronomical Society, 397,* 164–171 doi:10.1111/j.1365-2966.2009.14950.x

Science Daily. (2014, January 16). Hubble and galaxy zoo find bars and baby galaxies don't mix. Retrieved 2019-04-21. https://www.sciencedaily.com/releases/2014/01/140116085103.htm

Elliptical galaxies are discussed in the following sources:

Graham, A. W. (2016). Galaxy bulges and their massive black holes: A review. *Galactic Bulges, Astrophysics and Space Science Library, 418.* Retrieved from adsabs.harvard.edu/abs/2016ASSL..418..263G

Liller, M. H. (1966). The distribution of intensity in elliptical galaxies of the Virgo Cluster. II. *Astrophysical Journal, 146,* 28. doi:10.1086/148857

Irregular galaxies and interactions between galaxies are described in the following sources:

The Sloan Digital Sky Survey (SDSS) "First Discoveries" document includes a section about the Sagittarius Dwarf galaxy at cas.sdss.org/dr6/en/sdss/discoveries/discoveries.asp#halos

Cornell University's online "Ask an Astronomer" site has an article titled "What happens when galaxies collide?" at http://curious.astro.cornell.edu/about-us/96-the-universe/galaxies/formation-and-evolution/530-what-happens-when-galaxies-collide-beginner

Schweizer, F., Whitmore, B. C., & Rubin, V. C. (1983). Colliding and merging galaxies. II – S0 galaxies with polar rings. *Astronomical Journal, 88,* 909–925. doi:10.1086/113377

Whitmore, B. C., Lucas, R. A., McElroy, D. B., Steiman-Cameron, T. Y., Sackett, P. D., & Olling, R. P. (1990). New observations and a photographic atlas of polar-ring galaxies. *Astronomical Journal, 100,* 1489–1522, 1721–1755. doi:10.1086/115614

Edwin Hubble nicknamed the local group in Hubble, E. P. (1936). *The realm of the nebulae.* New Haven, CT:. Yale University Press.

Basic facts regarding M31 Andromeda can be found in the following sources:

Cox, T. J., & Loeb, A. (2008). The collision between the Milky Way and Andromeda. *Monthly Notices of the Royal Astronomical Society, 386*(1), 461–474. doi:10.1111/j.1365-2966.2008.13048.x

Karachentsev, I. D., & Kashibadze, O. G. (2006). Masses of the local group and of the M81 group estimated from distortions in the local velocity field. *Astrophysics, 49*(1), 3–18. doi:10.1007/s10511-006-0002-6

Karachentsev, I. D., Karachentseva, V. E., Huchtmeier, W. K., & Makarov, D. I. (2004). A catalog of neighboring galaxies. *Astronomical Journal, 127*(4), 2031–2068. doi:10.1086/382905

McConnachie, A. W, Irwin, M. J., Ferguson, A., M., N., Ibata, R. A., Lewis, G. F., & Tanvir, N. (2005). Distances and metallicities for 17 local group galaxies. *Monthly Notices of the Royal Astronomical Society, 356*(4), 979–997. doi:10.1111/j.1365-2966.2004.08514.x

Ribas, I., Jordi, C., Vilardell, F., Fitzpatrick, E. L., Hilditch, R. W., & Guinan, E. F. (2005). First determination of the distance and fundamental properties of an eclipsing binary in the Andromeda galaxy. *Astrophysical Journal Letters, 635*(1), L37–L40. doi:10.1086/499161

Basic facts about the Magellanic Clouds can be found in the following sources:

Besla, G., Martinez-Delgado, D., van der Marel, R. P., Baletsky, Y., Seibert, M., Schafly, E. F., ... & Neyer, F. (2016). Low surface brightness imaging of the Magellanic system: Imprints of tidal interactions between the clouds in the stellar periphery. *Astrophysical Journal, 825*(1), 20. doi:10.3847/0004-637X/825/1/20

Burnham, R., Jr. (1978). *Burnham's celestial handbook: Volume two.* New York, NY: Dover.

Buscombe, W. (1954). The Magellanic clouds. *Astronomical Society of the Pacific Leaflets, 7,* 9.

Hodge, P. W. (1998). Magellanic cloud. *Encyclopedia Britannica* (on-line). Retrieved 2019-04-21. https://www.britannica.com/topic/Magellanic-Cloud

Harvard University. (2007, January 9). Press release: Magellanic clouds may be just passing through. Retrieved 2019-04-21. https://www.cfa.harvard.edu/news/2007-02

Heydari-Malayeri, Meynaider, F., Charmandaris, V., Deharveng, L., Bertre, T. L., Rosa, M. R., & Schaerer, D. (2003). The stellar environment of SMC N81. *Astronomical Astrophysics, 411*(3), 427. doi:10.1051/0004-6361:20031360

Mathewson, D. S., & Ford, V. L. (1984). Structure and evolution of the Magellanic clouds. *IAU Symposium, 108,* 125.

Nemiroff, R., & Bonnell, J. (Eds.). (2006, June 17). The Small Cloud of Magellan. NASA. Retrieved 2019-04-21. https://apod.nasa.gov/apod/ap060617.html

Peñarrubia, J., Gomez, F. A., Besla, G., Erkhal, D., & Ma, Y. (2016). A timing constant on the total mass of the Large Magellanic Cloud. *Monthly Notices of the Royal Astronomical Society, 456*(1), 54–58. doi:10.1093/mnrasl/slv160

Peterson, B., & Ryden, B. M. (2009). *Foundations of astrophysics.* New York, NY: Pearson.

Pietrzynski, G., Graczyk, D., Gieren, W., Thompson, I. B., Pilecki, B., Udalski, A., ... & Karczmarek, P. (2013, March 7). An eclipsing-binary distance to the Large Magellanic Cloud accurate to two per cent. *Nature, 495*(7439), 76–79. doi:10.1038/nature11878

Basic facts concerning the Virgo cluster of galaxies, the local supercluster and the distribution of superclusters in the universe can be found in the following sources:

Abell, G. O. (1958). The distribution of rich cluster of galaxies. A catalogue of 2,712 rich clusters found on the National Geographic Society Palomar Observatory Sky Survey. *Astrophysical Journal Supplement Series, 3,* 211-88. doi:10.1086/190036

Boselli, A., Voyer, E., Boissier, S., Cucciati, O., Consalandi, G., Cortese, L., ... & Toloba, E. (2014). The GALEX Ultraviolet Virgo Cluster Survey (GUViCS). IV. The role of the cluster environment on galaxy evolution. *Astronomy & Astrophysics, 570*, A69. doi:10.1051/0004-6361-201424419. A69

Côté, P., Blakeslee, J. P., Ferrarese, L., Jordan, A., Mei, S., Merritt, D., ... & West, M. J. (2004). The ACS Virgo Cluster Survey. *Astrophysical Journal, 153*(1), 223–242. doi:10.1086/421490

Geller, M. J., & Huchra, J. P. (1989). "Mapping the Universe". *Science, 246*, 897. Retrieved 2019-04-21. https://science.sciencemag.org/content/246/4932/897/tab-article-info

Ferguson, H. C., Tanvir, N. R., & von Hippel, T. (1998). Detection of intergalactic red-giant-branch stars in the Virgo cluster. *Nature, 391*(6666), 461-463. doi:10.1038/35087

Fouqué, P., Soulanes, J. M., Sanchis, T., & Balkowski, C. (2001). Structure, mass and distance of the Virgo cluster from a Tolman-Bondi model. *Astronomy and Astrophysics, 375*(3), 770–780. doi:10.1051/0004-6361:20010833

Lea, S. M., Mushotzky, R., & Holt, S. S. (1982). Einstein Observatory solid state spectrometer observations of M87 and the Virgo cluster. *Astrophysical Journal, 262*(1), 24-32. doi:10.1086/160393

Mei, S., Blakeslee, J. P., Côte, P., Tonry, J. L., West, M. J., Ferrarese, L., Jordan, A., ... & Merritt, D. (2007). The ACS Virgo Cluster Survey. XIII. SBF Distance Catalog and the three-dimensional structure of the Virgo cluster. *Astrophysical Journal, 655*(1), 144–162. doi:10.1086/50959

Tully, R. B., Courtois, R. H., Hoffman, Y., & Pomarede, D. Westphal, J. A. (2014). The Laniakea supercluster of galaxies. *Nature, 513*(7516), 71. doi:10.1038/nature13674

"The Sloan Great Wall: Largest Known Structure?": https://apod.nasa.gov/apod/ap071107.html

The improvement of the Wide Field Planetary Camera (WFPC2) of the Hubble Space Telescope is described in

Trauger, J. T., Ballester, G. E., Burrows, C. J., Casertano, S., Clarke, J. T., Crisp, D., ... & (1994). The on-orbit performance of WFPC2. *Astrophysical Journal Letters, 435*(1), L3–L6. doi:10.1086/187580

The deep-field projects are discussed in the following sources:

Abraham, R. G., van den Bergh, S., Glazebrook, K., Ellis, R. S., Santiago, B. X., Surma, P., & Griffiths, R. E. (1996). The morphologies of distant galaxies. II. Classifications from the Hubble Space Telescope Medium Deep Survey. *Astrophysical Journal Supplement, 107*, 1–17. doi:10.1086/192352

Ferguson, A. S. (1998). The Hubble deep field. *Reviews in Modern Astronomy, 11*, 115.

Williams, R. E., Blacker, B., Dickinson, M., Dixon, W. V. D., Ferguson, H. C., Fruchter, A. S., ... & Hook, R. (1996). The Hubble Deep Field: Observations, data reduction, and galaxy photometry. *Astronomical Journal, 112*, 1335–1389. doi:10.1086/118105

https://phys.org/news/2019-01-hubble-deepest-images-deeper.html

https://www.sciencedaily.com/releases/2019/01/190124084812.htm

Credits

Fig. V.2: Source: https://commons.wikimedia.org/wiki/File:Hubble_ultra_deep_field.jpg.

Fig. 22.3a: Source: https://commons.wikimedia.org/wiki/File:Hubble2005-01-barred-spiral-galaxy-NGC1300.jpg.

Fig. 22.3b: Copyright © by ESA/Hubble (CC BY 3.0) at https://commons.wikimedia.org/wiki/File:M101_hires_STScI-PRC2006-10a.jpg.

Fig. 22.4: Source: http://adsabs.harvard.edu/abs/1964ApJ...140..646L.

Fig. 22.5a: Source: https://commons.wikimedia.org/wiki/File:M87-full_jpg.jpg.

Fig. 22.5b: Source: https://commons.wikimedia.org/wiki/File:MESSIER_110_2MASS.jpg.

Fig. 22.6a: Source: https://commons.wikimedia.org/wiki/File:Irregular_galaxy_NGC_1427A_(captured_by_the_Hubble_Space_Telescope).jpg.

Fig. 22.6b: Source: https://commons.wikimedia.org/wiki/File:Starburst_in_NGC_4449_(captured_by_the_Hubble_Space_Telescope).jpg.

Fig. 22.7: Source: https://commons.wikimedia.org/wiki/File:NGC2207%2BIC2163.jpg.

Fig. 22.8: Source: https://commons.wikimedia.org/wiki/File:NGC_4650A_I_HST2002.jpg.

Fig. 22.9: Copyright © by Richard Powell (CC BY-SA 2.5) at https://commons.wikimedia.org/wiki/File:Local_Group.svg.

Fig. 22.10a: Source: https://commons.wikimedia.org/wiki/File:Pic_iroberts1.jpg.

Fig. 22.10b: Source: https://commons.wikimedia.org/wiki/File:M31_-_Andromeda_Galaxy_by_Kees_Scherer.jpg.

Fig. 22.11a: Copyright © by ESO (CC BY 4.0) at https://www.eso.org/public/images/lmc-schmidt-1986-6000p/.

Fig. 22.11b: Copyright © by ESO/VISTA VMC (CC BY 4.0) at https://commons.wikimedia.org/wiki/File:VISTA%E2%80%99s_view_of_the_Small_Magellanic_Cloud.jpg.

Fig. 22.12: Source: https://commons.wikimedia.org/wiki/File:Virgo_Galaxy_Cluster_in_UV.jpg.

Fig. 22.13: Copyright © by JA Galán Baho (CC BY-SA 4.0) at https://commons.wikimedia.org/wiki/File:Observable_universe_r.jpg.

Fig. 22.14: Copyright © by Willem Schaap (CC BY-SA 4.0) at https://commons.wikimedia.org/wiki/File:2dfdtfe.gif.

Fig. 22.15: Source: https://commons.wikimedia.org/wiki/File:Improvement_in_Hubble_images_after_SMM1.jpg.

Fig. 22.16a: Source: https://commons.wikimedia.org/wiki/File:Hubble_Deep_Field_observing_geometry.svg.

Fig. 22.16b: Source: https://commons.wikimedia.org/wiki/File:2005-Dime-Obv-Unc-P.png.

Fig. 22.17a: Source: https://commons.wikimedia.org/wiki/File:HubbleDeepField.800px.jpg.

Fig. 22.17b: Source: https://commons.wikimedia.org/wiki/File:HDF_extracts_showing_many_galaxies.jpg.

Fig. 22.18: Source: https://commons.wikimedia.org/wiki/File:Hubble_Extreme_Deep_Field_(full_resolution).png.

Fig. 22.19: Source: https://phys.org/news/2019-01-hubble-deepest-images-deeper.html.

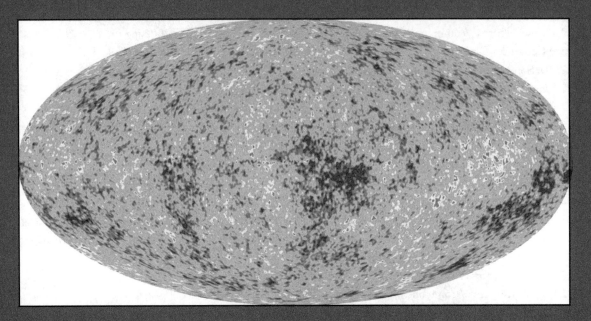

Nine years of data gathering by the Wilkerson Microwave Anisotropy Probe (WMAP) shows an incredible smoothness to the microwave background radiation of the universe. The most extreme deviations are on the order of only 200 microKelvin, or about 7 parts in 100,000. Credit: NASA.

CHAPTER 23

COSMOLOGY

PURPOSE

To review our current understanding of the origin and future of the universe

OBJECTIVES

- ▸ To address how scientific theories are constructed
- ▸ To answer why the sky is dark at night
- ▸ To present the evidence for the Big Bang
- ▸ To examine various milestones in the development of the universe
- ▸ To suggest possible futures for the universe

INTRODUCTION

How did the world begin?

However phrased, this question is one of the most fundamental ever asked by humans; indeed, we are the only species we know to pose it. Prior to modern science, this type of question was only addressed in myths and religion. The astonishing notion that we can say anything about the origin of the universe—and even more, where it is going—is very recent in human history. And while biology and geology have much to say, it is in astronomy where we seat the discipline of cosmology, the science of ultimate origins.

This chapter is therefore devoted to these ultimate questions: How did it all begin? How old is the universe? What will be its ultimate fate? Are there other universes (indeed, does this concept even make sense)? Perhaps surprisingly, we already know a great deal, but of course also have much yet to learn about where we come from.

Before we begin, it will help for us to go over some ground previously covered. Modern cosmology tells us that all matter and energy once inhabited a space smaller than the head of a pin, an absurd statement to say the least. Why do astronomers think this to be true? We start by revisiting the notion of a scientific theory.

KEY TERMS

Abundances of elements: The relative amounts of elements in the universe. Hydrogen and helium, the most popular of elements, were produced in the first few minutes of the universe

Accelerating universe: The notion that the universe is not only expanding, but that its speed of expansion is increasing

Big Bang: The nickname given to modern cosmology, most often associated with the first moments of the universe

Closed universe: The notion that, if the mass density of the universe is high enough, that the universe will eventually stop expanding and start contracting

COBE (Cosmic Background Explorer): A satellite launched in 1990 that made detailed observations of the CMBR and established the Hubble Constant with precision (see *CMBR, John Mather*)

Cosmological microwave background radiation (CMBR): Radiation, originally emitted when the universe was about 400,000 years old, that now is detectable as microwaves

Cosmology: The study of the beginning and end of the universe (see *Recombination*)

Dark energy: An unknown substance which is thought to be responsible for the acceleration of the universe

Dark matter: An unknown substance which does not interact with light and is thought to exert enough gravity to hold galaxies and galaxy clusters together

Electromagnetism: A force that can be either repulsive or attractive, has infinite range, and affects all objects possessing electric charges. One of the four fundamental forces of nature

False vacuum: A state of matter where the energy density is at its lowest possible value, but also where the state is unstable and liable to spontaneous decay

Fundamental forces: Any of four forces that underlie how all objects behave in nature (see *gravitation, electromagnetism, strong nuclear force, weak nuclear force*)

General relativity: Einstein's theory of gravity; very briefly, the idea that matter warps space/time and that space/time informs how matter moves

Gravitation: A force that is solely attractive, has infinite range, and affects all objects with mass and/or energy. One of the four fundamental forces of nature

Homogeneous (also cited as the **homogeneity problem**): The notion in cosmology that one's surroundings are the same no matter where one is

Hubble's constant: A measure of the rate of expansion of the universe, expressed as a speed per distance (often in km/s/Mpc)

Hubble's Law (a.k.a. the **Hubble-Lemaître Law**): A mathematical relationship between the speed of a receding cosmological object and its distance from us

Inflation: The notion that the universe underwent an incredibly rapid expansion in its first few moments

Isotropic: The notion in cosmology that the universe looks the same in and from all directions

Multiverse: The notion, supported by quantum mechanics, that our universe might be only one of a potentially infinite number of universes

Olbers' paradox: A simple question, "Why is the sky dark at night?" that leads to profound conclusions regarding the nature of the universe

Open universe: The notion that, if the mass density of the universe is not high enough, that the universe will continue to expand forever

Planck time: The earliest moment of the universe when we have anything reasonable to say about its conditions; conversely, when gravity was united (we think) with the other fundamental forces of nature. Or, 10^{-43} seconds

Principle of equivalence: Einstein's discovery that the effects of gravity and acceleration give the same results

Quark: A type of elementary particle. Quarks combine to form protons and neutrons. Quarks today are always bound together, but were free in the first few minutes of the Big Bang

Recombination: Occurred when the universe was approximately 400,000 years old, when electrons were able to recombine with atomic nuclei to form atoms (see *cosmological microwave background radiation*)

Special relativity: Einstein's theory of how objects move at speeds close to the speed of light. Does not include how gravity affects objects (see *general relativity*)

Strong nuclear force (also just **strong force**): A force that is attractive, is limited in range to atomic nuclei and smaller, and affects particles such as protons and neutrons (but not electrons). One of the four fundamental forces of nature

Theory: As used in science, a mental model and/or explanation of a natural process supported by enormous amounts of evidence

Type Ia supernovae: A specific type of exploding star that is virtually always the same size bomb, making it an excellent indicator of distances to far-away galaxies

Uncertainty principle: The notion that we cannot measure the energy of an object and the duration of its existence both perfectly well. Usually only matters at the subatomic level

Weak nuclear force (also just **weak force**): A force that is repulsive, is limited in range to atomic nuclei and smaller, and affects select particles such as certain atomic nuclei. One of the four fundamental forces of nature

KEY INDIVIDUALS

Eddington, Arthur: A British astronomer of the early 20th century who, among other discoveries, performed observations of a total solar eclipse in 1919 that confirmed Einstein's theory of general relativity

Einstein, Albert: A German-American physicist of the early 20th century who, among other discoveries, devised the special and general theories of relativity

Guth, Alan: An American physicist of the late 20th/early 21st century who, among others, suggested that the universe underwent an inflationary period of expansion very early in its existence

Heisenberg, Werner: A German physicist of the early 20th century who discovered the uncertainty principle in quantum mechanics

Hubble, Edwin: An American astronomer of the early 20th century who compiled spectral observations of galaxies arguing for the expansion of the universe

Humason, Milton: An American astronomer of the early 20th century who worked with Hubble to discover the expansion of the universe

Kitcher, Philip: An American philosopher of the late 20th century who discussed properties of scientific theories

Lemaître, Georges: A Belgian Catholic priest of the early 20th century who was the first to realize that general relativity suggests the universe must be expanding

Linde, Alexei: A Russian astronomer of the late 20th/early 21st century who, like Alan Guth, suggested the universe underwent an inflationary period of expansion very early in its existence

Mather, John: An American astronomer of the late 20th/early 21st century who headed up the COBE satellite project that examined the CMBR in detail (see *COBE, CMBR*)

Olbers, Heinrich Wilhelm: A German scientist of the early 19th century who first posed the question, "Why is the sky dark at night?"

Pensias, Arno: An American electrical engineer of the mid-20th century working for Bell Labs who, with Robert Wilson, discovered the CMBR (see *cosmological microwave background radiation*)

Smoot, George: An American astronomer of the late 20th/early 21st century who, with John Mather, worked on measurements of the CMBR

Whewell, William: An English philosopher of the early 19th century who invented terms such as "scientist," "physicist" and "consilience," and who emphasized the role of induction in the formation of scientific theories

Wilson, Robert: An American electrical engineer of the mid-20th century working for Bell Labs who, with Arno Pensias, discovered the CMBR (see *cosmological microwave background radiation*)

Section 23.1: Revisiting Scientific Theories

Prior to the early 1990s, the universe was assumed by most to be static (unchanging) and eternal. It is easy to forget the strangeness of the revolutionary idea of an origin of the universe, since virtually all astronomers now recognize that the universe had a beginning, but this was a watershed moment in the history of science. Throw in the complimentary idea that all space and matter was once concentrated into a point of infinite density and temperature, and what sticks out is the absurdity of it all. Why would anyone believe such fanciful notions? Or (to get "meta" about it), what is a scientific theory in the first place?

We originally covered scientific theories in chapter 3 when comparing astronomy (a science) to astrology (a pseudo, or fake, science). Here, we wish to discuss scientific theories in the context of the Big Bang, our nickname for modern cosmology. Previously, we made the following points:

+ A scientific theory is a comprehensive explanation and/or model for a natural process
+ A scientific theory offers a unified and consistent method for solving problems and making predictions

+ A scientific theory can be tested via observations and/or experiments (it is "falsifiable"), so that if it is wrong, or has sections of it that are wrong or incomplete, these issues can be identified
+ A scientific theory is "fecund"; that is, it not only addresses current questions, but also opens up new questions for investigation and study

Much of this cribs from the writings of Philip Kitcher (b. 1947), a British philosopher of science currently affiliated with the University of Minnesota. With these guidelines in mind, how is it that modern astronomers accept the Big Bang theory of cosmology? We will visit these in more detail as this chapter progresses, but we can preview our arguments:

+ The theoretical basis for the Big Bang starts with Einstein's theory of general relativity. General relativity is a geometric treatment of space and time (or "space/time," which are linked together in Einstein's view). Simply put, objects with mass and/or energy warp the geometry of space; the more massive an object, the stronger its warp. Conversely, objects moving through space/time follow paths in part determined by this warping effect
+ Other theoretical considerations for the Big Bang arise from quantum mechanics, which introduced the uncertainty principle, which in turn allows for the existence of "virtual" particles
+ Evidence for general relativity is found in places such as gravitational lensing effects (first discovered by Arthur Eddington in 1919 for the Sun), details of the orbit of Mercury, gravitational waves, and, interestingly, in modern global positioning satellites (GPS). Your cell phone's map features wouldn't work as well as they do if the Earth's warping of space/time weren't taken into account
+ Evidence for virtual particles is seen in various lab experiments such as the Lamb Shift and the Casimir effect
+ Evidence for the Big Bang proper comes from the following:
  · Observations of the motions of distant galaxies
  · Observations of the development (evolution) of galaxies over time
  · The cosmic microwave background radiation
  · Abundances of elements
  · Origins of fundamental forces

It is worth noting that the evidence is overwhelming. It is not merely that a few astronomers saw a few galaxies moving away from us and then leaped to the conclusion that the universe is expanding. Rather, we have nearly a century of hundreds of thousands, if not millions, of observations taken by thousands of astronomers showing this effect. Consider quasars, relics of ancient galactic activity. Quasars are only seen hundreds of millions to billions of light years away, meaning we are viewing them as they were hundreds of millions to billions of years ago. Yet, we also don't see quasars at the very beginning of the universe either; quasars came into existence long ago, lived for a long time, but eventually died out and/or transformed themselves into less exotic objects. We would not expect to see this if the universe were static and unchanging.

The combination of so many observations that "jump" to a conclusion was given the term "consilience" by the philosopher William Whewell (1794–1866), who also invented labels such as "scientist" and "physicist."[1] The notion of induction in science, that we build our models from the bottom up based on evidence from observations and experiment, owes much to him. Bear all this in mind as we introduce modern cosmology.

Section 23.2: Olbers' Paradox and Einstein's Lens

We start our study of cosmology by asking a simple question: Why is the sky dark at night? Or, conversely, why isn't the night sky bright?

---

[1] Whewell also invented several terms used in the physics of electricity, such as "ion," "anode," and "cathode."

While this has occurred to many people over human history, the person most famously associated with it is Heinrich Wilhelm Olbers (1758–1840), an astronomer from what is now Germany. In its modern form, we can phrase the situation as so: Assume the universe is (a) infinite in size, (b) infinite in age, and (c) homogeneous and isotropic, which is a fancy way of saying the universe behaves and looks the same from any location. If these conditions are met, then no matter where we look, we should see the surface of a star. It doesn't matter how small the star appears to us, since there are an infinite number of them, evenly spread out. It also doesn't matter how distant the star, because we have an infinite amount of time for its light to reach us. Therefore, no matter where we look, we should see the surface of a star; ergo, the night sky should be bright, not dark.

FIGURE 23.1. Olbers' paradox. If there are a small number of stars, they don't cover much of the night sky, and the overall effect is that the sky is dark. The more stars we have, and the longer we have for their light to reach us, the more of the sky is covered with stars. In a homogeneous, infinite universe, the night sky should be completely covered with stars.

The night sky <u>is</u> dark, of course, but why? One or more of the conditions hasn't been met: Either the universe is not infinite in size, not infinite in age, or not homogeneous and/or isotropic, or a combination thereof. But this implies an important result: It is unlikely that the universe is eternal; instead, it is more likely the universe had a beginning.

This question lay more or less dormant (with exceptions) for about a century. In order to answer it, we need both a deeper understanding of the shape of the universe and how objects inside it behave, both which needed to wait until the early decades of the 20th century for answers.

The first hint of a finite universe came about as a consequence of Einstein's general relativity. First published in 1915, it states the relationship between gravity and geometry. For example, acceleration due to gravity is indistinguishable from acceleration due to a change of motion, something Einstein called the *principle of equivalence*. Einstein illustrated it thus: Imagine you are in a spaceship, with no windows or other ways to detect the outside world. You can't tell the difference between gravity pulling you down on the Earth versus an equal amount of acceleration of the spaceship traveling upward.

Now, Einstein said, suppose a beam of light (nowadays we would say a laser) shines horizontally across the spaceship. In the case of the moving spaceship, because it is accelerating, and because the speed of light is finite, the beam will appear to bend downward as the ship moves. But if gravity and acceleration due to motion are indistinguishable, the beam will also bend downward in the same fashion if the spaceship is on the surface. Gravity and acceleration are equivalent.

From this, Einstein concluded that space (or more properly, space/time, since he found they are inextricably linked) is bent by the presence of mass, which, as we have discussed throughout this textbook, is the source of gravity. Conversely, he also discovered that objects—and we can include photons of light here—follow the curvature of space/time. The reason we are "held" to the surface of the Earth is not because, as Newton said, there is a force

FIGURE 23.2. Einstein's principle of equivalence. Inside a sealed spaceship, whether it is accelerating upward (left) or at rest on the surface of a planet (right), a beam of light will slightly bend downward.

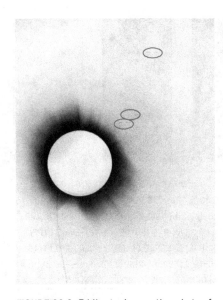

FIGURE 23.3. Eddington's negative photo of the total solar eclipse of 1919. The Sun is a white disk and its corona black streamers surrounding it. Indicated in red are some of Eddington's identifications of background stars.

of gravity between the Earth and us; rather, in Einstein's view, you feel a tendency to naturally follow the curvature of space around the Earth due to its large mass. In everyday life these two interpretations give us the same results, but Einstein's is the more accurate when dealing with astronomical bodies.

Of course, Einstein needed something more specific than a "thought experiment" to convince the scientists of his day. The amount of deflection of a beam of light was at the time too small to see in a laboratory setting, so he needed an extreme source of gravity. The Sun is the largest body in our solar system, and its gravity should warp space/time around it, deflecting starlight from its normal "straight" path to us. The Sun is too bright for us to see stars near it, but once every few years the Earth experiences a total solar eclipse. Arthur Eddington, the famous British astronomer, undertook an expedition to the island of Principe, off the western coast of Africa, to take pictures of a total solar eclipse and hopefully be able to spot the deflection of starlight. In the event, most of his images were not useful, but he was able to see enough to verify Einstein's predictions. Follow-up observations by various astronomers over the next decade convinced the scientific community of the veracity of Einstein's theory, and incidentally make him a worldwide celebrity in the process.

Einstein suggested that distant galaxies should also be capable of deflecting starlight due to their large masses but doubted their effects would be bright enough to ever be detected, an effect termed *gravitational lensing*. For a change, we can say Einstein was not foresighted enough. Gravitational lensing effects due to galaxies (and clusters of galaxies) have been observed since the 1970s, and astronomers now find them rather easily, all things considered, with the improvements since then in both equipment and computer modeling. Gravitational lensing has even been used to search for objects such as black holes and exoplanets within the Milky Way. Further, other types of observations—the precession of the orbit of Mercury, or the detection of gravitational waves by the LIGO project—also tell us that Einstein's version of gravity is correct.

Check Your Neighbor

General relativity states that masses warp space and space tells masses how to move. What do you think this implies about the motions of masses in space?

Einstein himself realized an important consequence of his theory of gravity. If the universe has even one object with mass inside it, and this is most definitely the case, then space (or, again, space/time) isn't stable. As an analogy, think of a baseball thrown into the air: It is either going up or coming down, depending on

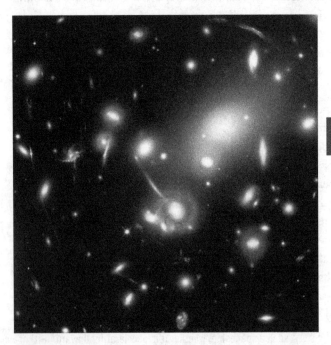

FIGURE 23.4. An image of a distant cluster of galaxies taken by the Hubble Space Telescope. Credit: NASA.

when you look. Gravity in both cases is acting to pull the ball back down to the ground. Extrapolate this to the entire universe, and the universe should either be growing (i.e., "going up") or shrinking (i.e., "coming down").

The prevailing view at the time, as mentioned earlier, was that the universe was eternal and static. Einstein thought the notion of a universe that changes size to be ridiculous. But his equation that governed the overall behavior of the universe required change to occur. To ensure the universe to be static, he introduced a "cosmological constant"—designated by the capital Greek letter lambda, or "Λ"—to exert a counterbalancing force.

This all went mostly unnoticed until a previously unknown Catholic priest and part-time lecturer of physics in Leuven, Belgium, published a review of the consequences of general relativity in 1927. Georges Lemaître (1894–1966) derived the expansion of the universe from Einstein's theory and estimated the rate of expansion, work done a few years before Hubble's observations came to light. Even more, Lemaître ran the clock backward; that is, he considered what now sounds obvious: If the universe is getting larger as we progress into the future, it must have been smaller in the past. Eventually, if we go back far enough in time, the universe must have all been concentrated into a single tiny object, which Lemaître called a "cosmic egg" and a "primeval atom."

FIGURE 23.5. A portrait of Arthur Stanley Eddington (left; artist unknown); a statue of Georges Lemaitre (right; Place des Sciences, Louvain, Belgium).

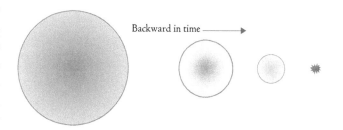

Backward in time ⟶

FIGURE 23.6. Lemaître's proposed "cosmic egg." If we run the clock back in time, the universe must have been smaller and smaller, until we reach a moment where the universe theoretically had no size whatsoever.

But in order for new ideas to be accepted in science—especially ideas apparently as outlandish as a point-sized "cosmic egg"—we need evidence. While Lemaître was publishing his theoretical work, another group was gathering the necessary data to prove him correct.

Section 23.3: Motions of the Galaxies

Edwin Powell Hubble (1889–1953) was raised in a variety of towns and cities in the Midwest and was better known for his athletic rather than his intellectual prowess while growing up; for example, he led the University of Chicago's basketball team to its first conference title in 1907. As a concession to his father's wishes, his early academic career had him concentrating on law rather than astronomy, to which he always had a strong interest. Upon his father's death in 1913, he spent a year as a high school teacher of a variety of subjects, then entered into graduate school in work toward a doctorate in astronomy at Yerkes Observatory outside William's Bay in Wisconsin. World War I accelerated his studies—he earned his Ph.D. before being called overseas—and

FIGURE 23.7. Edwin Hubble.

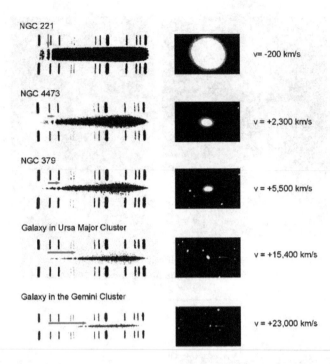

NGC 221

v= -200 km/s

NGC 4473

v = +2,300 km/s

NGC 379

v = +5,500 km/s

Galaxy in Ursa Major Cluster

v = +15,400 km/s

Galaxy in the Gemini Cluster

v = +23,000 km/s

FIGURE 23.8. Humason's comparison of the redshifts of various galaxies. Credit: Humason/NASA.

he served as an officer in an infantry unit, though he never saw combat. After the war, he spent a year in Cambridge (on what we might now call a "post-doc" appointment) before taking a position at Mount Wilson Observatory outside Pasadena, California, in 1919. He would later serve as a researcher for the U.S. Army during World War II, developing (for example) a high-speed camera that could analyze bombs and missiles in flight, leading to improvements in weapons design and performance.

Hubble's 1917 Ph.D. thesis had concerned itself with photography of nebulae, a topic which he continued to pursue, and which involved him in one of the premier arguments of the day, whether the Milky Way was equal to the universe or not (chapter 22). He arrived at Mt. Wilson during the completion of a new 100-inch reflecting telescope, then the largest in the world. Following the work of Henrietta Swan Leavitt (chapter 13) on Cepheid variables, he discovered several residing in the Andromeda "Nebula," as it was then known, and realized the nebula was too far away to be part of the Milky Way. This discovery, besides its connotations for cosmology, was important since it showed that other galaxies exist, and in fact is when the term "galaxy" itself took on a separate meaning from "universe."

Combining his findings with those of another astronomer, Vesto Slipher, and Hubble's assistant Milton Humason (1891–1972), a former mule-team driver who had helped cart equipment up Mt. Wilson to construct the telescope in the first place, Hubble made a series of important discoveries regarding these brand-new nebulae or "galaxies."

+ With the exceptions of a few nearby galaxies, all galaxies show redshifts in their spectra
+ Furthermore, the larger the distance to the galaxy, the greater the redshift

Figure 23.8 shows a series of spectra published by Humason in 1936. Each galaxy's spectrum shows both the rainbow of visible light from the galaxy (note the images are negatives) and various spectral lines. The horizontal axis depicts wavelength, increasing to the right. "Calibration" lines are photographed above and below each galactic spectrum, for comparison to laboratory (i.e., stationary) conditions. In the spectrum of NGC 221 (top image), the red arrow points to a particular spectral line of hydrogen gas. The line is almost at the same location as the calibration line; in fact, in this case the line is to the left (shorter wavelength) of the calibration line, meaning NGC is actually approaching us.

As we go down the figure, we see the line is moving to the right (longer wavelengths) for each galaxy. In each case, the red arrow now points to the right, showing the amount of shift from the stationary calibration line. When we get to the bottom of the figure, the line has shifted so much as to be halfway across the spectrum.

How to interpret these results? The simplest way to make a spectral line shift is via the Doppler effect (chapter 14). To recap, if a stationary object emits waves (light qualifies) then observers see its spectrum at the same wavelengths it emits (i.e., nothing changes). If an object is moving toward us (or we are moving toward it; it doesn't matter who does the moving), the spectrum we perceive is shifted toward shorter wavelengths, an effect astronomers nickname "blueshift." If the object is moving away from us (again, it doesn't matter who moves), the spectrum we perceive is shifted toward longer wavelengths, which is nicknamed "redshift." The amount of redshift (or blueshift) increases with increasing speed.

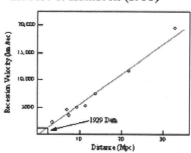

FIGURE 23.9. Hubble's original plot of recessional velocities versus distance (left) and the updated version by Hubble & Humason. Credit: NASA/ The StarChild Team.

Hubble and Humason therefore were able to draw the following conclusions:

+ With the exceptions of a few nearby galaxies, all galaxies are moving away from us.
+ Furthermore, the larger the distance to the galaxy, the greater the speed.

The speeds of galaxies and their distances can be plotted (Figure 23.9), showing what appears to be a very simple relationship. The formula that describes this is commonly known as *Hubble's law*:

Equation 23.1

$$v = H_0 d$$

where v is the velocity (recessional speed) of the galaxy expressed in kilometers per second, d is the distance to the galaxy in millions of parsecs ("megaparsecs", or Mpc), and H_0 is a new quantity called the *Hubble Constant*. The Hubble Constant relates the rate at which the galaxies are moving away from us at this time in cosmological history (note we would get a different value of H_0 if we were observing many millions of years in the past or future). Hubble and Humason's value of H_0 was significantly off, but astronomers have worked diligently over the past several decades to determine its value with a good amount of precision. Modern values of H_0 tend to cluster between 68 and 72 km/s/Mpc; we will adopt 70 for our purposes, knowing this will likely be further updated.

We can turn Hubble's law around to estimate distances to galaxies. The recessional speed of a galaxy is relatively easy to determine from its spectrum, but distance, as we have discussed many times in this text, is much more difficult. If we have a precise value for the Hubble Constant, we can use it to find distances to galaxies and other extragalactic objects.

Sample Calculation

In Figure 23.8, Humason estimated the speed of NGC 379 to be 5,500 km/s. Assuming that is correct, how far away from us is NGC 379?

Solution: Rearrange Hubble's law to solve for distance and plug in the values of the speed and the Hubble Constant:

$$d = \frac{v}{H_0} = \frac{5500 \text{ km/s}}{70 \frac{\text{km}}{\text{s}} / \text{Mpc}} = 79 \text{ Mpc}$$

Because of the theoretical contributions made by Georges Lemaître prior to the publication of Hubble's results, the International Astronomical Union in 2018 suggested renaming the formula the *Hubble-Lemaître Law.*

What is the redshift of NGC 379?

From chapter 14, we learned that the redshift of an astronomical object is given by

$$z = \frac{\Delta\lambda}{\lambda_0} = \frac{v}{c}$$

(This applies only when the redshift is small). The speed of NGC 379 was 5,500 km/s and the speed of light is 300,000 km/s, so the redshift is then

$$z = \frac{v}{c} = \frac{5500 \text{ km/s}}{300,000 \text{ km/s}} = 0.0183$$

If the red spectral line of hydrogen (656 nm) is used from NGC 379 to calculate its redshift, at which wavelength would it be?

The shift (change) in the wavelength is

$$\Delta\lambda = \lambda_0 z = (656 \text{ nm})(0.0183) = 12.0 \text{ nm}$$

But also, by definition, the change in wavelength is the difference between the observed and the lab (original) wavelength, so

$$\lambda = \lambda_0 + \Delta\lambda = 656 \text{ nm} + 12 \text{ nm} = 668 \text{ nm}$$

We note that, in practice, astronomers find the observed wavelength first, and go from there. We ran it backward here to show where results (like the 5,500 km/s recessional speed) come from.

Section 23.4: Expansion of the Universe

The modern interpretation of Lemaitre's theoretical work and Hubble's observations is that the universe itself is expanding, carrying galaxies and other extragalactic objects along with it, much like the flow of a river carries bits of debris downstream.

Not every scientist was enthusiastic about this. Hubble himself occasionally expressed doubts about the expansion idea. The most vocal of critics was a British astronomer named Fred Hoyle (1915–2001), who in 1949 mocked the idea of a beginning to the universe during a radio interview as a "Big Bang." As sometimes happens, a previously derogatory term (Hoyle and his opponents argued over how the term was viewed) was co-opted and now the Big Bang is the accepted term for the rapid expansion of the universe.[2]

When discussing the Big Bang, cosmologists often resort to a variety of analogies. The reason for this approach isn't because they are intentionally unclear; rather, the Big Bang is far removed from our everyday experiences and isn't easily understood. One of the ideas involves four physical dimensions.

---

[2] And, of course, the term has been incorporated into a highly successful sitcom of the 2010s.

If we run the clock backward, all the universe should end up at a single point, or center. But where is that center today? Recall Hubble's observations:

+ Distant galaxies are all moving away from us.
+ The larger the distance to the galaxy, the greater the speed.

This implies two possible results. One is that <u>we</u> are at the center. Since we see the same results in all directions, the only preferred position is the one we already hold. Astronomers are understandably reluctant to reach such a conclusion, though, since every other time our species thought it was at the center of everything (recall the geocentric versus heliocentric debate highlighted in chapter 3), we've found out we were wrong.

Another interpretation is that we are just like everybody else. Every observer in every other galaxy will see the same

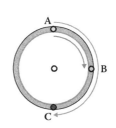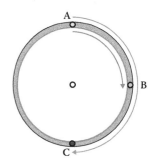

FIGURE 23.10. Suppose students (colored dots) make a ring around their instructor (central white dot). Students start by measuring the distance to their neighbors along the ring (left). The red arched arrow represents the closer pair of students (A and B) and the blue arrow a farther pair (A and C). Then the students expand the size of the ring (right). Not only have the distances between pairs of students increased, but the farther pair moved apart by more than the closer pair.

general behaviors: galaxies moving away from them, and the farther galaxies moving at faster speeds. There is no "center" in such a picture, then. Rather, the center—if there is one in the first place—is inaccessible to us. Let's consider a simple exercise to explore the consequences:

Imagine students form a perfectly circular ring surrounding their instructor (imagine doing this in a large space, like a gym or field). We want to measure the distance from one student to another, but with a catch: They can only measure distances <u>along</u> the ring, not across. Let's focus on one student's measurements. Student A notes that student B is currently 6 feet away and that student C is currently 12 feet away. Then the instructor has the students all step backward, so that the circle has expanded. Now student A notes student B is 15 feet away and student C is 30 feet away.

Speed is defined as the <u>change</u> of distance over change of time. The change of student B's distance from A is then (15 − 6) feet or 9 feet. But the change of student C's distance from A is (30 − 12) feet or 18 feet. From student A's perspective, student C covered more ground in the same time as student B, so student C moved faster than student B.

This is thought to be similar to our situation in cosmology: Simply increase the number of physical dimensions in the story. Our ring analogy shows students only allowed to observe events along the ring—one dimension, if you will—whereas the instructor, at the center of the ring, is inaccessible in two dimensions. In astronomy, we can observe galaxies in three-dimensional space, but the "center" of the universe is inaccessible in a fourth physical dimension.

Why would we think that the universe can possess another physical dimension beyond the three that we perceive? Recall Einstein's general relativity. Its major statement is that mass warps space. Now we can add that extra piece: Space (or space/time) is warped into a fourth physical dimension. We can't see this fourth dimension directly, but we can observe its effects via gravity.

Another analogy might help. Suppose we want to make a loaf of banana bread with pieces of walnut inside.[3] The bits of walnut are well mixed inside the batter, but otherwise are stuck inside it. After baking, the bread has expanded, carrying the pieces of walnut along with it. The walnuts haven't changed size, nor have they moved on their own; they simply have been carried along for

Check Your Neighbor

What other analogies or activities can you think of to get across the idea of the expansion of the universe?

_____

[3] If you're not fond of banana-nut bread, feel free to bake your own.

FIGURE 23.11. Banana walnut bread expands as it bakes, enlarging the distances between individual bits of walnut. Credit: Whitney.

the ride. Further, every walnut will "see" the same results when they look at other walnuts; nearby walnuts haven't moved very far, whereas distant walnuts have moved far away indeed.

One more thing: Hubble's constant can be used to estimate the age of the universe. If we look closely at the units for the Hubble constant, we see that distance units are in both the numerator and the denominator, and the result ultimately is inverse time units. We have to do some work to change units to get sensible answers, but this can be done.

Sample Calculation

Invert Hubble's constant in order to estimate the age of the universe. Use $H_0 = 70$ km/s/Mpc.

We need to first display megaparsecs (Mpc) in units of kilometers. Let's take a shortcut by assuming one parsec is the same as 3.086×10^{16} meters. Since "mega" is the prefix for "million," or 10^6, a megaparsec then equals 3.086×10^{22} meters.

Next, we note that the Hubble constant makes use of seconds for its time unit. But years are preferable, here. Let's take another shortcut by noting 1 year $= 3.156 \times 10^7$ seconds. So now

$$\text{age of universe} = \frac{1}{H_0} = \left(\frac{1}{70 \dfrac{\text{km}}{\text{s}}} \right) \left(\frac{3.086 \times 10^{22}\,\text{km}}{\text{Mpc}} \right) \left(\frac{1\,\text{year}}{3.156 \times 10^7\,\text{s}} \right) = \mathbf{14.0 \times 10^9\ years}$$

Extra considerations put the universe's current age at 13.8 billion years, so our quick estimate is not too far off.

Section 23.5: The Timeline of the Universe

We have enough background to begin discussing the development of the universe in detail. Since we know the most about our current time, we will start at the present and work our way backward. In the process, we will encounter several milestones in the life of the universe, some of which you may recognize.

1. The Current Time

The largest individual structures currently in the universe are galaxies. As we have seen (chapter 22), galaxies come in a variety of shapes and sizes but all share the same general theme of being constructed out of billions or more stars. Virtually all the various types of objects we have discussed in this text—from planets to globular clusters—live in some galaxy or another.

When we look at galaxies, we see evidence of maturity. Elliptical galaxies exhibit overall yellowish colors, indicating stars on the order of 10 billion years old or so. Spirals tend to have distinct arms and bars, with their globular clusters having sifted out of the rest of the galaxies. Even irregular galaxies, with no generally discernable shapes,

TABLE 23.1. Milestones in the History of the Universe

Time	Temperature	Event
0?	Infinite?	The beginning
10^{-43} s	10^{32} K	Planck time; all forces united
10^{-35} s	10^{27} K	Separation of strong force from electroweak force
10^{-11} s	10^{15} K	Separation of electromagnetism from weak force
~10 min	10^9 K	Formation of protons, neutrons and helium nuclei
~380 kyr	3000 K	Formation of atoms, recombination epoch
~500 Myr	~100 K	Formation of first stars, first galaxies
13.8 Gyr	3 K	Today

show evidence of past collisions and high metallicities, telling us they have been around for lengthy amounts of time.

Galaxies are ancient objects. The currently oldest galaxy known goes back to a time when the universe was "only" 400 million years old. To put that in perspective, 400 million years out of the 13.8 billion years of the current age of the universe means that the universe was only 3% of its way toward our time when galaxies first began forming. Galaxies were just then in the beginnings of their formations, and collisions between nascent galaxies were frequent. Associated objects that depend on collisions—such as quasars—are also seen at these ancient times.

Interstellar—or even intergalactic; that is, between the galaxies—space has a temperature. Some of this is from stars, of course, which emit light and heat, but stars are amazingly small compared to the vastness of space and don't really contribute much (think of the average temperature of an object like Neptune, which is only 1/2000th of the way to the next nearest star). Rather, space is filled with radiation left over from the initial Big Bang, giving it an overall temperature of about 2.7 K.

The story is famous in the history of astronomy. The 1960s were still relatively early in the use of radio transmitters and receivers, and the major telecommunications companies of the day were always interested in improvements. Bell Labs constructed a radio horn antenna (see Figure 23.13) in Holmdel, New Jersey, to test radio com-

FIGURE 23.12. Abell 2744, also known as Pandora's cluster, from the Hubble Space Telescope. Credit: NASA, ESA, and R. Dupke (Eureka Scientific Inc.) et al.

Check Your Neighbor

How old were you when you were 3% of your current age? Does this give you some perspective on how to view the universe when it was that old?

munications, including searching for sources of interference. Two Bell Lab engineers, Arno Penzias (b. 1933) and Robert Wilson (b. 1936), kept encountering interference around a wavelength of 7.5 cm. The interference was about a hundred times what they expected given terrestrial sources; it persisted regardless of weather conditions; it came from all locations in the sky; and it persisted whether it was day or night. They checked their equipment thoroughly (even to the extent of cleaning bird droppings from the antenna!), but the interference would not go away.

FIGURE 23.13. Arno Penzias and Robert Wilson stand with the radio horn antenna they used to discover the Cosmic Microwave Background Radiation. Credit: NASA.

Ironically, some astronomers had been working on the problem from the theoretical side. Less than 40 miles away at Princeton University (also in New Jersey), a team of astronomers led by Robert Dicke, Jim Peebles, and David Wilkinson were preparing their own radio experiment to search for background radiation. Serendipitously, Penzias and Wilson learned about the astronomers' upcoming experiment, realized the importance of their own discovery, and contacted the Princeton astronomers. Working together, the astronomers and engineers published a pair of papers discussing the theory behind the background radiation and their new measurements. Penzias and Wilson, despite not being physicists or astronomers themselves, won the Nobel Prize in physics in 1969 for this work.

What exactly did they discover? Some scientists had for several decades prior realized that the early universe must have been extremely hot and would release radiation (primarily in the near-infrared) at a specific time in its history. This radiation, like the light from galaxies, would be redshifted to longer wavelengths and would be detectable as radio waves (or microwaves) filling the sky. The radiation would correspond to a background temperature as well, much like a black body (chapter 14), though estimates of that temperature were much too high. Nevertheless, it remains one of the triumphs of 20th-century science and provides a key piece of evidence for the Big Bang.

2. The Recombination Epoch

When was this radiation released, and why? It comes from the notion that what we consider an "atom" is really a combination of particles. The simplest atom, hydrogen, has an electron in orbit about a proton. But if the temperature is too high, the electron will have too much energy too remain in orbit and won't "combine" with the proton to form an atom. Instead of atoms, the early universe was a mixture of protons, electrons, and various other particles.

As we know from earlier studies (chapters 10 and 17, for example), if a gas is forced to expand, its temperature will drop. The early universe started as an incredibly hot gas of elementary particles, but eventually expanded enough so that its temperature dropped to a point where electrons could permanently join with protons (or helium nuclei) to form permanent atoms. When an electron does this, it needs to emit a photon. Most of the photons emitted at this time were in the near infrared, though some would have been visible light. The temperature for this to happen for hydrogen is about 3,000 K (over 5,000°F), and since 90% of all atomic nuclei were protons (hydrogen), this process dominated. Electrons began emitting this

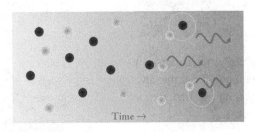

FIGURE 23.14. The early universe was too energetic for electrons (light dots) to bind themselves to protons (dark dots). Only when the temperature dropped to about 3,000 K, at an age of 380,000 years, were electrons able to join protons to form atoms. In the process, they released photons which we now see as the CMBR.

light when the universe was approximately 380,000 years old.[4] Since that time, the universe has expanded by about 1,000 times, and the temperature has dropped (as we saw) to an overall temperature of just under 3 K. The radiation we see from the recombination epoch, the microwaves detected by Penzias and Wilson, is titled the *cosmic microwave background radiation* (*CMBR* for short).

The sky is very smooth when it comes to the CMBR. A succession of satellites has made detailed observations, the first of which was the *Cosmic Background Explorer* (*COBE*), launched in 1989, and whose findings won the Nobel Prize in physics for John Mather (b. 1946) and George Smoot (b. 1945). The average temperature of the universe is very precisely known: 2.725 48 +/− 0.000 57 K, which corresponds to a wavelength of about 1 millimeter. The CMBR, despite being invisible to our eyes, is not trivial; some 99.97% of the universe's radiant energy (primarily photons) was emitted during this time. The smoothness of the CMBR is about 1 part per 100,000, which is like saying the Earth is a perfect sphere with its tallest mountain being only about 200 feet tall. The smoothness of the CMBR is so good, in fact, that it demands its own explanation, which we will discuss later in this chapter.

This era is somewhat confusingly called the *recombination epoch*. Electrons were always free to "try" to combine with protons prior to this time, but only when the temperature dropped below 3,000 K were they able to make it permanent, thus "recombination" rather than "combination".

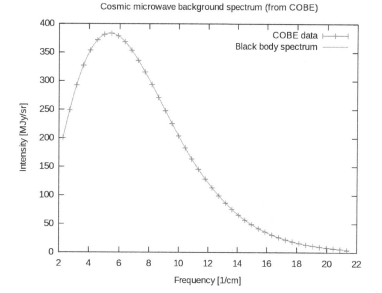

Cosmic microwave background spectrum (from COBE)

FIGURE 23.15. The black body curve of the universe, from the FIRAS instrument of the COBE satellite. The little crosses show the COBE data while the curve is for a black body of temperature 2.715 K. Credit: NASA.

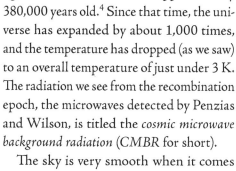
Check Your Neighbor

Given the current age of the universe is 13.8 billion years, and the recombination epoch occurred at an age of 380,000 years, what percentage of the universe's life had passed by when recombination happened? As a follow-up, how old would you have been if you had undergone "recombination" at the same (percentage) moment of your life?

By the way, this comes back to one of our first questions in this chapter: Why is the sky dark at night? It turns out the sky isn't dark at night after all, if you have microwave eyeballs!

3. Creation of the Elements

One of the seminal discoveries of early 20th century astronomy was by Cecelia Payne, who found that stars (and subsequently the universe) consist of 90% hydrogen by number, 9% helium, and 1% everything else.

Let's continue to run the clock further back. Elements are defined by the number of protons in their nuclei: hydrogen is thus element #1, helium element #2, lithium element #3, and so on. We also have isotopes, atomic nuclei where a neutron(s) has been added. Hydrogen can come in its most simple form—one proton only—but also shows up as deuterium (one proton + one neutron in the nucleus) and tritium (one proton + 2 neutrons). Tritium is radioactive, but deuterium is not, and plays a role in the generation of energy via nuclear fusion in the cores of

---

[4] The CMBR was not emitted all at once. Data from the WMAP satellite hints that the process took over 100,000 years to complete.

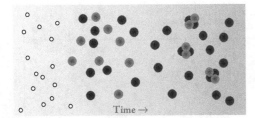

FIGURE 23.16. The very early universe was too energetic for quarks (small white dots) to bind themselves to protons (dark dots) and neutrons (brown dots). Only when the temperature dropped to about 10^9 K, when the universe was a few minutes old, did this become possible. Some helium nuclei (the combinations of 2 dark and 2 brown dots) and traces of other light elements were able to form before the universe's temperature dropped too low to build up heavier elements.

stars (chapter 17). When astronomers look at the stars, they note that 99% of all elements are isotopes of either hydrogen or helium, the two simplest elements. Why is that?

Similar to the questions regarding the CMBR, the temperature needed to be near a certain value for elements to form. Protons and neutrons themselves are not truly fundamental particles; rather, they both are combinations of more basic particles called *quarks*. As there was a time when the universe was too hot for electrons to join with atomic nuclei to form atoms, so there was an even earlier time when it was too hot for quarks to join together to form protons and neutrons. This corresponds to a temperature of the universe around 10^9 K (i.e., 1 trillion K) and an age of a few <u>minutes</u>.

It's even a little more complicated than that. The temperature continued to drop as the universe expanded. Protons and neutrons were not able to form when the temperature was too high; once they were able to form, they were also able to begin nuclear fusion processes. However (as we have seen), the temperatures need to go <u>higher</u>, not lower, as nuclear fusion becomes more and more complex. This meant there was a window of time of just a few minutes where the temperatures were low enough to allow protons and neutrons to form, but high enough to use those particles to make helium and a few other light elements. By the time it was carbon's turn (so to speak), the temperatures had dropped too low to make it. Thus, the universe's proportions of hydrogen and helium were determined rather early on.

4. Separation of the Fundamental Forces

Question: Have you ever dropped an ice cube into a glass of water, and heard (and/or seen) the ice cube suddenly crack? Physicists suspect that fundamental forces of nature behaved in a similar way during the first moments of the Big Bang.

FIGURE 23.17. Left: An ice cube, straight out of the freezer. Right: An ice cube after being dunked in liquid water. Photos by the author.

First, let's refresh our memories regarding the four fundamental forces. Other forces, "pushes" or "pulls," result from combinations of these four. For example, simply sitting on a chair combines gravity pulling you down versus the chair holding you up. The chair's force (called a "normal" force in physics[5]) ultimately comes from electrical repulsion between your atom's outer electrons and those of the chair.

---

[5] By "normal," physicists don't mean an average, well-adjusted-to-life force. Rather, they mean "perpendicular," as in perpendicular to the surface of the object in question, such as a chair. The term is borrowed from mathematics.

Two of these forces are present in our everyday lives: gravity and electromagnetism. *Gravity* is usually a "background" force, in the sense that it's always present and (on the surface of the Earth) always has the same effect. *Electromagnetism* is usually more complicated, but it is ultimately responsible for virtually all the other effects we see: the color of a shirt, the texture of a chair, the sound one hears from a lecture professor droning on about forces. Both have unlimited (infinite) range, though they do diminish with distance. Electromagnetism is far more powerful than gravity—recall how a refrigerator magnet defies the gravity of the entire planet Earth—but also has positive and negative charges, which tend to cancel each other at large distances. Gravity is weak but also only attractive, so gravity tends to win out more often than not for astronomy, whereas electromagnetism dominates at people scales.

TABLE 23.2. The Fundamental Forces of Nature

Name of Force	Range	Action(s)	Relative Strength
Gravity	Infinite	attractive	$\sim 10^{-39}$
Electromagnetism	Infinite	attractive or repulsive	$\sim 1/100$
Strong nuclear	10^{-15} m	attractive	1
Weak nuclear	10^{-17} m	effectively repulsive	$\sim 10^{-7}$

The strong nuclear force acts to hold quarks together inside protons and neutrons, and protons and neutrons together for atomic nuclei. The weak force is responsible for many forms of radioactive decay, which also acts at the scales of atomic nuclei. While essential for matter to exist as we know it, these forces don't usually announce themselves to us, except in certain circumstances like nuclear power plants or bombs. True to its name, the strong force is the strongest of all the fundamental forces. The weak force is significantly weaker than the strong force and the electromagnetic force, though actually much stronger than gravity.

Physicists are often captivated by the search for a "grand unified theory"; that is, a mathematical model that incorporates all the forces together under one banner. The first of these unifications occurred around 1860, when James Clerk Maxwell devised a set of equations linking electricity and magnetism. The next unification occurred when the weak force was linked to electromagnetism in the 1970s, and several versions of unification exist to link the strong force to these two. Only gravity is left on its own, and efforts continue to try to show that gravity and the other forces are really one and the same, just seen under different circumstances.

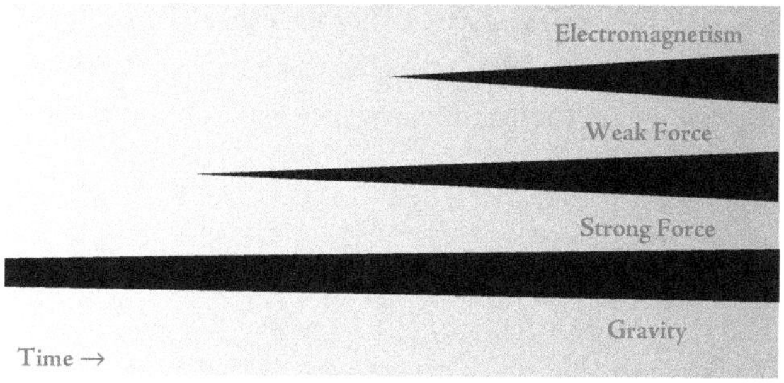

The forces act the same only under intense temperatures and densities. Such conditions are at best simulated by large particle accelerators; to achieve them we need to consider the earliest moments of the universe.

It is difficult to conceive of the conditions of the early universe. The earliest time we can make any reasonable statements about is a mind-boggling 10^{-43} seconds, a limit set due to our inability (yet?) to unite Einstein's general relativity with quantum mechanics. The moment, called the *Planck time*, represents a hard limit to the current state of our knowledge.

In case the scientific notation version of this number doesn't faze you, let's look at it written out in long form:

0.000 000 000 000 000 000 000 000 000 000 000 000 000 000 1

FIGURE 23.18. In the earliest moments of the universe, the four fundamental forces were united. As the universe cooled, the forces separated from each other. Gravity is depicted as separate from the beginning here, as we do not yet have a theory uniting gravity with the others.

It is officially true we don't know what happened at <u>the</u> beginning. But if we're not at zero seconds, we're pretty close!

One prevailing thought is that (assuming this is possible) gravity and the other fundamental forces of nature act as one and the same before this time. The temperature—again, if the concept has any meaning at these values—was an incredible 10^{32} K. After this time, gravity separates from the others and went its own way as a force of nature.

It didn't take long for the other forces to follow suit. The strong force separated out at 10^{-35} seconds and 10^{27} K. The final split between the weak force and electromagnetism occurred around 10^{-11} s and 10^{15} K. From then on, the universe would be governed by four separate fundamental forces.

Cosmologists wonder about the transitions from unified to separated forces. In some ways, these transitions resemble phase changes. Let's return to our ice cubes for a moment. When water is poured into an ice cube tray, it is smooth all the way through. But as the water turns to solid ice inside the freezer, imperfections arise, and the resultant ice cube develops cracks—cracks we can see by suddenly dunking the ice cube in a glass of liquid water. Did the universe undergo such a severe phase change? It's possible; in fact, it's likely.

5. Cosmic Inflation

As stated before, the CMBR is very smooth, to one part in 100,000. This isn't what we would expect from a "simple" Big Bang, though. Here's why:

Einstein also showed—through his theory of *special relativity*—that information cannot travel faster than the speed of light. How does this affect the smoothness issue? Suppose we have two regions in space, separated by a large distance. If they are so far apart that light cannot have traveled between them during the life of the universe, then they cannot "know" what the other region is like and therefore are more likely to be very different. The amount of separation isn't trivial; at the time of the recombination epoch (380,000 years), the universe would have been many tens of millions of light years in diameter. Yet, when we look at the CMBR in opposite parts of the sky, we see almost exactly the same behaviors.

Consider an analogy from history. The Mongol armies of Ghengis Khan were the most effective of his time, allowing him and his heirs to conquer more territory than any other empire on Earth, before or since. A standard tactic of the Mongols was to send separate armies along different paths, then meet together at the target. In order to keep the armies in sync with each other, the Mongols employed fast horses to convey riders continuously back and forth between the armies, allowing for rapid messaging in times long before modern telecommunications. Now suppose one of those armies engaged in sudden battle before the riders could get the information to the other armies.

The armies would no longer be in perfect harmony with each other.

In cosmology, this is called the *homogeneity problem*. The universe, at the largest of scales, shouldn't look the same because there hasn't been enough time for the riders (photons) to convey information back and forth. Yet the universe is smooth, especially in the CMBR. How could this happen?

In 1979, a theoretical physicist at Cornell University named Alan Guth (b. 1947) proposed a detailed model of cosmological inflation. Very early in the history of the universe, it was in a state cosmologists call a *false vacuum*; "vacuum" meaning that it was in the lowest possible energy density, "false" in that it is not a permanent situation, but rather that it is unstable. It is perhaps an unfortunate term for the rest of us, since "vacuum" tends to imply "empty," and the early universe was anything but empty.

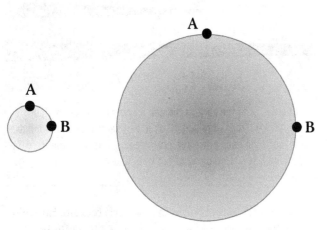

FIGURE 23.19. Cosmic inflation: In an early moment of the universe, points A and B are close enough together that they can share information via light and therefore can appear similar. The universe then underwent an incredibly rapid expansion, which preserved the similarities between A and B, even they are no longer close enough to communicate with each other.

In the process of decaying from its false vacuum state, the universe would expand at a fantastic rate, and also experience a sudden drop in temperature (by a factor of 100,000 or so). The false vacuum would have begun its decay at 10^{-36} seconds and continued until 10^{-32} seconds—an unmeasurable time for us, but not zero. The universe might have expanded by 10^{50} or more times during this incredibly short interval. To follow up with our Mongols analogy, suppose the armies were in direct contact right before a battle, then magically transported in an instant to opposite sides of the opposing forces. The Mongol armies would retain information on how their brethren armies were about to fight, and coordination would still be possible.

Guth's idea has been reworked and modified to account for a variety of issues, most notably by Alexei Linde (b. 1948), a Russian physicist who has spent most of his career at Stanford University in California. Inflation as a theory has several holes left to fill—notably the discovery of a subatomic particle and/or field that can instigate the inflation—but observations from the WMAP satellite in 2006 support the general idea. If true, inflation brings us yet another mind-blowing concept: The visible universe, which is on the order of several tens of billions of light years across, is but the smallest corner of what actually exists. Some estimates from inflation yield a universe on the order of 10^{28} light years across!

Section 23.6: The Future of the Universe

One of our most reliable distance indicators is the Type Ia supernova. Type Ia supernovae originate from the explosions of white dwarfs that exceed their mass limits of 1.44 $M_\odot$ (chapter 18), meaning that a Type Ia supernova is, ideally, always the same-sized bomb (or, in astronomy lingo, a "standard candle"). Since such an event can shine as brightly as a moderately sized galaxy, with its luminosity concentrated in a point of light, we can observe them from almost anywhere in the observable universe.

In 1998, two separate research groups were using Type Ia supernovae to determine distances to far-away galaxies. Inexplicably, the supernovae were dimmer than expected, and the effect was more pronounced for the farther away supernovae. Independently, they came to the same conclusion: The universe is actually larger than previously thought; or, equivalently, the rate of expansion of the universe itself is expanding. The speeding up of the universe's rate of expansion has since been confirmed by further observations of Type Ia supernovae, clustering of galaxies over time, and oscillations of acoustic (sound) waves in the universe. Since scientists use the term "acceleration" to describe the change of an object's velocity, this became the *accelerating universe* model.

The acceleration of the universe brings us back to Einstein and his cosmological constant. While Einstein and his contemporaries considered the inclusion of Λ as an ad-hoc device to keep the universe static, currently we recognize

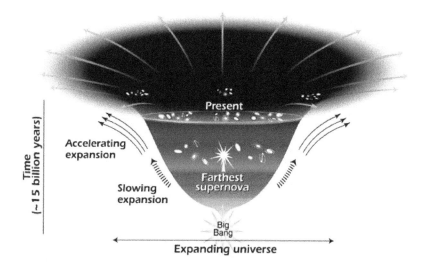

This diagram reveals changes in the rate of expansion since the universe's birth 15 billion years ago. The more shallow the curve, the faster the rate of expansion. The curve changes noticeably about 7.5 billion years ago, when objects in the universe began flying apart at a faster rate. Astronomers theorize that the faster expansion rate is due to a mysterious, dark force that is pushing galaxies apart.

FIGURE 23.20. The expansion of the universe. The direction of time is up. The rate of expansion slowed down until the universe was about 5 billion years old, after which the rate began to increase. Credit: NASA/ESA/Ann Feild (STScI).

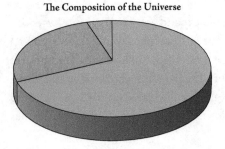

The Composition of the Universe

■ Dark energy ■ Dark matter ■ "Normal" matter

FIGURE 23.21. The relative percentages of dark energy, dark matter, and "normal" matter in the universe.

it represents a new type of behavior ("negative pressure") that is pushing the universe apart. The generic term for the cause of this activity is *dark energy*, which, like dark matter, is simply a place-holding name until we determine its specifics. So far, cosmologists have only detected the consequences of dark energy, but like dark matter do not yet know what it is. It is worth noting that the accelerating universe model is a separate issue from the cosmic inflation of the first moments of the universe.

This situation does present a few entertaining propositions. For example, for the dark energy and dark matter to contribute what is needed to make the universe operate as observed, they must dominate the universe. Approximately 68% of the universe's total mass-energy must consist of dark energy and another 27% consists of dark matter. In other words, the part of the universe we know in everyday life, "normal" matter, only counts for 5% of what exists.

Another issue is the future of the universe. Prior to 1998, cosmologists had debated the end of the universe. The basis of the argument was the amount of gravity (expressed by astronomers as the "mass density") of the universe acting upon itself. If the universe has enough matter, then its gravity will be strong enough to eventually overcome the expansion of the universe and bring it back together, a situation nicknamed the "Big Crunch." If the universe does not have enough matter, then the universe expands forever. Due to cosmic inflation and our moment in time in the history of the universe, the two options have until recently been difficult to tell apart, though most astronomers would probably have leaned toward a forever-expanding universe, albeit one that does slow down due to the universe's self-gravity.

Check Your Neighbor

What do you think the terms "dark energy" and "dark matter" mean? Keep in mind that cosmologists, like most other astronomers and physicists, are very literal people.

Suppose we were to plot the changing size of the universe over time (figure 23.22). The different values of Omega ("Ω") tell us which option we're considering. What would we see? If the universe were to collapse upon itself, we get a curve arcing back down ("$\Omega_M = 6$" in the figure). If the universe continues to expand, but at an ever-slowing rate, we get a virtually straight line ("$\Omega_M = 1$"). If, however, the universe's rate of expansion is indeed accelerating, we get a curve arcing upward ("$\Omega_M = 0.3, \Omega_\Lambda = 0.7$"). Since 1998, the answer appears to be that the universe is expanding, though it's not a completely done deal amongst cosmologists. If the acceleration is true, and does not stop, it will eventually begin to tear apart galaxies, then stars and planets, and even atoms, a fate nicknamed the "Big Rip." Whether a Big Rip is in our future—or any of these options—it is reassuring to know that its potentially baleful effects won't matter until many billions of years into our future.

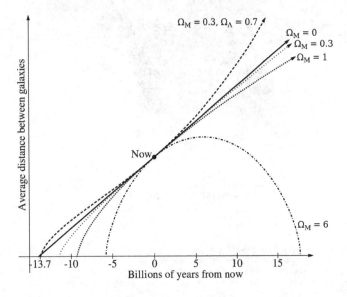

FIGURE 23.22. The size of the universe plotted as a function of time. The different values of Ω refer to different possible outcomes. Note they are difficult to distinguish at our current moment in cosmological history ("Billions of years from now" equaling zero).

Finally, we come to one of the most speculative ideas in all science. A few people—Max Tegmark and Brian Greene are notable popularizers—think that our universe might not be alone. Rather, there exists a large, possibly infinite, number of universes, a concept called the *multiverse*. Although the idea sounds like science fiction, there is some support for the idea from quantum mechanics. Here's an example of how it might work (Figure 23.23):

In quantum mechanics, one of the most important, and strange, properties is called the *uncertainty principle*. One interpretation of it states that we can perfectly measure the amount of energy possessed by a particle, or perfectly measure the time it exists (most subatomic particles are susceptible to radioactive decay), but not both at the same moment. This leads to an odd interpretation: Could there be

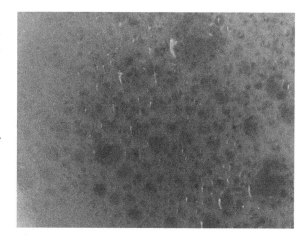

FIGURE 23.23. One version of the multiverse hypothesis is that individual universes "pop" up like bubbles.

particles that "pop" into existence but disappear again before we have time to detect them? Such "virtual particles" sound like a staple of science fiction, but several physical processes and lab experiments show they do exist. The energy to make virtual particles comes from the fabric of space/time itself (which, by the way, is one suggestion as to the source of the acceleration of the universe).

Now suppose conditions allow for one of these virtual particles to stick around; that is, it doesn't disappear or get absorbed by space/time, but instead becomes permanent. Some versions of the beginning of the Big Bang go with this theme, except the virtual particle becomes an entire universe. Furthermore, there is no reason why this can't occur again and again; universes, like virtual particles, may be popping back and forth across a larger continuum. While extremely speculative—and difficult to test!—the mathematics of quantum mechanics makes it a serious possibility, one we should take seriously. Our entire universe may therefore be nothing but an expanding bubble amongst innumerable other bubbles—a sobering thought indeed!

Summary

In this chapter, we did the following:

▸ Revisited the notion of a scientific theory

▸ Reintroduced Einstein's theory of general relativity

▸ Showed how general relativity implies the universe cannot be static

▸ Presented evidence for the expansion of the universe

▸ Recapitulated various milestones in the history of the universe

▸ Reviewed current ideas regarding the acceleration of the universe

▸ Briefly introduced the notion of the multiverse

Questions

1. Which of the following are better supported as scientific theories and which are more speculative?
   + Expansion of the universe
   + Inflation
   + Acceleration
   + Multiverse

2. Einstein's most famous formula is $E = mc^2$, saying that energy is equivalent to mass and vice versa. Consider the Sun: Does the Sun's energy contribute to the overall gravitational influence of the Sun?

3. Starlight passes by the edges of both the Sun and the Earth. In which case does the starlight experience more bending? Briefly defend your answer.

4. Which of the assumptions of Olbers's paradox are likely true and which are likely false?

5. The galaxy NGC 1316 in the constellation of Fornax has a redshift of 0.0587. Assume the Hubble constant has a value of 70 km/s/Mpc.
   + What is the recessional speed of NGC 1316?
   + What is the distance to NGC 1316?

6. 3C 273 was the first quasar discovered. Suppose a near-ultraviolet telescope observes a spectral line of hydrogen at 1,056 nanometers. In the lab, the same spectral line is at 912 nm. Assume the Hubble constant has a value of 70 km/s/Mpc. Find
   + the redshift of 3C 273
   + the recessional speed of 3C 273
   + the distance to 3C 273
   + How much time has gone by since the light we see originally left 3C 273? Hint: One parsec equals 3.26 light years

FIGURE 23.24. The famous quasar 3C 273. The spikes coming from the center are artifacts of the optics and are not real, though the "thread" to the upper left is actually a jet of material shot out from the quasar's core. Credit: ESA/Hubble & NASA.

7. The "Einstein Cross" is the result of a foreground galaxy (nicknamed "Huchra's Lens", after the extragalactic astronomer John Huchra) lensing the light of a more distant quasar (Q2237+0305) and breaking the quasar's light into four separate components in the process. The redshift of Q2237+0305 is 1.695. Assume the Hubble constant is 70 km/s/Mpc.
   + If the wavelength of a spectral line in the lab was 912 nm, at what wavelength was it observed from the quasar Q2237+0305?
   + Find the speed of the quasar using the formula given in the text. Do you notice a problem with your answer?
   + A more general formula for determining the speed of an object, regardless of the value of its redshift, is given by

$$v = cz \left(\frac{z+2}{z^2 + 2z + 2} \right)$$

Use this formula to determine the speed of the quasar
   + How old was the universe when the light we now see was originally emitted by the quasar? Use the formula

$$\text{age} = (13.8 \text{ billion years}) \left(\frac{1}{z^{3/2}} \right)$$

   + How long ago did the light leave the quasar to get to us? Hint: Assume the universe is 13.8 billion years old.

8. Suppose instead of redshifts we were seeing blueshifts from distant galaxies. What would that imply about the universe?

FIGURE 23.25. The "Einstein Cross," an extreme example of gravitational lensing.

Activities

▸ *Astrophysics activity 23.1:* A class walk-through of the Hubble expansion.

Works Referenced

The philosophy behind how modern scientific theories are constructed is discussed in the following sources:

Kitcher, P. (1982). *Abusing science: The case against creationism.* Cambridge, MA: MIT Press.

Whewell, W. (1840). *The Philosophy of the Inductive Sciences, Founded upon their History.* John W. Parker, West Strand, London. https://archive.org/details/philosophyofindu01whewrich/page/n8 Retrieved 2019-04-21.

Einstein's prediction regarding starlight and Eddington's solar eclipse expedition are in the following sources:

Dyson, F. W., Eddington, A. S., & Davidson, C. (1920). A determination of the deflection of light by the Sun's gravitational field, from observations made at the total eclipse of May 29, 1919. *Philosophical Transactions of the Royal Society of London, 220*(579), 291–333. doi:10.1098/rsta.1920.0009

Longair, M. (2015, April 13). Bending space–time: A commentary on Dyson, Eddington and Davidson (1920) "A determination of the deflection of light by the Sun9s gravitational field." *Philosophical Transactions of the Royal Society A., 373*(2039), 20140287. doi:10.1098/rsta.2014.0287

Lemaître's predictions regarding the expanding universe, and their impact today, are in the following sources:

Lemaître, G. (1927, April). A homogeneous universe of constant mass and growing radius accounting for the radial velocity of extragalactic nebulae. *Annales de la Société Scientifique de Bruxelles, 47,* 49.

Gibney, E. (30 October 2018). "Belgian priest recognized in Hubble-law name change", Nature.com. https://www.nature.com/articles/d41586-018-07234-y Retrieved 2019-04-21.

Biographical and research information about Hubble and Humason can be found in the following sources:

Humason, M. L. (1936). The Apparent Radial Velocities of 100 Extra-Galactic Nebulae. *Astrophysical Journal, 83,* 10. http://adsabs.harvard.edu/abs/1936ApJ....83...10H

NASA. Edwin P. Hubble. https://asd.gsfc.nasa.gov/archive/hubble/overview/hubble_bio.html Retrieved 2019-04-21.

StarChild Team. (n.d.). *Redshift and Hubble's law.* Retrieved from https://starchild.gsfc.nasa.gov/docs/StarChild/questions/redshift.html

Thoughts and interpretations regarding the Big Bang can be found in the following sources:

Mitton, S. (2011). *Fred Hoyle a life in science.* Cambridge, UK: Cambridge University Press.

The Telegraph. (2001, August 22). "Professor Sir Fred Hoyle." Retrieved 2019-04-21. https://www.telegraph.co.uk/news/obituaries/1338125/Professor-Sir-Fred-Hoyle.html

The history and science of the recombination epoch and/or the cosmic microwave background radiation is discussed in the following sources:

Fixsen, D. J. (2009). The temperature of the cosmic microwave background. *Astrophysical Journal, 707*(2), 916–920. doi:10.1088/0004-637X/707/2/916

Mather, J. C. et al. (1994). Measurement of the cosmic microwave background spectrum by the COBE FIRAS instrument. *Astrophysical Journal, 420,* 439. http://adsabs.harvard.edu/abs/1994ApJ...420..439M Retrieved 2019-04-21.

Penzias, A. A., & Wilson, R. W. (1965). A measurement of excess antenna temperature at 4080 Mc/s. *Astrophysical Journal, 142*(1), 419–421. doi:10.1086/148307

Smoot, G. F., Bennett, C. L., Kogut, A., Wright, E. L., Aymon, J., Boggess, N. W., ... & Wilkinson, D. T. (1992). Structure in the COBE differential microwave radiometer first-year maps. *Astrophysical Journal Letters, 396*(1), L1–L5. doi:10.1086/186504 https://lambda.gsfc.nasa.gov/data/cobe/firas/monopole_spec/firas_monopole_spec_v1.txt

White, M. (1999). Anisotropies in the CMB. *Proceedings of the Los Angeles Meeting*, DPF 99. University of California, Los Angeles.

Thoughts about the fundamental forces of nature can be found in the following sources:

Georgia State University. (n.d.). Coupling constants for the fundamental forces. *HyperPhysics*. http://hyperphysics.phy-astr.gsu.edu/hbase/Forces/couple.html Retrieved 2019-04-21.

Sirola, C. (2018, February). May the forces be with you! *Physics Teacher*, 56, 118–119.

A popular account of the early versions of inflationary theory can be found in Guth, A. H. (1997). *The inflationary universe: The quest for a new theory of cosmic origins*. New York, NY: Basic Books.

The accelerating universe, including the concept of dark energy, is described in Peebles, P. J. E., & Ratra, B. (2003). The cosmological constant and dark energy. *Reviews of Modern Physics, 75*(2), 559–606. doi:10.1103/RevModPhys.75.559

Ade, P. A. R. et al. (2013, March 22). Planck 2013 results. I. Overview of products and scientific results – Table 9. *Astronomy and Astrophysics, 571*, A1. doi:10.1051/0004-6361/201321529

Carroll, S. (2007). Dark Matter, Dark Energy: The Dark Side of the Universe. *The Teaching Company*. https://www.thegreatcoursesplus.com/show/dark_matter_dark_energy_the_dark_side_of_the_universe Retrieved 2019-04-21.

National Aeronautics and Space Administration. (n.d). Content of the universe: Pie chart. *Wilkinson Microwave Anisotropy Probe*. https://map.gsfc.nasa.gov/media/080998/index.html Retrieved 2019-04-21.

Planck. (2013, March 21). Planck reveals an almost perfect universe. *ESA*. https://www.esa.int/Our_Activities/Space_Science/Planck/Planck_reveals_an_almost_perfect_Universe Retrieved 2019-04-21.

Credits

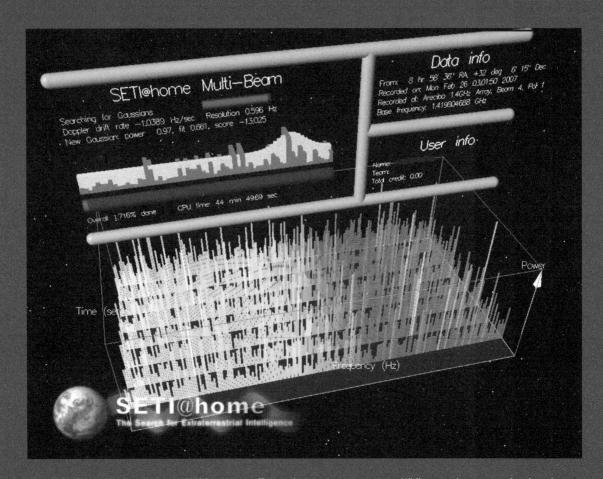

The SETI (Search for Extraterrestrial Life) program offers an interesting screen saver. While a user's computer is otherwise idle, the screen saver processes radio signals to search for evidence of intelligent life elsewhere in the Milky Way. It is available at http://setiathome.ssl.berkeley.edu/.

EXTRATERRESTRIAL LIFE

PURPOSE

To review the current status of the possibility of extraterrestrial life

OBJECTIVES

- To cite examples of claimed contact from extraterrestrial beings
- To describe the realities of interstellar space travel
- To use the Drake equation as a guideline for research
- To review current numbers of Earth-like planets
- To carefully define terms like "intelligence" and "technology"

INTRODUCTION

Our final chapter goes off in a different direction: the possibility of intelligent life elsewhere in the universe. Science fiction aside, what are the chances?

Some, of course, will claim we've already been visited by aliens from other planets. We will look at some of those examples and investigate their claims. It will probably come as no surprise that astronomers view these stories with extreme skepticism.

However, astronomers are also very interested in true science concerning life elsewhere. Short of an actual discovery, what can we reasonably say about all this? It turns out we can say quite a lot, especially with research into extrasolar planets conducted just within the past few decades.

We also need to talk a bit about how interstellar space travel might work—how fast could we actually travel through space, how much time it would take to get to a destination, and potential benefits and costs. How close are we to flying to the stars?

KEY TERMS

Bussard Ramjet: A proposed spaceship that would use the hydrogen floating in interstellar space as fuel, allowing the spaceship to reach speeds close to the speed of light

Close Encounter of the Third Kind: Jargon used by UFO enthusiasts (people convinced that extraterrestrial beings visit the Earth) to describe direct contact between extraterrestrials and humans

Crop circle: A large indentation (not necessarily circular) made in a farmer's field typically indicating it was made on purpose

Drake equation: A step-by-step process to estimate the number of technological civilizations in the Milky Way

Extraterrestrial: Simply, something or someone that does not come from or live on the Earth

Flying saucer: (also **flying disk**): A shape often ascribed by UFO enthusiasts to supposed extraterrestrial spacecraft

Frame of reference (also **inertial frame etc.**): How the universe looks for one particular observer, especially regarding questions involving motion

Goldilocks zone (also **habitable zone**): A region surrounding a star where it is possible for water to exist on a planet or moon in liquid form. Also a region in a galaxy where conditions allow for the possibility of life

Habitable zone (also **Goldilocks zone**): A range of distances from a star that water could exist on a planet or moon in its liquid phase

Length contraction: The fact that the travel distance for an object moving close to the speed of light significantly shortens compared to the distance perceived by objects that aren't moving so fast

Mass increase: The fact that the mass of an object moving close to the speed of light appears significantly larger to those who aren't moving so fast

Miller-Urey experiment (also **Urey-Miller experiment**): An experiment in 1953 to see if conditions of the early Earth could give rise to biological molecules

Optical infinity: When an object is so far away that its rays come to us along parallel lines

Planetary Society: An organization founded in 1980 to promote exploration of the solar system

Project Mogul: A classified U.S. Army program that used weather balloons to search for evidence of Soviet atomic bombs, carried out from 1947 to 1949

Project Ozma: The first systematic attempt in 1960, led by the astronomer Frank Drake, to search for radio signals from extraterrestrial beings

SETI (short for **Search for Extraterrestrial Intelligence**) **Institute:** A privately funded research program founded in 1984 dedicated to searching for evidence of extraterrestrial life

Special relativity: Einstein's theory that describes how objects behave when traveling near the speed of light

Super Earth: An exoplanet larger across and larger in mass than the Earth, but otherwise made of similar materials as the Earth and possessing a surface gravity similar to that of Earth

Time dilation: The fact that the travel time for an object moving close to the speed of light appears much longer to objects that aren't moving so fast

UFO (**unidentified flying object**): Literally what the term says: a flying object that we haven't identified. <u>Not</u> synonymous with flying saucer or alien spaceship

UFO enthusiast (also **ufologist**): A person convinced that UFOs often represent extraterrestrial spaceships visiting the Earth

KEY INDIVIDUALS

Drake, Frank: An American astronomer of the late 20th century who suggested a method for estimating the number of technological civilizations in the Milky Way

Einstein, Albert: A German physicist of the early 20th century who, among other discoveries, formulated the *special theory of relativity*

Hill, Betty and Barney: An American couple who claimed they were abducted by aliens in the early 1960s

Miller, Stanley: An American chemist of the mid-20th century who, with Harold Urey, performed experiments analyzing conditions of the early Earth

Sagan, Carl: An American astronomer of the late 20th century who addressed the science of extraterrestrial life for the public

Urey, Harold: An American chemist of the mid-20th century who, with Stanley Miller, performed experiments analyzing conditions of the early Earth. Also the discoverer of heavy hydrogen (deuterium)

Section 24.1: Encounters of the "Third Kind"?

It's one of the most common questions asked of an astronomer: "Do you believe in aliens?"

An astronomer's answer will probably not satisfy, at least at first. As scientists, we need to be clear and concise. The astronomer will first want to pin down what is meant by "aliens," which usually means some type of intelligent being from beyond the Earth (truly *extraterrestrial*), though not always. The second item to check is what is meant by "believe." To a scientist, a belief is a shorthand way of stating the acceptance that a proposition is true, given the current evidence, though open to reevaluation should better and/or conflicting evidence present itself. If our hypothetical questioner hasn't already given up and moved on, the astronomer will likely (again, not a guarantee) state that the evidence for visits to Earth by extraterrestrial beings is scant, to say the least, though it's an interesting question and an exciting possibility.

The Steven Spielberg movie *Close Encounters of the Third Kind* (1977) popularized a term used by UFO enthusiasts regarding possible contact between beings from other worlds and humans. Let's take a look at some celebrated cases of supposed alien visitation in order to assess the evidence.

1. The Hill Case

On September 19, 1961, a couple was driving home through New Hampshire after a vacation at Niagara Falls and Montreal. During a portion of their drive taking them through a relatively deserted region at night, they saw a variety of lights that moved and changed shape. Then a spacecraft landed and prevented them from traveling further. The couple then lost track of the next several hours. Eventually they awoke at their car and continued home, though deeply disturbed over what had happened. Over the next few weeks, they sought out government officials—including Air Force officers—to report their experience; otherwise they were reluctant to discuss it with others for fear of ridicule. But by the spring of 1963 they were talking about the event with fellow church members, and within 2 years both of them underwent sessions of hypnosis to recover their missing memories.

Such is the story of Betty and Barney Hill, residents at the time of Portsmouth, New Hampshire. It is one of the more famous (and early) examples of a supposed encounter with extraterrestrials. By 1965, some details of their episode made it into a newspaper based in Boston, and in 1966 journalist John G. Fuller wrote up their account as a book titled *Interrupted Journey*, which went through several printings. The Hill case was the basis for at least two movies, an episode of the *X-Files* TV show and numerous other pop culture references.

One of the more compelling portions of the Hill story is a star map. Part of the Hills' tale is that they were brought aboard the alien starship for several hours. While on board, Betty claimed she was shown a map of stars by the aliens, who told her it depicted routes of travel and interstellar commerce. Later, in 1968, an amateur astronomer named Marjorie Fish searched through updated star charts and compiled a map of her own from Betty's testimony. Fish's version supposedly included stars that had not been known to astronomers prior to 1961, with several invisible to the naked eye, and therefore Betty could not have known about them before the alien visitation.

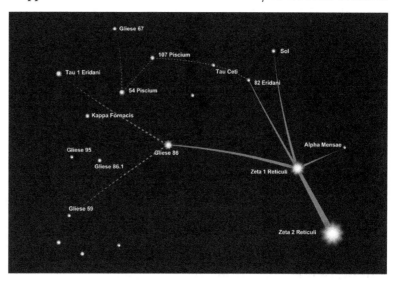

FIGURE 24.1. A star map, based on testimony from Betty Hill, supposedly shown to her by extraterrestrials in 1961. The original version of the map was created by Marjorie Fish, an amateur astronomer, in 1968.

What do people think when they hear the Hills' story? Many *UFO enthusiasts* (also called *ufologists* for short)—that is, people who already think that extraterrestrials are

Check Your Neighbor

Before going on, let's pause a moment. What do you think about the story so far? Are there parts (claims) that are believable at face value? Are there parts that require further scrutiny?

FIGURE 24.2. An object at optical infinity (like the Moon) will appear to follow you as you move, because its rays come in parallel.

visiting the Earth—consider this important evidence buttressing their views. But virtually all scientists are skeptical it ever happened, or happened in the manner claimed. Air Force personnel suggested the Hills had seen a pair of weather balloons or the planet Jupiter. Lest this appears dismissive, even experienced pilots often have difficulty identifying objects in the sky, especially bright planets like Venus, which seem to follow one around. We can call this the *optical infinity* problem; if an object is far enough away (the Moon and Sun qualify, as do planets, comets, stars, etc.), it will appear to follow you wherever you go. The rays of light from the object come in parallel, meaning there is no way to triangulate them (it takes a good telescope and months of time for astronomers to do this for real), and unless you're willing to wait several hours to watch how the object has changed its position due to the Earth's spin, you might think it is dogging your every step. Combine optical infinity with the lack of landmarks in the sky (no trees, buildings, etc.) with which to compare the object, and it's very easy to mistake the apparent motion of a celestial object for the real thing.

Other objections include the following: The event occurred late at night, and skeptic Robert Schaeffer makes the point that sleep deprivation can cause waking hallucinations and account for "missed" time. Psychologists stated that being a bi-racial couple in 1960s America caused stress, though Betty insisted theirs was a happy marriage. An article written by Martin Kottmeyer in 1990 noted that aliens were staples of science fiction TV and movie lore in the 1950s and 1960s, and the descriptions of the aliens by Barney resembled those from pop culture. The hypnosis sessions occurred nearly 2 years after the supposed events, and psychologists are far more cognizant nowadays that memories can be easily influenced under such conditions.

The star map seems at first like a special case. But Carl Sagan, a famous astronomer and popularizer of science, pointed out that the map was a case of observational bias; in other words, the map was chosen to fit a particular description, meaning that it was almost a certainty that stars could be found to make the pattern work. In other words, if you already know the answer before you begin your investigation, you're fairly likely to find it.

2. Crop Circles

Another candidate for extraterrestrial visitations is *crop circles*. Crop circles, indentations in farmers' fields, though not always circular, have actually been around for centuries. For example, a tale from Hartfordshire, England, tells of a farmer whose field was mowed down by the Devil.[1] Another story from 1948 Germany invoked dancing fairy princesses to explain circular flattening of a farmer's grain. Other circular flattenings have been blamed on odd weather patterns or storms. But it wasn't until the modern UFO craze ramped up in the 1970s that they were associated with extraterrestrials. Crop circles have now become a worldwide phenomenon, with over 2,000 different versions catalogued as of 2011. Almost always the crop circles—despite the wild variety of patterns, the name persists—are large enough to be visible from low-flying planes or (nowadays) drones.

Crop circles made their modern debut in the fields of English farmers. Originally the patterns were simply perfect circles (or disks), which led some UFO enthusiasts to claim they were the indentations of flying saucers landing in the fields. Soon, though, the patterns became more and more elaborate (see Figure 24.3), dispelling the simple notion of a landing, and UFO enthusiasts came up with complicated explanations for the patterns; for example, perhaps the aliens were leaving complex messages, to either their own compatriots or to humans. Others linked crop circles to "Ley lines," supposed lines of magical power running through the Earth, or to magical and/or advanced beings manipulating ball lightning. There is even a name for a person who studies crop circles: "cereologist."

---

[1] To be fair, the Devil supposedly cut down the oats instead of trampling them, so it doesn't qualify as a "true" crop circle. Semantics …

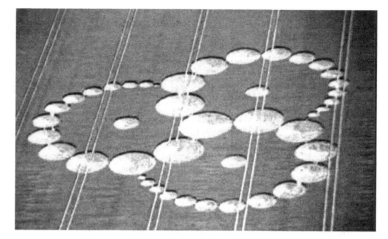

FIGURE 24.3. Left: A possible precursor to crop circles is the tale of the "Devil Mower" from 1689 England. Right: A modern crop circle (Credit: Thomas J. Sutter Jr.).

In 1991, two English artists named Doug Bower and David Chorley announced publicly that they were responsible for starting the current round of crop circles back in 1978. They filmed themselves demonstrating how to create straight lines, circles, and more elaborate patterns with relatively simple tools. They had created, by their own account, some 200 crop circles by 1991, and inspired others to create thousands more.

Once a mystery has been given a plausible, simple, naturalistic solution, any claims at supernatural or extraordinary origins have incredibly high hurdles to leap before being taken seriously. Crop circles are almost always found in fields near roads, meaning the creators have easy access, and arguing further that people, not aliens, are responsible. Some companies have been known to carve out advertising messages in fields, and even the 2012 Summer Olympics held in London commissioned a crop circle to depict its famous Olympic Rings logo. Due to the obvious and utterly mundane nature of their origin, crop circles as extraterrestrial artifacts have died down.

Check Your Neighbor

Suppose you have access to some simple items: a long rope, a plank of wood, and wooden stakes, to start. How could you use these items to help you make a circle in a field of wheat? How about making a straight line?

Check Your Neighbor

Crop circles became a craze in England and other countries, but not so much in the United States. Why not? Hint: How do you think a farmer from America would react when confronted with people smashing her or his wheat field?

3. Roswell, New Mexico

The most famous location for extraterrestrials is probably Roswell, New Mexico. The town supports several museums dedicated to the notion that aliens from outer space have visited Earth. One can take a short drive out of town to a farmer's field where a spaceship supposedly crashed back in the 1940s. A parade is held annually through the middle of the town to celebrate our "guests."[2]

The story, in its simplest form, goes like this: A spaceship crash landed outside Roswell, New Mexico, in 1947. The army swooped in immediately, cordoned off the area, and took away the remains of both the spaceship and deceased aliens, which are now in storage in a government complex famously labeled Area 51. Some versions go as

---

[2] The author personally visited Roswell back in the summer of 2005; unfortunately, we got to town too late to see the parade, though we did check out one of the museums.

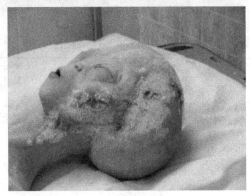

FIGURE 24.4. Top: The entrance to the International UFO Museum in Roswell, New Mexico. Right: A model of a supposed deceased alien at the museum.

far as to claim that many of our modern inventions (such as the transistor) owe their existence to our adapting of captured alien technology. Several people have come forward as eye witnesses, a variety of books and articles have been published, and even a 1995 TV special showcased an autopsy of one of the aliens.

As with our previous cases, the true explanation is more prosaic than extraterrestrials, though a bit complicated. In 1947, World War II was over and the ideological battle between the United States and Soviet Russia called the Cold War had just begun. While Russia had not yet gotten hold of an atomic bomb, the American government assumed it was only a matter of time, and was even at that early date taking steps to guard against a potential attack. *Project Mogul* was part of this effort. The program sent microphones up with weather balloons to listen for shockwaves generated by Soviet tests of nuclear weapons. The program ran only from 1947 to 1949, when it was superseded by cheaper and more sensitive detection methods.

In late June or early July of 1947 (the date is uncertain), one of the balloons crashed about 30 miles outside of Roswell. A foreman named William Brazel working on a local homestead (ranch) noted odd-shaped debris and took some of it home. After hearing about flying saucers, Brazel brought his find to the attention of the local sheriff, who in turn contacted a major at a nearby Army Air Force base, who then traveled to review the wreckage. Eventually, the Army sent out personnel to gather up the debris and take it away. To conceal the true purpose of the program, the Army sent out a press release that a weather balloon had crashed (which was somewhat true), and the story died a dull death for 3 decades.

By the late 1970s, UFOs and flying saucers had come into the public eye, and several ufologists revisited the Roswell "incident." The timing was ripe—besides Spielberg's movie, the 1970s and early 1980s were a period of severe mistrust by the American public of its government (somewhat understandable after the Vietnam War and Watergate), and people were more likely to believe in a government cover-up than the plain facts of the case.

To add to the confusion, jet planes were invented near the end of World War II, promising

FIGURE 24.5. A newspaper account from the Roswell Daily Record on July 8, 1947, covering the crash of a "Flying Saucer" outside of the town.

faster fighter planes capable of reaching higher altitudes than ever before. The U.S. Army Air Force asked if pilots could survive if they needed to bail out of a jet, and so (not wanting to experiment with actual human pilots) dropped manikins from high heights to test the possibility. Manikins are human-shaped objects, but often without distinguishing features (there is no reason to get too detailed) which was later often conflated with the notion of aliens having humanoid features.

So how does the "Roswell incident" stack up? Most of the supposed eye witnesses aren't. Declassified files tell how balloons ended up in rural New Mexico; ditto for crashed manikins. The TV special of 1995 was quickly debunked; the "alien" wasn't even a high-quality fake alien by Hollywood standards, artifacts such as a telephone in the video were from the wrong time period, the environmental suits worn by the doctors performing the autopsy weren't any such thing, and so on to the point that the same TV network that originally broadcast the special broadcast a follow-up debunking it! Far from being the slam-dunk case of an alien visitation, the Roswell "incident" is now one of the most debunked of all such claims.

4. Flying Saucers

One of the features of the Roswell story is that the supposed alien spaceship was a flying disk or saucer. In 1956, the U.S. Air Force[3] decided that if flying saucers are good enough for aliens, they're good enough for us.

The Air Force had specific and demanding requirements for their craft, including a top speed between Mach 3 and Mach 4 (i.e., three to four times the speed of sound), a ceiling over 100,000 feet, and a range over 1,000 nautical miles. The cost of the original contract (with a Canadian aeronautics firm) was $3,168,000, which translates to over $25,000,000 today.

FIGURE 24.6. The U.S. Air Force's initial proposed flying saucer, in 1956. Credit: National Archives.

But in December of 1961, the project was canceled. Why? The Army could have saved itself a lot of time and trouble (and taxpayer's money) by consulting any competent physicist. A flat disk is simply not stable in flight unless it spins rapidly; without this, the disk quickly crashes. Any aliens would either be dizzy from continuously spinning or would be crash landing every time they entered an atmosphere. This is why we don't have flying saucers today: The design is horrible.

Why are so many scientists skeptical of the UFO idea? Don't the hundreds of claims (we've only covered a few) all add up to something? No, they don't.

Check Your Neighbor

Play catch with a friend using a frisbee. Notice you "flick" your wrist to get it to your partner. Now hold the frisbee with both hands and "shove" it toward your partner. What happens to the frisbee?

The previous chapter opened with an in-depth description of how science is conducted, and what makes a science in the first place. One of the key points made was that claims require evidence, and extraordinary claims require extraordinary evidence. In cosmology (chapter 23), we stated that astronomers are convinced that the universe (our universe, specifically) began as an incredibly tiny—maybe even infinitely tiny—dot which then dramatically

---

[3] Part of the U.S. Army during World War II, the U.S. Air Force became its own service branch in 1947.

expanded. This is an extraordinary claim by any reasonable sense of the term: astronomers are stating that all we know and see was once stuffed into a space smaller than the period at the end of this sentence. Yet astronomers buy into it because they have also gathered thousands upon thousands of pieces of independent, corroborated evidence that points to this conclusion.

The idea that Earth has been visited by aliens from another planet is also extraordinary. But when we investigate particular claims, we find they are explained better by more mundane happenstances or fail to present any evidence at all. While hundreds of people tell stories of flying saucers, or tales of alien abductions, none of them work. A story without evidence to back it up, by definition an anecdote, carries no explanatory "weight." No matter how many times we add the number zero to itself—no matter how many anecdotes we hear—the sum is still zero.

Section 24.2: Thoughts About Interstellar Space Travel

Besides the lack of any credible evidence for extraterrestrial visitations, another reason astronomers give for doubting the idea is that space travel is <u>hard</u>.

For example, why don't we routinely send astronauts to explore other objects in the solar system? After all, we did land astronauts on the Moon over six separate missions (Apollo 13 had to come back without landing) from 1969 to 1973, 50 years ago. Surely we've improved space travel since then? Why aren't we reveling not in movies about missions to Mars, but actual reports back from astronauts currently <u>at</u> Mars?

FIGURE 24.7. Left: The launch of Apollo 11 in 1969. Right: The command module of Apollo 15 in lunar orbit in 1971. Credit: NASA.

One of the answers is that space is BIG. It's easy to get lost in the immensity of extragalactic space as we did in the past several chapters, where numbers like megaparsecs are tossed around so freely. But the fact remains that even the Moon, our nearest neighbor, is very far away by human standards. The Moon is 384,000 kilometers (223,000 miles) from the Earth, and the round-trip of the first landing mission, Apollo 11, took about 7 ½ days. The next nearest potential target for manned space flight is Mars, which is about 78 million kilometers (48 million miles) away at closest, and we wouldn't be able to simply travel there in a straight line. While our computers have improved dramatically since Apollo—you have more computing power in your cell phone than did the entire Apollo mission—rockets haven't. The laws of chemistry govern the energy we can get from a rocket, and the rocket fuel of the Moon missions is still the same fuel we have today. While one can dream about better sources of energy— nuclear fusion is a favorite—we don't have them yet. This is all to say that the quickest trip to Mars with current technology would last at least 9 months, one way.

Using Mars as our goal, the trip there won't be easy. Space is a vacuum, meaning there are no impediments to travel. But that also means we can't pick up any supplies along the way, or stop to fix broken parts. The expense of such a mission means rescue efforts are problematic at best (any reasonable estimate of the cost begins in the hundreds of billions of dollars) and realistically impractical. Space is also deadly to people; besides being a vacuum (no air to breathe, etc.), it's also full of high-energy radiation and micro-meteorites. The lack of apparent weight means that astronauts will be floating for the entire trip; experiences with Russian cosmonauts who spend months aboard the International Space Station show serious health problems upon returning to Earth, especially regarding bone and muscle loss.

Once on Mars, we assume our astronauts aren't going to sightsee for a few days and then return home. Rather, they would probably need to spend close to a year or more to make the effort worthwhile. But Mars doesn't have any useful materials at hand: The air is too thin and made of the wrong components to breathe; water can't exist as a liquid above the surface, and we don't know of reliable channels of underground water to tap; astronauts would need to bring all of their food, drink, and supplies; Martian summers incorporate abrasive dust storms that reach above 100 mph; and again there is no prospect of rescue should the astronauts run into trouble.

This isn't meant to say that a Martian mission isn't an exciting prospect or not worth pursuing. It's to give a realistic appreciation of the difficulties involved. Apollo was always more of a political statement to the world (it was a major achievement to rub in the faces of the Soviets) than a scientific enterprise,[4] and certainly never a stepping stone to creating a permanent presence on the Moon. It's no surprise that our explorations of the solar system have used robotic probes rather than people. As expensive as the Juno spacecraft currently in orbit about Jupiter is ($1.13 billion), it's still two to three powers of ten less than a comparable mission involving people. And if Juno fails, while we've lost an expensive spacecraft; we haven't lost any people.

The above discussion is concerned with travel within our solar system. But the question in

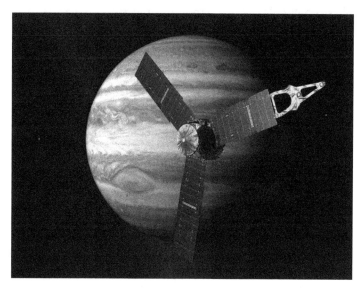

FIGURE 24.8. The robotic spacecraft Juno silhouetted against Jupiter to celebrate its arrival in the Jupiter system in 2016. Credit: NASA.

front of us is the possibility of interstellar space travel. To tackle this problem, we must enjoy a quantum leap in our space-traveling abilities. To put this into perspective, the fastest spacecraft ever launched is Voyager II, which a few years ago passed a distance of 100 astronomical units from the Sun. Suppose it is pointed toward Barnard's Star (it isn't), at 1.83 parsecs away the second-closest star system to us. A parsec is not 100 au, but 206,265 au. Instead of the 40-plus years Voyager II has spent exploring our solar system, to get to Barnard's Star at this rate would require over <u>80,000 years</u>. Fast space travel, as depicted by science fiction movies, remains in the realm of science fiction, not fact.

Of course, another important feature of this question is that the aliens are visiting us, not the other way around, and so perhaps they've found a way to make interstellar travel work. A few suggestions involve such ideas as hibernation (where the passengers sleep away most of the journey) or multi-generational ships, where it's the remote descendants of the original travelers who reach their destination. But we'd probably still like to explore the concept of fast space travel, meaning that a traveler has a chance of reaching a nearby star system in a reasonable amount of time.

---

[4] For all seven Apollo missions, and the 12 people who walked on the Moon, only one person was a scientist of any kind (specifically, a geologist).

Einstein pointed out a possible way to do this via his *theory of special relativity*. Whereas his general theory is an explanation of gravity, the special theory focuses on how objects behave if they move at speeds close to the speed of light. In formulating the special theory, Einstein noted several properties or postulates:

* The speed of light in a vacuum is a fixed speed for all observers
* No material object can travel at (or faster than) the speed of light in a vacuum
* The laws of nature are the same for everybody

The theory has the name it does for two reasons: First, it's a "special" case because it doesn't include gravity; second, it talks about how observers perceive motion "relative" to one another.

To get this second point across, Einstein introduced (or re-introduced) the notion of a *frame of reference*. Sometimes also called an inertial frame, this simply means that each observer (it doesn't have to mean a thinking person; it can also include objects, etc.) perceives the motions of other observers relative to their own motion. All motions, from our points of view or frames, are always measured relative to something else. And all of us, from a physics point of view, appear not to be moving, with the rest of the world moving instead. Suppose you walk toward the east inside a hallway in your house. It is equally valid to say the entire house is walking toward you—that is, toward the west—at the same speed. Of course, we know from everyday life that houses don't walk. What we mean here is that if you posed a physics motion problem, you would get the same results if you walk to the east or the house moves to the west. The same applies to cars on a highway, planets orbiting the Sun, galaxies moving through the universe, and so on.

FIGURE 24.9. The principle of relativity. Left: The red car appears to slowly pass by the blue car, because their velocities are in the same direction. Right: The blue car appears to pass by the red car very quickly, because their velocities are in opposite directions.

The term "relativity" itself is not an invention of Einstein's and goes back at least to the days of Galileo. It's simply this recognition that when we measure an object's velocity, it's always compared to a frame of reference. When we say something like "That red car is moving at 60 miles per hour," we usually mean it's moving at 60 mph compared to the road. Now, suppose two cars are both moving east on a highway (Figure 24.9). If the red car is moving at 60 mph and the blue car at 55 mph, the red car slowly passes by the blue car at a relative velocity of 5 mph. Next, suppose the red car is moving east at 60 mph and the blue car west at 55 mph. In this case, the blue car appears to zip past the red car at 115 mph. This notion of subtracting or adding velocities is a consequence of *Galilean relativity* and is a feature of everyday life.

Where Einstein's version of relativity is different is the restriction on an object's speed: "Thou shalt not go faster than the speed of light." Let's imagine next a spaceship with an unlimited fuel supply, so it can keep adding more thrust to increase its speed. At first, adding thrust does what we expect it to—the more thrust, the faster the speed. But as the spaceship approaches the speed of light, a strange thing happens. The same amount of thrust that (for example) increased the speed of the spaceship from 10% to 20% of the speed of light doesn't increase the speed from 90% to 100% of the speed of light. This is the physics version of "diminishing returns": Larger and larger increases in thrust do not go into increasing the speed of the spaceship very much.

So where does the thrust (or more properly, the energy) go? This invokes one of the odd properties of special relativity. Instead of speed, the spaceship becomes more <u>massive</u>. This *mass increase* isn't noticed directly by the astronauts inside the spaceship, but its consequences are. In fact, even an infinite amount of fuel turned into thrust would simply go into making the spaceship (as seen by observers standing still watching from a distance) infinitely massive. No matter how much energy is poured into propelling the spaceship, the speed of light is never reached.

TABLE 24.1. A Spaceship Traveling at High Speeds

Percentage of the Speed of Light	Mass of Spaceship	Distance to Destination (ly)	Travel Time (yr)
0	1	10	N/A
10	1.005	9.95	99.5
20	1.021	9.78	48.9
50	1.155	8.66	17.3
90	2.294	4.36	4.84
95	3.203	3.12	3.28
99	7.089	1.41	1.42
99.9	22.36	0.45	0.45
99.99	70.71	0.14	0.14

Table 24.1 shows how this progresses. Einstein found a formula that calculates the mass of the spaceship as it gets closer to the speed of light. If the spaceship has 1 unit of mass before starting its journey, it has 1.005 units of mass at 10% the speed of light, not much of a change. But the same spaceship has a mass of 2.294 units (over double its original mass) at 90% the speed of light, and by the time it's moving at 99% the speed of light, its mass is over seven times its original "rest" mass. While this sounds unbelievable, physicists accelerating protons for particle physics experiments (such as at the Large Hadron Collider in Europe) need to compensate for increases in the masses of the protons in order to keep them confined. Cosmic rays—usually, but not always, protons—traveling through the galaxy that hit our upper atmosphere exhibit the same behavior. Mass increase is a law of nature.

This sounds like bad news for any potential space travelers, but there are positive tradeoffs. Not only did Einstein finds that mass changes, but also the amount of time it takes to travel through space and the perceived distance to the destination. Specifically, the change of time (*time dilation*) and length (*length contraction*) help our travelers by shortening the journey. Suppose the distance to the star system in question is 10 light years. If the travelers move at speeds similar to our current fastest spacecraft, 1/10,000 the speed of light, then a 10–light year trip requires 100,000 years to get there. But traveling close to the speed of light changes things. If the spaceship moves at 10% the speed of light, the travelers will actually perceive the distance to be 9.95 light years and the time to get there 99.5 years. Getting up to 90% of the speed of light shortens the trip to 4.36 light years and 4.84 years, respectively; 99% of the speed of light makes it sound humanly possible at 1.41 light years and 1.42 years, or about 17 months.

However, we need to keep in mind that these reductions only apply to those on board the spaceship, not anybody who stays at home. To those of us left behind, we still see a distance of 10 light years for the travel distance, regardless of how fast the space travelers move. And while their trip will of course take less time if they go faster, the gains are not as much; from home, a traveler moving at 90% the speed of light will take 11.11 years to make the trip, not 4.84 years. The longer the trip, and the faster the spaceship, the larger the discrepancy the perception of time (what year is it?) between the two groups.

One more thing: How could it possibly work? Where could a spaceship get a virtually unlimited supply of fuel? One suggestion—very much still in the science fiction stage—is called the *Bussard Ramjet*. It makes use of the observation that interstellar space is not a perfect vacuum, but instead contains

FIGURE 24.10. A Bussard Ramjet is a proposed spaceship that makes use of hydrogen in interstellar space as fuel and can move at speeds close to the speed of light. Credit: NASA.

hydrogen atoms. As the spaceship moves through space, a large scoop would capture these free-floating atoms, use them as fuel in a hydrogen fusion reactor (a technology we do not yet have), and blow them out the back as exhaust. The resulting thrust could theoretically get the ramjet to 90% the speed of light or more.

The ramjet sounds like a possibility (we don't know of any laws of nature that forbid it) but it does come with its own problems. The density of hydrogen atoms in interstellar space is on the order of a single atom per 10 cubic centimeters. In order to capture enough hydrogen to make propulsion work, the scoop would need to be hundreds or thousands of kilometers across. When the ramjet gets up to high speeds, passengers (due to relativity) would perceive the atoms as moving at those speeds, meaning that there would need to be a way to protect them from the hard radiation thus induced. A potential solution is to have lasers projecting from the ramjet strip electrons off the neutral atoms and use powerful magnets to direct the protons away from the passengers and into the engine.

The size and scale of such a spaceship is daunting; the spaceship would be the size of a large asteroid or small moon. Any such spacecraft is hundreds or thousands of years in our future. But Einstein's special relativity does make it possible for space travelers to cruise the galaxy. Our next question is thus: Are there any extraterrestrials out there in the first place?

Section 24.3: Searching for Extraterrestrials

In large part due to the overzealousness of ufologists, and also due to some of the difficulties of space travel noted, astronomers tended to downplay the question of extraterrestrial life, especially as a theme for serious research. But a few people did take the question seriously, among them Frank Drake.

Frank Drake (b. 1930) is an American astronomer whose career centered about radio waves. After a few astronomers had published speculations about the notion of extraterrestrial intelligences, he decided to search for them.

Using the 25-meter radio dish at the National Radio Astronomy Observatory (NRAO) in Green Bank, West Virginia, he set up a systematic program called *Project Ozma* looking at two nearby Sun-like stars, Epsilon Eridani and Tau Ceti. Drake scanned the 21-centimeter line (chapter 16) and nearby wavelengths, following a suggestion by the physicist Philip Morrison, but found no signals over 3 months of observations in 1960.

FIGURE 24.11. Left: Frank Drake giving a speech at Cornell University in 2017. Right: Carl Sagan at the founding of the Planetary Society in 1980.

In 1961, Drake hosted a meeting amongst several interested parties at Green Bank. He recounted his thoughts decades later on his preparations:

> As I planned the meeting, I realized a few day(s) ahead of time we needed an agenda. And so I wrote down all the things you needed to know to predict how hard it's going to be to detect extraterrestrial life. And looking at them it became pretty evident that if you multiplied all these together, you got a number, N, which is the number of detectable civilizations in our galaxy. This was aimed at the radio search, and not to search for primordial or primitive life forms.

> "The Drake Equation Revisited: Part I". *Astrobiology Magazine*. Sep 29, 2003.

Two organizations sprang from these and other like-minded scientists, both interested in the question of extraterrestrial life. One was the *Planetary Society*, founded in 1980, devoted to space exploration in the solar system.

The other was the *SETI ("Search for Extraterrestrial Intelligence") Institute*, founded in 1984. Both organizations are still active today.

The Drake equation, as it soon came to be called, is less an attempt at a specific answer and more of a way to think about all the factors that come into pondering such a problem, absent direct evidence. The equation looks like this:

Equation 24.1

$$N = R_* f_p n_e f_l f_i f_c L$$

N is the number of technological civilizations in the Milky Way. Drake restricted his discussion to our galaxy, since even other nearby galaxies (like Andromeda) are so far away in human terms that, even if teeming with life, they simply can't be communicated with. The various symbols on the right represent individual steps in the logic used by Drake. In order they are as follows:

- R_*: The rate of star formation in the Milky Way
- f_p: The fraction of stars that possess planets
- n_e: The number of planets in a star system capable of evolving life
- f_l: The fraction of capable planets that actually do evolve life
- f_i: The fraction of life-bearing planets that evolve intelligent life
- f_c: The fraction of planets with intelligent life that develop the ability to communicate across galactic distances
- *L*: The amount of time such a technological civilization exists

Many of the factors are fractions of some kind. Some factors are related to astronomy, some to biology, and some (perhaps) even to sociology and psychology. A few of these factors have in recent years gotten reasonably precise answers, but most have not, and it may that be some factors cannot be answered at all.

Let's take some time to look at each factor and see what, if anything, we can say about it:

1. Rate of Star Formation

Going in, we are assuming that stars are essential. Stars provide the energy needed for life to exist, and there aren't other reliable sources of energy available. While not all stars may be suitable for life (O and B stars in particular don't live long enough), the majority at least provide an opportunity. The more stars we have in the Milky Way, the more chances we give life.

It's also worth focusing on current star formation rates rather than simply the total number of stars in the Milky Way. Many stars from previous populations (chapter 16) don't have enough heavy elements to form Earth-like planets (or life forms), and so much of the galactic bulge and halo can be tentatively ruled out. Nor are the bulge and/or halo making new stars today. On the other hand, the disk possesses stars (including the Sun) with the needed mix of elements and is where star formation occurs today.

Estimates are difficult to come by, and previously rates have been cited as high as 20 stars per year. But observations by telescopes such as Spitzer, which look in the infrared (where most star formation shows itself) hint at anywhere from *1.5 to 3 new stars per year.*

2. Fraction of Stars with Planets

This is actually a little easier to gauge recently than the rate of star formation. Studies from planet-hunting satellites such as Kepler (chapter 7) and searches for microlensing effects almost guarantee that planets are a key component of star formation. It is reasonable lately to assume that all stars have planets; or, the fraction of stars with planets is approximately *1.*

3. Number of Planets per Star Capable of Evolving Life

Studies of life-capable exoplanets is still in its infancy, the field only really going back to the mid-1990s. Early observations tended to emphasize Jovian-sized planets—thought to be unsuitable for life—versus terrestrial-like planets. Even so, astronomers can make a few statements with confidence.

NASA runs an "Exoplanet Archive" where it tracks the latest statistics of not only how many exoplanets have been found, but also their estimated radii and masses, most of them coming from the Kepler satellite. One thought, which we aren't completely sure about yet, is that a planet should have a surface gravity near that of the Earth's—not too small and not too large –in order to promote the formation of life. Tables 24.2 and 24.3 show the most recent numbers (as of January 18, 2019) for confirmed discoveries:

A quick glance shows that there are relatively few planets with small radii (less than 1.25 times the radius of the Earth) and small masses (less than 3 times the mass of the Earth), and many more exoplanets known that are both larger across and more massive than the Earth. Astronomers suspect that the statistics are skewed, not because the galaxy actually has many more giant planets than Earth-sized planets, but because giant planets are easier to find. As our techniques improve, we expect to find more and more smaller planets.

These numbers also don't rule out potential sites for life. For example, a planet with 3 times the mass of the Earth and 1.5 times the radius of the Earth would have a density of 4.92 grams per cubic centimeter, meaning its composition would be dominated by rock and metal like the Earth, but also have a surface gravity of 13 meters per second squared, or 1.33 times the surface gravity of Earth. Such planets that are larger than Earth but still have densities and gravities similar to ours are often nicknamed *super Earths* and could serve as potential homes for life.

Another requirement for an object to possibly support life is to be warmed to just the right amount by its parent star. Usually astronomers start this discussion by noting the range of distances a planet can be from its star in order for water to exist in a liquid state, a region known as the *habitable zone*, or sometimes the "Goldilocks zone," since it is "just right" (Figure 7.16 in chapter 7). Astronomers also wonder about such issues as the composition of a planet's atmosphere, whether or not it has active tectonic plates, whether or not its rotation is tidally locked to its star, whether planetary migration of a Jovian exoplanet has disrupted the orbits of terrestrial exoplanets, whether the planet has a moon, and so on. Astronomers now even include the possibility that a sufficiently large moon in orbit about a Jovian exoplanet (recall that Titan, orbiting Saturn, has an atmosphere and active weather) could host life.

The astronomers at the 1961 Green Bank meeting thought the number of suitable planets could be between 3 and 5 per star. Extrapolating from the Kepler satellite's findings, there might be as many as 40 billion terrestrial-sized exoplanets orbiting suitable stars.

This is where our estimates begin to wander. While there are some telescopes in the planning stages to address some of these questions (for example, to capture detailed spectra of an exoplanet's atmosphere), it will likely be many decades before we can state any numbers with confidence for this factor in the Drake equation.

4. Fraction of Capable Planets That Actually Evolve Life

Now we move away from astronomy proper and into other sciences, particularly geology, chemistry, and biology, and a glaring lack of data.

TABLE 24.2. Radii of Exoplanets

Range (R_{Earth})	Number Found
≤1.25	388
1.25 to 2	827
2 to 6	1295
6 to 15	397
≥15	146

TABLE 24.3. Masses of Exoplanets

Range (R_{Earth})	Number Found
≤3	27
3 to 10	113
10 to 30	70
30 to 100	78
100 to 300	186
≥300	323

Life arose fairly quickly after the Earth formed, which might suggest that life (at least simple forms of life) is easy for the universe to make. But we need to be cautious with such a conclusion. So far, we know of a grand total of <u>1</u> world that supports life, or ever supported life. Several candidates have been talked up for the solar system—Mars, Europa, Titan, and others—but no other location has yet shown evidence of life of any kind. The rapidity of life (astronomically speaking, as we always do) arising on Earth may be a special case. We simply don't know yet.

The classic statement regarding life on the early Earth was the *Miller-Urey experiment*. In 1952, two chemists, Stanley Miller (1930–2007) and Harold Urey[5] (1893–1981) attempted to replicate the conditions of the primitive Earth. Various gases—methane, ammonia, and hydrogen—were placed in a flask containing liquid water, and lightning was

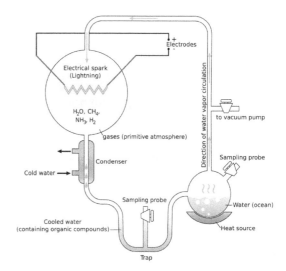

FIGURE 24.12. A schematic of the Miller-Urey experiment.

simulated by sending electric sparks through the flask. Their results have become famous: Within a week, they had produced several amino acids, which are a class of molecules used by life on Earth.

We now know the early atmosphere of the Earth contained a different mix of molecules, leading some critics to dismiss the experiment. But several other experiments replicated the basic results using different mixtures. We still don't know for sure what the earliest atmosphere of the Earth was like, but we can reasonably guess it contained very simple molecules—nitrogen, carbon dioxide, hydrogen sulfide (H_2S) and sulfur dioxide (SO_2) would have been ejected from early volcanoes in the air—and reproductions of the Miller-Urey experiment with these components also return amino acids. The Miller-Urey experiment did not create life in the lab (nor did they ever claim that it did). Rather, it showed the building blocks of life are fairly easy to make under the conditions of the early Earth.

Earth isn't the only place we find amino acids in nature. For example, the Murchison meteorite (which landed in Australia in 1969) has been shown to contain 14,000 (!) different molecular compounds, including 70 distinct amino acids, 19 of which are found in life on Earth. Astronomers also suspect many comets are covered in organic matter, meaning that the vacuum conditions of the solar system are not a barrier to the formation of such molecules. Some scientists (the co-discoverer of DNA, Francis Crick, has speculated about this) think that it is more likely that Earth was "seeded" from space, rather than developing its own organic supply. Again, life has not been discovered elsewhere, but the materials with which to build life are.

5. The Fraction of Life-Bearing Planets with Intelligent Life

This is a rather contentious topic, where values range from virtually 0 to 1 and seem to depend as much on the outlook of the person promoting their number as opposed to much in the way of scientific evidence. However, it will help to take a step back and decide what we mean by "intelligence" first.

To do that, it also matters to go back to the original intent of the Drake equation and the problem it addressed. In order to know that other extraterrestrial intelligences exist, we need to be able to communicate with them, whether it be in-"person" visits (highly unlikely, as we have seen) to signals sent through interstellar space. It's not even vital to answering the question that we can <u>understand</u> anything our galactic neighbors may have to say; it's that we can recognize an attempt at communication in the first place.

Thus, the question of intelligence should devolve not into problem-solving skills, the ability to reason abstractly, or the construction of complex machines, but the ability to communicate. Obviously, we need to narrow this a

---

[5] By 1952, Harold Urey had already led a distinguished scientific career, winning the Nobel Prize for chemistry in 1934 for the discovery of deuterium.

bit; a tree sending pollen into the fields during spring is communicating in some sense, but we would not consider a tree therefore "intelligent." Rather, we mean the ability to communicate complex concepts—both transmitting and receiving—within one's own species, and perhaps to other species.

In this vein, several species of dolphins and whale can be considered intelligent, as we have large amounts of evidence indicating they trade complicated thoughts back and forth. That we can't understand the clicks of dolphins or the "songs" of whales isn't the point; it's that we recognize these creatures are communicating in sophisticated manners. Other candidates (no doubt you can think of some of your own) could also include other primates besides humans. A famous case involves a gorilla named Koko (1971–2018), who was taught a modified version of American Sign Language from birth and, according to her handlers, had an active vocabulary of over 1,000 words. How much Koko ultimately understood is debatable—she did not appear to use complex syntax or grammar—but that she could communicate via signs is undisputed.

On the other hand, the number of species of animals (never mind plants, etc.) incapable of more than rudimentary language skills lies in the billions. Biologists such as Ernst Mayr (1904–2005) thought this drives the intelligent life fraction toward zero. Only one species (humans) have achieved anything resembling complex intelligence, and therefore the odds are extremely low. On top of that, the planet Earth has been in existence for 4.5 billion years; life has been here for 4 billion of those years, but anything more complicated than bacteria didn't arise until the Cambrian explosion of 500 million years ago, and it is only within the past 100–200,000 years that our species arrived, so humans have only been on Earth for about two one-thousandths of the Earth's existence. Nor are we explicitly considering the dangers of living on an active planet such as Earth, which has experienced at least five worldwide ice ages and several extinction events (the Chicxulub asteroid that may have killed the dinosaurs was not even the worst) argues for a tiny answer.

It depends in part, as was said, on your attitude. If you prefer to look at just the number of species Earth has had, or the length of time it has been here without intelligence, you will derive a very small fraction. But if your mind-set is that humans (or something like us) was inevitable—and we are here, after all—then your fraction may be close to 1. Until we learn much more about this subject, the fraction of planets that develop intelligent life will remain an unknown.

FIGURE 24.13. Left: An African Gorilla using a stick as a tool to search for food. Right: A humpback whale breaching off the coast of Tahiti.

6. The Fraction of Intelligent Species That Develop Intergalactic Communications

We may be able to say more about this factor, at least via astronomy, since this brings us back to talking about space. But again, before we begin, we need to discuss the term "communication" in this setting.

Suppose we consider humpback whales. By all indications, they talk with each other constantly. The acoustic frequencies they prefer—sound waves are a much superior method for communication in the oceans than light waves—allowed them, at least in theory, to talk to each other on opposite sides of the globe, until modern shipping introduced great amounts of noise over the past 100-plus years. But we don't ever expect humpbacks to develop technology to communicate over interstellar distances. The kind of technology to build the machinery necessary involves (among other things) the use of hands and fire, neither of which humpbacks can nor ever will possess. Here then is an example of an "intelligent" species incapable of the kind of skills needed to communicate with another intelligent species somewhere else in the galaxy.

FIGURE 24.14. Left: The 100-meter Robert C. Byrd Telescope at Green Bank, WV, the largest steerable telescope in the world. Right: A close-up of a single antenna of the Allan Telescope Array outside of San Francisco, used by SETI.

Out of the few intelligent species (however we care to define that number) we humans are the only ones to build technology capable of talking with other like-skilled alien species elsewhere in the galaxy. We are not able (yet?) to send spacecraft to other stars, but for these purposes, we don't need to. Radio waves are relatively easy to manipulate, are cost effective, and travel at the speed of light. Our radio instruments are, and have been for decades, able to transmit and receive signals in nearly any portion of the Milky Way.

There may be a few downsides. First, other intelligent species in the galaxy may not use radio waves for communications. We think of radio as having several advantages that prefer it to other methods, but our interstellar neighbors may not look at it that way. Second, while the speed of light is very fast, it isn't infinitely fast, and radio signals take time to travel. We have had this technology for about a century. Any signals we have sent have only had time to go outward about 100 light years (30 parsecs) into the galaxy, but the diameter of the disk of the Milky Way is about 100,000 light years (30,000 parsecs) across. Plus, assuming our new friends

FIGURE 24.15. Forbes Field in Pittsburgh, PA, prior to 1916. The first radio broadcast of a major league baseball game was by KDKA out of Pittsburgh in 1921. Those radio signals have now traveled through space for about a century.

cared to respond, their radio signals would take the same amount of time to get here. True in-time conversations are not possible.

How likely is it for an intelligent species to develop radio technology or its galactic equivalent? We don't know for sure—a theme running through the Drake equation—but here are a few thoughts. The human species has been in existence anywhere from 100,000 to 400,000 years, depending on the expert questioned; let's take the lower estimate here. We've had radio for 100 (again, rounded off) of those years. So humans have possessed this capability for just 1/1000th of the life of our species. Of course, as time goes by, this fraction will increase, but it's still a sobering assessment.

7. Lifespan of a Technological Civilization

The last factor of the Drake equation involves sociology, psychology, and history as much or more than it does astronomy. How long has such a species been in existence in order to do the communicating?

Science author and founder of the Skeptics Society, Michael Shermer (b. 1954) performed a survey of 28 human civilizations (such as the Roman Empire) and found their average lifetimes to be 304 years, a very tiny number in an astronomical context. Others have made the contrary argument that once a civilization has developed enough, it becomes essentially immortal (this does not imply its individual members are immortal), and so the lifespan of a technological civilization for our purposes here is essentially indefinite. Another counter argument is that Shermer's use of the term "civilization" is too limiting; after all, when the Ottoman Turks conquered Constantinople in 1453, there was no real "break" in the existence of a civilization, just the transfer of political power from one group to another. The victory of the allies over Germany and Japan in World War II did not eliminate radio technology simply because their empires fell.

But, back to the pessimistic view, we have also developed the ability to harm the Earth (via climate change, nuclear war, biological weaponry, etc.) where it either becomes uninhabitable or plunges humanity back into a new dark age where modern technology no longer exists. There is no guarantee of our survival in the laws of nature.

One final thought: There may be extraterrestrials out there fully capable of communicating with us, but purposely have not done so. The "Prime Directive" of *Star Trek* fame incorporates the notion that civilizations shouldn't interfere with each other. Or perhaps another civilization doesn't want to communicate, even if they are fully capable of doing so. Absolute privacy may be a value held very strongly by others in the galaxy.

The Drake equation isn't a final answer to the question, "Are we alone"? Rather, as the previous pages point out, it is the beginning. The famous science fiction writer Arthur C. Clarke once put it this way:

> *Two possibilities exist: Either we are alone in the universe or we are not. Both are equally terrifying.*

If that sounds a little depressing (you'd prefer to look at this question as an exhilarating one instead) perhaps some humor from Arthur C. Clarke would fit the bill instead:

> *I'm sure the universe is full of intelligent life. It's just been too intelligent to come here!*

Summary

In this chapter, we did the following:

▶ Reviewed the case for UFO/alien visitations to Earth

▶ Discussed the possibility of fast space travel

▶ Talked about the possibility of extraterrestrial intelligences in the Milky Way

Questions

1. Suppose astronomers sent out a radio signal inviting prospective extraterrestrials for a talk 50 years ago. How far has the signal traveled?

2. Suppose extraterrestrials living 25 light years away receive a signal from us and respond immediately. How long will we have to wait to receive their reply?

3. The first radio broadcast of a baseball game, between the Pittsburgh Pirates and the Philadelphia Phillies, was aired in 1921. The Pleiades cluster is 136 parsecs away. Assuming aliens living on a planet orbiting Merope (one of the bright Pleiads) love baseball, when can they first enjoy the game?

4. Taking an optimistic point of view, suppose the various factors in the Drake equation are thus: $R_* = 3$ stars per year, $f_p = 1$, $n_e = 3$, $f_l = 1/10$, $f_i = 1/10$, $f_c = 1/10$, and $L = 1000$ years. How many technological civilizations can we expect to be in the Milky Way?

5. The Milky Way is thought to possess about 400 billion stars. Using the previous results, about how many stars are there per technological civilization?

Activities

▸ *Astrophysics activity 24.1:* With help from the instructor, discuss the various factors involved in the Drake equation and use it to come up with an estimate of the number of extraterrestrial civilizations in the Milky Way.

Works Referenced

Supposed cases of UFO/Alien encounters (including fictional portrayals) are surprisingly well documented. In order of presentation in the text they are as follows:

The Hill case is discussed in the following sources:

Spielberg, S. (Producer). (1977). *Close encounters of the third kind* [Movie]. United States: Columbia Pictures.

Sagan, C., Druvan, A., & Soter, S. (Writers). (1980). *Cosmos: A personal voyage* [TV series]. PBS. United States. UFOs, the Drake Equation etc. are discussed in episode #12, "Encyclopaedia Galactica."

Fuller, J. G. (1975). *The Interrupted Journey*. The Dial Press. New York.

Dunning, B. (October 21, 2008). Skeptoid #124: Barney and Betty Hill: The original UFO abduction. *Skeptoid* (podcast) https://skeptoid.com/episodes/4124 Retrieved 2019-04-21.

Kottmeyer, M. (1990, January). *Entirely Unpredisposed: The Cultural Background of UFO Abduction Reports.* https://www.debunker.com/texts/unpredis.html Retrieved 2019-04-21.

* Crop circles are discussed in the following sources:

Peter J. M., & Roodenburg, H. (2007). *Reframing Dutch culture: Between otherness and authenticity. Progress in European ethnology* (illustrated ed.). Ashgate Publishing Inc.

Sagan, C. (1997). *The Demon-Haunted World; Science as a Candle in the Dark.* Ballentine Books. New York.

Eddie, L. (2004, November 4). *The Skeptics SA guide to: Crop circles.* Retrieved from Skepticssa.org.au

Taylor, R. (August 2011). Coming soon to a field near you. *Physics World.* https://physicsworld.com/a/coming-soon-to-a-field-near-you/ Retrieved 2019-04-21.

Brough, G. (September 9, 1991). "Men who conned the world." *Today.* https://menwhoconnedtheworld.weebly.com/new-11-today-september-9-1991.html Retrieved 2019-04-21.

Vidal, J. (June 5, 2009). "The bizarre revival of crop circles—and advice on how to make your own." *The Guardian*. https://www.theguardian.com/uk/2009/jun/05/ruralaffairs Retrieved 2019-04-21.

* The Roswell "Incident" is discussed in the following sources:

Roswell UFO incident, season 8, episode 2. (1997) *Scientific American Frontiers*. United States: PBS. https://www.tvguide.com/tvshows/scientific-american-frontiers/episode-2-season-8/beyond-science/194931/ Retrieved 2019-04-21.

Frazier, K. (2017). The Roswell incident at 70: Facts, not myths. *Skeptical Inquirer*, 41(6), 12–15.

Olmsted, K. S. (2009, March 11). *Real enemies: Conspiracy theories and American democracy, World War I to 9/11*. Oxford, UK: Oxford University Press.

Broad, W. J. (1994, September 18). Wreckage in the desert was odd but not alien. *New York Times*. https://www.nytimes.com/1994/09/18/us/wreckage-in-the-desert-was-odd-but-not-alien.html Retrieved 2019-04-21.

Associated Press. (1947, July 9). New Mexico "disc" declared weather balloon and kite. *Los Angeles Examiner*, p. 1.

Goldberg, R. A. (2001). The Roswell incident. In *Enemies within: The culture of conspiracy in Modern America* (pp. 189–231). New Haven, CT: Yale University Press.

CNN. (1997, June 15). Poll U.S. hiding knowledge of aliens. http://www.cnn.com/US/9706/15/ufo.poll/ Retrieved 2019-04-21.

Harding, S., & Stewart, K. (2003). Anxieties of influence: Conspiracy theory and therapeutic culture in millennial America. In H. G. West & T. Sanders (Eds.), *Transparency and conspiracy: Ethnographies of suspicion in the new world order* (pp. 258–286). Durham, NC: Duke University Press.

Klass, P. (1997). The Klass files. *The Skeptics UFO Newsletter*, 43.

Klass, P. (1998). The Klass files. *The Skeptics UFO Newsletter*, 49.

* The declassified proposal for a U.S. Air Force flying saucer is now online at the following sites:

https://apps.dtic.mil/dtic/tr/fulltext/u2/a606604.pdf

https://apps.dtic.mil/docs/citations/ADA606604 (gives a short summary)

https://airwingmedia.com/news/2012/usaf-project-1794-plans-for-a-mach-4-flying-saucer-aircraft/ (shows a downloadable image of the flying saucer blueprints)

Space travel, including references to special relativity, are discussed in https://www.jpl.nasa.gov/news/press_kits/juno/facts/

The Drake equation and attempts to estimate the possibility of extraterrestrial intelligences is discussed in the following sources:

Drake, N. (2014, June 30). "How my dad's equation sparked the search for extraterrestrial intelligence." *National Geographic*. https://cacm.acm.org/opinion/articles/176351-how-my-dads-equation-sparked-the-search-for-extraterrestrial-intelligence/fulltext?mobile=true?mobile=false Retrieved 2019-04-21.

Astrobiology Magazine. (2003, September 29). "The Drake equation revisited: Part I." https://www.astrobio.net/alien-life/the-drake-equation-revisited-part-i/ Retrieved 2019-04-21.

The Planetary Society's home page is www.planetary.org

The SETI Institute's home page is seti.org

Robitaille, T. P., & Whitney, B. A. (2010). The present-day star formation rate of the Milky Way determined from Spitzer-detected young stellar objects. *Astrophysical Journal Letters*, 710(1), L11. doi:10.1088/2041-8205/710/1/L1

Kennicutt, R. C., & Evans, N. J. (2012, September 22). Star formation in the Milky Way and nearby galaxies. *Annual Review of Astronomy and Astrophysics*, 50(1), 531–608. doi:10.1146/annurev-astro-081811-125610

Cassan, A, Kubbas, D., Beaulieu, J. P., Dominik, M., Horne, K., Greenhill, J., ... & Wyrzykowski, L. (2012, January 11). One or more bound planets per Milky Way star from microlensing observations. *Nature*, *481*(7380), 167–169. doi:10.1038/nature10684

NASA Exoplanet Science Institute: NASA Exoplanet Archive. https://exoplanetarchive.ipac.caltech.edu/docs/counts_detail.html

Petigura, E. A., Howard, A. W., & Marcy, G. W. (2013 October). Prevalence of Earth-size planets orbiting Sun-like stars. *Proceedings of the National Academy of Sciences of the United States of America*, *110*, 19273–19278. doi:10.1073/pnas.1319909110

Crick, F. H. C., & Orgel, L. E. (1973). Directed panspermia. *Icarus*, *19*(3), 341–346. doi:10.1016/0019-1035(73)90110-3

Miller, S. L. (1953). A production of amino acids under possible primitive Earth conditions. *Science*, *117*(3046), 528–529. doi:10.1126/science.117.3046.528

Miller, S. L., & Urey, H. C. (1959). Organic compound synthesis on the primitive Earth. *Science*, *130*(3370), 245–251. doi:10.1126/science.130.3370.245

Kvenvolden, K. A., Lawless, J., Pering, K., Peterson, E., Flores, J., Ponnamperuma, C., ... & Moore, C. (1970). Evidence for extraterrestrial amino-acids and hydrocarbons in the Murchison meteorite. *Nature*, *228*(5275), 923–926. doi:10.1038/228923a0

Schmitt-Kopplin, P., Gabelica, Z., Gougeon, R. D., Fekete, A., Kanawati, B., Harir, M., ... & Hertkorn, N. (2010, February 16). "High molecular diversity of extraterrestrial organic matter in Murchison meteorite revealed 40 years after its fall. *PNAS*, *107*(7), 2763–2768. doi:10.1073/pnas.0912157107

Thompson W. R., Murray B. G., Khare B. N., & Sagan, C. (1987, December). Coloration and darkening of methane clathrate and other ices by charged particle irradiation: Applications to the outer solar system. *Journal of Geophysical Research*, *92*(A13), 14933–14947. doi:10.1029/JA092iA13p14933.

Science Engineering Themes (February 2, 2010). "Can SETI Succeed? Carl Sagan and Ernst Mayr Debate." http://scifi-harrykar.blogspot.com/2010/02/can-seti-succeed-carl-sagan-and-ernst.html Retrieved 2019-04-21.

Haviland, W. A., Prins, H. E. L., Walrath, D., & McBride, B. (2012). *The essence of anthropology* (3rd ed.). Cengage/Wadsworth, Belmont, CA.

Hu, J. C. (2014, August 20). "The Story Behind 'What do talking apes really tell us?'" *Slate*. https://slate.com/technology/2014/08/koko-kanzi-and-ape-language-research-jane-c-hu-talks-about-how-she-got-the-story.html Retrieved 2019-04-21.

Shermer, M. (2002, August). Why ET hasn't called. *Scientific American*, 21.

Both Arthur C. Clarke quotations are found at https://www.goodreads.com/quotes/tag/universe

Credits

LAGNIAPPE

Here, we give students a *Lagniappe*, a "little something extra," a glimpse at more complex ideas and formulae that were mentioned in the textbook but not explicitly covered.

"Clearing the Neighborhood"

How do we define a planet? The International Astronomical Union (IAU) put forward three criteria in 2006. The first two—that a planet orbits the Sun and is massive enough to be spherical—are straightforward. But the third criterion—that a planet "clears" its "neighborhood"—is more abstract. What does it mean?

Several researchers have worked on this question. Here, we summarize the results from a study published by Jean-Luc Margot in 2015.

The table lists the major planets, and some dwarf planets, comparing their masses and one version of these "discriminants":

TABLE L.1. Distinguishing Between Major and Dwarf Planets

Planet	Mass (ME)	Planetary discriminant
Mercury	0.055	1.3×10^2
Venus	0.815	9.5×10^2
Earth	1	8.1×10^2
Mars	0.107	5.4×10^1
Ceres	1.6×10^{-4}	4.0×10^{-2}
Jupiter	317.8	4.0×10^4
Saturn	95.19	6.1×10^3
Uranus	14.54	4.2×10^2
Neptune	17.15	3.0×10^2
Pluto	2.2×10^{-3}	2.8×10^{-2}
Eris	2.8×10^{-3}	2.0×10^{-2}

The "discriminant" relates the mass of the object to the size of its orbit and its orbital period. It thus estimates the gravitational influence of the object on its surroundings. Several versions of discriminants exist; we are showing the simplest version, here. If the discriminant is greater than 1, we can say the object's gravity "dominates" its neighborhood; if the discriminant is less than 1, the object does not.

The planetary discriminant for the eight major planets are each both several orders of magnitude larger than 1 and larger than the discriminants for the dwarf planets. It suggests there really is a way to tell the difference between planets and other objects in the solar system. Further, such criteria can be applied to planets orbiting other stars, and they too show similar results. It gives us a reason as to why each planet has its own "neighborhood."

Work Cited

Margot, J-L. (2015). "A Quantitative Criterion for Defining Planets". https://arxiv.org/pdf/1507.06300.pdf Retrieved 2019-04-21.

Kelvin-Helmholtz Contraction

In 1887, Sir William Thomson (later named Lord Kelvin) suggested a mechanism for the enormous power output of the Sun. At the time, astronomers were engaged in an informal debate with biologists and geologists regarding the age of the Earth, and Thomson decided to estimate the maximum amount of time the Earth could have existed by looking at the Sun. A German physicist, Hermann Ludwig Ferdinand von Helmholtz, made a similar suggestion.

The Sun is made of gas. Suppose the Sun's gravity acts to shrink the gas. The shrinking of the Sun would turn gravitational potential energy into heat.

The formula for the potential gravitational energy between two masses is given by

$$U_g = -G\frac{m_1 m_2}{r}$$

How do we assess the gravitational potential energy of a single object? Or, what are the two separate objects if we're considering one object?

The Sun is nearly a perfect sphere. Assuming that it is a sphere, we can separate the Sun into two parts—an extremely thin shell on the outside, and the rest of the Sun on the inside.

We also assume the Sun's density is the s ame throughout. This isn't true, but the assumption simplifies the calculation and still gives us an order-of-magnitude answer (i.e., the answer we get should be within a factor of 10 of the "real" answer). If we do this (and skipping a quick calculus-based calculation), we get this for the Sun:

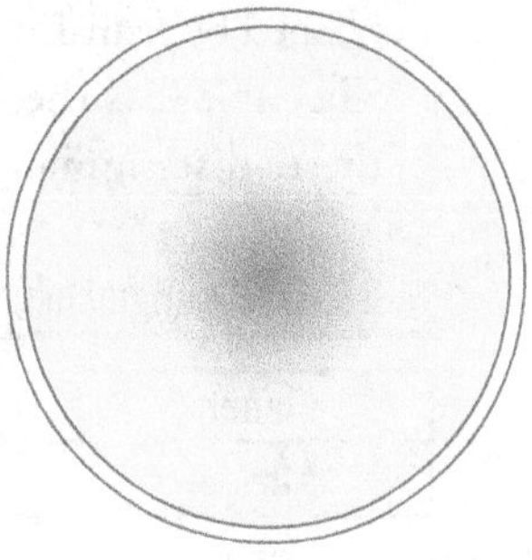

FIGURE L.1. The Sun represented as having an extremely thin spherical shell surrounding the rest of the Sun.

$$U_\odot = -\frac{3GM^2}{5R}$$

Plugging in values for the universal gravitational constant (6.67×10^{-11} N·m²/kg²), the mass of the Sun (1.99×10^{30} kg), and the radius of the Sun (6.96×10^8 m), we get

$$U_\odot = 2.28 \times 10^{41} \text{ joules}$$

The luminosity (power output, or change of energy) of the Sun is $L_\odot = 3.84 \times 10^{26}$ watts. Assuming the luminosity (i.e., the brightness of the Sun) remains constant, we can find the maximum lifespan of the Sun by dividing the two numbers:

$$t = \frac{U_\odot}{L_\odot} = 9{,}000{,}000 \text{ years}$$

While this amount of time is rather long, it was not nearly long enough to satisfy the biologists and geologists. With the discovery of nuclear processes (first radioactive decay, then nuclear fusion) as more energy-efficient options, astronomers were able to revise their estimates of the lifespan of the Sun and Earth, and found they were more in line with the requirements of the other disciplines.

Black Body Radiation

Max Planck's formula for the emitted flux (per unit wavelength) of a black body object is

$$F_\lambda = \frac{8\pi hc}{\lambda^5} \frac{1}{e^{hc/\lambda kT} - 1}$$

where h is Planck's constant (6.63×10^{-34} J·s), c is the speed of light, λ is the wavelength of the light, k is Boltzmann's constant (1.38×10^{-23} J/K), and T is temperature. Astronomers call this emitted flux; physicists tend to call it emitted intensity, and so sometimes you may find the symbol for flux (intensity) as an I_λ instead of F_λ, or even S_λ, an older version of physics notation.

Mass-Luminosity Relations

A shorthand version of the mass-luminosity relationship estimates that the luminosity of a main sequence star scales as the mass of the star to the 3.5 power. It turns out that, for various reasons, this isn't strictly true for certain masses:

TABLE L.2. Mass-Luminosity Relationships

Range of masses ($M_\odot$)	M-L relation (in solar units)	Comments
$M < 0.43$	$L \sim M^{2.3}$	Energy transport in these stars is solely via convection
$0.43 < M < 2$	$L \sim M^4$	Energy generated primarily via proton-proton chain
$2 < M < 20$	$L \sim M^{3.5}$	Energy generated primarily via CNO cycle
$M > 20$	$L \sim 3200\, M$	Radiation pressure becomes important

The first person to attempt deriving such relationships was Arthur Eddington in 1924. Concepts to incorporate include black body radiation, gravity, gas pressure (treat the gas inside the star as an ideal gas), hydrostatic equilibrium, opacity, and so on.

Relaxation Times for Stellar Clusters

After its formation, the ability of a cluster of stars to hold itself together depends on the mass and size of the cluster, compared to the tidal forces from the rest of the galaxy. Because clusters do not have set boundaries, astronomers sometimes use an idea called "half-radius" to represent the extent (size) of a cluster; that is, the distance from the center of the cluster at which half of the mass of the cluster is included.

The "disruption time scale" for a cluster is given by Binney and Tremaine (2008) as

$$\tau_{\text{dis}} = 250 \text{ Myr} \left(\frac{M}{300\, M_\odot} \right)^{1/2} \left(\frac{2 \text{ pc}}{r_h} \right)^{3/2}$$

where r_h is the half-radius of the cluster in parsecs and M the total mass of the cluster in solar masses.

For example, the Pleiades has an estimated 800 $M_\odot$ and a half-radius of about 2.45 pc. Then we find its disruption time scale to be about 300 million years. The Pleiades are estimated to be between 115 and 125 million years old.

The time scale does not mark the date at which the cluster has completely disintegrated; rather, it suggests an exponential decay (much like radioactivity) such that about 2/3 of the cluster will have dissipated within that time. 2/3 of the remaining cluster will have dissipated after another time scale, and so on. These are approximations; clusters also consist of stars that are themselves aging, of binary systems which both interact with the overall cluster and the individual stars making up the binary system; tidal forces from the galaxy or other passing objects can speed up the disintegration, and so on. The Pleiades are expected to live as a cluster for about a billion years or so.

Jeans Instability

The first person to propose a detailed mechanism for star formation was James Jeans in 1902. Essentially, a nebula will begin to collapse if the gas pressure exerted by particles in the nebula is less than the pressure exerted by the mutual gravitation of the particles.

We can use these ideas to derive a formula for the minimum mass needed by an interstellar cloud to initiate a collapse. We can start by assuming the nebula is dominated by hydrogen gas, acts like an ideal gas, and is spherical in shape.

The work (energy) exerted by such a cloud's particles is

$$\Delta W = nTR^2 \Delta R$$

where n is the number density (i.e., number of particles per unit volume), T is the temperature, and R is the radius of the nebula. The triangle symbol Δ (the capital Greek letter "delta") represents change, and so this is the amount of energy needed to be used in order to attempt to push the nebula outward over a small change of radius.

In opposition, the energy exerted by the mutual gravitational attraction of the particles is given by

$$\Delta U = \frac{M^2}{R^2} \Delta R$$

Where M is the total mass of the nebula. Equilibrium occurs when these two energies equal each other. We also note that the total mass of the nebula depends on the density and volume of the nebula, which is approximately $M = nR^3$. Using these facts, and including all the constants involved (which are not explicitly shown, here), we get the Jeans mass:

$$M_J = (3 \times 10^4 \ M_\odot) \left(\frac{T^3}{n} \right)^{1/2}$$

For example, if a nebula has an average temperature of 100 K, and a number density of 1 million particles per cubic meter, then the Jeans Mass is 30,000 $M_\odot$. If such a nebula has a larger mass, then it will collapse under its own weight.

The Virial Theorem

Borrowed from the branch of physics known as statistical mechanics, the virial theorem relates the time-averaged kinetic energy of a system of particles to the sum of the potential energies between all the particles. For stars, the potential energy comes from gravity, and the relationship becomes

$$(K) = -\frac{1}{2}(V)$$

where K is the kinetic energy, V the potential energy, and the brackets refer to the time averaging of the energies.

We can take this a step further. Kinetic energy for a gas is both related to the time-averaged speed of the particles and the overall temperature of the gas. If we assume protons (i.e., the nuclei of hydrogen atoms) are the dominant particles for a forming star, then we get

$$\frac{1}{2}m\bar{v}^2 = \frac{3}{2}k_BT = \frac{3}{5}\frac{GMm}{R}$$

where m is the mass of the proton, $\bar{v}$ the time-averaged speed of the protons, k_B is the Boltzmann constant, T the temperature, G the universal gravitational constant, M the total mass of the star, and R the radius of the star. Note the fractions are actually rough estimates, not exact numbers.

Other things being equal, this states that the larger the mass of the star, the higher its temperature is likely to be. It also states the smaller the radius of the star, the higher its temperature is likely to be. Therefore, as a protostar gathers mass to itself and shrinks, it heats up.

The Chandrasekhar Limit

White dwarfs are made of degenerate matter, and this phase of matter behaves differently than others. Specifically, the larger the mass of the white dwarf, the smaller it is. We can derive this result like so.

The total energy contained in a white dwarf is its gravitational potential energy plus its kinetic energy (or more specifically, the sum of the kinetic energies of all of its particles). The gravitational potential is on the order of

$$E_g = -G\frac{M}{R}$$

where G is the universal gravitational constant, M the mass of the white dwarf, and R the radius of the white dwarf.

The total kinetic energy contained in the white dwarf is a bit more complicated to calculate and explicitly uses quantum-mechanical properties, specifically the uncertainty principle. The uncertainty principle states that we cannot determine the momentum p of a particle and the position x of a particle perfectly well at the same time. The principle is most often expressed in terms of the uncertainties Δp and Δx of the particles:

$$\Delta p \Delta x \geq \hbar$$

where $\hbar$ is the reduced Planck's constant (i.e., $h/2\pi$). In this case, because the electrons are essentially locked in place, the uncertainties in their positions is the reciprocal of the cube root of the number density n (i.e., $n^{-1/3}$) in the white dwarf. The average kinetic energy of an individual electron can be expressed as

$$\bar{K} = \frac{1}{2}mv^2 = \frac{p^2}{2m}$$

where the m is the mass of the electron. In the case of the white dwarf, we can replace the momentum p with its uncertainty Dp. The total kinetic energy of the white dwarf is simply then the number of electrons N multiplied by the average kinetic energy, or

$$E_k = N\bar{K} = N\frac{(\Delta p)^2}{2m}$$

The number density of the white dwarf will be on the order of NM/R^3. Using this and the uncertainty principle, we can make substitutions that lead us to

$$E_k = \frac{M^{2/3} N^{5/3} \hbar^2}{2MR^2}$$

The total energy is minimized (that is, the pull of gravity inward balances the push of the degenerate matter outward) when the gravitational potential energy equals the kinetic energy. If we do this and solve for the radius, we get

$$R = \frac{N^{5/3} \hbar^2}{2mGM^{1/3}}$$

which states that the radius changes with the inverse of the cube root of the mass. Or, in plainer language, the <u>larger</u> the mass, the <u>smaller</u> the radius.

However, this derivation assumes that the white dwarf is non-relativistic. But the electrons will be moving at nearly the speed of light. This means we should substitute the relativistic formula for kinetic energy, pc (where c is the speed of light) for $p^2/2m$. If we do this, then we get a new result for the total kinetic energy:

$$E_k = \frac{M^{1/3} N^{4/3} \hbar c}{R}$$

Notice that the gravitational potential energy also has R in its denominator. Setting these energies again equal to each other and solving this time for the mass yields

$$M = N^2 \left(\frac{\hbar c}{G} \right)^{3/2}$$

These calculations are approximations; doing this more carefully tells us the radius approaches zero (it can't get any smaller) when the mass of the white dwarf reaches 1.44 $M_\odot$. This result is known as the *Chandrasekhar limit*. Finally, this calculation does not account for other factors such as rotation. The mass limit does not change much for a uniformly rotating white dwarf, but could potentially become meaningless if the rotation isn't uniform.

Approximate Shapes of Roche Lobes

The gravitational interaction between two stars is complicated enough that solutions to their shapes can only be found by numerical calculations (these days, via computer). But a good analytic solution was found by P. P. Eggleton that looks like this:

$$\frac{r_1}{a} = \frac{0.49q^{2/3}}{0.6q^{2/3} + \ln(1 + q^{1/3})}$$

where a is the orbital distance between the stars, r_1 is the radius of the sphere that approximates the Roche lobe for star #1, and q is the ratio of the two masses of the stars (i.e., m_1/m_2). The formula is accurate to within 1% of the actual shape of the Roche lobe.

Work Cited

Eggleton, P. P. (1983, May 1). Approximations to the radii of Roche lobes. *Astrophysical Journal, 268*, 368. doi:10.1086/160960

Neutron Stars

Most of the discussions regarding neutron stars are beyond our scope here, but we can cite two interesting results. Bear in mind that neutron stars, like white dwarfs, are supported by degeneracy pressure, but in this due to neutrons (naturally), not electrons.

Our first result is the size of a neutron star. The approximate radius R of a neutron star is

$$R = (11 \text{ km})\left(\frac{1.5 \, M_\odot}{M}\right)^{1/3}$$

where M is the mass of the neutron star. For example, if the neutron star's mass is $1.5 \, M_\odot$, then it has a radius of 11 km (about 7 miles). Like white dwarfs, the radius of a neutron star decreases with increasing mass. Neutron stars also have a mass limit, but at $3.0 \, M_\odot$ rather than the $1.44 \, M_\odot$ for white dwarfs.

Assuming a spherical shape, the density ρ of a neutron star is given by

$$\rho = \frac{3M}{4\pi R^3} = \frac{4.5 M_\odot}{4\pi(11 \text{ km})^3}$$

which yields a density around $5 \times 10^{17} \text{ km/m}^3$, on the order of the density of an individual neutron or proton. Which is to say, a neutron star is very much like (to first approximation) a giant atomic nucleus.

Our second result is the energy E lost by the progenitor star (via Type II supernova) in order to form the neutron star. This ends up being

$$E \approx (1.6 \times 10^{46} \text{ J})\left(\frac{M}{1.5 \, M_\odot}\right)^2 \left(\frac{11 \text{ km}}{R}\right)$$

Or, to form a neutron star of $1.5 \, M_\odot$, the star must release about 1.6×10^{46} J of energy. To put this into perspective, recall the Sun's luminosity is 3.96×10^{26} W. In order to release this much energy, the Sun must do so for

$$\text{Time} = E/L_\odot = (1.6 \times 10^{46} \text{ J})/(3.96 \times 10^{26} \text{ W}) = 4 \times 10^{19} \text{ s} = 1.3 \text{ trillion years}$$

which is a fancy way of saying that either (a) this supernova releases as much energy as the Sun would if it shone for 1.3 trillion years, or (b) the supernova releases as much energy in one second as 1.3 trillion Suns.

The majority of the energy (about 90% of the total) goes into the production of neutrinos (during photodisintegration), which leaves a small amount used to blow apart the star (9%) and an even tinier amount to visible light (1%). If we want an estimate as to the brightness of a supernova, then take 1% of the number found above, or 13 billion Suns, a result in agreement with observations of supernovae in distant galaxies.

Work Cited

Cardall, C. (2008). Degeneracy, the virial theorem, and stellar collapse. *American Journal of Physics*. Retrieved from https://arxiv.org/pdf/0812.0114.pdf

The Shapes of Spiral Galaxies

The most common method for modeling the shapes of spiral arms historically has been via a logarithmic curve. But this does not account for why the spiral arms begin at the end of the bulge, nor why there may or may not be a bar.

Recent work by Ringermacher and Mead (2009), using non-Euclidean geometry (i.e., taking general relativity into account), suggests a more general formula:

$$r(\phi) = \frac{A}{\log[B\tan(\phi/2N)]}$$

where *A*, *B*, and *N* represent various parameters and ϕ is the angle around the galaxy. *A* is a scale factor for the entire structure (disk) of the galaxy, *B* controls the relative sizes of the bar to the arms, and *N* controls for the tightness of the winding of the arms. An example is shown next:

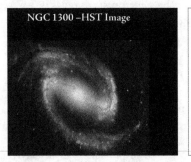
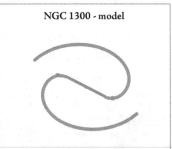

FIGURE L.2. An image of NGC 1300 at left; a mathematical model of the shape of the arms and bar of NGC 1300 at right.

One of the most important consequences of this work is that it implies all spiral galaxies possess bars, whether they are visible or not. Some bars are so small that they are subsumed inside their respective bulges, but they are still there, and the arms naturally come "off" of the ends of the bars regardless.

Work Cited

Ringermacher, H. I. & Mead, L. R. (July 10, 2009). "A new formula describing the scaffold structure of spiral galaxies." Monthly Notices of the Royal Astronomical Society (MNRAS). 397, 1, pp. 164–171. https://onlinelibrary.wiley.com/doi/pdf/10.1111/j.1365-2966.2009.14950.x Retrieved 2019-04-21.

The Cosmological Constant

Einstein's equation governing the overall behavior of the universe invokes some of the most complicated math applied to physics. Physics recognizes different types of quantities: (a) scalars, which are just numbers (i.e., you could measure them on a scale), examples of which include mass, time, and even money; (b) vectors, which are both numbers and directions, examples of which include velocity (imagine driving 55 mph due north on a highway); and (c) tensors, which are grids of numbers. Einstein's general relativity uses tensors.

Tensor notation uses two super- or subscripts after the quantity's symbol. The first script is the horizontal row of the grid of numbers, and the second script is the vertical column of the grid. General relativity commonly uses 4 × 4 grids.

Einstein's equation looks like this:

$$R_{\mu\nu} - \frac{1}{2}Rg_{\mu\nu} + \Lambda g_{\mu\nu} = \frac{8\pi G}{c^4}\, T_{\mu\nu}$$

We aren't going to calculate with this (fortunately!), but we can look at the symbols and discuss what they represent. "*R*" discusses the structure of space/time, "*g*" discusses the effects of gravity, "*G*" is the universal gravitational constant, "*c*" is the speed of light, and "*T*" discusses the effects of matter—energy, momentum, and so on—at that point of space/time. "Λ" is Einstein's famous "cosmological constant," the factor he placed in the equation to represent a counterbalance to gravity.

If $T = 0$, then the universe is completely empty of matter, and we are dealing with vacuum. If $\Lambda = 0$, then the universe does not have a counterbalance. If Λ is positive, then the universe experiences a negative pressure that pulls it apart; if Λ is negative, then the universe experiences a positive pressure that pushes it together.

Modern measurements (of the Hubble constant and the mass density of the universe) suggest a value of

$$\Lambda = 1.1056 \times 10^{-52} \ m^{-2}$$

which is very small, but not zero. Since Λ is positive, it suggests the universe should not only be expanding, but that the expansion is getting faster, or "accelerating"—which is what astronomers discovered in the mid-1990s.

Length Contraction and Mass Increase

Einstein (and others) showed that an object traveling close to the speed of light experiences a variety of strange effects. One of those is *length contraction*.

Suppose two observers, both at rest, measure the distance between two objects as L_0. Then one observer moves between those objects at near the speed of light. The moving observer then perceives the distance between the objects L to shrink:

$$L = \frac{L_0}{\gamma}$$

where γ is called the gamma factor and incorporates the effects of high-speed motion. The gamma factor itself is

$$\gamma = \frac{1}{\sqrt{1 - (v^2 \ / \ c^2)}}$$

where v is the speed of the moving observer and c is the speed of light.

If the observer is not moving, then $v = 0$, $\gamma = 1$ and the length doesn't change. But as the observer's speed increases, the gamma factor also increases. For example, if $v = \frac{1}{2} \ c$, then $\gamma = 1.15$. If $v = 90\%$ of c, then $\gamma = 2.29$.

The length of the trip for our moving observer goes down correspondingly. If the observer is moving at 50% the speed of light, then the trip is 87% of its length if the observer is not moving. If the observer is moving at 90% the speed of light, then the length is 44% of its unmoving length, and so on.

Finally, the mass of the moving object goes up with the gamma factor:

$$m = \gamma m_0$$

So, a spaceship has a mass 115% larger when moving at 50% the speed of light than it did at rest, 229% of its rest mass when moving at 90% the speed of light, and so on.

Credit

Fig. L.2a: Source: https://commons.wikimedia.org/wiki/File:Hubble2005-01-barred-spiral-galaxy-NGC1300.jpg.

INDEX

Aurora, 246, 256, 262, 265, 267

Autumnal equinox. *See* equinox, autumnal

Axial tilt. *See also* inclination

Axis, 28–29, 33–35, 40–41, 53–55, 67, 74–75, 98, 150–152, 218, 264–265, 301, 403, 504

Azimuth, 13, 28, 33–35, 115

B

Bar magnet, 253–254, 262

Barnard's Star, 14–15, 118, 296–297, 366, 468–470, 531

Barred spiral galaxy. *See* galaxy, spiral barred

Baryon, 377

Basalt, 138, 214, 216

Becquerel, Antoine-Henry, 213

Bell, Jocelyn. *See also* Bell, Jocelyn Burnell

Bessel, Friedrich Wilhelm, 296

Beta Pictoris, 383

Betelgeuse, 11, 31, 321, 419

Bethe, Hans, 378–380

Bias, 526

Big Bang, 123, 211, 304, 499–500, 506, 509–510, 512, 514, 517

Big Crunch, 516

Big Rip, 516

Binary, 97, 298–301, 345–346, 384–385, 405–409, 421, 440–442, 449, 451. *See also* binary star
  astrometric, 301
  contact, 183, 323, 345–346, 385–386, 406, 510, 515, 525, 528
  detached, 243, 301, 345–346, 385, 405–408, 447
  eclipsing, 300–301, 385, 406, 451
  semi-detached, 301, 345–346
  spectroscopic, 5, 222, 300, 336, 343–344
  visual, 17, 31, 197, 299–300

Binding energy, 423

Bi-polar jets, 445, 453

Black body, 279–280, 319–323, 338, 382, 447, 453, 510, 547

Black body radiation. *See* radiation, thermal

Black hole, 118–119, 123–124, 126, 183, 303, 346, 391, 393, 417, 422, 426–427, 435, 441–452, 454–457, 469, 472–474, 480, 490, 502

Black smoker, 257

Blazkho, Sergey, 392

Bode's Law, 135

Bohr, Niels, 324–327, 336

Bok, Bart, 356, 361

Bok globule, 356, 361

Boltzmann constant, 234, 320

Boltzmann, Ludwig, 234–235, 318, 320, 547, 549

Boson, 423

Brahe, Tycho, 72, 118, 294, 296, 407

Brown dwarf, 364

Brown, Michael, 17–18, 151, 192, 246, 364, 465, 467–468, 480

Bulge. *See also* galactic bulge, galactic nucleus

Bunsen, Robert, 323

Bussard ramjet, 533

C

Calendar, 51–52, 71, 304
  Egyptian, 51, 301, 304, 314, 465
  Gregorian, 52
  Julian, 51–52

Callisto, 191, 217–221, 262–263

Cambrian explosion, 198

Cambridge University (with the Cavendish Laboratory), 324, 341

Cannon, Annie Jump, 95, 182–183, 305, 336–338, 342

Cantaloupe terrain, 222

Carbon, 64, 146, 278, 284–285, 380, 397, 399, 403, 405, 408, 420–421, 424, 453, 512

Carbon-nitrogen-oxygen (CNO) cycle, 379–380, 397, 547

Cassini (i.e. the probe), 223, 243, 263

Cataclysmic variable. *See* variable star, cataclysmic

Catastrophism, 211–212

Cavendish, Henry, 324, 442

Celestial equator, 29, 33

Celestial sphere, 28–29, 54, 68–69, 72, 292, 294, 296

Center for High Angular Resolution Astronomy (CHARA), 301, 374, 386, 406

Center of mass, 96–98, 163, 168, 384

Central engine, 454

Centripetal acceleration. *See* acceleration, centripetal

Cepheid variable, 305, 336, 478, 485–486

Ceres, 135, 139–140, 143, 217, 545

Chandra (i.e. the telescope), 402, 405, 407–408, 424, 440, 443, 549–550

Chandrasekhar Limit, 405, 408, 424, 440, 549–550

Chandrasekhar, Subhartha, 402, 405, 408, 424, 440, 549–550

H

Habitable zone. *See also* Goldilocks zone

Halley, Edmond, 144–145, 294–295, 421

Halley's comet, 294

Halo, 366–367, 469–472, 481, 535
  galactic, 344, 366, 407, 454–455, 461, 468, 472, 491, 500, 504–506, 509, 530, 537–538, 540

Haro, Guillermo, 151, 193, 363, 537

Hartley (e.g. a comet), 218

Hartmann, Johannes, 194, 353

Hartmann, William K., 194, 353

Harvard classification scheme, 338

Harvard College Observatory, 305, 341

Harvard Observatory. *See also* Harvard College observatory

Hawking radiation, 446

Hazard, Cyril, 452–453

HDE 226868, 451

Heat, 319, 355–356, 382, 399–400, 404, 467

Heisenberg Uncertainty Principle. *See* uncertainty principle

Heliocentrism. *See also* heliocentric model

Helium, 91, 136–137, 139, 162, 172, 175, 215, 225–226, 236, 324, 353–354, 363, 393, 398

Helium flash, 398, 405

Helix Nebula, 358

Hellas Planitia. *See also* Hellas Impact Basin

Henyey, Louis George, 364

Henyey track, 364

Herbig, George, 363

Herbig-Haro object, 363

Hercules X. *See also* Her X-1

Hershel, Caroline, 78, 161, 353, 358, 401, 421

Hershel, John, 78, 161, 353, 358, 401, 421

Hershel, William, 78, 161, 353, 358, 401, 421

Hertzsprung, Ejnar, 305, 339, 357

Hewish, Antony, 438

HII region, 303, 357, 359, 465, 467, 480

Hill, Barney, 261, 319, 340, 525–526

Hill, Betty, 261, 319, 340, 525–526

Hipparchus, 31, 54, 118, 294, 332

Hipparcos (e.g. telescope), 297, 339, 392

HI region, 303, 357, 359, 465, 467, 480

HL Tauri, 162

Horizon, 27–28, 33, 151, 243, 446–448, 455

Horsehead Nebula, 19, 165, 356

Hot Jupiter, 163

Hot spot, 146, 214, 224

Hour angle, 10, 25–26

Hubble constant, 11–12, 305, 505, 508

Hubble, Edwin, 304–305, 357, 479, 503

Hubble's Law. *See also* Hubble-Lemaitré Law

Hubble Space Telescope, 169, 174, 245, 265, 293, 301, 305, 345, 362, 404, 488, 490

Hubble tuning fork, 479

Huchra, John, 487

Humason, Milton, 304, 479, 504–505

Hutton, James, 211

Huygens, Christiaan, 100, 243, 312–313

Huygens (e.g. probe), 100, 243, 312–313

Hyashi, Chusiro, 364

Hyashi track, 364

Hydrogen, 17, 225, 260–261, 282, 317, 337, 379, 393, 511
  atomic, 279, 355–356, 359
  metallic, 225, 261–262, 275
  molecular, 355

Hydrogen alpha, 118

Hydrostatic equilibrium, 276–277, 376, 404, 547

Hypernova, 422

I

Icy dwarf, 151

Ida, 91, 142–143

Ideal gas. *See also* ideal gas law

Impact, 187–192, 194, 259

Impactor, 188–190

Inclination. *See also* axial tilt

Inflation, 514–517

Infrared, 111, 118, 123, 137, 186, 226, 262, 279, 317, 338, 355, 363–364, 535

Inner solar system. *See* solar system, inner

Intensity. *See* flux

Interferometry, 120–121, 123

Interior, 215–218, 276–279
  of planet, 79, 360
  of Sun, 426

International Space Station (ISS), 531

Interplanetary kite-craft accelerated by radiation of the Sun (ICAROS), 283

Interstellar medium (ISM), 283, 302, 353, 355, 358–359, 381, 393, 401–403, 407, 426, 440–441, 454

Inverse square law, 303, 316

R

S